MATTER, EARTH, AND SKY

GEORGE GAMOW

University of Colorado

PRENTICE-HALL, INC.

Englewood Cliffs, New Jersey

Printed in the United States of America

5 6 5 7 5

Typographical design by Walter Behnke

Third printing . . . . March, 1959

MATTER,
EARTH,
AND
SKY

Archimedes in his laboratory, from a sixteenth-century text by Walther Riff.

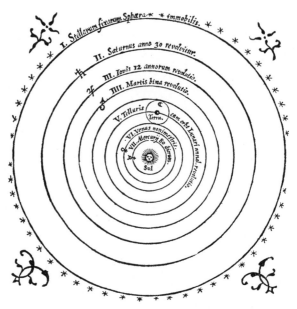

The Copernican system of the world, from *De revolutionibus orbium celestium*, A.D. 1543.

Dedicated to
ASPIRING YOUTH

PREFACE

If one has a large library composed of books written by many different authors in many different languages on many different subjects and published over a period of many years, it is impossible to arrange them on the shelves in such a way that they will form a consistent sequence in all respects. This is the situation that faces any author who attempts to present as a continuous narrative any broad subject such as the entire field of the physical sciences. Thus, one has to resort to trickery and put things together in such a way that they will at least look like a continuous presentation running from alpha to omega.

The plan selected for this book is that of a trilogy dealing first with things our size, secondly with things much smaller, and finally with things much larger than ourselves. In the first part the reader will find a discussion of phenomena that are more or less familiar to him from his everyday experience: the motion of the pendulum in a grandfather's clock, the boiling of water in a teakettle, rainbows in the sky, the electric current in a telephone wire, etc. This is the field of so-called "classical physics," which is not very exciting and challenging for our imagination but is absolutely necessary for an understanding of the events that take place in the physical world to which we belong.

In the second part, the reader will be taken into the

wonderful world of modern physics and chemistry. Down will he go through the crowds of molecules that restlessly rush about without any order in gases and that form most unusual architectural structures in crystals. He will meet the atoms and learn how they stick together to make different chemical substances, from such simple ones as table salt to such complex, and still to a large extent mysterious, ones as proteins. He will enter the interior structure of the atom with its swarms of unruly electrons, and finally the atomic nucleus itself. He will become acquainted with newly discovered particles with such strange names as "muons," "pions," and "hyperons," some of which may well be the ultimate building blocks of matter.

Leaving this microcosmic world, the reader will now be taken into the world of things that are much larger than himself. He will see the interior structure of our globe, the depths of the ocean, and the outer fringes of the atmosphere. He will get acquainted with the planets of the solar system, the sun, the stars, and the giant stellar systems known as galaxies. And at the end he will learn about the history of the universe, about the origin of the earth, stars, and galaxies, and also about the origin of the tiny atoms of the various chemical elements of which our universe is made.

In covering such a wide field of science with the intention of not omitting any important topics, I have found it somewhat difficult to keep the presentation at the same level, for of course it is intrinsically more difficult to understand the difference between the positive and negative curvature of space discussed in the last chapter than the difference between the levers of the first and the second kind discussed in the beginning. It is hoped, however, that as the pages go by the reader will become more and more trained in the mental gymnastics that are necessary for an understanding of modern science, so that the Heisenberg principle of uncertainty discussed in the thirteenth chapter will not appear to him much more complicated than Bernoulli's principle of hydrodynamics discussed in the first chapter. In any case, the author has tried to do his best to present the most difficult fields of modern physical science in as simple a way as possible.

In conclusion the author must express his gratitude to Professor J. M. Cleveland of the University of Colorado, who read through the original text and corrected the numerous mistakes that the author usually makes in all his writings, and to Mr. J. M. Guiher, Jr. of Prentice-Hall, Inc., whose efforts transformed the original mess of the manuscript into printable form.

G. G.

CONTENTS

MATTER, EARTH, AND SKY

OUR PLACE

IN THE UNIVERSE

In our everyday life we encounter objects of widely differing sizes. Some of them are as large as a barn and others are as small as a pinhead. When we go beyond these limits, either in the direction of much larger objects or in the direction of much smaller ones, it becomes increasingly difficult to grasp their actual sizes. We know that mountains are very large, but at a distance they look quite small, while at a short range we can see but a few rocks and cliffs. We know that bacteria are very small, but to see them we have to use a microscope, through which they look quite big.

Objects that are much larger than mountains, such as our earth itself, the moon, the sun, the stars, and stellar systems, constitute what is known as the *macrocosm* (i.e., "large world" in Greek). Very small objects, such as bacteria, atoms, and electrons belong to the *microcosm* (i.e., "small world" in Greek). If we use the standard scientific unit, a *centimeter* (0.3937 inch), for measuring sizes, objects belonging to the macrocosm will be described by very large numbers, and those forming the micro-cosm by very small ones. Thus, the diameter of the sun is 139,000,000,000 cm, while the diameter of a hydrogen atom is only 0.0000000106 cm. Scientists customarily express such numbers in terms of positive or negative powers of ten, and write 1.39×10^{11} cm for the diameter of the sun and 1.06×10^{-8} cm for the diameter of a hydrogen atom. Sometimes special very large or very small units are used. Thus, in the macrocosm we use the so-called *astronomical unit* (symbol: A.U.), which is defined as the mean distance of the earth from the sun and is equal to 1.4964×10^{13} cm, or a still larger unit known as a *light-year* (symbol: l.y.), which is defined as the distance traveled by light in the course of one year and is equal to 9.463×10^{17} cm. In the microcosm we often use *microns* (symbol: μ), defined as 10^{-4} cm, and *Angstroms* (symbol Å), defined as 10^{-8} cm.

In Fig. I-1 the relative sizes of various objects in everyday life, in the macrocosm, and in the microcosm are shown in a decimal logarithmic scale, i.e., in the scale in which each factor of ten is represented by one division of the yardstick. The sizes range from the diameter of an electron —and other elementary particles that are about one hundred-thousandth of an Angstrom—to the diameter of giant stellar galaxies, which often measure a hundred thousand light-years across. It is interesting to notice that the size of the human head is just about halfway between the size of an atom and the size of the sun, or halfway between the size of an atomic nucleus and the diameter of the planetary system (on the logarithmic scale in both cases, of course).

Similar vast variations will be found in the time intervals encountered in the study of the microcosm and the macrocosm. In human history we ordinarily speak about centuries; in geology the eras are usually measured in hundreds of millions of years, while the age of the universe itself is believed to be about five billion years. The revolution period of an electron in the hydrogen atom, on the other hand, is 10^{-15} sec, and the oscillations of particles constituting atomic nuclei have a period of only 10^{-22} sec. A comparison (on the logarithmic scale again) of various durations encountered in the macrocosm, microcosm, and in our every-day life is also given in Fig. I-1. Notice that the wink of an eye is just halfway between the age of our stellar system and the rotation period

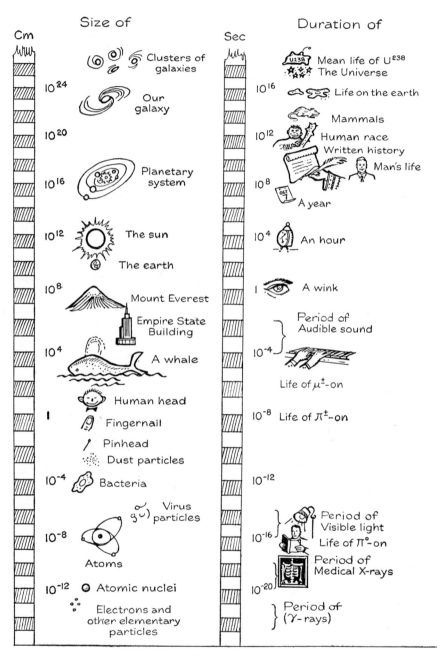

Fig. I-1. Space and time scales of the universe.

of an electron in an atom. Thus, it seems that we are located pretty well in the middle (logarithmically again) between the macro- and microcosm and can look up at the stars and down at the atoms with an equal degree of infer- and superiority.

Units Used in Physical Sciences

Until the beginning of the nineteenth century, the situation in the field of weights and measures was not much better than the linguistic situation at the Tower of Babel. The units of length varied from country to country, from town to town, from one profession (such as tailor) to another (such as carpenter), and were mostly defined, rather loosely, by reference to various parts of the human body. Thus, an "inch" was defined as a thumb-width, a "hand" or "palm" (still used for measuring the height of race horses) as the breadth of a hand, a "foot" as the length of a British king's foot, a "cubit" as the distance from the elbow to the tip of the middle finger, a "fathom" (used in measuring ocean depths) as the distance between the tips of the middle fingers of the two hands when the arms are outstretched in a straight line, etc. In the year 1791 the French Academy of Sciences recommended the adoption of an international standard of length and suggested that the unit of length be based on the size of the earth. *This unit, called a meter, was to be equal to one ten-millionth of the distance from the pole to the equator.* To prepare a standard meter it became necessary to measure, with all possible precision, at least a part of the earth's meridian, and two French scientists, M. Delambre and M. Méchain, were charged with the task. It took them seven years to measure, by an improved triangulation method, a stretch of meridian from Barcelona in Spain to Dunkirk in Normandy. On the basis of these measurements the academy prepared a "standard meter"— a platinum-iridium bar with two marks on it that was supposed to represent one ten-millionth part of a quarter of the earth's meridian. The original meter is kept at the Bureau des Poids et Mesures in Sèvres (not far from Paris), and faithful copies are distributed among all the countries in the world.

Although the United States, along with Great Britain, has chosen not to accept the metric system as all other countries do, it possesses a copy of the standard meter at the National Bureau of Standards in Washington, D. C. (Fig. I-2). While in stores and factories in this country, length is customarily measured in yards, feet, and inches, scientific measurements are always expressed in *kilometers* (one thousand meters or 0.62 miles), *meters, decimeters* (one-tenth of a meter), *centimeters* (one-hundredth of a meter), *millimeters* (one-thousandth of a meter), etc.

A peculiar situation exists in the Los Alamos Scientific Laboratory of the AEC in New Mexico where atomic and hydrogen bombs are developed. The nuclear components of the bombs, which involve pure physics, are described in terms of the metric system, while the over-all dimensions and the weight are usually given in inches and pounds. It should be mentioned here that the original intention of the French academicians to have a unit of length with a simple relationship to the size of the earth was not exactly fulfilled. Subsequent, more exact, measurements have shown that the length of a quarter of the earth's meridian is actually 10,022,288.3 meters. The error does not matter, however, as long as we know the exact amount of discrepancy.

Along with the standard unit of length, the metric system also introduced a new unit for the amount of matter, or mass. Disposing of "short and long tons," "pounds," "ounces," "drachms," "grains," etc., it uses a *gram*, defined as *the mass of a cubic centimeter of water at the temperature (about 4°C) at which it has the greatest density.* A standard *kilogram* (i.e., one thousand grams) equivalent to the mass of one liter (i.e., one cubic decimeter) of water under the above conditions was made of platinum and iridium alloy; the original is kept together with the original meter in Sèvres, and copies are distributed all over the world. The "American kilogram" is shown in Fig. I-2 resting alongside the "American meter" on a soft velvety background. While one gram is the standard unit used in physical measurements, we also use *milligrams* (one-thousandth of a gram) and *micrograms* (one-millionth of a gram) to express the mass of very small amounts of matter.

Fig. I-2. The standard meter and the standard kilogram at the National Bureau of Standards in Washington, D. C. The idea of standard time is shown by the sundial in the upper right corner. *Courtesy National Bureau of Standards.*

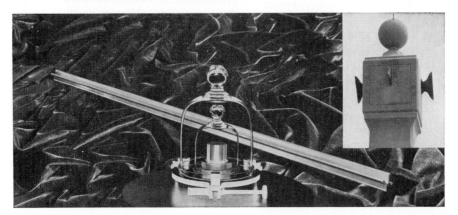

The inset in the upper right corner of Fig. I-2 symbolizes the third fundamental physical unit: a unit of time. A day is divided into 24 hours, and each hour is subdivided into 60 minutes, with each minute further divided into 60 seconds. This system of time measurement is based upon that used in ancient Babylon and Egypt, and even the French Revolution (not to mention the Russian one) was unable to convert it into a decimal system. Since we use a decimal system for length and weights, we should logically divide a day into "decidays" (2.4 hours each), "centidays" (8.4 minutes each), and "millidays" (59.4 seconds each). This would necessitate, however, the introduction of "decadays" (10 days each), "hectodays" (3.3 months each) and "kilodays" (2.6 years each), and would lead to chaos in speaking about the phases of the moon or the seasons of the year. In the scientific measurement of time intervals much shorter than a second, however, the decimal system is used, and we speak about *milliseconds* (one-thousandth of a second) and *micro-seconds* (one-millionth of a second).

Having defined the units for length, mass, and time, we can express through them the units for all other physical quantities. Thus, the unit of velocity becomes *a centimeter per second* (cm/sec), the unit of material density, *a gram per cubic centimeter* (gm/cm³), etc. This system of units is known as the "CGS system" and is always used in scientific literature. Being a unique system accepted by all scientists in the world, it represents a definite advantage over the Anglo-American system of units where the velocity, for example, may be expressed at will in "feet per second," "miles per hour," or even in "furlongs per weekend."

The Method Used in Physical Sciences

The immediate observation of physical phenomena in the surrounding world leads us to the establishment of definite relations between the various quantities observed. Thus, we find that the viscosity of oil depends on its temperature, the pull of an electromagnet on the strength of the current flowing through the wire, the rotation period of planets on their distance from the sun, and the brightness of stars on their mass. Such relations, based on direct measurements, are known as the *empirical laws of nature,* and the progress of observational and experimental science leads to the accumulation of ever larger and larger numbers of such empirical laws. The role of theoretical science is to find the hidden inter-relations between the empirical laws and to interpret them in the light of certain hypothetical assumptions concerning the internal structure of matter and various material objects which are not subject to direct obser-vation. For example, the viscosity of liquids and its dependence on temperature can be explained by a molecular hypothesis which assumes that all material bodies are formed by a very large number of very small particles known as molecules. The dependence of the brightness of stars on their mass can be understood if we make certain assumptions about the physical properties of the material deep in the interior of the stars and about the nature of their energy sources. In this connection the word *model* is often used, such as "Bohr's model of the atom," or "Eddington's model of a star." It goes without saying that the word "model" is used here in a rather different sense than when we speak about a model railroad or a model of an Indian pueblo village. A model in the physical sciences is a hypothetical picture of the hidden, directly unobservable structure of certain objects, and this picture is used to explain the various observed properties of such objects. Although the assumptions underlying such models and the laws that are supposed to govern them often cannot be tested by direct observation or experiment, numerous theoretical consequences can be drawn by means of mathematical reasoning and then compared with experimental and observational evidence. When the theory based on a certain model agrees with the direct empirical evidence, the belief of the correctness of the model is strengthened, and if the theory not only coincides with previously observed facts but also permits us to predict some new phenomena or regularities that are later confirmed by direct experiment or observation, the validity of the theory is further enhanced.

After these preliminary remarks, we proceed with the study of the wonderful world of nature, starting with ordinary things we observe in our everyday life, then plunging into the abyss of the microcosm—the world of atoms and their nuclei—and finally soaring up toward the stars and the giant stellar systems that constitute the macrocosm.

PART ONE

MATTER AND ENERGY

ONE

MATTER

AT FIRST SIGHT

Going about our daily tasks, we deal with what we usually call "material" objects. They may be solid, such as a fountain pen, a frying pan, or a five-ton truck. They may be liquid, such as the water we drink and in which we swim. They may be gaseous, such as the air we breathe and through which we fly in airplanes.

11

Solids

Solids are rigid and stubbornly resist any attempt to change their shape. They yield to force, but return to their original shape as soon as the force is removed, provided that the force has not been too great. This property of solids is known as *elasticity* and is used in many practical devices, such as springs. If the deformation of a solid object exceeds a certain limit (different for different materials), the object will not return exactly to its original shape, but will retain a certain amount of residual deformation. Some materials, such as steel, can undergo considerable elastic deformation, whereas others, such as lead, cannot. Some solids, such as sealing wax, will yield slowly to a force acting over a long period of time. Thus, a stick of sealing wax will crack if we try to bend it in our hands, but if the same stick is fastened at one end and left for a long time in a horizontal position, it will slowly bend under its own weight. This property that some solids have to be rigid in respect to "sharply" acting forces and to flow as a liquid if given enough time is known as *plasticity*. An interesting example of such material is provided by so-called "silicone rubber." It is as soft as putty, and if left overnight in a small container will spread out evenly over the container's bottom. But if we roll it into a small ball and drop it on the floor, it will bounce like a ping-pong ball.

CENTER OF GRAVITY

In solid objects that possess a definite shape, we can single out an important point known as the *center of gravity*. It is often defined as the point of application of gravitational pull, but such a definition may be misleading as it was to the man who went to a surgeon and asked him to cut out his center of gravity so that he could soar up to the clouds. The forces of gravity act, of course, on all parts of any given object, and the center of gravity can be defined more properly by saying that objects subjected to gravity behave as if there were only a single force applied at that point. In other words, if an object is supported at its center of gravity, it will remain in a state of equilibrium.

A simple experiment that demonstrates the properties of the center of gravity can be carried out by means of a ruler and a golf club. Take a ruler and place it on your index fingers. Now move your hands closer and closer together and note that the stick will slide somewhat over your right finger, then over the left one, then over the right, then over the left again, etc. Finally, when your two fingers come together, the ruler will still be in equilibrium, and its middle point (which in this case, of course, is the center of gravity) will be located between the two fingers. If you repeat the same experiment with a golf club, which has a heavy piece of iron at one end (Fig. 1-1), you will find that the center of gravity is located closer to the heavy end of the club. The alternating sliding of the ruler or the golf club over your fingers is caused by the fact that the friction force between any two objects is larger the more strongly they are pressed together, and by the fact that the finger which is located closer to the center of gravity is supporting the larger fraction of the total weight of the ruler or the club. To make the experiment more quantitative, we may use a light but sturdy aluminum tube, at the two ends of which different weights can be attached. When equal weights are placed on both ends, the tube will remain in equilibrium if it is supported in the middle (Fig. 1-2a). If, however, the weight on the left is twice as large as the weight on the right, the tube must be supported at a point located closer to the heavier weight in such a way that the length *AB* is equal to one-half the length *BC* (Fig. 1-2b). Similarly, if the ratio of weights is 3 to 1 (Fig. 1-2c), the ratio of lengths *AB* and *BC* should be 1 to 3. Thus, we arrive at the conclusion that **the distances of the center of gravity from the two ends of a stick stand in inverse proportion to the weights attached at these ends.** A reverse situation is encountered in the case of two men carrying a heavy load that is suspended from a stick but not from the middle of it (Fig. 1-2d). In this case, **the distribution of the total load between two carriers will be inversely proportional to the distances between the point of suspension and the two ends of the stick.**

In the case of an object of more complicated shape, the center of gravity can always be found by suspending it on a string attached first at one point and then at another point on its surface. An object always comes to rest with its center of gravity directly under the point of suspension. Suppose we cut an object out of plywood with the shape shown in Fig. 1-3. If we suspend it at the point, *A*, it will hang in the way shown

Fig. 1-1. A simple method, demonstrated by Mrs. S. Barry, for finding the center of gravity of a golf club. *Courtesy Convair, San Diego, Calif.*

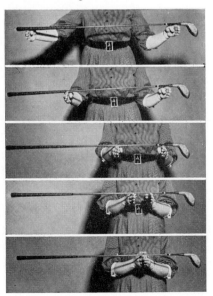

in Fig. 1-3 (left), and its center of gravity must be located somewhere on the line *AB*. If we suspend it at another point, *C*, the object will hang as shown in Fig. 1-3 (right), and the center of gravity must be

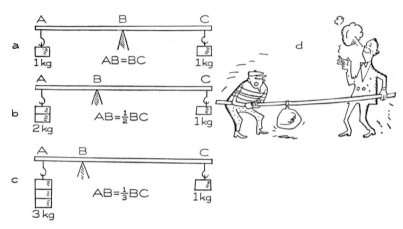

Fig. 1-2. The relationship between the shoulder ratios of a bar and the weights on the ends of it.

somewhere on the line *CD*. Thus, the exact location of the center of gravity is determined by the intersection, *E*, of the lines *AB* and *CD*.

To conclude our discussion concerning the center of gravity, let us consider the following interesting problem. Suppose we have a large number of books of equal size and want to pile them at the edge of a table in such a way that the top book will protrude as much as possible beyond the table's edge. How can we do it? If the first book is placed so that it protrudes by almost one-half its length, the second and all the following books cannot project any more without falling, and nothing will be gained by piling

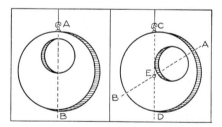

Fig. 1-3. A simple way of finding the center of gravity of oddly shaped objects.

up more of them. For a more reasonable solution, then, we know that the first book must protrude by less than half its length. But by how much less? Suppose that, instead of starting the arrangement with the bottom book, we first consider the book that is on top. Since all that is required from it is that it not fall from the pile below it, it can project out by just a little less than half its length. By inspecting Fig. 1-4 we see that the common center of gravity of the first and the second books will be located a quarter-book length to the right of the edge of the second book. Thus, if these two books are placed on top of the third one and overhang it a quarter length (or just a little bit less), they will not fall.

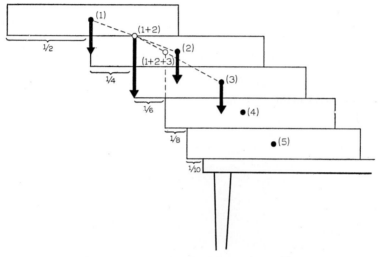

Fig. 1-4. The best way to pile books that edge beyond a table. The point (1 + 2) is the center of gravity of the two top books. The point (1 + 2 + 3) is the center of gravity of the three top books and is located one-third of the way between the double weight applied at (1 + 2) and the single weight applied at (3).

Let us go one step further and find the center of gravity of the system of the three top books. The way the books are stacked, the center of gravity of the first two is halfway between them, and the center of gravity of the third book is, of course, in its middle. Since the combination of the first two books is twice as heavy as the third book, according to the law illustrated in Fig. 1-2b, we should expect the center of gravity of all three books to be located twice as close to the center of gravity of the first two as it is to the center of gravity of the third one. A glance at Fig. 1-4 shows that the overhang of the third book should be one-sixth of its total length. If we proceed in the same way down the pile, we will find that the next two overhangs will be one-eighth and one-tenth, respectively. With five books, the distance of the outer edge of the top book from the edge of the table will be:

$$(\tfrac{1}{2} + \tfrac{1}{4} + \tfrac{1}{6} + \tfrac{1}{8} + \tfrac{1}{10}) \text{ book lengths} = 1.14 \text{ book lengths}$$

Thus, by piling books up in a rational way, we can do much better than a half-book overhang, in fact, better than a full-book overhang. If we use more than five books, the sum in the bracket above must be extended by adding $\tfrac{1}{12}$, $\tfrac{1}{14}$, $\tfrac{1}{16}$, etc., and it can be proven mathematically that the sum of a series of terms of this kind can become as large as we want, provided that we add enough terms. By stacking an unlimited number of books, therefore, we can make the top book protrude any desired distance beyond the edge of the table. Because of the rapidly decreasing contribution of each new book, however, we will need the entire Library of Congress to make the overhang equal to three or four book lengths!

In Fig. 1-5 we see a photograph of five books actually piled up in the above described manner. Although, in piling up these books, the photog-

Fig. 1-5. A photograph of an actual protruding column of books. *Photograph by Dr. Philpot.*

rapher placed the centers of gravity well within the underlying edges, the top book protrudes beyond the edge of the table by slightly more than its full length.

LEVERS

The principles discussed in the previous section are applied in practice through the use of various kinds of levers (Fig. 1-6). The *lever of the first kind* (Fig. 1-6a) is identical with the arrangement shown in Fig. 1-2a, b, and c, except that the weight on the left is replaced by a force exerted by a human hand. If the ratio of lever arms (i.e., the distance from the point of support to the points at which forces are applied) is sufficiently large, a small effort applied at the end of the longer lever arm can easily move a heavy rock at the other end. In the example shown in Fig. 1-2c, the ratio of lever arms is 3 to 1 and the force applied by hand is augmented correspondingly. The ancient Greek scientist, Archimedes (287-212 B.C.), who was the first to formulate the basic mechanical principles involved in the use of levers, exclaimed once: "Give me a point of support and I can turn over the entire world" (Fig. 1-6b).

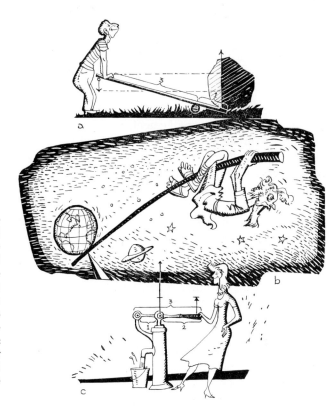

Fig. 1-6. The levers in (a) and (c) produce a resultant force 3 times that applied by the man and woman; in (b) Archimedes is proving his legendary boast: "Give me a point of support and I can turn over the entire world."

In the *lever of the second kind* (Fig. 1-6c), the point of support is located on the same side of both acting forces, but the condition of equilibrium remains the same: The forces must be inversely proportional to the distances between their application points and the point of support. Thus, in case (c), where the distance from the woman's hand to the pivot point is three times as long as the distance from the pivot point to the pump's piston, the force exerted by the hand is increased by a factor of three.

FRICTION

We have already mentioned friction forces in connection with the golf club sliding over two supporting hands. We have also stated that the friction force is larger when the two objects are pressed more strongly together. More detailed studies of friction phenomena have shown that **the friction force is directly proportional to the force that presses the moving object to the surface along which it is supposed to slide;** the numerical value of the coefficient of proportionality is known as the *friction coefficient.* If we push an object along a level surface, as western cowboys do with their silver dollars at a bar, friction forces will slow down the sliding object and will finally bring it to a stop. Most of the power spent by locomotive and automobile engines is used to overcome the friction forces that tend to slow down the motion of the train and the car.

An interesting experiment with friction can be carried out by means of the following simple arrangement. Suppose we have two rollers rotating in opposite directions and a wooden board placed on top of them. If the board is originally placed so that its middle point (which is, of course, its center of gravity) is located just halfway between the two rollers, no motion will ensue because the friction forces that exist at the two rollers will be equal and opposite. If, however, the board is placed to the right of its equilibrium position, its center of gravity will be closer to the right-hand roller and will cause that roller to carry a larger fraction of the total weight. Consequently, according to the law of friction, the friction force at this roller will be proportionately larger than the opposing force at the other roller, and the board will start moving to the left. When it reaches the equilibrium position, it will have a certain velocity directed to the left and will continue to move in this direction until its center of gravity comes close to the other roller. It will then be stopped by the increased friction force at that roller, and the motion will be reversed. Thus, the board will swing to the right and to the left in much the same way as a swinging pendulum. With a little more mathematics we could show that under the above stated law of friction the board will execute the same kind of harmonic vibrations as an oscillating pendulum or a vibrating tuning fork.

Liquids

Liquids possess fluidity. They usually do not have any definite shape of their own (though don't forget the morning dew on leaves) and readily assume the shape of the vessel into which they are poured. But, in doing so, they always retain their total volume, and a gallon of water will remain a gallon whether it is poured into a flat dish or into a tall, narrow cylindrical vessel. Consider water in a glass. Because of its weight, water exerts a pressure on the bottom of the glass, a pressure that is the same as that which would be produced by a cylindrical piece of ice if the water were frozen and the glass walls removed. "Pressure" here is not the same thing as "force." It is the force per unit area, that is, the total force divided by the area over which it is exerted. But, whereas in the frozen state water does not have any tendency to spread sideways, in the liquid state it presses on the walls of the vessel containing it. Since the pressure at any given point is due to the weight of the water column between that point and the free surface, it is greatest near the bottom of the vessel and gradually decreases as we go up towards the free surface. If we make little holes up the sides of a vessel (better use a cardboard container for such an experiment), we can observe the difference in pressure at the various levels by comparing the shape of the water jets coming from the different holes (Fig. 1-7a).

PASCAL'S LAW

If we subject the water contained in a vessel to an additional external pressure by fitting a piston into the vessel and placing a heavy weight on top of it (Fig. 1-7b), the situation will be entirely different. Water will spray from the upper openings almost as fast as from the lower ones, and, if the weight we place on the piston is very large compared with the weight of the water, the water jets from the upper and lower openings will show almost exactly the same velocity. Since the velocity of the

Fig. 1-7 (left below). The velocity of water jets spouting from holes in the side of a container, (a) without pressure and (b) with pressure.

Fig. 1-8 (right below). A demonstration of Pascal's law.

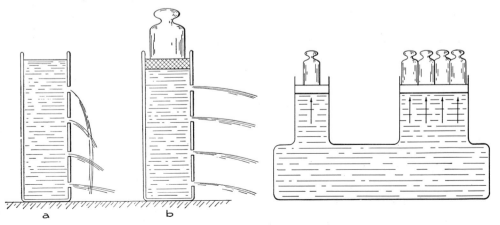

a   b

water jets is determined by the pressure inside the vessel, we conclude that **a liquid compressed inside a closed vessel exerts the same pressure at all points along its walls.** This basic law was discovered by the French physicist, Blaise Pascal (1623-1662), and carries his name. Imagine a closed vessel with two vertical cylinders of different diameters protruding from its upper part (Fig. 1-8). These cylinders are fitted with pistons that can be loaded with various numbers of heavy weights. If we place one weight on the piston in the narrower cylinder, it will produce a pressure within the liquid, and this same pressure will be transmitted to all parts of the vessel including the surface of the larger piston. Since, however, the area of that piston is larger, the total force acting on it will be larger, too. In the example shown in Fig. 1-8, the cylinder on the right is twice as large in diameter so the areas of the two pistons stand in the ratio 4 to 1. Since the total force of hydrostatic pressure acting on the right piston will also be four times larger, we will have to place four weights on it to maintain the equilibrium. The above described principle forms the basis of the so-called "hydraulic press" in which the pressure built within a liquid by a comparatively small force acting on a small piston exerts a much stronger force on another piston of considerably larger diameter.

ARCHIMEDES' LAW

We turn now to the important subject of solids floating in liquids. Everybody knows that a piece of wood will float in water because its density is smaller than that of water (i.e., it has less weight per unit volume), and that a piece of metal will sink because its density is greater. There is a story, however, of a student in a freshman course in physics who was asked whether a solid iron sphere would float in mercury and who could not give the answer. "I can tell you this much," said the professor, trying to help him, "the density of iron with respect to water is 8, and the density of mercury is 13."

"Oh!" said the lad brightly, "then almost two iron spheres can float in mercury."

Although a solid metal object will not be supported by water and will sink to the bottom, the fact that it is submerged in a liquid will diminish its weight. This phenom-

Fig. 1-9. A silver spoon (a) and a "watery" spoon (b) submerged in a glass of water.

a   b

enon can be easily seen in Fig. 1-9. On the left is a spoon suspended in water on a string. On the right there is no spoon, but the volume that was previously occupied by the spoon and now is, of course, filled by water is shown by dotted lines. If we consider this part of the water separately from the rest of the water in the glass (think of it as a thin-walled plastic container which has the shape of a spoon and is filled with water), we can see that it is completely supported by the surrounding water and moves neither up nor down. If in the place of the "watery spoon" we put a real silver spoon, only the difference in the weights of the two kinds of spoons will act on it. Thus, we can conclude that **any material body suspended within a liquid loses weight in the amount equal to the weight of the liquid it displaces.**

This famous law of hydrostatics was discovered by Archimedes, who, as the story goes, thought of it while sitting in a bathtub (see frontispiece, top), and then, in his excitement, rushed through the streets of Alexandria shouting "Eureka, Eureka!" ("I have found it, I have found it," in Greek). The populace of the city was not impressed by the great discovery, however; undoubtedly they thought he had found a missing cake of soap in the tub. Whether the above account is true or not, a more credible story is that Archimedes used this law while checking the authenticity of a golden crown that was suspected of being made of a gold-plated cheap metal rather than of pure gold. He had to determine its worth without breaking or scratching its surface, so he weighed it when it was suspended on a string in a basin of water and then compared the result with its normal weight. Since the ratio of these weights turned out to be 0.948, according to his law he could write the equation:

$$\frac{\text{weight of the crown} - \text{weight of displaced water}}{\text{weight of the crown}} = 0.948$$

from which follows:

$$\frac{\text{weight of displaced water}}{\text{weight of the crown}} = 0.052$$

or:

$$\frac{\text{weight of the crown}}{\text{weight of displaced water}} = 19.3$$

Since one cm^3 of water weighs one gm, the weight of the displaced water represents the volume of the crown, and, therefore, the ratio on the left is simply the density of the metal of which the crown was made. The figure he got coincided with the known density of pure gold, and he declared the crown authentic. Archimedes' law applies also, of course, to objects floating on water and only partially submerged. In this case, the weight of a floating object such as a ship is the same as the weight of the water it displaces.

BERNOULLI'S PRINCIPLE

Pascal's and Archimedes' laws pertain to the field of *hydrostatics,* i.e., the study of equilibrium of liquids. We will now take up one of the important items from the field of *hydrodynamics,* i.e., the study of liquids in motion. Consider water flowing through a pipe with a varying diameter (Fig. 1-10). In the narrow part of the pipe, the water flow is faster than

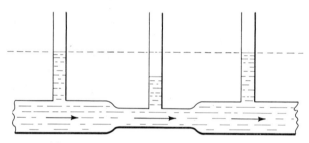

Fig. 1-10. The pressure is *lower* in the narrow part of the tube where the water moves *faster.*

it is in the wider part because the same amount of water must go through it per unit time as goes through the wide part. Since the water is accelerated when it enters the narrow section, there must be a force that makes it move faster, and the force can be due only to the pressure difference between the wider part of the pipe on the left and the narrower middle part. Thus, in the narrower part of the pipe the pressure is lower than in the wider part. Similarly, when the water enters the wider part on the right, it is slowed down in its motion and we can see that the pressure here must be higher. This fact can be easily demonstrated by attaching narrow vertical pipes to the three parts of our horizontal pipe, as shown in Fig. 1-10. The water in the middle pipe will stand lower and thus indicate a lower pressure. The statement that **in the regions where the velocity of fluid is smaller, the pressure is higher, and vice-versa,** is known as the *principle of Bernoulli,* after a Swiss physicist, Daniel Bernoulli (1700-1782), who discovered it.

Bernoulli's principle is quite general and applies to all kinds of fluid motion. Consider, for example, the stream of air around the wing of a flying plane. The profile of the wing and the lines of air flowing around it

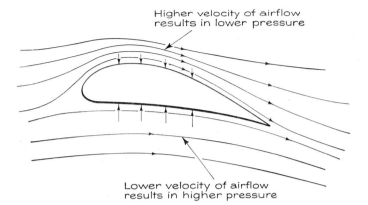

Higher velocity of airflow
results in lower pressure

Fig. 1-11. The explanation of the lift of an airplane wing.

Lower velocity of airflow
results in higher pressure

are shown in Fig. 1-11. Airplane wings are shaped in such a way that the total distance traveled by the air flowing over the wing is longer than that of the air flowing under it. Thus, the velocity of airflow above the wing must be higher, and the pressure correspondingly lower, than that of the airflow under the wing. This difference of pressure above and below the wing results in an upward force that supports the flying airplane in the air.

SURFACE TENSION AND CAPILLARITY

Before we leave the subject of liquids, we must say a few words about the phenomenon of *surface tension*. As we implied above when we reminded you of dewdrops, liquids show some tendency to assume a characteristic shape which, for small quantities of the liquid, competes with the force of gravity that forces liquids to assume the shape of their containers. We may think of droplets of water falling from a faucet or from the sky, small water droplets resting on an oily surface, drops of mercury on a glass plate, etc. Another example is provided by a glass heaping full of water in which the water level stands slightly above the rim of the glass and slopes down towards the edges. The behavior of liquid in all these cases is caused by certain forces acting along the liquid surface that tend to shrink that surface to the smallest possible size. Since, for a given volume, a sphere possesses the smallest surface, these surface tension forces will give to liquid bodies a regular spherical shape, if not interfered with by other forces. If a liquid drop rests on a surface that does not "wet," (we will return to this notion in a minute), a conflict arises between gravity forces, which tend to spread it thinly over the entire surface, and the surface tension forces, which tend to keep it spherical. As a result, the drop assumes the shape of a flattened ellipsoid.

Closely connected with surface tension are the *capillary forces* that act on the boundaries between solid and liquid (or two liquid) bodies. If we put a narrow glass tube into a dish of mercury (Fig. 1-12a), we will find that, although the liquid enters the tube, its level on the inside is somewhat lower than that on the outside. In addition, the surface inside the tube will have the shape of a convex meniscus because the liquid (mercury) "does not want anything to do" with the solid (glass) that is pushed into it. The surface of the mercury in the dish, therefore, behaves as an inflated rubber balloon does when we push our finger into it, or, to use the technical term, the mercury *does not wet* the glass (although it would wet a copper tube, for example).

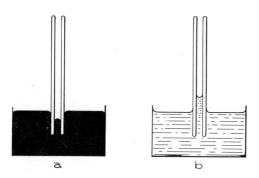

Fig. 1-12. Capillary forces depress mercury in a glass tube (a) and raise water in the same tube (b).

In Fig. 1-12b, the same glass tube is put into a dish of water, and the behavior of the water is the reverse of that of the mercury. It forms a concave meniscus, and the water level inside the tube is higher than on the outside. The water *does wet* the glass and spreads over it in the form of a very thin layer. The weight of the water column is supported by the surface tension forces along the rim of the meniscus. If we put a tube of waxed paper into the water, however, the water reacts to it in the same way that the mercury reacted to the glass tube, because the water does not "wet" the waxed paper.

Since capillary force is proportional to the periphery of the meniscus (i.e., to the diameter of the tube), and the weight of the liquid column is proportional to its area (i.e., to the square of the diameter of the tube), the elevation (for a wetting case), or depression (for a non-wetting case), of the liquid in the tube will be inversely proportional to its diameter.* When very narrow capillaries are wetted by the liquid contained in them, the liquid will rise to a considerable height against the

---

* If h = height of the column and r = its radius, then the volume of the column = $\pi r^2 h$, and its weight is $\pi r^2 h D$, where D = the density of the liquid. (This, for a liquid that wets the tube, will be the weight of the water that surface tension holds above the outside liquid surface.) The amount of surface tension = the strength of the surface tension film, T, times the circumference of the tube, or $2\pi r T$. Thus, since the pull of surface tension is what holds up the weight of the column, we have $\pi r^2 h D = 2\pi r T$, and $h = 2T/Dr$.

force of gravity. If there were no capillarity, kerosene lamps and cigarette lighters would be completely impossible, since the fluid would not climb up along the wick. There would be no blotting paper and, what is still worse, no plants on the earth, since capillarity is to a large extent responsible for raising water from the soil up to the green leaves

Gases

Gases, like liquids, possess fluidity and assume the shape of their container, but, unlike liquids, they do not show any tendency to retain their volume and will expand beyond any limit if not confined in a completely enclosed container. On the other hand, gases are much less resistant to compression than liquids, and although very high pressures are needed to compress water by any noticeable amount, air can be easily compressed into twice or more of its normal density by a simple pneumatic pump. The high compressibility of gases is employed to operate an amusing toy known as the "Cartesian diver," which consists of a cylindrical glass vessel that is completely filled with water and covered with a rubber membrane, and contains a figure of a diver attached to an upside-down test tube with some air in it (Fig. 1-13a). By pressing on the rubber

Fig. 1-13. The classical "Cartesian diver" (a) and its more modern modification (b).

a   b

membrane, we push water into the test tube, thus compressing the air in it and making the diver heavier than the surrounding fluid. As a result, he sinks to the bottom. If we release the pressure, the air in the tube will expand and push the water out of it, and the diver will float up.

Figure 1-13b illustrates a modification of the diver experiment that is both much more striking and easier to perform. Take an ordinary bottle with not too wide a neck and fill it heaping full of water. Then take three paper matches, break each in two near the middle to get the proper buoyancy, and drop the ends with the heads into the water. The matches will float at the surface of the bottle because the buoyancy of their paper bodies will support their heavy heads. But if you cover the opening tightly with your thumb and push in to build up some pressure (it requires some but not much practice), you will see the matches dive to the bottom. Release the pressure and up they come! The explanation is that the submerged matches still contain some air, either in capillaries in the paper or in the form of small air bubbles attached to their surfaces. Under the pressure produced by your thumb, this air compresses—just as the air did inside the Cartesian diver—and the matches lose their buoyancy and sink. When you release the pressure, the bubbles expand, the buoyancy is regained, and the matches rise. The interesting point of this experiment is that it is always possible to adjust the pressure in such a way that one match stays at the bottom, one at the surface, and the third in the middle of the bottle. This is due, of course, to the fact that there is always enough difference in the air content of the three matches (under a properly adjusted pressure) to make one of them buoyant, one sinkable, and the third just in between.

BOYLE'S LAW

Returning to more serious facts concerning the compressibility of gases, we will formulate the basic law discovered by an Irish physicist, Robert Boyle (1627-1691). Take a closed glass tube with some air trapped in it and an open tube and connect them with a mercury-filled rubber tube a couple of meters long, as shown in Fig. 1-14. Start the experiment with the two glass tubes in the relative positions shown in Fig. 1-14a, in which the mercury stands at the same level in both of them. Under these conditions the trapped air is under normal atmospheric pressure. Now move the open tube up until the trapped air is compressed to one-half of its original volume. You will find that, in this case, the difference in the mercury levels will be about 760 mm (Fig. 1-14b).* Move the open tube higher until the trapped air is squeezed into one-third of its original volume, and you will find that the difference in the mercury levels is now 1,520 mm, or 2×760 mm (Fig. 1-14c). To interpret this finding, take a closed glass tube about one meter long, fill it up with mercury and, closing the open end with a finger, put it upside down into a dish filled

---

* It will vary slightly depending on atmospheric pressure.

with mercury. You will observe that the column of mercury drops down somewhat leaving a vacuum in the upper part of the tube (Fig. 1-14d). The height of the mercury column will be about 760 mm, and this device

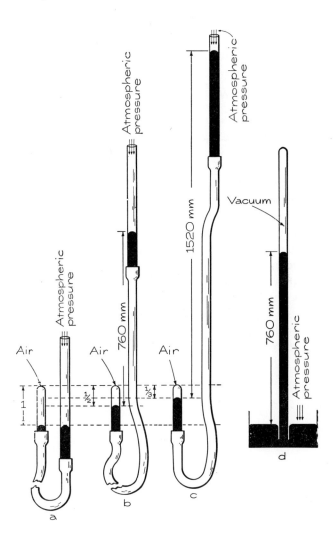

Fig. 1-14. An apparatus for determining the compressibility of gases.

is, of course, nothing but an ordinary barometer for measuring atmospheric pressure. Now let us sum up the results of our experiment.

In case (a) the trapped air was subject to atmospheric pressure, i.e., 760 mm of mercury. In case (b) the pressure was increased 760 mm to a total of two atmospheres. In case (c) the pressure was that of three atmospheres. Since the volumes of trapped air were in the rations 1:½:⅓, we can conclude that **the volume of gas is inversely proportional to the pressure to which it is subjected,** which is the classical *Boyle's law of gases.* Air and other gases follow this law very precisely, but at very high compressions (by a factor of several hundred) deviations are observed toward lower compressibility. This is quite understandable since in these cases the density of gas approaches that of liquids, which possess very low compressibility.

STATES OF MATTER

The three states of matter described above—solid, liquid, and gaseous —do not, of course, represent a unique attribute of any given material. Since water, as we all know, is ordinarily a fluid, it freezes into a solid block of ice at a low temperature and turns into a vapor at a sufficiently high temperature. (We avoid here the use of the word "steam" for water vapor, because the popular notion is that the steam coming from a teapot or a steam engine is something that can be seen as white puffs. The white coloring, however, as in the case of clouds or fog, is caused by tiny water droplets and not by the water vapor itself.) All other substances can also be found in all these three states, but their melting and evaporation points vary quite widely. Iron, for example, melts only at $+1,525°C$ and does not turn into vapor, under atmospheric pressure, until its temperature reaches $+3,000°C$. Nitrogen, on the other hand, the main component of air, liquefies only at $-196°C$ and does not become solid until its temperature drops to $-210°C$.

THE LAWS
OF MECHANICS

Work and Energy

Let us return now to the two cases discussed in the previous chapter: 1) two forces applied to the ends of a solid bar supported at a certain point in between, and 2) two forces applied to the pistons of different diameters in two hydrostatically connected cylinders. We will assume here that the bar and the pistons have a negligibly small weight. These two cases with lever arms or area ratios, 1:2, are shown in Fig. 2-1a and b.

If the two forces satisfy exactly the conditions specified in the previous chapter, both systems will be in the state of equilibrium and no motion will ensue. But if there is a very slight preponderance in one of the forces (say, the one on the left), the system will start to move: The left end of the bar and the left piston will move down and the right end and the right piston will move up. By inspecting Fig. 2-1a and b, we find that the

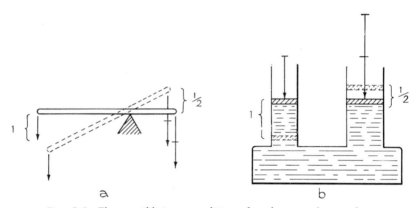

Fig. 2-1. The equilibrium conditions for the two forces that are applied at the ends of a solid bar, and to the pistons in two hydrostatically connected cylinders. The directions of both forces are indicated by the arrows and their relative strengths by the length of the arrows. Notice that the displacements of the ends of the bar, and of the pistons, are inversely proportional to the strengths of the two forces.

end of the bar or the piston acted upon by the double force moves only half the distance the other does. If the ratio of forces is 1:3, the displacement of the point of application of the larger force will be only one-third that of the other side. Thus we conclude that **the product of an acting force and the displacement of the point of its application is the same for two nearly balanced forces that oppose one another.**

This product is known in mechanics as the *work* done by the force, and we say that in the above cases the work done by two opposing forces is numerically the same. But, and it is an important "but," the force on the left did *positive work*, since it moved the object in the direction in which it was acting, and the force on the right did *negative work*, since it was "executing a strategic retreat under the enemy's pressure," as the military would say. Thus, if we ascribe to work done by forces a positive or a negative sign, as is done in algebra, the total work done by both forces in the above example is zero. This principle is the basis of a funicular railway, in which two carriages of equal weight and with about the same number of passengers are attached to the same cable, which passes over a pulley, so that the two carriages move in opposite directions up and down the side of a steep mountain. The only work done by the motor operating the funicular is that against friction and against the small difference in the weights of the passengers in the two carriages (the latter, however, averages zero in the long run).

The above definition of mechanical work is quite consistent with our common notion of the subject, at least in the case of crude physical work. We will all agree that it takes twice as much work to move twice as much furniture to the same floor of an apartment building or to move the same amount of furniture to an apartment located twice as high. Thus, **the work of raising a certain weight against the forces of gravity can be defined as the product of the total weight raised by the height to which it is raised.** Using various units for measuring the weight and length, we can express this work in "gram-centimeters," "kilogram-meters," "pound-feet," or even in "stone-hands."

POTENTIAL ENERGY

When an object is located at a certain height, it has the potentiality of producing work if and when it falls to the ground, and this amount of work is known as the *potential energy* of the object. It is, of course, equal to the amount of work that had to be done in order to place the object in its elevated position. Thus, the potential energy of water upstream from a dam is equal to the weight of water multiplied by the difference in water levels created by the dam. In this case, it is convenient to speak about the potential energy that can be released per unit of time, and this rate of release of energy depends on the rate at which water is supplied by the river. If we multiply the difference in the heights of the two water levels by the weight of water that flows per unit time through the hydroelectric installation of the dam, we get the amount of potential energy released per unit time, or the *power* of that installation (in $\frac{\text{kg} \times \text{m}}{\text{hour}}$, for example).

It goes without saying that the notion of potential energy is not necessarily associated only with the force of terrestrial gravity. A tightly wound spring or a gas compressed in a metal cylinder are also able to produce mechanical work that can be measured in the same units. Potential energy is also stored in an automobile tank filled with gasoline, in a charge of high explosive in an artillery shell, or, for that matter, in the plutonium core of an A-bomb.

KINETIC ENERGY

Returning now to our original experiments shown in Fig. 2-1, suppose that the force on the left is considerably larger than the force on the right. In this case "the orderly strategic retreat" will turn into "a rout in the face of the vastly superior enemy." Since the forces now are not balanced, the solid bar in the first example, as well as the pistons and the liquid in the second, will come into a state of accelerated motion and, gathering speed, will acquire the ability to produce a certain amount of mechanical work by virtue of that motion. **The ability of moving bodies to produce mechanical work is known as their kinetic energy** and can be expressed either in terms of the work done to bring them into that state of motion or in terms of the work they can do before coming to rest. We can investigate the situation by means of the simple experiment shown in Fig. 2-2. A light carriage that can be loaded with a variable amount of

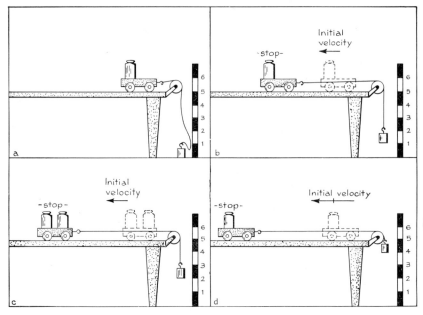

Fig. 2-2. The work that can be done by a moving object increases in proportion to its weight and to the square of its velocity.

heavy weights is rolled with a certain velocity along a table. A string attached to the carriage passes through a pulley and its other end is attached to a certain weight resting on the floor at the side of the table (a). When the string tightens up, the weight will be lifted from the floor and will reach a certain maximum elevation at the moment the carriage comes to rest (b). If we double the load of the carriage, keeping its initial velocity the same, however, we will find that the weight will be raised twice as high (c). If, on the other hand, we use the same load but propel the carriage with a double velocity, the weight will be raised to four times the height recorded in the first experiment. Similarly, if we triple the load of the carriage, we will raise the weight to a triple height, and if we triple the velocity we will find that the weight will be lifted nine times as high. Thus we must conclude that **the kinetic energy of moving objects is proportional to their total weight and to the square of their velocity.** We can therefore define kinetic energy as the product of these two quantities multiplied by a certain constant factor. The value of that factor depends on the choice of units of measurement and will be discussed at the end of this chapter.

In most examples of mechanical motion, there is a constant interplay between kinetic and potential energies. Thus, if we hold a ping-pong ball in our hand some distance above the floor, it has potential energy but no kinetic energy. If we release it, it falls faster and faster towards the floor, and when it reaches the floor, it will have no potential energy left; all of it will have been turned into kinetic energy. At the moment of impact with the floor, the ball will stop for a split second, and all its kinetic energy will be turned into the energy of the elastic deformations in its body. (In the case of an inelastic lead ball, the kinetic energy will be transformed into heat—by a process that we shall explain later—and it will not bounce.) The elastic energy is then changed back into kinetic energy and this sends the ping-pong ball up into the air, with the result that the kinetic energy is turned into potential energy. The ball will rise to approximately its original height. This process is repeated again and again until the friction forces gradually rob the system of its initial energy and the ball comes to a standstill on the floor.

The above discussion provides an interesting explanation of the fact that, although a man is several thousand times larger than a flea, a flea can jump to about the same height that a man can (Fig. 2-3). Why is this so? If we use what we already know about work and energy, the explanation is simple. The body of any jumping animal is lifted into the air by the work done by its muscles. The larger the animals, the larger are its muscles, and the greater is the total work they can produce. But how much greater? When a muscle contracts, the work it does is the product of the force with which it pulls and the length by which it shrinks. Since muscle tissue is about the same in all animals, the tension produced per unit area of a muscle's cross-section is also the same, so that the total force produced by a muscle is proportional to the square of the size of the muscle or, what is the same, to the square of the size of the animal.

In the case of a flea which is, say, 2,000 times smaller than a man, the cross-section of leg muscles, and also the force exerted by them, is $(2,000)^2$ times smaller than the cross-section of leg muscles in a man. The length by which a muscle contracts is a fixed fraction of its original length and therefore is proportional to the animal's size. Thus, the total work done by a contracting muscle is proportional to the cube of the

Fig. 2-3. A flea and a man can jump to about the same height.

size of the animal, which in the case of a flea is $(2,000)^3$ times smaller than in the case of a man. But the weight of the animal is also proportional to the cube of its size, and a flea weighs $(2,000)^3$ times less than a man. Using the formula, *work = weight × height*, we find that, since the work of the muscle and the weight of the animal change by approximately the same factor, the resulting height of a jump remains about the same. Of course, this is only an approximate relation, for there are good and poor jumpers among the animals of any one size.

CONSERVATION OF MECHANICAL ENERGY

The law of conservation of mechanical energy is a generalization that is based upon what we have observed in both the ping-pong ball and muscle experiments. It states that **the total amount of potential and kinetic energy in a mechanical system does not change unless some work is done on it from the outside or unless some of the energy of the system is removed.** For example, a ball will not bounce higher and higher unless, as children often do, we hit it with our palm each time it starts down. Nor would the height of its bounces be reduced if there were no friction forces (against the air, against the floor, and within its own body) that gradually deplete its energy. Before the establishment of scientific mechanics and the formulation of the law of conservation of mechanical energy, people played with the idea of "getting mechanical energy out of nothing" and were continually trying to design various so-called "perpetual motion" machines. One such machine consists of a wooden wheel placed halfway through a watertight slit in the wall of a vessel filled with water. Since one side of the wheel, being submerged in water, has the tendency to float, and the other half outside the vessel has the tendency to descend, it was argued that the wheel would rotate indefinitely clockwise and produce an unlimited amount of work. We will leave it to the reader to disprove this theory.

How Things Fall

The Leaning Tower of Pisa, besides being one of the architectural wonders of the world, is also inseparably connected with the history of physics because of the part it played in an experiment that was alleged to have been performed more than three centuries ago by the famous Italian scientist, Galileo (1564-1642). From the upper platform of the tower, Galileo simultaneously released two spheres, a heavy one made of cast iron and a lighter one made of wood (Fig. 2-4). In spite of a large difference in weight, both spheres dropped side by side and hit the ground almost at the same moment. By this simple experiment, Galileo established the important fact that **independent of their weight, all material bodies fall**

Fig. 2-4. Galileo's experiment.

Iron

Wood

with exactly the same speed. He thus disproved, once and for all, the belief of his contemporaries that heavier bodies must fall faster than lighter ones. The fact that a feather lingers in the air considerably longer than a stone or a coin is due to the resistance of air, which affects the motion of lighter bodies more than that of heavier ones. To test Galileo's finding, we place a feather and a coin in a long, evacuated glass tube and turn the tube rapidly upside down. In the absence of air, the feather drops just as fast as the coin.

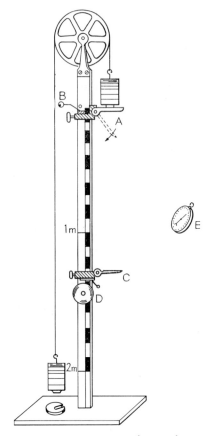

Fig. 2-5. Atwood's machine.

The study of falling objects is an excellent way to learn about the basic laws of motion. Since ordinary free fall is much too fast for convenient observation, it is necessary to slow the fall down by means of an ingenious device known as Atwood's machine (Fig. 2-5). It consists essentially of a long, vertical pole with a light pulley on top and a collection of metal weights that can be piled in desired quantities on two light supports attached to both ends of the string that runs over the pulley. A platform, A, placed at the zero point of the vertical scale plotted on the pole, supports the pile of weights on the right side. It can be dropped quickly, by pressing the lever B, thus releasing the pile of weights for its downward movement. Another adjustable platform, C, can be placed at any height along the pole, and it rings the bell D when it is hit by the descending pile of weights. Using stop watch E, we can measure rather accurately, at least for our purpose, the time between the release of the pile of weights from the upper platform and the moment that it hits the lower one.

UNIFORM MOTION

We can start our experiments with Atwood's machine by putting an equal number of weights (it does not matter how many) on each end of the string. If we remove the support under the pile on the right, nothing will happen. Since the gravitational pull on both piles is the same, the system will remain in equilibrium. To start it moving, we must give the upper pile a slight push downwards or the lower one a push upwards. Once on the move, the pile on the right will continue downwards—with the pile on the left moving upwards—until it hits the lower platform. The motion in this case proceeds at a constant speed, since there are no forces to speed it up and only a negligible friction force to slow it down. The situation is not much different from that of a billiard ball or a bowling ball rolling along a smooth horizontal surface. The famous British physicist, Isaac Newton (1642-1727), considered the generalization of these simple facts to be one of the basic laws of mechanics in his book, *Philosophia Naturalis Principia Matematica*, i.e., "Mathematical Principles of Natural Philosophy." (In olden times the expression "Natural Philosophy" meant the Physical Sciences and is still retained in the title of one of the leading British physical journals, "Philosophical Magazine.") Because of its historical interest, we give here the exact English translation of the original Latin text

First law of motion: every body continues in the state of rest or uniform motion in a straight line, except insofar as it is compelled by forces to change that state.

Newton's first law was severely criticized some time ago by the well-known British astronomer, Sir Arthur Eddington (1882-1944), who argued, quite correctly, that in general we can tell whether a force is acting on a material body only by the fact that the motion of the body deviates from a uniform motion or from a state of rest. He altered Newton's first law by changing the passage following the comma to: . . . **except insofar as it does do otherwise.** In fact, Newton's first law should not be considered so much a law of nature as the definition of a force.

ACCELERATED MOTION

Returning to our experiments with Atwood's machine, let us now place 51 weights on the right string and 49 on the left string. If we remove the support, the heavier weights will descend, slowly at first and then faster and faster. The motion, however, will be considerably slower than a free fall, because the driving force, which in this case is the gravitational pull on only two weights (51 − 49), has to set in motion the total mass of one hundred weights. The passive resistance of all material bodies to any attempt to set them in motion from a state of rest, or to change their velocity or the direction of their already existing motion is known as *inertia*. A locomotive trying to pull a long train from a station has to overcome the inertia of heavily loaded cars that would rather remain standing. But when the train rolls at full speed, it takes powerful brakes to slow down or bring to a stop the happily rolling cars.

Since we have conveniently slowed down the motion of the weights in Atwood's machine, we can easily make some quantitative measurements concerning the relation between the distances covered and the time intervals of the drops. If we put the adjustable platform 10 centimeters below the upper one, we will find that the bell rings just about one second after we release the weights. The velocity of the moving weights increases with time, so it will take them less than a second to drop the next ten centimeters. By the end of the second second, therefore, we can expect the descending pile to be considerably further down. By placing the lower platform at different positions and measuring the time of each fall, we can eventually place it where the descending weights will take two seconds to reach it, and we will find that this position is 40 centimeters below the starting point. By further experimentation, we will find that it takes three seconds for the descending pile to hit a platform placed 90 centimeters below and four seconds to hit one 160 centimeters below. Since 1, 4, 9, and 16 are the squares of the numbers 1, 2, 3, and 4, we conclude that **the distances traveled by objects in (slowed-down) free fall increase as the square of the time of travel.**

It can easily be shown that such a dependence between the time of travel and the distance traveled corresponds to the case when the velocity is increasing in direct pro-

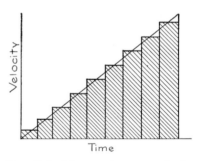

Fig. 2-6. The total area of the rectangles represents the distance covered by a uniformly accelerated moving object when the rectangles become infinitely thin and infinitely numerous.

portion to time, or, as we say, when the motion of the weights is *uniformly accelerated*. Indeed, in this case, the graph of velocity versus time (Fig. 2-6) will be represented by a straight line and we can write: *velocity* = $a \times$ *time*, where a is a constant that characterizes the *rate of change of velocity* and is known as the *acceleration*. Let us now divide the entire time interval into a large number of short intervals and construct narrow vertical rectangles as shown in Fig. 2-6. Since the height of each rectangle represents approximately the velocity during each successive short interval, the areas of these rectangles must correspond to the distances traveled during these intervals. Thus, the total distance traveled is approximately represented by the shaded area in Fig. 2-6. If we reduce the rectangles to infinitely narrow rectangles, we find that the distance is represented by the area of the large triangle, with the time of travel as its base and the final velocity as its height. According to a theorem of elementary geometry, we now have:

$$\text{distance traveled} = \tfrac{1}{2} \text{ final velocity} \times \text{time of travel}$$

Since, as we have just seen,

$$\text{final velocity} = a \times \text{time of travel}$$

we can substitute this in the above equation and get:

$$\text{distance traveled} = \tfrac{1}{2}a \times (\text{time of travel})^2$$

Thus, we conclude that the slowed-down free fall, as observed with Atwood's machine, is a uniformly accelerated motion and that the acceleration a is twice the ratio of distance traveled to the square of the time of travel. Using the figures we got from the above experiment, we can calculate the value of a. Since in a 4-second interval the weights dropped 160 centimeters, $a = \dfrac{2 \times 160}{16}$ cm per sec per sec or 20 cm per sec per sec or, more simply, 20 cm/sec².

If we now repeat the experiment but place 52 weights against 48 (a pulling force of 4 unit weights), 53 against 47 (a pulling force of 6 unit weights), etc., we will find that the distances traveled during the same time intervals (and consequently the values of the constant a) are correspondingly 2, 3, etc. times larger for each increase in pulling force. We can therefore conclude that **the acceleration of motion is directly proportional to the acting force, provided the total mass to be moved remains the same.**

Suppose we use only one-half of the weights used before. In this case, we will find that for the same amount of difference in weights, the motion will be faster. Thus, if we place 26 weights on the right and 24 on the left, we will find that the distances traveled by the end of the 1st, 2nd, 3rd, and 4th seconds will now be: 20 cm, 80 cm, 180 cm, and 320 cm (the latter distance will, of course, be off the scale on our 2-meter high pole). Since the distances traveled during a given time for 50 weights are twice as large as those for 100 weights, we conclude that **the acceleration of motion caused by a given force is inversely proportional to the total number of weights to be moved.**

The two conclusions reached above are partially contained in **Newton's second law of motion: a change of motion is proportional to the force and takes place in the direction of the straight line along which the force acts.**

ACCELERATION OF GRAVITY

As we have just seen, when 100 weights are driven by a gravitational pull of only 2 weights, the acceleration of motion is about 20 cm/sec². Using the law of motion derived above, we conclude that the acceleration of motion in a free fall—when the number of weights driven is the same as the number of driving weights—must be $\frac{100}{2} = 50$ times larger, or about 1,000 cm/sec². More exact measurements of gravitational acceleration, usually denoted by the letter g, give:

$$g = 980 \frac{cm}{sec^2}$$

The numerical value of g varies, however, from place to place on the surface of the earth. The observed force acting on a material object is actually the difference between two forces: 1) Newtonian attraction towards the center of the earth, and 2) centrifugal force due to the earth's rotation. Both forces vary with latitude. Since, because of its rotation, the earth is not exactly spherical but has an ellipsoidal shape, the equator is farther away from the center than the poles and this fact causes the surface gravity to decrease from the poles towards the equator. Centrifugal force, caused by the earth's rotation, increases from the poles towards the equator, and, since it acts in the opposite direction to the force of gravity, it further reduces the force of gravity on material bodies in the equatorial zone. The force of gravity also decreases with the elevation above the surface of the earth. Just to amuse the reader and not for any practical purpose, we give here an exact formula which permits us to calculate the value of g at any geographical location and at any altitude above the earth's surface. It reads: $g = 980.616 - 2.5928 \times \cos 2\varphi + 0.0069 \times \cos^2 2\varphi - 0.3086 \times h$, where φ is the latitude in degrees and h is the altitude in kilometers. But even this formula does not take into account the numerous gravitational anomalies that are due to the uneven distribution of masses in the crust of the earth.

On the moon, the acceleration of gravity is considerably less than that on the earth (only 167 cm/sec²) because the moon is much smaller than the earth (only one-81st of the earth's mass) and therefore attracts the objects on its surface with a much weaker force. A man who on the earth can jump, say, 2 feet into the air would soar up 12 feet on the moon. On the surface of the sun, on the other hand, the force of gravity is almost 30 times larger than on the earth (27,440 cm/sec²), and a man on the sun would be crushed by his own weight if he were not first burned and turned into thin gas.

Closely related to the acceleration of gravity is the notion of *escape velocity*, i.e., the velocity that must be communicated (vertically) to an object to enable it to break the bonds of gravity and to escape into space. According to a formula which we will not attempt to derive here, escape velocity is given by the square root of the product of acceleration of gravity and the diameter of the celestial body in question. For the earth, the escape velocity is 11.2 km/sec, while for the moon it is only 2.4 km/sec. Various rockets developed by the armed forces today attain velocities of about 2 km/sec and with slight improvement could be used as escape vehicles from the surface of the moon. To attain the velocities of 11.2 km/sec and more that are necessary to escape from the gravity of the earth, however, takes much more mechanical ingenuity, and we will return to this question in the next chapter.

MASS VS. WEIGHT

In the above discussion, we have always referred to the weight of material bodies and have used the word "mass" only in the colloquial sense. However, if properly defined, the notion of mass is more basic and general than that of weight. Suppose we take Atwood's machine to the moon and repeat the experiments there. Since on the moon gravity is considerably weaker than on the earth, the gravitational pull on each individual weight will be correspondingly less. The inertial resistance of the weights against a change in their state of motion, however, will remain exactly the same, and as a result, all movements of the machine will be correspondingly slower.

Consider another experiment. Suppose we have two balls of equal diameter—one made of solid iron and the other of balsa wood—lying on a hard, smooth surface. If we try to lift the balls, it will take much greater effort to lift the iron ball than to lift the wooden one, and we say that the iron ball is much heavier. If we push the balls along the surface, we will find that again the heavy one resists more stubbornly and requires a much stronger push to get rolling. This resistance of balls to the push has nothing to do with their weight or with the pull of gravity, since they are supported by the surface on which they rest, and the friction forces in this case can also be readily ignored. The iron ball resists our push more than the wooden one because of its larger *inertial mass*. Imagine now that we take the balls to the moon and repeat the experiment. Because of the moon's lesser gravity, we will be able to raise the iron ball without much effort, while the wooden ball will feel almost like a rubber balloon. If we try to push these balls along the surface, however, it will take just as much effort as it did on the earth. Thus, **although the weight of material bodies varies from place to place, their inertial mass, or simply their mass, remains always the same.** This law makes it clear that we should use the (inertial) mass of an object rather than its weight for characterizing the amount of matter it contains. We do not need to construct a new universal unit for mass, since "standard kilogram," originally defined as the unit of weight, can also serve as the unit of mass. Although an object, if weighed on a spring scale, will not weigh the same on the north pole as it will on the equator, it will always have the same resistance to any attempt to shove it along a horizontal, slippery surface.

Fig. 2-7. Newton's third law: the equality of action and reaction.

a   Rough surface

b   Slippery surface

Action vs. Reaction

"Push me and I'll push you back!" are fighting words between schoolboys. Sir Isaac Newton puts it in slightly different words in his **third law of mechanics: to every action there is always opposed an equal reaction.** This means that if there is an interaction between two material bodies, the force acting on one of them is exactly equal and opposite to that acting on the other. When a nurse pushes a perambulator along a smooth sidewalk, the perambulator pushes back at the nurse with exactly the same force. The reason that it is the nurse and not the perambulator who wins the competition is because her white Oxfords hold more strongly to the ground (because of friction) than do the wheels of the perambulator (Fig. 2-7a). If, however, the nurse gives a strong shove to the perambulator while standing on a slippery surface—especially if the perambulator is heavily loaded (large inertial mass)—the situation will be different; the perambulator will move forward and the nurse will move backwards (Fig. 2-7b).

Since the forces of action and reaction between the two objects are equal to one another, and since the acceleration communicated to any object by a given force is inversely proportional to the mass of that object, the acceleration of the more massive of the two interacting objects will be smaller than that of the lighter one. When we shoot a rifle, for instance, the powder gases in the barrel force the bullet out towards the target, but they also push equally strongly towards the rear of the barrel and produce what is known as *recoil*. The recoil in an ordinary rifle is relatively small because the rifle is much more massive than the bullet, but even then, it is quite appreciable. The principle of recoil is used in the construction of all kinds of rockets, from those used on the 4th of July to those that will some day fly to the moon and beyond. Small rockets are usually propelled by the burning of black powder, such as that used in the Army's "bazooka." Large rockets usually carry two liquid fuels, gasoline and liquid oxygen, which are burned, for example, in the Army's "Redstone" and Convair's "Atlas," shown in Fig. 2-8. A rocket's speed at the end of its burning period depends essentially on the ratio between the weight of its fuel and the weight of the rocket itself. According to the equality of action and reaction, this speed will be higher the smaller is the mass of the rocket's body and the larger is the mass of the gases that stream back from its nozzle. The quality of the fuel used also plays an essential role: The more energy liberated per unit weight of the fuel, the stronger is the push or thrust and the larger is the maximum speed of the rocket.

The rockets like "Redstone" and "Jupiter" that are being developed by the armed forces today attain maximum velocities of only about 2 km/sec, which, although approaching the escape velocity from the moon, are still too small for the escape from the earth's gravity. Even if we make the ratio of fuel weight to the empty rocket weight 8:1, which is the ratio of the weight of an egg to the weight of its empty shell, the maximum velocity will be raised only to 5 km/sec.

There are, however, two possible ways to increase the initial speed of a rocket. One is the use of a *multi-stage rocket*, which is a combination of several rockets, each one smaller than the next, located one on top of the other. The flight starts by firing the rear (largest) rocket, which rises into the air and attains the maximum speed permitted by its fuel load. At the moment its fuel is exhausted and it begins to slow down in its

Fig. 2-8. (Left) The Jupiter-C rocket blasting off on the night of January 31, 1958, with the United States' first satellite, Explorer, on the tip of its nose. *United Press.* (Right) The ICBM Atlas—possible launcher of a rocket to the moon. *Courtesy Convair, San Diego, Calif.*

vertical rise, the second (smaller) rocket is disengaged and its fuel is ignited. The process is repeated with the third rocket, etc., until finally the last (smallest) rocket, carrying the payload, gets under way. Since for the maximum efficiency of such a rocket system, each rocket must be considerably larger than the one above it, the whole system becomes quite sizable, and a three- or four-stage rocket powerful enough to carry a small cabin with a few space travelers would be about the size of an ocean liner.

Another way to improve the performance of a rocket is to use nuclear power for its propulsion. In an ordinary chemical rocket, the gases that are expelled from the nozzle and that provide the thrust are the products of a combustion process that involves mostly carbon dioxide and water vapor. It is known that, for a given weight of ejected material and for a given temperature of the jet, a lighter exhaust gas will produce a stronger thrust than a heavier one. Since carbon dioxide and water vapor are comparatively heavy gases, the performance could be considerably improved if the lightest gas, i.e., hydrogen, could be used as the ejected material. Hydrogen can be carried in the rocket in liquid form, but before it enters the nozzle it must be heated to a temperature of several thousand degrees, and that is where nuclear power comes into the picture. In the nuclear-powered rocket of the future, liquid hydrogen from the rocket's tanks will be sent through the channels of a perforated nuclear reactor, where it will be heated to the desired temperature and then ejected through the nozzle. Whether or not nuclear rockets will outperform multi-stage chemical rockets is an unresolved question because a suitable nuclear reactor is very difficult to design and because heavy shielding will be required around the reactor if the rocket is to carry human beings.

ARTIFICIAL SATELLITES

Although only a few decades ago rockets were used almost exclusively for amusement purposes of the coronation and 4th of July type, they are now gaining paramount importance in the life of humanity, both for constructive as well as for destructive purposes. During World War II, German engineers developed the famous V-2 rockets which carried loads of high explosives across the British Channel into the industrial and residential areas of London. Though initially designed for destructive purposes, the unshot V-2's turned out to be very useful for the study of the upper layers of the atmosphere (see Chapter 17) and of the properties of sunlight unmarred by passage through the atmospheric air. The only changes that were necessary to transform these war birds into peaceful pigeons was the replacement of the TNT warhead by an assortment of scientific instruments of about the same weight, and to shoot the rocket straight up instead of sending it along a slanting trajectory from the green shores of Normandy to the white cliffs of Dover.

The next stage in the development of military rocketry is the *Intercontinental Ballistic Missile* (ICBM for short) which will be able to deliver a hydrogen bomb warhead to any point on the surface of the earth from any other point. The steppingstone towards the ICBM is known in this country as the IRBM (*Intermediate Range Ballistic Missile*) and is supposed to carry the thundering warheads as far as 1,500 miles. While, in its peaceful application, the V-2 rocket could lift a package of scientific instruments for a very short time towards the limits of the terrestrial atmosphere, the IRBM can do something better than that: It can lift instruments beyond the limits of the atmosphere and leave them there for a very long period of time circling round and round our globe in practially empty space. In other words, a rocket of the IRBM type can throw into space a compact package of instruments which becomes at least a temporary satellite of the earth—a little baby moon of a very small stature but with a rather big brain.

To accomplish this task, the rocket should be brought to altitudes of over 500 km (300 miles), where the resistance of the air ("drag") becomes negligibly small, and to a horizontal speed of about 7 km/sec (17,000 miles per hour), which corresponds to a circular orbit close to the surface of the earth. On October 4, 1957, Russian rocketeers shot up the first satellite rocket known as *Sputnik I* (pronounced spootnick) which means in Russian a "traveling companion" and also a "satellite." Since Sputnik's launcher was apparently a military rocket of the IRBM type, no information about the site and the method of its launching was revealed, but it seems likely that it was a three-stage chemically fueled rocket launched from a point somewhere between the Caspian and Aral Seas. In Fig. 2-9a, b, c, and d we show the trajectory of Sputnik I during the first day of its flight (the dashed line represents the actual trajectory while the solid line corresponds to its projection on the surface of the earth) in which it made almost exactly 15 revolutions around the globe. The continuous shift of Sputnik's orbit is due to the rotation of the earth around its axis. During the following three months of its existence, Sputnik I made about 1,500 revolutions but gradually lost its altitude, and early in January, after entering the denser layers of the atmosphere, was burned and gone. The launching of Sputnik I was followed on November 3 by another satellite rocket, *Sputnik II*, which was considerably heavier than Sputnik I, (1,120 pounds instead of 184 pounds), climbed to higher altitudes (Fig. 2-10), and also had a passenger—a dog called *Laika* (barker).

The first American satellite, *Explorer*, went up from the Cape Canaveral, Florida, rocket testing grounds on January 31, 1958. It was put into orbit by a missile known as *Jupiter-C*, a four-stage rocket developed by the Army at its Redstone Arsenal. Explorer is shaped like a bullet, weighs about 30 pounds, and carries equipment for cosmic ray studies which signals the collected information by radio to the ground. The orbit of Explorer is considerably more elliptical than that of the first two sputniks, with a minimum and maximum altitude of 200 and 1,700 miles. Also, whereas the sputniks follow essentially meridian trajectories, Explorer follows an equatorial trajectory and can be seen only from the southern United States.

Artificial satellites of the earth are of great importance for the solution of many geophysical problems. First of all, they give us new information about the structure of the earth's crust. If our globe were exactly ellipsoidal and its crust of a uniform thickness, the orbit of a terrestrial satellite would be comparatively easy to calculate. We know, however, that this is not the case, and that the surface of the earth presents highly variable features such as ocean basins, continental mas-

Fig. 2-9. Sputnik I circled the globe 15 times its first day. Presumably launched between the Caspian and Aral Seas, it took 96 min for one revolution. Its orbit is dashed line, its trace on the earth's surface solid lines. From l. to r.: the completion of the 1st, 2nd, 6th, and 16th revolutions. These drawings are somewhat idealized; they assume the orbit to be stationary in space. Courtesy *Scientific American*.

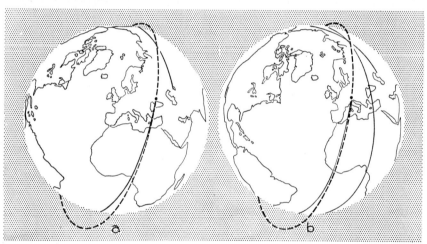

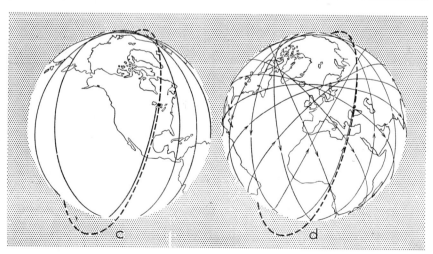

sifs, and elevated mountainous regions. As we will see in Chapter 8, which is devoted to the physical structure of our globe, these surface features are reflected in the structural characteristics of the rocky material deep under our feet, and the entire picture becomes rather involved. All these deviations in the distribution of masses through the crust of the earth affect the field of gravity surrounding the earth and, consequently, the motion of artificial satellites circling it. Thus, by closely studying the orbits of these satellites, earth scientists are able to obtain valuable additional information concerning the detailed structure of our globe.

Another important branch of geophysics that will benefit from the observations made by means of artificial satellites is the study of the upper atmosphere, since the instruments carried by the satellites record the density, temperature, and other properties of the atmospheric air at very high altitudes. Also, as was mentioned above, the satellites' instruments permit them to collect important information of a purely astronomical nature concerning the sun, the planets, and the stars. These little moons are really small observatories located beyond the limits of the disturbing terrestrial atmosphere. And last, but not least, the animals and probably in the future the human beings riding the satellites will enable us to make the first steps in the field of "space

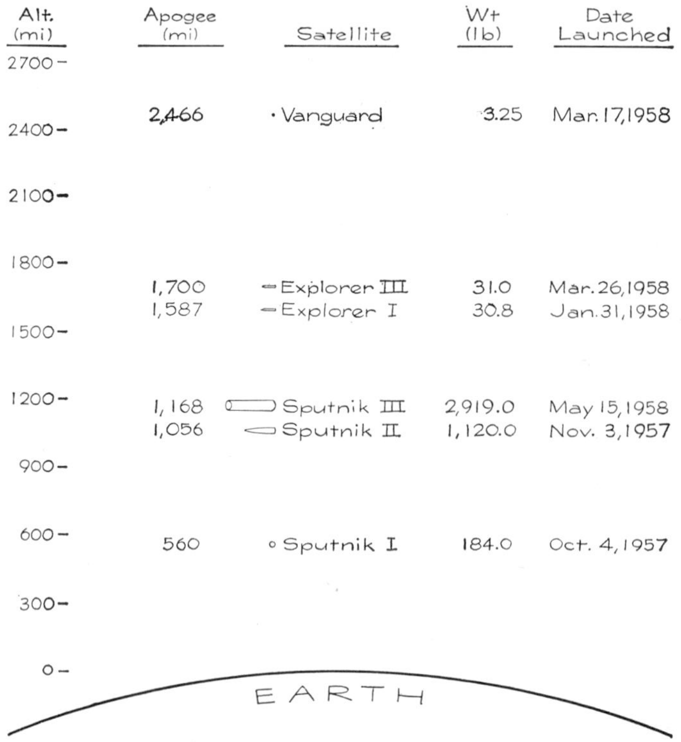

Alt. (mi)	Apogee (mi)	Satellite	Wt (lb)	Date Launched
2700 –				
2400 –	2,466	· Vanguard	3.25	Mar. 17, 1958
2100 –				
1800 –				
	1,700	⊸ Explorer III	31.0	Mar. 26, 1958
1500 –	1,587	⊸ Explorer I	30.8	Jan. 31, 1958
1200 –	1,168	⊂⊃ Sputnik III	2,919.0	May 15, 1958
	1,056	⊂⊃ Sputnik II	1,120.0	Nov. 3, 1957
900 –				
600 –	560	∘ Sputnik I	184.0	Oct. 4, 1957
300 –				
0 –				

EARTH

Fig. 2-10. The first satellites to be launched (3 by the United States, 3 by Russia). Sputniks I and II and Explorer III have fallen from their orbits and disintegrated in the earth's atmosphere. On July 26, 1958, the United States launched Explorer IV, weighing 38.43 lb and with an apogee of 1,386 miles.

medicine" as preparation for future manned flights into interplanetary space.

ASTRONAUTICS

While the rockets of the IRBM type can throw into space little baby moons that circle just beyond the limits of terrestrial atmosphere, the bigger and more powerful ICBM's should be able to reach the old man moon itself. Although no information is, of course, released about the size and weight of H-bomb warheads, it can be assumed that it weighs a few thousand pounds, which is much larger than the necessary weight of instruments needed for purely scientific studies. Thus, it should be possible to re-convert a military ICBM into a scientific moon vehicle by replacing its warhead with an extra stage rocket and using most of the extra weight for additional fuel. This extra power will be able to communicate to the instrument head, which need not weigh more than a few hundred pounds, a velocity in excess of 11.2 km/sec, the *escape velocity* that is necessary to break the bonds of terrestrial gravity and to fly out into space. Beyond this velocity, the kinetic energy of the rocket exceeds its potential energy on the earth's surface, so that the force of gravity is unable to pull the rocket back to the surface. Velocities in excess of 11.2 km/sec are not much higher than the initial velocity needed to launch an artificial satellite,* and the construction of an "escape rocket vehicle" will undoubtedly be the next step in rocket development. The first interesting flight of such an escape rocket will be, of course, a flight around the moon, the trajectory of which is shown in Fig. 2-11. This rocket will enable us to photograph the opposite side of the moon (which undoubtedly looks very much like this side), measure the moon's magnetic field, and maybe even, with some luck, get some samples of the moon's material. The latter task may be done without landing on the moon. It can be accomplished with the use of two rockets. The first would carry a small A-bomb, which would blast the surface of the moon and raise a giant cloud of dust. The second rocket, following immediately behind the first one, would fly through this cloud and collect some of the material. But, shooting a rocket around the moon is a delicate matter. A small mistake in aiming may change the trajectory shown in Fig. 2-11 into that shown in Fig. 2-12, and, instead of returning to the earth, the rocket will be catapulted by the gravitational pull of the moon out into interplanetary space.

As in the case of an artificial satellite, the returning moon rocket will

---

* It can be shown, in fact, that the velocity necessary for escape is larger than the orbital velocity of the satellite by a factor: $\sqrt{2} = 1.414$.

burn on re-entering the terrestrial atmosphere, and all the data collected by it will have to be sent by radio to the earth before this happens. People looking into the future visualize the return of space rockets to the surface of the earth unharmed, through the use of a winged rocket that can spiral lower and lower and slower and slower around the globe. But this task, which is necessary before a human being can take a space trip, is really a very difficult one. A possible model of such a manned space vehicle is illustrated in Fig. 2-13.

The next step in astronautics is a visit, first by unmanned and then by

Fig. 2-11. The calculated orbit of a rocket that will circumnavigate the moon. The rocket will climb vertically to a height of 345 miles and then be aimed in the proper direction for the moon flight. The simultaneous positions of the rocket and the moon are connected with solid lines. The rocket will come closest to the moon's surface (within about 5,000 miles) 194 hours after its launching. Note the effect of the moon's gravity on the trajectory of the rocket when the distance between the two bodies becomes small. The gravity force exerted by the moon will deflect the rocket from its original elliptical trajectory, so that it will be necessary to fire an additional charge (correction impulse) on the way back to ensure that the returning rocket does not miss the earth. *Courtesy Krafft Ehricke, Astronautics Division, Convair, San Diego, Calif.*

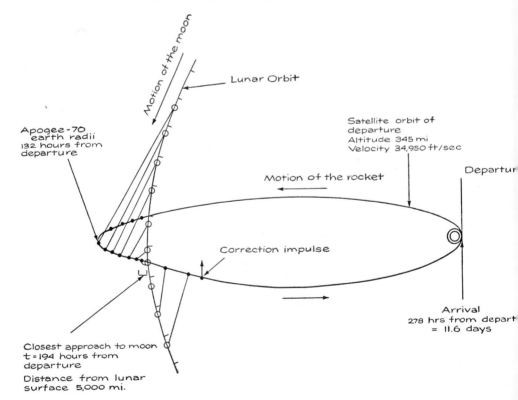

manned rockets, to the planets of the solar system, and in particular, to our two neighbors, Venus and Mars. To send a rocket to Mars, we will have to supply an additional acceleration to the escape vehicle so that, after leaving the gravity of the earth, it will still have enough velocity to travel to Mars against the sun's attraction. To get to Venus, the vehicle will have to be slowed down so that it will sink closer to the sun towards Venus' orbit. There is a possibility that the two trips can be combined, as shown in Fig. 2-14.

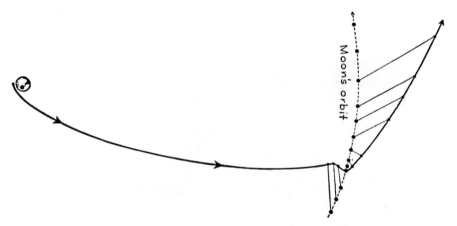

Fig. 2-12. The path of a rocket catapulted out into space by the gravitational pull of the moon, calculated at the Astronautical Division of Convair. Such orbits could be used for interplanetary travel.

Although trips to the moon and to the planets of our solar system seem to be quite feasible sometime in the future, the voyage to distant stars and to the giant stellar systems known as "galaxies" seems to lie completely outside the realm of possibility.

Mechanical Units and "Dimensions"

Now that we have become acquainted with the basic notions and laws of mechanics, let us spend some time in setting up a rational and consistent system of units to express such things as work, energy, force, etc. In the metric system we have the three basic units: a gram, a centimeter, and a second. Velocity, of course, is measured in centimeters per second or cm/sec, and as we have seen above, the unit for acceleration is centimeters per second per second or cm/sec^2. But we run into trouble with

Fig. 2-13. (Top) Three-stage manned space vehicle of the future at take-off. The rocket motors of the first stage (large cylinder) give to the vehicle the initial push upwards. The second-stage tanks and motor are located behind the main vehicle. (Middle) The third stage on its way out into space. The cutaway wall shows the arrangement of the passengers' cabin. (Bottom) In case of motor trouble during the ascent, the passenger cabin can be disconnected and glide back to earth. *Courtesy Krafft Ehricke, Astronautics Division, Convair, San Diego, Calif.*

the gram, which is by definition one-thousandth of the cylinder made by French academicians and kept in Sèvres near Paris. Is it one-thousandth of its weight, i.e., of the force with which it is pulled by terrestrial gravity, or one-thousandth of its mass, which is the amount of inertial resistance it offers to any force trying to move it? In the discussion on weight and mass, we made it clear that the notion of inertial mass is much more fundamental than the notion of weight. Therefore, *we define a gram as a unit of mass, i.e., as the resistance of a body to any change in its motion.*

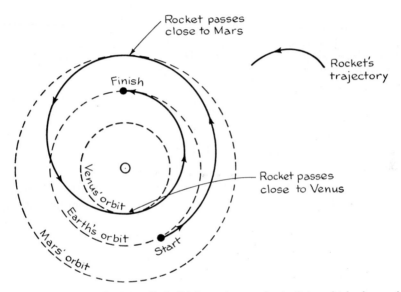

Fig. 2-14. The so-called "Hohman's round trip," in which the rocket fired from the earth goes close to the orbits of Mars and Venus and then returns to the earth.

Since we have now the unit of (inertial) mass and the unit of acceleration, and since we know that the acceleration is proportional to the acting force and inversely proportional to the mass on which it acts, it is rational to define a unit of force as a force that acts on a unit of mass and gives it a unit of acceleration. Thus *we define the unit of force or a "dyne" as a force that gives a mass of one gram an acceleration of one centimeter per second per second.* If we measure force in dynes, we can write:

$$\text{dyne} = \text{gm} \times \frac{\text{cm}}{\text{sec}^2} = \frac{\text{gm} \times \text{cm}}{\text{sec}^2}$$

Suppose an object weighing 1 gm falls freely in the field of terrestrial gravity. Since, as we have seen before, it moves with an acceleration of 980 cm/sec², we have to say, following the above definition, that the force of gravity acting on it is equal to 980 dynes. And, since we have defined work as the product of force and the distance that the object is displaced under the action of that force, we have to say that the work done against the force of terrestrial gravity in moving one gram upwards by one centimeter is, not one unit, but 980 units of work. In general, although the acceleration of gravity varies from place to place, we can write:

$$\text{work} = g \times \text{mass} \times \text{elevation}$$

where the value of g pertains to the place where the work is done. *The unit of work is called an erg, and is defined as the work done by a force of one dyne displacing the object on which it acts by one centimeter.* Since potential energy was defined as the work that can be done by an object by virtue of its elevated position in the field of gravity, it is also measured in ergs.

The problem now is to express kinetic energy in terms of the mass and the velocity of a moving object. Let us consider again a gram falling freely from a certain height in the field of gravity. As we have seen above, this height (it is the distance the gram moves vertically from its starting point to the ground) is connected with the final velocity and the time of travel by the relation:

$$\text{height} = \tfrac{1}{2} \, (\text{final velocity}) \times (\text{time of fall})$$

Since, however:

$$\text{final velocity} = g \times \text{time of fall}$$

if you substitute this second equation into the first and then multiply by g/g (which does not change its value), you will be able to rearrange things a little and come out with:

$$\text{height} = \frac{1}{2} \times \frac{1}{g} \times (\text{final velocity})^2$$

or, multiplying by the mass of the object and by g:

$$g \times \text{height} \times \text{mass} = \tfrac{1}{2} \, \text{mass} \times (\text{final velocity})^2$$

Since the expression on the left represents the work done by gravity accelerating the falling object, the expression on the right is the kinetic energy it acquired as the result of that work. We therefore define *the kinetic energy of a moving object as one-half the product of its mass and the square of its velocity,* which agrees with what we said about kinetic energy earlier. Notice that, according to this definition, kinetic energy is measured in the same units of $\frac{gm \times cm^2}{sec^2}$ as potential energy, although its formula was derived from the basic units of mass, length, and time in a different way:

$$gm \times \frac{cm}{sec^2} \times cm, \text{ in the case of potential energy, and}$$

$$\frac{1}{2} gm \times \frac{cm^2}{sec^2}, \text{ in the case of kinetic energy.}$$

In speaking about all kinds of engines, we use the notion of *power,* which is the rate of energy production. In the CGS system, power is expressed in *ergs per second,* and its dimension is: $gm \times \frac{cm^2}{sec^3}$. Later on we will see that we can construct similar units based on cm, gm, and sec for measuring even more complicated physical properties, such as the elasticity of solids, the amount of electricity, and the strength of a magnetic field. This system of units is known as the *CGS system* and is the one used almost exclusively in scientific research.

Another system of units sometimes used in physics texts is known as the *MKS system.* It is based on a meter and a kilogram instead of a centimeter and a gram. In this system, velocity is measured in meters per second, and the numerical value of any given velocity in the MKS system is therefore 100 times smaller than in the CGS system. The same is true of acceleration, which is measured in meters per second per second. Since force is defined as the product of acceleration and mass, and since a kg is 1,000 times larger than a gm, the unit of force in the MKS system —called a *newton*—is 10^5 times larger than a dyne. Energy, which is proportional to mass and the square of velocity, is expressed in the MKS system in a unit known as a *joule,* which is $(10^3) \times (10^2)^2$ or 10^7 larger than an erg. This unit of power, i.e., one joule per second, is known as a *watt.* The power of engines is usually expressed in kilowatts (kw or 1,000 watts) or in horsepower (one horsepower is equal to 0.745 kw). The MKS system is convenient in technical fields because it contains the units of energy and power used in engineering. But, since scientific literature around the world and all the standard tables of physical constants use the CGS system, we will stick to it in order to prevent the confusion that always results when two different terminologies are employed.

The unit to be used for measuring any physical property can always be expressed in terms of our three basic units. The formula telling how it is composed of gm, cm, and sec is known as the *physical dimension* of that property. Thus velocity is composed of cm and sec in this way: cm/sec, while the unit of acceleration has a different physical dimension: cm/sec². The dimensions of the erg are gm × cm²/sec², etc. This concept, of course, has nothing to do with the notion of geometrical dimension or size. Physical entities that do not have the same "dimensions," on the other hand, cannot be compared in this way. It is just as meaningless to ask whether an acceleration of 100 cm/sec² is larger or smaller than a velocity of 1,000 cm/sec as it is to ask whether an income of $15,000 per year is larger or smaller than a capital sum of $100,000.

The process of dimensional analysis is often useful for checking the final answer of a complicated theoretical formula; if the right and the left side of the final equation are found to have different physical dimensions, there must have been a mistake made somewhere in the derivation of that equation. This type of analysis is used sometimes—without the application of more complicated mathematical analysis—in the derivation of relations between different physical quantities that characterize a certain phenomenon. We will illustrate this process by deriving the relationship between the period T of a pendulum and its length l, its mass m, and the acceleration g of the gravitational field in which it is suspended. We can write quite generally:

$$T = l^x\, m^y\, g^z$$

where x, y, and z are unknown. Remembering, however, that T is measured in seconds, l in centimeters, m in grams, and g in the composite unit cm/sec², we can write:

$$\text{sec} = \text{cm}^x \times \text{gm}^y \times \left(\frac{\text{cm}}{\text{sec}^2}\right)^z = \text{cm}^{x+z} \times \text{gm}^y \times \text{sec}^{-2z}$$

Comparing the exponents of cm, gm, and sec on both sides, we conclude that:

$$0 = x + z \qquad 0 = y \qquad 1 = -2z$$

from which it follows that:

$$z = -\tfrac{1}{2} \qquad x = +\tfrac{1}{2} \qquad \text{and, of course, } y = 0$$

Thus, the formula for a pendulum becomes:

$$T = \alpha \sqrt{\frac{l}{g}}$$

which means that **the period of a pendulum is proportional to the square root of its length and independent of its mass,** a law that was first discovered by Galileo about three centuries ago. Dimensional analysis does not permit us to estimate the value of the numerical (dimensionless) constant α that stands in the formula, and its value (in this case $\alpha = 2\pi$) has to be obtained by mathematical anlysis. But, since numerical coefficients in the formulas of theoretical physics are usually close to unity (rarely larger than 10 and rarely smaller than 0.1), dimensional analysis may be quite adequate if we are interested only in finding the order of magnitude of the quantities in question. This method is also satisfactory if we do not care about absolute magnitude but are interested only in the way in which one quantity (in this case, T) depends on other quantities (l, m, and g).

THREE

ELASTIC VIBRATIONS

AND WAVES

Elastic Deformations

As we stated in Chapter 1, and, in fact, as we all knew at an early age, solid bodies tend to maintain their shape, and, when deformed (within limits) by an external force, return to their original shape as soon as the force is removed. This property of solids is known as *elasticity* and is of great importance in many practical devices, such as, for example, those based on various types of springs. A fun-

58

damental law in this field, the so-called *Hooke's law of elasticity*, named after its discoverer, Robert Hooke (1635-1703), states that **the deformation of a solid body is proportional to the force acting on it,** provided the force does not exceed a certain limit. The coefficient of proportionality between the applied force and the deformation caused by it is known as the *coefficient of elasticity*. The numerical value of this coefficient varies for different materials and for different kinds of deformation.

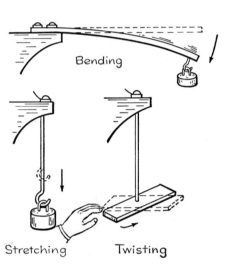

Bending

Stretching   Twisting

Fig. 3-1. Three types of elastic deformations.

The three principal types of deformation are known as *stretching, bending,* and *twisting,* examples of which are shown in Fig. 3-1. When we remove the forces acting on these three objects they will behave in a way that is similar to the action of the ping-pong ball that we discussed in the previous chapter. The stress caused by the deformation will tend to bring the body back to its original shape: the stretched rope will begin to shrink, the bent bar to straighten out, and the twisted wire to untwist. The resulting motion will be accelerated (though not uniformly accelerated as in the case of free fall), and the potential energy stored in the deformation will be transformed rapidly into the kinetic energy of motion. When the objects reach their original (undeformed) state, the acquired kinetic energy will prevent them from coming to rest, and they will swing beyond this position almost equally far in the other direction. To and fro, to and fro they will go until the friction finally drains all the energy out of them.

Imagine a weight of W dynes hung from the end of a wire that is 1 meter long and that has a cross-sectional area of 2 mm². W is supported by 2 mm² of metal all along the wire, so that the stress in the wire is $W/2$ dynes/mm². If the wire were thicker, with a cross-sectional area of 4 mm², there would be more material to support W, and the stress would be reduced to $W/4$ dynes/mm². It is plain to see that the elongation of the second wire will be only half as much as for the first one, since each mm^2 of cross-sectional area supports only half as much weight. Mathematically, then, we can say that the lengthening is inversely proportional to the cross-sectional area of the wire.

If we again hang W on a wire 2 meters long, each meter of length will stretch just the same amount as it did before, so the lengthening will be twice as great as for a 1-meter wire. This means the lengthening is directly proportional to the length.

It is also plain from Hooke's law that the lengthening is directly proportional to the force W that the suspended weight exerts. Putting all these ideas together gives us:

$$\text{lengthening} = \frac{k \times \text{force} \times \text{length}}{\text{cross-sectional area}}$$

where k is a proportionality constant we want to investigate. Similar expressions can also be written for bending and twisting.

We have written the formula for stretching in order to give another example of the dimensional analysis described at the end of the previous chapter. What are the physical dimensions of the coefficient k? We know that:

$$k = \frac{\text{cross-sectional area} \times \text{lengthening}}{\text{force} \times \text{length}}$$

Since length and lengthening have the same dimension (both are expressed in cm or any other unit of length), they cancel out in the formula above. Force is measured in dynes, the dimensions of which are gm $\times$ cm/sec^2, and area is of course cm^2. So the physical dimensions of k must be:

$$k = \frac{\text{cm}^2 \times \text{cm}}{\text{gm} \times \text{cm/sec}^2 \times \text{cm}} = \frac{\text{cm}^2 \times \text{cm} \times \text{sec}^2}{\text{gm} \times \text{cm}^2} = \frac{\text{cm} \times \text{sec}^2}{\text{gm}}$$

This k is obviously a constant that tells us about the stretchability of the material the wire is made of. Engineers prefer a constant that describes a material's *resistance* to stretching, and they use a constant Y (for Young's Modulus, called that for an engineer named Young), which is equal to $1/k$. Hence,

$$Y = \frac{\text{force} \times \text{length}}{\text{cross-sectional area} \times \text{lengthening}}$$

This could be reduced, of course, to gm/cm $\times$ sec^2, but ordinarily only the lengths are cancelled out to leave $Y = $ force/cross-sectional area, or dynes/cm^2.

Young's modulus, in dynes/cm², is about 2×10^{12} for steel and 2×10^9 for rubber.

Elastic Vibrations

We can now use dimensional analysis to derive the formula for the vibration period of an object suspended on a rubber band in the same way that we derived the formula for the oscillation period of a pendulum. In this case, however, the force of gravity, which produces a certain elongation of the rubber band when the object hangs motionless, does not participate in determining the motion because the motion depends entirely on the change of the tension of the rubber band when the suspended object moves up and down in respect to its equilibrium position. Thus, the vibration period T depends only on the length and thickness of the band, on the Young's modulus of its material, and on the mass of the suspended object. Furthermore, only the ratio of the mass m of the object to the cross-section s of the elastic band can enter the formula, since the increase of the mass and of the elastic force by the same factor will not change the motion in any respect.

Thus, we can write:

$$T = \beta Y^x l^y \left(\frac{m}{s}\right)^z$$

where β is a numerical factor. Using CGS units, we get:

$$\sec = \left(\frac{\text{gm}}{\text{cm} \times \sec^2}\right)^x \times \text{cm}^y \times \left(\frac{\text{gm}}{\text{cm}^2}\right)^z$$

$$\sec = \frac{\text{gm}^x}{\text{cm}^x \times \sec^{2x}} \times \text{cm}^y \times \frac{\text{gm}^z}{\text{cm}^{2z}}$$

Combining all these, and separating out each dimension, we get:

$$\sec = \text{cm}^{-x+y-2z} \times \text{gm}^{x+z} \sec^{-2x}$$

Since the powers of cm, gm, and sec on both sides of the equation must be the same, we have:

$$0 = -x + y - 2z$$

$$0 = x + z$$

$$1 = -2x$$

which leads to:

$$x = -\tfrac{1}{2} \qquad y = z = \tfrac{1}{2}$$

Thus, our formula becomes:

$$T = \beta \times Y^{-1/2} \times l^{1/2} \times \left(\frac{m}{s}\right)^{1/2}$$

$$= \beta \times \frac{l^{1/2} \times m^{1/2}}{Y^{1/2} \times S^{1/2}}$$

$$= \beta \sqrt{\frac{lm}{Ys}}$$

where the numerical factor β can be found only by an exact mathematical calculation of the motion. But, even without knowing the value of β, we can draw many useful conclusions from the derived formula. For one thing, it tells us that the vibration period depends on the length of the suspension band in the same way as in the case of an ordinary pendulum. It also tells us that unlike the period of the pendulum, which does not depend on the mass, the vibration period of an elastically suspended object will increase with its increasing mass. This relationship between the period and the mass is due, of course, to the fact that, in contrast to the case of the pendulum, where both the acting force and the inertia are proportional to the mass of the object, the force in this case depends only on the relative lengthening of the rubber band. Similar formulas can be derived for the elastic vibrations caused by bending (in, for example, a tuning fork) and twisting.

RESONANCE

A very important notion in the study of all kinds of vibrations is that of resonance. **Resonance is the specific response of a system, which is able to oscillate or vibrate with a certain period, to an external force acting with the same period.** Consider a child on a swing. The swing is, of course, nothing but an ordinary pendulum, and its period is determined by the length of the ropes and is independent of the weight of the child sitting on the swing. In order to put the swing in motion and to make it move with a larger and larger amplitude, the child must pull periodically on the ropes and stretch out its legs at the same time. But to be successful these muscular efforts must be made with the same period as the natural oscillation period of the swing, for if this condition is not satisfied, the swing will hardly move at all. The situation can be demonstrated by the simple experiment shown in Fig. 3-2. A horizontal metal bar *A* is inserted loosely through the two holes in the supporting frame *B*, and a number of light wooden balls *C*, C^1, C^2, etc. are suspended from the bar on strings of different lengths. A heavier metal ball *D* is also suspended from the bar's protruding extremity in such a way

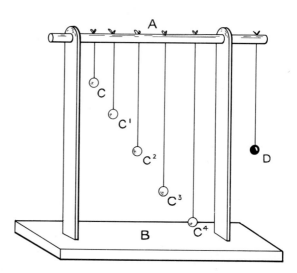

Fig. 3-2. The principle of resonance.

that its length of suspension can be changed. If we make this length equal, say, to the length of suspension of the third wooden ball and swing the iron ball in the plane perpendicular to the bar, some of the ball's energy will be transmitted through the small movements of the bar to the wooden balls hanging inside the frame. Although the other balls will show only a very slight tendency to take up this motion, the ball with the same suspension length (and, consequently, with the same oscillation period) will begin to swing more and more until its amplitude becomes even larger than that of the iron ball. By changing the suspension length of the iron ball, we can in turn set into motion the other balls hanging on the bar.

The principle of resonance is used in the construction of an instrument called a *tachometer*, which is used for measuring the speed of rotation of various motors. It consists of a number of steel bars of different lengths mounted on a common support. When put in contact with a running motor, the tachometer receives slight vibrations caused by the rotation of the motor's axis. If the period of the motor's rotation coincides with the vibration period of one of the bars, this particular bar begins to vibrate with an appreciable amplitude while all the other bars remain practically at rest. By reading the figures printed on a scale that runs along the row of bars, we can quickly find the number of rotations per minute (rpm) the motor is making.

This experiment has a "tricky" counterpart that can easily be demonstrated at the dinner table. Take an ordinary silver fork, which, when pinched by the ends of the two outer prongs (Fig. 3-3), emits a not

Fig. 3-3. "Putting the sound" of a vibrating fork into a glass.

very strong but audible sound. After pinching the fork with two fingers, move the fingers quickly towards a glass or a cup standing on the table and "drop the sound" into it. The audience will distinctly hear the increase of sound intensity after the sound is "dropped" into the glass. Next, "put the sound" taken from the fork's prongs into the open mouth of somebody in the audience and there will again be a noticeable increase in intensity. This experiment will ordinarily astonish everyone present (the author has even succeeded in confounding a few physics professors), but it is, of course, nothing but a trick. The increase in sound intensity is actually caused by the fork being held in the way shown in Fig. 3-3 and the handle of it (hidden within the palm) being pressed onto the surface of the table at the desired moment, which makes the surface of the wooden table vibrate. The presence of a tablecloth helps to eliminate the click of the fork against the wood, but, needless to say, the demonstration will not succeed if the hostess has a thick mat below the tablecloth.

Waves

SURFACE WAVES

"If you are dropping pebbles into a pond and do not watch the spreading rings, your occupation should be considered as useless," said the fictional Russian philosopher, Kuzma Prutkoff. And, indeed we can learn much by observing these graceful circles spreading out from the punctured surface of calm water. When one of the waves encounters an obstacle such as, for example, the wall of the pond, it is reflected backwards as shown in Fig. 3-4. The reflected wave looks as if it had been caused

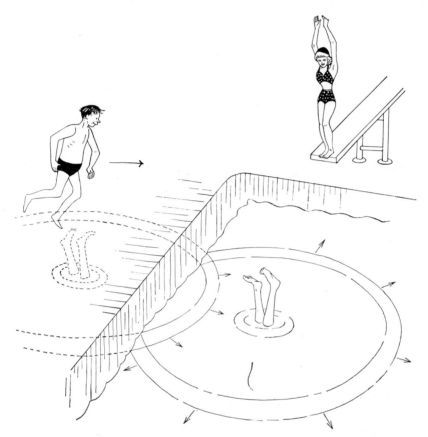

Fig. 3-4. The reflected wave off the side of a swimming pool caused by a diver looks as if it were caused by a diver who plunged in at an exactly opposite point on the other side of the pool's wall.

by a pebble dropped in the water at an exactly opposite point on the other side of the pond's wall. Thus, the wall of the pond acts as a mirror in respect to the surface waves, and, indeed, an optical mirror is based on the same principle except that it reflects waves of light instead of water waves.

A propagating wave can be characterized by its *period, frequency,* or *wave length. Period* is defined as the time interval during which the source emits one single wave or during which a propagating wave passes any given point on its way. *Frequency* is the number of waves emitted by the source per unit time or the number of individual waves which pass during a unit time through any given point. These two quantities are related by an obvious formula:

$$\text{frequency} = \frac{1}{\text{period}}$$

Thus, if a wave has a period of one-hundredth of a second, a hundred waves will pass by during a one-second interval. The *wave length,* measured from crest to crest or from hollow to hollow, is related to the period (or frequency) of the wave and also to the velocity of its propagation. The wave velocity, which is the distance through which the wave motion spreads out in a unit time, is obviously equal to the number of waves emitted during that unit of time multiplied by the length of individual waves:

$$\text{wave velocity} = \text{frequency} \times \text{wave length}$$

or, in terms of the period:

$$\text{wave velocity} = \frac{\text{wave length}}{\text{period}}$$

For a more detailed study of the propagation of surface waves, it is more convenient to move from the pool to the laboratory and to use the arrangement illustrated in Fig. 3-5. It consists of a dish filled with water or mercury and an electrically driven elastic bar which operates on much the same principle as an ordinary electric bell. To the end of the bar are attached two vertical needles that barely touch the surface of the

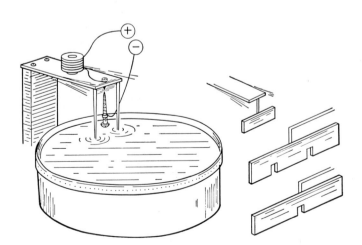

Fig. 3-5. Two electrically operated needles produce waves on the surface of a water tank.

liquid. When the bar vibrates, the needles periodically disturb the surface of the water and send out two sets of concentric circular waves. The overlap of these two sets of waves produces a phenomenon known as

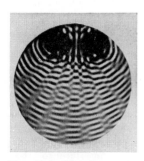

interference, which is demonstrated in the photograph in Fig. 3-6. The surface of the liquid breaks up into a number of narrow segments of alternately disturbed and calm water. The explanation of this phenomenon is given in Fig. 3-7, which shows two waves propagating from the points O_1 and O_2 on the left to a screen on the right. Since the distances O_1A and O_2A are equal, the two waves will travel to point A, with the ridges and hollows of one coinciding with the ridges and hollows of the other. We say that the two waves are *in phase* with one another, and it is apparent that the resulting motion will be increased. On the other hand, if we select a point B in such a way that the difference $O_1B - O_2B$ is equal to one-half of the wave length, the two waves will arrive *out of phase,* with the ridges of one overlapping the hollows of the other. It is clear in this case that the motion will practically cease. If we now select a point C so that the difference $O_1C - O_2C$ is equal to the entire wave length,

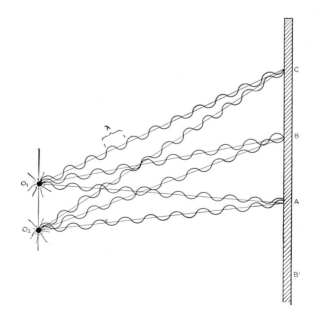

Fig. 3-7. The inter-
ference of two
waves coming from
the points, O_1 and
O_2.

the two waves will be in phase again, and the motion will again be increased. We can proceed in this way selecting points D, E, etc. (not shown in the figure) that correspond to alternating in-phase and out-of-phase positions in which the surface motion will be alternately increased and obliterated. A similar interference pattern will exist, of course, in the lower part of the screen.

Figures 3-8a and 3-8b show another experiment in which the two

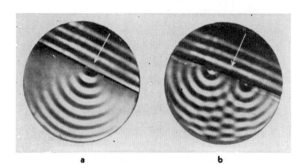

a   b

Fig. 3-8. The diffraction of a plane wave passing through a small opening in a breakwater (a), and the interference between two waves formed by two openings (b). *Courtesy Ealing Corp.*

needles attached to the vibrating spring are replaced by a long vertical plate (shown on the right of Fig. 3-5). In this case we get what is known as a *plane wave* propagating across the surface of the liquid. If we place in its way a "breakwater" plate with a single opening in it (see Fig. 3-5), the wave will pass through and produce a pattern (shown in Fig. 3-8a) that is similar to the pattern produced by a single oscillating needle. The pattern resulting from two openings in the "breakwater" plate (see Fig. 3-5) is reproduced in Fig. 3-8b, and it again shows an interference phenomenon similar to that shown in Fig. 3-6. The wave phenomena shown in Figs. 3-6 and 3-8 will have an important bearing on our study of light waves in Chapter 6.

Before we leave the subject of waves on the surface of a liquid, we must say a few words about the forces that produce them. There are two kinds of forces—gravity and surface tension—that are responsible for the propagation of these waves, and which one predominates in a particular case depends on the length of the wave. In the case of ordinary ocean waves, the main operating force is the force of gravity. Since the water in the crest of the wave is elevated above the mean water level, when it comes down it pushes up the water in the trough next to it and thus makes the crest look like it is moving forward. But there is actually no horizontal or translatory motion at all. The particles of water execute periodic circular or elliptic motions as shown in Fig. 3-9a and b. The deeper under the surface, the smaller are the orbits described by the particles, and at the bottom the particles are motionless. Let us consider the lines AA^1, BB^1, etc. in Fig. 3-9 as flexible boards attached to the bottom of a body of water. If all the boards are vertical and at rest, the surface of the water is smooth, but if the boards move as indicated in the drawing, the water levels between them will rise and fall periodically and thus form a propagating wave.

In the case of waves operated by gravity, the velocity of propagation increases with the wave length; the long high waves in a stormy sea roll much faster than the ripple caused by a gentle breeze. Those of you who have been thrown rudely upon the shore by an incoming comber will probably object to the statement that waves have no translatory motion. Well, the waves that roll onto a beach can carry people and heavy objects for quite a distance, but contrary to the situation in the open

Fig. 3-9. The motion of water particles in a propagating wave. At the situations shown in (a), the crest of the wave is in F and the hollows in B and J. When the water particles move 45° along their trajectories, the crest is shifted to E and the hollows to A and I, giving the impression that the wave "runs" from right to left.

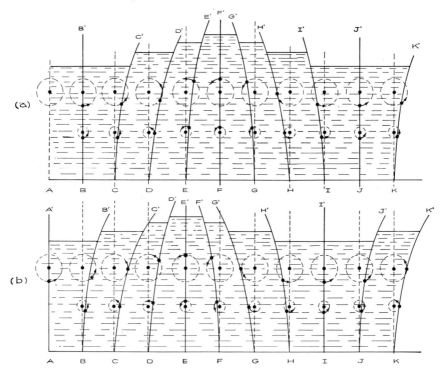

ocean, the waves that come into shallow water become unstable, break up, and throw tons of water up onto the shore.

If we turn now to an analysis of short waves like those shown in Figs. 3-6 and 3-8, we find that they are operated, not by the force of gravity, which is here quite small, but by the forces of surface tension. Since a plane surface has a smaller area than a wavy one, surface tension forces try to eliminate the crests and hollows in the same way that gravity forces do in the case of longer waves. Although the short surface tension waves look much the same as the long gravity waves, they obey different laws of propagation; in particular, the velocity of these waves decreases as the wave length increases.

There are other differences, also, between the two kinds of waves. Since long waves are operated by gravity and since their propagation results from the interplay between the weight of water elevated above the mean level and the mass of water to be moved, their velocity would remain the same even if the oceans were filled with a lighter liquid such as alcohol or a heavier liquid such as mercury. We have here the same situation as that in Galileo's experiment of dropping a light and a heavy body from a tower. Ocean waves on the moon (if there could be any oceans there), on the other hand, would have a different propagation velocity than those on the earth because the moon's gravity is less. The properties of surface tension waves, however, largely depend on the substance in which they are propagating. Thus, if we substituted mercury for water in Figs. 3-6 and 3-8, the waves would run considerably slower, but it would not make any difference whether the photographs were taken on the earth or on the moon.

Returning to the waves produced by a pebble in a pond, we may ask whether these waves are "long" waves operated by gravity or "short" waves operated by surface tension. As it turns out, in the case of water, the demarcation point between "long" and "short" waves is a wave length of about two centimeters. Since this length is just about that of the waves that are produced in water by a pebble, we can conclude that the waves of the type shown in Fig. 3-4 are operated by both gravitational and surface tension forces.

Although we ordinarily see surface waves only on the surface of water or some other liquid, such waves also occur on the surfaces of solids and gases. In an earthquake, for instance, although the main destructive force propagates right through the body of the earth, some surface waves are also created that may be quite destructive over a comparatively small distance. To get an example of surface waves in a gas, we have to turn to the terrestrial atmosphere, the upper boundary of which, though not as sharply defined as the surface of the ocean, is still some kind of a boundary. When in the year 1883 the volcano Krakatoa exploded in the Dutch East Indies with an energy of thousands of 10-megaton hydrogen bombs, a wave of disturbance in the atmosphere traveled several times around the earth. The pressure changes observed at that time at meteorological stations all around the globe were interpreted to be the result of a surface wave that propagated along the outer boundary of the terrestrial atmosphere.

WAVES IN SOLIDS

Elastic disturbances that propagate through solid bodies are of two different kinds: *transverse waves* and *longitudinal waves*. Suppose a horizontally suspended metal bar is struck by a hammer at one end in the direction perpendicular to its length (Fig. 3-10a). The impact of the hammer will cause a deformation (bending) near the point of impact, and this deformation will propagate along the bar just as the surface wave did in the pond of water. If we continue to hit the bar periodically, we will produce a steady train of waves along it. Waves of this kind are known as *transverse* or *T-waves*, and the motion of the material particles is perpendicular to the direction of propagation.

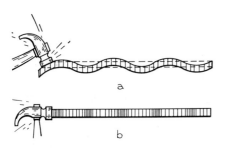

Fig. 3-10. Transverse and longitudinal waves in a solid bar.

If, instead of hitting the bar sideways, we hit it in the direction of its axis as shown in Fig. 3-10b, we will produce a rather different kind of wave. The material of the bar will be compressed at the point of impact, and this compression will propagate along the bar without causing any sidewards motion at its surface. This type of wave is a *longitudinal* or *L-wave*, and the particles of metal move back and forth along the direction of the propagation. The two kinds of waves, *T* and *L*, will, generally speaking, move at different speeds since they depend on different mechanical characteristics of the material: the resistance to bending (or shearing) in the first case and the resistance to compression in the second. This is all we will say here about waves in solids, but in the third part of this book we will return to them in more detail when we discuss earthquakes and the basic problems of seismology.

SOUND WAVES

Since a fluid substance, whether it is a poorly compressible fluid such as water or a readily compressible fluid such as air, does not offer any resistance to the changing of its shape (such as bending or shearing), transverse waves cannot exist in a fluid. The only waves that can propagate through a fluid are longitudinal compression waves. These compression waves, as they propagate through the water of the oceans and the air of the atmosphere, play a very important role in all walks of life. They warn a convoy ship of the presence of an enemy submarine, a peaceful gazelle of the approach of a vicious beast of prey, and a motorist of the on-rushing engines of the fire department. They carry the love calls of birds and red Indians (but not those of fish!),* they bring high profits to music halls; and they help professors communicate their knowledge to classrooms full of students. These waves are, of course, those that are commonly known as *sound waves*. Because of the practical importance of sound waves, the branch of physics dealing with this comparatively narrow subject is highly developed and is known by the special name of *acoustics*.

The first question that usually comes up in this field concerns the velocity of sound. If we watch an artillery battery practice some distance away, we will see the flash of light a few moments before we hear the sound of the shot. And, we all know that the clap of thunder follows the lightning with a delay that depends on how far away the thunderstorm is. Since light propagates practically instantaneously (by our everyday standards, of course), the velocity of sound can easily be found by timing the lag between the flash of light and the roar of the shot and then measuring the distance between the observer and the artillery piece. In this way we find that *the velocity of sound in air under normal atmospheric conditions is 330 meters per second.* In water, sound waves propagate about four and one-half times this fast, and in solid bodies such as a steel bar, they propagate fifteen times as fast. We also know that the velocity of sound in air is not affected by any changes in air density, but it noticeably increases with increasing temperature.

Sound waves differ from each other by their vibration frequency and wave length. Compression waves in air can have any frequency and any wave length, but when we speak about sound, we usually mean *audible sound*. The classic device for studying the vibration frequency or *pitch* of sound is a siren. A metal disc, containing a number of holes along its rim, is driven by a motor at varying speeds. A steel cylinder sup-

---

* It has been recently demonstrated, however, that sperm whales talk to each other by producing squeaking noises.

plies the compressed air that comes out in a puff each time an open-ing in the rotating disc aligns with the end of the pipe that releases the compressed air. If the disc rotates comparatively slowly, we will hear: "puff, puff, puff . . . ," not unlike the sound that comes from the ex-haust pipe of an automobile when the engine is idling. As the rotation velocity of the disc increases, we will hear a musical tone that will sound first like a bassoon, then like a flute and, finally, like a piccolo. If we speed up the rotation of the disc still more, the sound will fade out and we will hear practically nothing. Knowing the rotation veloci-ties of the disc in each case and the number of holes along its rim, we can easily calculate the number of "puffs per second" that correspond to the different sounds we hear (or don't hear). In this way we find that the lowest frequency which our ear accepts as a tone is somewhere around 20 oscillations per second and that the highest audible fre-quency is nearly 20,000 oscillations per second. By remembering that sound propagates at the rate of 330 meters per second, we can calcu-late the wave lengths of audible sound and find them to range from about 1.5 centimeters to about 15 meters.

SPEECH AND HEARING

In human relations, the primary role of sound is, of course, to carry conversation; one person speaks and another listens. The sounds are pro-duced by vibrations in our *vocal cords,* which are located at the opening of the throat, and amplified by the resonance action of our mouth and nasal cavities. When a person is silent, his vocal cords are wide open, a position that permits the air to circulate freely and facilitates the process of breathing. When a person starts to speak or sing or shout, the vocal cords come close together and begin to vibrate under the action of the stream of air expelled from the lungs. By changing the tension in the vocal cords, we can regulate the pitch of the sounds we produce.

The sounds that come from the human throat during an ordinary con-versation are certainly not the pure musical tones that are produced by tuning forks and, to a certain extent, by most musical instruments (ex-cluding drums!). They are a conglomeration of many different fre-quencies, and the way these frequencies are mixed together determines whether a sound is "Ah," "Oh," or "Rrr . . ." In Fig. 3-11 the curves show how different frequencies (pure tones) participate in the formation of the sound of various letters in the alphabet. It is interesting to note that the open "a" has a single broad frequency maximum (with the average about 1,025 vibrations per second), that the letter "i" in tip, drip, etc. has two distinct maxima (at 510 and 2,050 vibrations per second), and that the letter "m," like all other consonants, has a wide spectrum of frequencies (the consonants, indeed, are much closer to noise than they are to pure musical tones).

Another interesting point about the sound of letters is the amount of

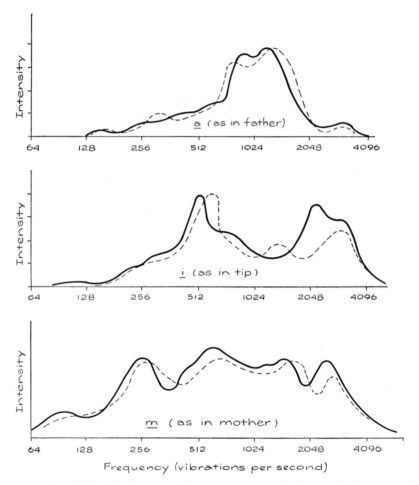

Fig. 3-11. The acoustical frequencies participating in different sounds of the human language. The solid curve is the male voice, the broken curve the female voice.

energy we expend in pronouncing them. It has been found that vowels take much more energy than consonants, as you can see by inspecting Table 3-1. To pronounce an average syllable, a speaker uses about 200 ergs of energy. Since, in the course of a one-hour lecture, a professor pronounces about ten thousand syllables, the total energy he spends on

TABLE 3-1 RELATIVE ENERGY INVOLVED IN
PRONOUNCING DIFFERENT LETTERS

Sound	as in	Relative mean energy
a	talk	1,870
a	tape	810
i	tip	365
s	sit	40
k	kit	15
d	dot	3
v	vat	1

talking is about 2×10^6 ergs or 0.00000006 kilowatt hours, in the terminology of an electric light bill. Since the commercial cost of energy is about 5 cents per kilowatt hour, professors should be paid 0.0000003 cent for each lecture they deliver. Or, to put it mildly, from this point of view, professors are highly overpaid!

The *ear* has a rather complicated structure (Fig. 3-12), consisting of three different compartments: The *outer ear* is a chamber (though not a

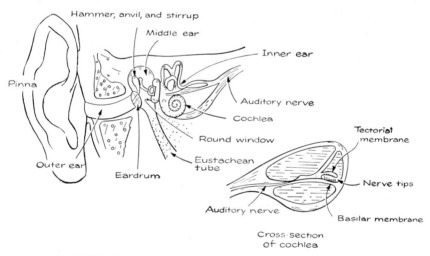

Fig. 3-12. The ear.

very effective one) for catching the sound, and at its inner end is the *eardrum*. The *middle ear*, which is connected by a channel with the mouth cavity, contains a joint system of three bones known as the *hammer*, the *anvil*, and the *stirrup*, names that describe the shape of these bones remarkably well. The *inner ear*, which receives vibrations from the eardrum via this triple bone system, contains the important structure known as the *cochlea,* which looks like a snail shell. In contrast to the outer and middle ears, the inner ear is filled with a fluid that transmits the pressure of the sound waves brought in by the three bones. As shown in the cross-section drawing in Fig. 3-12, the long spiral-shaped tube forming the inner ear contains a membrane known as the tectorial membrane, which runs all along it. It contains another membrane known as the *basilar membrane,* which looks like a brush and is covered with a multitude of tiny, hair-like cells that are the endings of nerve cell extensions (dendrites) which run all the way into the auditory center of the brain. Because of varying tension, and maybe also because of the varying thickness of the membrane along the spiraling channel of the cochlea, the inner ear possesses vibration frequencies that range from rather high values at the broad entrance of the channel (where high pitches are received) to comparatively low values at its narrow end (where low pitches are received). When a musical tone of well-defined frequency comes into the ear, it is transferred by the triple bone system to the inner ear where it produces vibrations in the fluid filling the inner ear, and the part of the membrane that is in resonance (i.e., has the same frequency) with the incoming sound begins to vibrate and, by exciting the nerve endings, sends the signal to the brain. The brain can then decide that "the singer took his E flat a bit too high."

That's how the ear works. It is certainly a very complicated gadget, but it does its job perfectly well.

SOUNDS, PLEASANT AND UNPLEASANT

Music is a series of sounds that give pleasure to the person listening to them. Since the notion of "pleasure" does not fall within the scope of the physical sciences, all we can do here is give a cold-blooded description of the different sound frequencies used in musical performances. "Scientific acoustics" uses a scale composed of eight notes, the vibrations of which stand in the proportions:

$$24 : 27 : 30 : 32 : 36 : 40 : 45 : 48$$

In this scale, the note "middle C" has a frequency of 256 vibrations per second, and the other notes of the scale have the frequencies listed under them:

C	D	E	F	G	A	B	C'
256	288	320	341.33	384	426.67	480	512

These eight notes form an *octave* of the so-called *diatonic scale*. The intervals between successive notes are not equal but have the values:

$$9/8, \ 10/9, \ 16/15, \ 9/8, \ 10/9, \ 9/8, \ 16/15$$

The 1st, 3rd, and 5th notes have vibration frequencies standing in the ratios of 4:5:6 and are known as a major triad. Other major triads are formed by the 4th, 6th, and 8th notes, and also by the 5th and 7th notes and the 2nd note of the octave above. The human ear, or, more likely, the human brain, is so constructed that we find it pleasing to hear the notes whose frequencies stand in simple proportions sounded simultaneously. Such notes produce what is called *consonance*. On the other hand, the simultaneous sounding of frequencies that are not in a simple proportion produces an unpleasant sound known as *dissonance*.

The strings of a piano or the pipes of an organ can be tuned to any set of frequencies desired. Musicians agree that the diatonic scale is the most pleasing to the ear, but with this scale the instrument must be tuned to one particular key. The frequencies given above are for one tuned to the key of C, and if one tried to play a scale beginning on any other note the intervals would come out wrong.

To avoid this difficulty the *equally tempered* scale was devised. As in all scales, each note is twice the frequency of the note an octave below and is half the frequency of the note an octave above. But rather than using the exact frequency ratios of the diatonic scale, the octave was divided into twelve equal parts (or half-tone intervals). Each note has a frequency 1.0595 times the one just below it, so that we may start anywhere on the keyboard, and the chords and scales for any key will be alike. The frequency ratios will be a little off from those of the diatonic scale, but the increased flexibility of the instrument is worth this small compromise with perfection. And now, if you are really interested in music, go and listen to a Beethoven concert.

ULTRASONICS

A dog's ear can hear sounds of higher frequency than the human ear can, and this canine ability is often utilized in police work. Police dogs receive "silent" orders from an ultrasonic whistle that cannot be heard by the human ear of the criminal. In the laboratory, *ultrasonic vibrations* are produced by a special device known as a *transducer*, an apparatus that consists essentially of a crystalline plate which is submerged in a liquid, with two thin metal films attached to its upper and lower surfaces. The two metal films are connected by cables to an electronic oscillator, the frequency of which can be adjusted to any desired value. The alternating electric field acting on the crystal plate causes it to contract and expand periodically and to send compression waves through the liquid. By adjusting the frequency of the electronic oscillator to various sonic frequencies in the audible range, we have what, in effect, is a tuning fork sounding under water, and, if we increase the frequency beyond the range of hearing, we will produce ultrasonic waves. These waves create in the liquid violent internal disturbances that have a variety of practical applications. They rapidly clean dirty metallic objects placed in the liquid; they kill frogs and other amphibians who are unfortunate enough to be swimming in the liquid; and they tear to pieces tiny bacteria and virus particles and thus provide biophysicists with an invaluable aid in their studies of the nature of life.

SUPERSONICS

Supersonics, which should not be confused with ultrasonics, is the study of the motion of objects that move with velocities higher than the velocity of sound. Since no objects can move very well through a solid and since even the most daring Navy designers would not dream of constructing a submarine that could move faster than the velocity of sound in water, the problems of supersonics are essentially limited to planes and missiles that fly through the air. The difference between subsonic and supersonic motion is shown in Figs. 3-13 and 3-14. Since, by definition, a subsonic vehicle moves slower than sound, the disturbance in the air caused by its motion runs far ahead of it. Thus, the inhabitants of cities bombed from the air in World War II could hear the whistle of the falling bombs before the bombs hit them. Tearing through the air, the fast-

Fig. 3-13. A metal sphere traveling with 84 per cent of the speed of sound (mach number 0.84) produces a turbulent wake in the air. *Courtesy Ballistic Laboratory, Aberdeen Proving Grounds, Md.*

moving objects leave behind them a turbulent wake similar to that caused by the propeller of a ship (Fig. 3-13). The situation is entirely different when a vehicle is moving with supersonic speed. Since in this case the air does not have time to adjust itself to the disturbance imposed on it by the object's motion, a sharp discontinuity of pressure, known as a *shock wave,* is created around the advancing edge of the object (Fig. 3-14). Since these discontinuities of pressure move along with the object and are thus stationary in respect to it, they are known as *standing shocks.* These standing shocks are of great importance in supersonic flight and

Fig. 3-14. A metal sphere traveling through the air with about twice the velocity of sound (mach number 2) produces a turbulent wake and a set of shock waves The dark band in the lower part of the photograph is a metal plate with a series of holes drilled through it. As the frontal shock wave passes the holes, it sends impulses into the air below the plate, producing spherical sound waves which form the linear front of a sound wave. The dark dashes below the plate are the parts of the shock wave that have passed through the holes. Courtesy Ballistic Laboratory, Aberdeen Proving Grounds, Md.

must be taken into consideration in the structural specifications of a supersonic vehicle. In fact, many of the experimental supersonic planes that have crashed have been torn apart by these standing shocks.

When a plane or a guided missile moves through the air at subsonic speed, the resistance of air to its motion, known as *drag,* decreases slowly with its velocity, as indicated in Fig. 3-15. When the velocity of the plane approaches the speed of sound, the plane needs a lot of additional energy to overcome the standing shocks, and the air resistance to further acceleration sharply increases. This resistance encountered in the transition from subsonic to supersonic speed is known as the *sonic barrier*. As soon as the velocity of the plane exceeds the velocity of sound, however, the in-

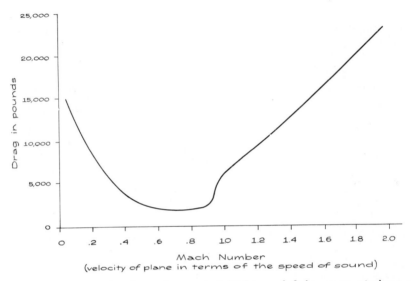

Fig. 3-15. The drag of a typical high-speed fighter-type airplane at 35,000 ft. Courtesy Convair, San Diego, Calif.

crease of drag slows down again, and the resistance to further acceleration becomes normal.

SHOCK WAVES

The *shock waves* produced in various kinds of explosions are similar to the standing shocks that accompany a supersonic vehicle. In fact, when an ordinary or atomic bomb goes off, its material moves outwards at very high supersonic speeds. This leads to the formation of a discontinuity of pressure in the surrounding medium which immediately precedes the expanding material of the exploded bomb (Fig. 3-16a). But, whereas a supersonic vehicle proceeds with a constant speed (since it is driven by its motor), the hot gases formed in a bomb explosion lose their power and slow down as their volume increases. Under these circumstances, the shock wave separates from the expanding hot gas sphere (Fig. 3-16b) and travels through the surrounding medium causing damage to any objects it encounters on its way. It is the underwater shock wave produced by depth charges that disables enemy submarines; it is the shock wave of an A-bomb that flattens buildings as if they were constructed of playing cards; and it was the shock wave of the H-bomb explosion at Eniwetok that turned the coral island Elugelab into a pool of water one mile wide and 175 feet deep. Since the problems of this book concern the physical sciences and not military engineering, we will not go into further details concerning the propagation and the effects of shock waves.

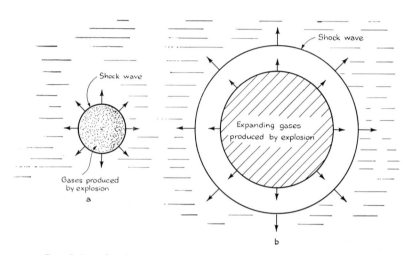

Fig. 3-16. The formation of a shock wave in an explosion. (a) At the early stage of the explosion, the gases formed by the exploded material push through the surrounding medium; (b) at the later stages, the discontinuity of pressure separates from the expanding gases and propagates freely through the surrounding medium.

HEAT

AND TEMPERATURE

The only way to explain to a person the meaning of the words "hot" and "cold," if he claims that he does not know what they mean, is to put him first into a tub filled with almost boiling water and then into one with ice cubes floating in it. Fortunately, such drastic treatment is never necessary since we all possess a well-developed sense of temperature. All physical bodies, such as a piece of solid material or a certain amount of liquid, respond to temperature changes in a simple way: They expand when the temperature rises and contract when it drops. The author cannot resist reproducing here an illustration from a booklet, "Physics For Fools," published in Russia half a century ago (Fig. 4-1). The original caption for this picture runs: "Every body expands when heated; that is why the railroad tracks are always made shorter than they should be. The same simple experiment can be performed in everybody's home. Put a not very bad natured relative of yours on a cold kitchen stove with his feet against the wall and place a pile of books behind his head. Start the fire and you will observe that your relative will begin to expand, moving the books until they finally fall on the floor. With a further increase of temperature, the character of the phenomenon will change: your relative will jump up and run away. This demonstrates another important physical phenomenon: the transformation of heat into motion."

Temperature and Thermometers

The expansion of heated material bodies can be used for determining the "degree of heating," usually known as temperature. Thermometers used for this purpose are usually constructed in such a way that a small thermal expansion results in a large displacement of the indicator. In thermometers based on the expansion of a liquid, a comparatively large amount of the liquid (usually mercury or alcohol) is confined in a container, and its expansion causes the excess liquid to rise in a narrow, capillary tube (Fig. 4-2a). In thermometers based on the expansion of solids, a double plate is often used, composed of two metals with different abilities to expand when heated (Fig. 4-2b). The difference of expansion between the two parts of such a double plate causes it to bend

Fig. 4-1. A demonstration of thermal expansion. From "Physics for Fools," published in St. Petersburg, Russia, in 1908.

with its free end moving along a scale. Although all such devices will behave, generally speaking, in a similar way and give us a clear indication of whether the temperature goes up or down, they will disagree between themselves in smaller details since different materials react somewhat differently to an increase of temperature. Thus, if we mark by 0 and 100 the freezing and boiling points of water (centigrade scale) on thermometers filled with mercury, alcohol, and water, we will find that, as the temperature increases from zero, the mercury and alcohol columns will rise while the water column will first drop and will begin to rise only after the other two columns have covered four per cent of the total distance to the boiling point. Even the mercury and alcohol columns, which are ad-

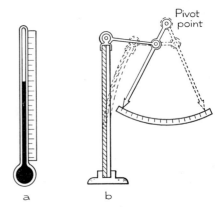

Fig. 4-2. (a) Mercury thermometer; (b) a metal-expansion thermometer.

justed to show identical values at the two ends of the scale, will be in slight disagreement in between because they expand at different rates in different temperature intervals.

Since the physiological sense of heat is too vague to be used for any exact definition of temperature and since we have no reason whatsoever to give preference to any particular one of the liquid thermometers filled with mercury, alcohol, water, or olive oil, or to a particular solid one formed by iron-copper, silver-zinc, or pine-oak plates, we have to look somewhere else for the exact and universal definition of the temperature scale. The solution is provided by gases, since it has been found that **all gases subjected to heating expand in exactly the same way.** This property of gases, which is in contrast to that of solid and liquid materials, is due to the extreme simplicity of the inner structure of gases as compared with the structure of solids and liquids. We will discuss this in more detail in the next part of the book devoted to the internal structure of matter. Meanwhile, we can accept as a standard the temperature scale provided by a gas thermometer (Fig. 4-3), regardless of what gas is used to fill it. Having this as a standard scale, we can then "calibrate" properly any other temperature-measuring gadget.

ABSOLUTE ZERO

When a gas, any gas, is heated from the freezing point of water to its boiling point, its volume increases by about one third or, to be more exact, by 1/2.73 of its original value. Since we have agreed to measure the temperature by the volume changes of gas and to divide the temperature interval between the freezing and boiling points of water into 100 equal parts, or *degrees centigrade*, we say that one degree centigrade corresponds to the volume change of gas by one 273rd part. If we now begin to cool the gas below the freezing point of water, it will contract by that fraction for each degree of cooling so that, at the temperature of 273°C below the freezing point, the volume of any gas should be expected to become zero. This point is known as the *absolute zero* of temperature, and the temperature counted from that point is known as *absolute temperature* (°abs.) or *Kelvin temperature* (°K). In Fig. 4-4 we give a graphic presentation of volume changes in gases as the function of absolute temperature. As long as a gas remains a gas, the graph is a straight line passing through absolute zero, and the gas shows every intention of shrinking to zero volume at that temperature. These intentions are never exactly fulfilled, however, since all gases liquefy before they reach zero. Some do it sooner, some do it later, and helium does it last of all, at only about 4 degrees before reaching absolute zero. And, of course, as soon as a gas turns into a liquid, its volume decreases much slower and does not tend to zero any more. But, although no real gas actually goes to the end of the track, the notion of absolute zero temperature is very important in physics and can be, if desired, used in reference to an

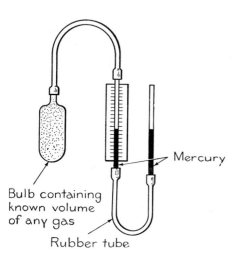

Mercury

Bulb containing known volume of any gas

Rubber tube

Fig. 4-3. Gas thermometer. The changing volume of the trapped gas is read from the height of the mercury column in front of the scale. If, in order to keep the mercury level the same on both sides, the right-hand tube is lowered as the gas heats, the gas in the bulb will remain at atmospheric pressure at all times.

imaginary "ideal gas" which remains a gas no matter how much we cool it.

AMOUNT OF HEAT

If we take a glassful of water at, say, 80°C and mix it with an equal amount of water at, say, 50°C, we will find that the mixture will have a temperature of 65°C, i.e., just in between. But if we mix one glass of water at 80°C with two glasses at 50°C, we find that the temperature

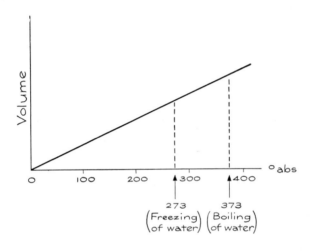

Fig. 4-4. The behavior of gas at low temperatures.

of the mixture will be only 60°C. This and similar observations can be interpreted in the following way: *Each material body contains in itself a certain quantity of what we call "heat," and the total amount of that heat increases with increasing temperature.* When we mix a glass of hot water with a glass of colder water, the excess of heat in the former is equally distributed between the water of both glasses. Since each volume of mixed water now has only one-half of the heat excess formerly existing in the first glass, the temperature of the mixture will drop halfway. In the case of the glass of hot water mixed with two glasses of cold water, the original heat excess is "diluted" by a factor of three and the temperature excess above the original cold water mark will be only one-third of the difference between 50°C and 80°C.

Having established the notion of the amount of heat, we can now define the unit for measuring it. In scientific measurements, we use the unit known as the *calorie*, which is defined as *the amount of heat necessary to raise the temperature of one gram of water by one degree centigrade.* A larger unit, the *kilocalorie*, is defined as one thousand calories.

Different substances have different heat capacities, which are called *specific heats* (if they refer to unit mass)—that is, they require different amounts of heat to raise the temperature of one gram of the substance by one degree. It is interesting to notice that water has an exceptionally high heat capacity so that the figures for other substances are, as a rule, considerably smaller than unity; for instance, the specific heat of alcohol is 0.232 and that of mercury 0.033.

LATENT HEAT

When we place a teakettle on the fire, the temperature of the water gradually rises to 100°C, at which point the water begins to boil. But, once the boiling has started, the temperature stays at 100°C until the last drops of water are turned into steam. Although the heat is still flowing into the kettle from the flame, it does not make the water any hotter. What happens to that heat? The answer is, of course, that this heat is used to transform the water into vapor, and measurements show that to do it we must supply 539 calories per each gram of water to be vaporized. This amount of heat is known as the *latent (hidden) heat of evaporation,* and is, of course, different for different substances. Thus, to evaporate one gram of alcohol and one gram of mercury we need only 204 and 72 calories respectively. The heat absorbed in the evaporation of water plays an important role during hot weather in the cooling of our body through the process of skin perspiration. Indeed, one glass of water evaporated from the surface of our body removes enough heat to cool the entire body by a few degrees. If the weather is "sticky," with a high content of vapor in the atmosphere, the evaporation is considerably slower; a layer of water is formed on the skin, and we begin to sweat. Meteorologists use the same principle for measuring the relative humidity of air. The apparatus used for this purpose is known as a "psychrometer" and consists of two identical thermometers with the ball of one of them covered by a wet cloth. This thermometer, because of evaporation, shows a somewhat lower temperature, and from the difference between the two readings the weatherman can calculate the rate of evaporation and, consequently, the amount of humidity present in the atmosphere.

A similar phenomenon is encountered when water turns into ice. When the temperature of water comes down to 0°C and the first crystals of ice begin to form, the temperature remains at zero until all of the water freezes. The *heat of fusion of water* (i.e., the amount of heat that must be taken away from one gram of water at zero to freeze it, or be given to one gram of ice at zero to melt it), amounts to 80 calories. The heat of fusion of alcohol (which freezes at −114°C) is only 30 cal/gm, whereas for mercury (freezing at −39°C) it is only 2.8 cal/gm. To melt lead (at +327°C) it takes about 6 cal/gm, whereas in the case of copper (at +1,083°C), the figure is as high as 42 cal/gm.

Mechanical Energy Versus Heat

In the second chapter of this book, we mentioned that the law of conservation of mechanical energy is challenged by the friction forces that gradually rob mechanical systems of their energy and eventually bring them to a standstill. On the other hand, we know that where there is friction there is always heat, be it in the two sticks of a Boy Scout trying to build a fire in the old Indian way or in the axles of a railroad car overlooked by the oil man. What is the relation between the mechanical energy lost to friction and the amount of heat produced by it? This question was answered in the middle of the last century by a British physicist, James P. Joule (1818-1889), in his famous experiment on the transformation of mechanical energy into heat. Joule's apparatus, schematically shown in Fig. 4-5, consists of a water-filled vessel containing a rotating axis with several stirring paddles attached to it. The water in the vessel was prevented from rotating along with the paddles by special vanes attached to the walls of the vessel. The whole system looked very much like the modern gearless hydromatic transmission of an automobile and provided a perfect stage for the play of internal friction forces. The axis with the paddles was driven by a

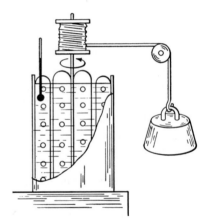

Fig. 4-5. Joule's apparatus.

weight suspended across a pulley, and thus the work done by the descending weight was transformed into friction heat communicated to the water. Knowing the amount of water in the vessel, Joule could measure the rise of its temperature and calculate the total amount of heat produced; the driving weight and the distance of its descent gave the total amount of mechanical work done. Repeating this experiment many times and under different conditions, Joule established that there is a direct proportionality between these two quantities and that "the work done by the weight of 1 lb through 772 feet at Manchester will, if spent in producing heat by friction in water, raise the temperature of 1 lb of water one degree Fahrenheit." In metric units, it means that one calorie of heat is the equivalent of 4.18×10^7 ergs of work.

Joule's work confirmed the basic idea that was "floating in the air" at the time, namely, that **heat is energy in the same sense as mechanical energy is, and, while one form of energy can be transformed into another, the sum of the two always remains constant.** This law represents one of the basic pillars of the entire system of physics.

HEAT CONDUCTION

If we take a long iron rod and heat one end of it, by a lighted candle, let us say, heat will propagate along the rod and gradually raise the temperature at points more and more distant from the heated end (Fig. 4-6). If the rod is perfectly insulated by, say, a layer of asbestos, it will finally acquire the temperature of the flame throughout its entire length,

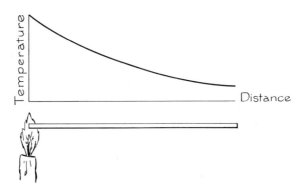

Fig. 4-6. The relationship between distance and temperature in a heated rod.

and the flux of heat will stop. If the rod is permitted to lose heat through its surface to the surrounding air, however, there will be established a certain state of equilibrium with the temperature gradually dropping along the rod. If, instead of an iron rod we take a glass rod, the sequence of events will be the same except that the establishment of the final temperature distribution will take a considerably longer time; thus we say that glass is a poorer heat conductor than iron. The basic law of heat conduction states that **the rate of heat flow, that is, the amount of heat passing through a unit cross-section per unit time, is proportional to the gradient of the temperature,** and we can define the heat conductivity of different materials as *the number of calories passing through a square centimeter cross-section per second, if the temperature drops by one degree centigrade per centimeter.* The heat conductivities of several familiar materials are shown in Table 4-1, and we notice right away that metals are, in general, much better heat conductors than non-metals. There is a very good reason for this, as we will learn later when we discuss the internal structure of matter and the hidden mechanism of heat conductivity.

TABLE 4-1   HEAT CONDUCTIVITY OF DIFFERENT MATERIALS EXPRESSED IN CALORIES PER SEC FLOWING THROUGH 1 CM^2, WHEN THE TEMPERATURE GRADIENT IS 1°C PER CM

Material	Heat Conductivity (at 18°C)
Silver	0.97
Copper	0.92
Aluminum	0.48
Iron (cast)	0.11
Lead	0.08
Mercury	0.016
Glass	0.0025
Brick	0.0015
Water	0.0013
Wood	0.0003
Asbestos	0.0002
Cotton-wool	0.00004
Air	0.00006

The heat conductivity of various materials plays an important role in all kinds of heat insulation. Since cotton-wool and similar materials present forty times more resistance to the flow of heat than ordinary brick, we can clearly see the advantages of their use for insulating homes. And, since the escape of heat is proportional to the surface of an object, to conserve heat it is advantageous to build houses as compact (as close to a spherical shape) as possible—hence the difference in construction styles in southern California and northern Canada. Following the same principle, many animals roll up almost into a ball when it is cold and stretch out when it is too warm.

Another important point in heat conductivity pertains to the size of the building to be heated. If we compare a modern apartment house with a log cabin, we will see at once that, per unit space, the heating of the former is much more economical. In fact, if a large building has the same geometrical shape as a small one, the total number of rooms (each of which is to be heated) increases as the cube of linear dimensions, whereas the surface through which the heat escapes increases only as the square. Thus, in larger buildings the amount of heat needed per room to maintain a comfortable temperature is considerably lower than that needed for smaller buildings. The same applies to various-sized animals who maintain their body temperature by chemical reactions between the food they assimilate and the air they inhale (metabolism). In Fig. 4-7, the metabolic rates of different animals are plotted in respect to their weight. We see that hummingbirds, who have a very unfavorable surface-

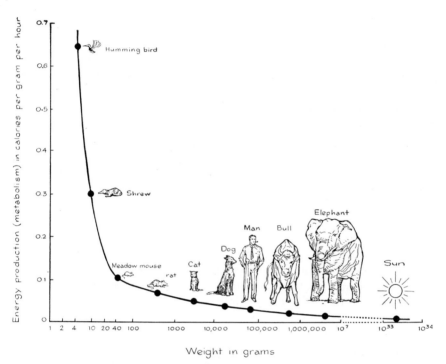

Fig. 4-7. The relationship between weight and heat production in various animals ranging in size from the hummingbird to the elephant. The graph is extended to the right to include the sun's interior.

to-volume ratio, have to metabolize at a terrific rate, which is, by the way, just about the same as the power production per unit weight in a modern helicopter. On the other hand, large animals can be very economical in their internal heating systems and, in fact, if an elephant metabolized at the same rate as a hummingbird, it would be a roasted elephant, since the temperature of its body would rise to that usually encountered in kitchen ovens. In this connection it is interesting to notice that the rate of "metabolism" inside the sun (the point on the far right in Fig. 4-7) is extremely low—only a fraction of a per cent of that in the human body. If the heating unit in an electric coffeepot produced heat at the same rate as it is produced in the interior of the sun, the pot would take months to make water boil (assuming, of course, that the coffee pot were perfectly insulated against heat losses). Only the extremely low surface-to-volume ratio of the sun enables its meager rate of energy production to keep its body and surface much hotter than that of a roasted elephant!

HEAT CONVECTION

In the case of poor heat conductors, the propagation of heat into the heated body is very slow, and in the case of water, for example, it would take hours to heat the water in a teakettle standing on the fire if there were no other heat-carrying processes. In fluids, the propagation of heat is considerably accelerated by the process of convection, which has its basis in the fact that heated bodies increase their volume and hence decrease their density. In our teakettle, the water near the bottom is heated by immediate contact with the hot metal, becomes lighter than the rest of the water in the kettle, and floats up, its place being taken by the cooler water from the upper layers. These convection currents carry the heat up "bodily," and they mix the water in the kettle so that the tea is ready in practically no time. A similar phenomenon takes place in our atmosphere when, on a hot summer day, the air heated by contact with the ground streams up to be replaced by cooler air masses from above. As the air rises to higher and cooler layers of the atmosphere, the water vapor in the air condenses into a multitude of tiny water droplets and forms the cumulus clouds so characteristic of hot summer days. Convection processes are also very important in the life of our sun and stars. In them, the atomic energy produced in the hot central regions is carried towards the surface by the streams of heated stellar gases.

Sometimes the notion of "convective" heat transfer gets mixed up with the notion of heat conduction. We have seen from Table 4-1, for example, that the heat conductivity of cotton-wool is about the same as that of air. Wool, fur, and other materials used to make warm clothes also have about the same degree of conductivity. But if the heat conductivity of air is the same as that of warm clothing materials, why then is a naked man less comfortable in cold weather than a man in a fur coat or under a thick woolen blanket? The reason is that the heat is removed from the skin of a naked man not by heat conduction in the air but by heat convection: The cold air warmed by contact with the skin rises and is replaced by more of the cold air. The role of warm clothing materials is to prevent this circulation and to keep the air from moving by trapping it between the numerous interwoven fibers of the materials. If we compress a woolen sweater or a mink coat under a hydraulic press, they will immediately lose their ability to keep us warm.

VERY HOT AND VERY COLD

We human beings are very sensitive to the temperature. If it is in the "upper eighties" (Fahrenheit) we feel uncomfortably hot, and if it is "below freezing" we feel pretty cold. Actually, life can survive much wider temperature variations. Algae living in hot springs can stand temperatures almost as high as the boiling point of water, while on the other hand plant seeds are not killed by temperatures approaching absolute zero. The lowest temperature we encounter in everyday life is probably that of dry ice (frozen carbon dioxide), which is about −80°C, and the highest is that of the kitchen range flame, which is about +1,700°C. High-temperature engineering goes well beyond this in the production of high temperatures; a "plasma-jet" torch, for instance, reaches a temperature of almost 15,000°C (Fig. 4-8). All solid bodies

Fig. 4-8. A "plasma jet" produced by blowing a stream of noble gas through a high-current electric arc discharge. Consisting of positive ions and free electrons, the plasma jet reaches temperatures of 15,-000°K, i.e., two and a half times the temperature of the sun's surface. Courtesy G. M. Gianini.

melt and then evaporate when the temperature is sufficiently high, and in Table 4-2 we list some melting and boiling points of solids just to give an idea of the range of temperatures between these two points.

TABLE 4-2   MELTING AND BOILING POINTS OF METALS

Material	Melting point, (°C)	Boiling point, (°C)
Tin	+232	+2260
Lead	+327	+1620
Aluminum	+660	+1800
Copper	+1083	+2300
Iron	+1535	+3000
Platinum	+1773	+4300
Tungsten	+3370	+5900

At temperatures of 6,000°C and above, all (even the most heat resistant) materials are turned into gas, which is the state of all materials in the atmosphere of our sun.

To produce very low temperatures, we use cryogenic equipment, which is similar to the mechanism of a refrigerator or a room air conditioner and is based on the fact that compressed air escaping through a small opening gets cooler when it expands into a larger volume. You can verify this fact by blowing air out of your lungs, first with your mouth wide open, and then with your lips forming a small hole. In the first case, the palm of your hand placed in front of your mouth will feel quite warm; in the second case, it will feel much cooler. The principle of a cryogenic apparatus is shown in Fig. 4-9. The apparatus consists of an electrically driven "compressor" that pumps the gas from the "expansion chamber" up into the "compression chamber" when the valve on the right connecting the two chambers is closed. The compressed gas is heated above room temperature, and the excess heat escapes into the surroundings, be it into the kitchen in which the refrigerator stands or into the air outside the window in which the air conditioner is installed. When the valve separating the compression chamber and the expansion chamber is opened, the gas expands again and "sucks in" heat from the surroundings. Then air from the expander is brought back into the compressor and the process is repeated. Thus, the sequence of successive compressions and expansions serves as a "thermal pump" that takes the heat away from the expander and "pumps" it into the compressor. The refrigerator, of course, warms up the kitchen while it cools the food inside it, and the air conditioner warms up the outside air while it cools the room, but nobody cares.

By using the above described principle, it is possible

Fig. 4-9. The principle of cryogenics. The gas, heated by compression in the upper chamber, loses heat to the surroundings, while the gas that is cooled by expansion in the lower chamber absorbs heat from the surroundings. (Direction of heat flow is shown by wavy-tailed arrows.)

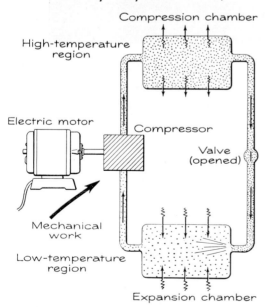

Compression chamber

High-temperature region

Electric motor

Compressor

Valve (opened)

Mechanical work

Low-temperature region

Expansion chamber

to build complex cryogenic equipment (Fig. 4-10) capable of reducing the temperature so much that it can first liquefy air and then freeze it into a solid block. In the same way, all other gases, such as hydrogen and helium, can be liquefied and frozen, but at much lower temperatures. Table 4-3 gives the temperatures of the liquefaction and freezing points of several common gases.

TABLE 4-3   LIQUEFYING AND FREEZING POINTS OF GASES

Substance	Liquefying point, (°C)	Freezing point, (°C)
Chlorine	− 35	−102
Oxygen	−183	−218
Nitrogen	−196	−210
Hydrogen	−253	−259
Helium	−269	−272

Turning Heat into Motion

We know that any amount of mechanical energy can be completely transformed into heat and, thus, that all the kinetic energy of a heavily

Fig. 4-10. Hydrogen liquefiers at the cryogenic laboratory of the National Bureau of Standards in Boulder, Colorado, which produce 350 liters of liquid hydrogen per hour. On the top of the large dewar vessels, Dr. F. Brickwedde, the expert in low-temperature physics, is testing the vacuum-jacketed pipes that deliver the liquid hydrogen. Courtesy National Bureau of Standards.

loaded, fast-moving train is transformed into heat when the train stops by the friction in the brakes. But is the process reversible? Can the entire amount of heat contained, let us say, in a pot of boiling water be transformed into mechanical energy? We know, for sure, that steam engines do transform heat into mechanical energy, but if we look at the problem closer we will find that they always transform only a part of the entire heat available into mechanical energy. What happens to the other part? Well, as any mechanical engineer will tell you, it is delivered into the "cooler" which receives the steam after it has done its work in the cylinders. Figure 4-11 is a simplified diagram of a common reciprocating steam engine. Hot steam produced in the boiler is sent into the cylinder (by opening the "incoming" valve), pushes the piston, and thus transforms a part of its thermal energy into mechanical work. The piston then moves and pushes the steam that has been used through the "outgoing" valve into the cooler where it condenses back into water.

"Coolers" are always used in steamship engines; since sea water is no good for running steam engines (too much salt deposits on the boiler's walls), the water collected in the cooler is again transferred to the boiler. In railroad locomotives, the role of the "cooler" is played by the surrounding air into which the steam is released from the cylinders (the air acts as a "cooler," of course, only as long as it is cooler than the boiler). Summing up, we see that the principle of the operation of a steam engine can be formulated in the following way: *The heat from the hot region (the boiler) streams down into the colder region (the cooler) and, on the way, a certain part of it is transformed into mechanical energy.* If Q_1 is the amount of heat coming from the boiler, and Q_2 the amount received by the cooler, the amount of mechanical energy produced is given by:

$$E = (Q_1 - Q_2) \times \text{(mechanical equivalent of heat)}$$

From the point of view of economy, of course, it would be best to reduce Q_2 to zero, throw away the cooler, and have the entire heat contained in the hot steam turned into mechanical energy. But this is

Fig. 4-11. The principle of a steam engine.

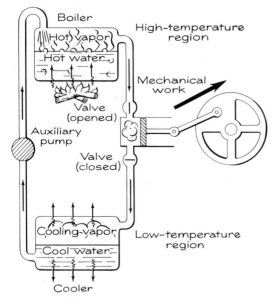

Boiler

Hot vapor

Hot water

High-temperature region

Mechanical work

Valve (opened)

Auxiliary pump

Valve (closed)

Cooling-vapor

Cool water

Low-temperature region

Cooler

impossible. To understand why, let us consider the following problem, which at first sight has nothing to do with heat or steam engines. Suppose there is a house on a hill and a creek running swiftly through a ravine a dozen feet below it (Fig. 4-12). Can we manage it so that the creek by its own power will supply the household's water needs? The answer is: yes. If we build a dam A and install a waterwheel B that will produce a certain amount of power, the waterwheel can operate a pump C that will pump a certain amount of water up the hill and into the house. Very simple indeed! But, if the owners of the house become too ambitious and try to get all the water carried by the creek up the hill, they will be heading for trouble. The amount of water they are getting is being pushed 12 feet uphill by the rest of the water dropping 3 feet in the waterwheel. If all the water in the creek were brought up to the house, there would be no water left to drive the wheel and to operate the pump! The best we can do is to arrange things in such a way that the potential energy liberated by the water operating the wheel is the same as the potential energy necessary to raise the water to the house. If X is the fraction of the total water supply of the creek that can be brought up to the house, we have:

$$X \times 12 = (1 - X) \times 3$$

so that:

$$X = \frac{3}{12 + 3} = \frac{1}{5}$$

Thus, at best, we can get one-fifth of the water of the creek "self-propelled" to the house, but any demand beyond that would contradict the laws of physics.

The situation with the steam engine is quite similar, and it was shown by a French engineer, Sadi Carnot (1796-1832), that **the largest fraction of original heat "descending" from the temperature T_1 to the temperature T_2 that can be turned into mechanical energy is, at best, equal to the ratio of the temperature difference to the higher tem-**

Fig. 4-12. Pumping water uphill by means of a water wheel.

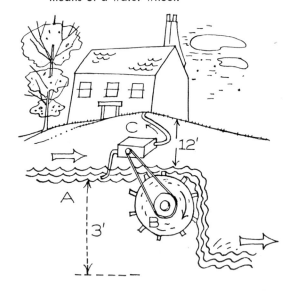

perature $(T_1 - T_2)/T_1$, where the temperatures are counted from absolute zero. If, for example, a locomotive engine operates between a boiler temperature of 100°C and an outside temperature of, say, 40°C (373 and 313 in the absolute scale), the maximum fraction of heat from the boiler that can be transformed into mechanical work is:

$$\frac{373 - 313}{373} = \frac{40}{373} = 0.107, \quad \text{or about 11 per cent}$$

The simple reciprocating steam engine, described above, in which the "to and fro" motion of a piston is transformed into the rotational motion of a crankshaft, was invented during the second half of the eighteenth century by the Britisher, James Watt, and it has been used extensively ever since for stationary power production as well as for the propulsion of steamships and locomotives. More recently, reciprocating steam engines have yielded, in many instances, to *steam turbines,* which have the advantage of continuity of motion and the absence of valves. The scheme of a steam turbine is shown in Fig. 4-13. It consists of a fixed drum, A,

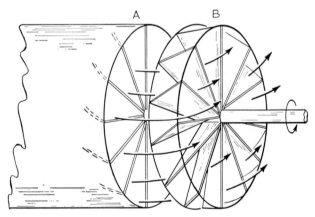

Fig. 4-13. The scheme of a steam turbine. Steam turbines operate by using hot water vapor, while gas turbines use the hot gases that result from the burning of fuel.

on the left, containing tilted metal paddles arranged in such a way that the high-pressure steam that passes through the drum from the boiler whirls around them in a counterclockwise direction. Another similar, but movable, drum B is placed right in front of drum A and contains paddles that are tilted oppositely to those in A. The impulse of the hot vapor streaming from *A* will then cause drum *B* to rotate in the direction indicated by the arrow.

INTERNAL COMBUSTION ENGINES

In the ordinary reciprocating steam engine, as well as in a steam turbine, the fuel (wood, coal, or oil) is used to produce high-pressure water vapor ("working fluid") which is then introduced into the working parts of the engine. In an *internal combustion engine,* however, the burning of fuel takes place within the moving system itself. The fuel, in this case generally a liquid, is either directly injected into the cylinder or is mixed with the air that is sucked into the cylinder by the receding piston.

One of the best-known engines of this type was invented in 1892 by a German engineer, Rudolph Diesel, and is named after him. Figure 4-14

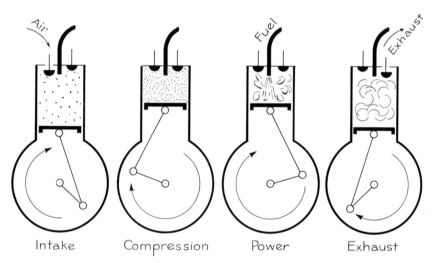

Fig. 4-14. The four-stroke cycle in a Diesel engine.

shows the operational cycle of the *Diesel engine,* which consists of the following:

A. The "suction stroke" during which air is drawn into the cylinder.

B. The "compression stroke" in which the air is compressed and heated by the inward inertial motion of the piston. At the end of this stroke, the fuel is injected into the cylinder and it ignites when it comes into contact with the hot air.

C. The "working stroke" when the ignited mixture pushes the piston back.

D. The "expulsion stroke" during which the burned products are expelled from the cylinder.

Its high efficiency and low fuel consumption made the Diesel engine very popular in all fields of industry, and stationary power plants as well as steamship companies rapidly substituted it for the old-fashioned steam engine. Diesel engines are sweeping the locomotive field, and the old steam locomotive, picturesque as it is, is quickly disappearing from the railroad scene. In the Diesels used in locomotives, the energy produced by the engine is first converted into the energy of electric current by large dynamos and then fed into electric motors attached to the wheels. This method insures a smoother transfer of power and permits the train to slow down or accelerate without changing the rate of the driving Diesel. The excess power of the Diesel may be stored in large storage batteries to be used as extra power when needed.

Diesel engines, which use inexpensive, heavy oil (such as that used for heating a house), are rather large and heavy and cannot be used for propelling vehicles such as passenger automobiles and airplanes. For these vehicles, the modern *gasoline engine* was developed, and it stands in about the same relation to the Diesel engine as a race horse does to a draft horse. The two principal differences between the Diesel and the gasoline engine are: (1) the latter uses a much lighter (and also a more expensive) fuel, which is obtained by distilling natural oil, and (2) instead of being injected into the compressed air in the cylinder, the fuel in a gasoline engine is mixed with the air in the carburetor before the air is sucked into the cylinder. In most gasoline engines, the mixture is ignited by an electric spark at the most favorable point of the compression cycle.

So-called *turboprop* engines that are designed to propel airplanes are analogous to steam turbines, with the difference that the hot gas in a turboprop engine that pushes the paddles of the turbine is produced by the burning of gasoline rather than by boiling water. In this engine, the fuel is injected into the air that is sucked in through the forward ducts of the airplane and is ignited in the burning chamber located next to the turbine wheel. The rotating turbine wheel communicates its motion to the propeller which drives the airplane through the air.

Ramjets and *turbojets* used for the propulsion of airplanes, as well as for various kinds of guided missiles, are based on the recoil principle discussed in connection with rockets in Chapter 2. Although rockets carry both the fuel and the oxidizer in their bodies and are thus independent of the air through which they fly, jets carry only the fuel and use the air for burning it. The principle of a ramjet, which was once rightly called a "flying smokestack," is very simple and is shown in Fig. 4-15. As the vehicle moves through the air at high speed, air is forced through the front ducts, passes around an ellipsoidal body known as a "diffuser," and enters the "burning chamber" into which the fuel is injected. The hot burning products rush out through the nozzle at the rear and push the vehicle forward. Before the system can function, the vehicle must move through the air at high speed, and a ramjet, therefore, clearly cannot raise itself off the ground. It has to have a "booster" in the form of an ordinary rocket to propel it into the air and to communicate to it a sufficiently high speed. When the rocket booster has done its job, it falls off and the ramjet proceeds on its own.

The scheme of a turbojet, which makes the rocket booster unnecessary, is shown in Fig. 4-15. In this system, two paddle wheels are placed

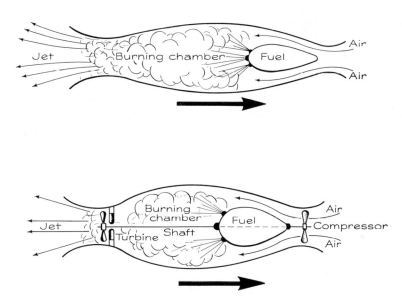

Fig. 4-15. Two types of air-breathing jet engines: (top) ramjet; (bottom) turbojet.

on a common axis. The turbine wheel at the rear of the jet is driven by the hot gases that originate in the burning chamber, and it in turn drives the compressor wheel at the front of the jet which sucks the air into the body of the vehicle and also compresses it above atmospheric density. An auxiliary engine that starts the whole thing running is needed, of course, to get the vehicle off the ground. In Fig. 4-16 we see the U. S. Air Force turbojet known as F-102.

Fig. 4-16. The Air Force's supersonic fighter, F-102, built by Convair, flying over the coastal ridges of California. Notice how the mountains look smeared when seen through the jet of gases streaming from the plane's tail. *Courtesy Convair, San Diego, Calif.*

Mysterious Entropy

If we could transform one hundred per cent of a given amount of heat into mechanical energy, we would be almost as well-to-do as we were with the "perpetual motion" machines described in the chapter on mechanical energy. Instead of "producing energy from nothing," we could turn the heat content of any surrounding medium into mechanical energy. An ocean liner could pump in sea water, extract the heat energy from it to drive its propellers, and throw overboard the resulting blocks of ice. An airplane could take in air, turn its heat content into kinetic energy, and throw the ice-cold jet out through the nozzle in the rear. In fact, since the air, the water, and the ground are heated well above the temperature of absolute zero, these "perpetual motion machines of the second kind" would be just as effective as the "perpetual motion machines of the first kind." But, as we have seen before, such machines are also impossible. We cannot use the heat content of our surroundings to produce mechanical work any more than we can use the water in the oceans to run hydropower installations. The potential energy of the water in the oceans is useless because there is no lower water level to which this water can flow; the heat content of our surroundings is useless because there is no lower temperature region to which this heat can flow.

Summarizing the above facts, we may say that **the natural direction of heat flow is from hot regions to cold regions and the natural direction of energy transformation is from mechanical energy into heat energy.**

In the "natural" direction, both processes can proceed by themselves one hundred per cent, but if either of them is to run in the "unnatural" direction, there must always be an accompanying process running in the "natural" direction which is sufficient to compensate for the "unnatural" behavior of the first one. Thus, it is "unnatural" for heat to escape from the cool interior of a refrigerator into the warm kitchen air, but this process can take place because it is compensated for and even over-compensated for by the "natural" transformation of the electric energy driving the refrigerator's motor into heat. It is "unnatural" for the heat of the steam in a locomotive's boiler to go over into mechanical energy and drive the wheels, but, here again, the "unnaturality" of the process is over-compensated for by the "naturality" of the flow of a part of the heat from the hot boiler to the cool air outside.

In *thermodynamics,* i.e., the study of the relation between heat and mechanical motion, the degree of "naturality" of heat transformation is called *entropy.* We say that the entropy increases when the process goes in the "natural" direction and decreases when it goes in the opposite direction. When a hot object cools down upon being thrown into cold water or an automobile is stopped by application of its brakes, the total entropy of the system goes up. In the work of steam engines or refrigerators, the entropy of the working parts (cylinder and piston or the cooling unit) of the machine goes down, but it is compensated for (or over-compensated for) by an increase of entropy elsewhere. **But in the grand total, the entropy of the entire system cannot decrease and it either remains constant or, in most cases, goes up.** If this were not so, engineers would be able to construct the fabulous perpetual motion machines of the second kind, described in the beginning of this section, and we would have an unlimited supply of free energy for industrial and other uses. Technically, the change of entropy of a given body is measured by the amount of heat it gains or loses (a negative sign in the second case) divided by its (absolute) temperature. In the earlier example of the steam engine that operated between the temperatures T_1 and T_2, the change of entropy of the boiler when the amount of heat Q_1 is taken from it is $-Q_1/T_1$, and the corresponding change in the cooler is $+Q_2/T_2$. Since the total change of entropy must be equal to or larger than zero, we easily arrive at Sadi Carnot's law quoted above. In fact, we can write:

$$\text{Entropy change} = -\frac{Q_1}{T_1} + \frac{Q_2}{T_2} \geq 0$$

so that:

$$\frac{Q_2}{T_2} \geq \frac{Q_1}{T_1} \quad \text{or} \quad \frac{Q_2}{Q_1} \geq \frac{T_2}{T_1}$$

The efficiency η of the engine is given by:

$$\eta = \frac{Q_1 - Q_2}{Q_1} = 1 - \frac{Q_2}{Q_1} \leq 1 - \frac{T_2}{T_1} = \frac{T_1 - T_2}{T_1}$$

The reader must have noticed that both examples given above for the local decreases of entropy (a steam engine and a refrigerator) are man-made machines. Indeed, all, or almost all, processes in nature run in "natural" directions, with the entropy increasing more or less uniformly everywhere. The trick of producing local entropy decreases that are compensated for by an increase elsewhere is essentially the product of human ingenuity, the brain child of clever engineers. The notable exception is that of living organisms, which operate on principles very similar to those used in man-made machines. But in building his machines, of course, man simply imposes on inorganic matter the same ingenious principles that operate in his own body. We will return to this problem at the end of Chapter 8.

FIVE

ELECTROMAGNETISM

Atmospheric Electricity

Electric phenomena have been known to man from time immemorial. Our earliest ancestors were horrified by the lightning striking down from thunderclouds and ascribed the flash to the fury of the gods. But, even in the absence of a thunderstorm, strong electric tensions exist above the surface of the earth, and we can produce miniature artificial lightning any time we want. To do this we must collect electricity from the layers of the air high above the ground and discharge it into the ground through a wire. This can easily be achieved by placing an "electric collector" at the end of an insulated bar protruding from the roof of some tall building and running an insulated wire down from it to the ground. An electric collector is simply a metal plate covered with a thin layer of some radioactive material (the luminous paint used for watch dials would do) which makes the surrounding air electrically conductive and thus permits electric charges to flow towards it. If we wait for a while until enough electric charge is collected by such a device, we can produce an impressive spark by touching the end of the wire with our finger (Fig. 5-1). It was found that electric

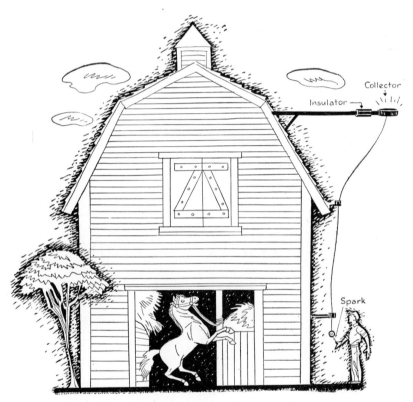

Fig. 5-1. Collecting electricity from the air.

tension in the air above the ground is about 100 volts for each meter of height, so that the electric tension between the head and the feet of a standing man is more than the voltage in an electric plug in the wall. Why then do we pay our electric bill instead of connecting the outlets of electric appliances to the roof and to the basement floors of our homes? The answer is that electric tension alone is not enough to run electric bulbs or motors; we must also have sufficiently large *amounts of electricity* flowing under this tension.

A simple hydrodynamical example will clarify the situation. Consider a hydroelectric installation, such as that at Niagara Falls, in which 5,000 tons of water come down every second from a height of about 50 meters. As we have seen, the mechanical power of this installation is the product of the two above given quantities and equals 250 million kilogram meters per second. But, to produce that power we need both the large amount of water and the large height of fall. A glass of water per second will not produce much power even if dropped from the top of the Empire State Building, and all the water of the Mississippi River would be useless for producing power if this water fell only a few centimeters. Similarly, high electric tension cannot produce much power if there is not enough electricity, because *electric power is the product of the electric tension (or potential difference) and the strength of electric current.* Thus, any attempt to use the 40,000 volts of electric tension that exist in the air between the base and the top of the Empire State Building for producing power is just as useless as building a hydroelectric installation at a creek that falls from a height many times that of Niagara Falls but carries only a few barrels of water per minute.

Triboelectricity

In the early experiments with electricity carried out by William Gilbert (1544-1603), a personal physician of Queen Elizabeth I, electric charges were produced mainly by "rubbing a galosh against a fur coat" (Fig. 5-2) or a glass stick against a silk handkerchief. When a lady with a fur coat tries to get into a car with plastic seat covers or a gentleman wearing rubber-soled shoes walks across a carpet, sparks may fly when they touch

Fig. 5-2. An elementary experiment with triboelectricity. From "Physics for Fools," published in St. Petersburg, Russia, 1908.

the handle of the car door, or the radiator in the room (this happens only when the air is dry, however, since humidity increases the electric conductivity of air and thus helps to neutralize electric charges). Electricity produced in this way is known as *triboelectricity,* and it served to establish the first laws of electric interactions.

If we suspend side by side two light metallic spheres and touch them both with a hard rubber stick rubbed against a piece of fur, we will find that the two spheres repel each other (Fig. 5-3b). The same happens if

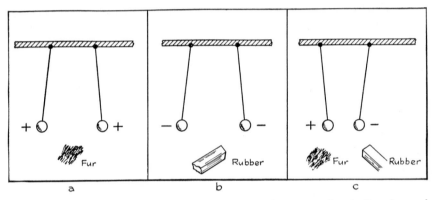

Fig. 5-3. The repulsion and attraction between electrically charged bodies.

we touch both spheres with the piece of fur against which the stick was rubbed (Fig. 5-3a). However, if one sphere is touched by the hard rubber stick and the other by the fur, the two spheres will attract each other (Fig. 5-3c). On the basis of these elementary experiments, Gilbert concluded that there are two kinds of electricity and that **electric charges of the same kind repel each other while those of the opposite kind attract each other.** He called electric charges produced by friction on the fur *positive,* and those produced on the rubber *negative.* Studying in more detail the interactions between electric charges, the French physicist, C. A. Coulomb (1736-1806), found that **the force of attraction or repulsion between two electrically charged bodies varies in direct proportion to the product of their charges* and in inverse proportion to the square of the distance between them.** This so-called *Coulomb's law* formed the cornerstone for all further studies in the field of electricity. Following

---

* Coulomb could experiment with half-unit, one-third-unit, and smaller integral fractions of charges by taking a charged sphere and bringing it in contact with one or more uncharged ones of equal size.

the general method of defining the units for new physical quantities, *we can define the unit of electric charge as the amount of electricity which acts with a force of one dyne on an equal amount placed one centimeter away.* This unit, known as an *electrostatic unit* of electricity, is, however, too small for practical purposes, and in electrical engineering a much larger unit known as a *coulomb* is used which is equal to three billion (3×10^9) electrostatic units.

ELECTRIC CURRENT

If we connect a conductor charged with, let us say, positive electricity (fur's kind) with the ground by a metallic wire (Fig. 5-4a), the conductor

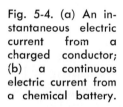
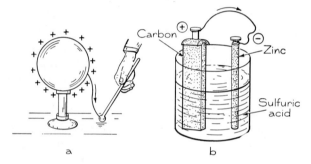

Fig. 5-4. (a) An instantaneous electric current from a charged conductor; (b) a continuous electric current from a chemical battery.

will be discharged, and for a split second an *electric current* will flow through the wire. The duration of such an electric discharge is, however, too short for convenient study, and it is desirable to have an arrangement that provides us with a steady current. This became possible after the discovery that steady electric current can be produced by the so-called *electric cell,* invented by an Italian physicist, A. Volta (1745-1827). It consists of two plates made of two different substances, such as carbon and zinc, placed in some acid solution such as sulfuric acid (Fig. 5-4b). During the early studies of electricity, it was believed that electric charges were caused by a hypothetical "electric fluid" and that the positive and negative charges corresponded to the excess and deficiency of that fluid in the charged object. The phenomenon of triboelectricity was interpreted as the transfer of a certain amount of that fluid from the rubber to the fur in the process of rubbing. Since in an electric cell made of carbon and zinc plates, the electric charge appearing on the carbon plate is similar to that produced on the fur and the charge appearing on the zinc plate is similar to that produced on the rubber, the cell was considered to produce an excess of electric fluid on carbon and a deficiency of that fluid on zinc. Thus, the current was considered as the flow of electricity from the carbon electrode (known as the *anode*) to the zinc electrode (known as the *cathode*).

As we shall see later in the book, the actual situation that exists when an electric current flows through a metallic wire is exactly the opposite. Electricity is actually carried by a flow of tiny negatively charged particles, the *electrons,* which make their way through the lattice of atoms forming metallic bodies, and although according to conventional terminology the current flows from anode to cathode, the actual motion of the charged particles takes place in the opposite direction. It would, however, be pointless to change the terminology because of our better knowledge of electric phenomena. In fact, when an electric current passes through a liquid or a gas, it is carried by both positively and negatively charged particles moving in opposite directions. Also, if we would take the direction of motion of electrons in metallic wires as the "correct" direction of the electric current, we would be placed in an awkward situation in the case of atom-smashing machines (see Chapter 14), which produce beams of fast-moving positively charged particles, and would have to say that, instead of going out of the machine, the beam is going in!

We can define the unit of electric current as the flow of one unit of electricity per unit time. Thus, the *CGS unit of electric current* is the current that carries one electrostatic unit of charge per second, while the practical unit, or one *ampere,* is a current carrying one coulomb per second. Earlier in this chapter we introduced the notion of *electric tension,* or the *difference of electric potentials* that makes the current flow, and defined the *power* of an electric installation as the product of the current flowing through it and the electric tension. The practical unit of electric tension is one *volt, defined as an electric tension which, in conjunction with a current of one ampere, produces one watt of power.* Thus a 100-watt bulb in a table lamp operating under a tension of 110 volts takes a current slightly less than one ampere.

Terrestrial Magnetism

The fact that certain natural iron ores, known as "lodestones," when suspended on a string, assume a definite position with one end pointing roughly to the north pole and another to the south pole, was known to the ancient Chinese. The magnetic compass developed on that principle is of immense value for finding one's way, both for the ships sailing across the oceans of the world and for boy scouts lost in the woods. The magnetic field of the earth that orients the needle of the compass manifests itself in many other ways; for example, it deflects towards the poles the beams of electrically charged particles which come to us from the sun, thus producing the magnificent phenomena of *aurora borealis* (polar lights).

We can use the magnetic field of the earth to "magnetize" steel rods by holding them in the direction of the magnetic field of the earth and hitting them repeatedly with a hammer. The violent impacts shake the tiny particles constituting the internal structure of metal and orient them, at least partially, in the direction of the field. As a matter of fact, all steel objects possess a certain small degree of magnetization induced by the terrestrial magnetic field, and during the war much effort was spent to "demagnetize" warships and transports so they would not trigger the magnetic mines laid by the enemy.

If we bring close together two magnetized steel rods, we will find that *the "homologous" ends, i.e. the ends that pointed the same way during the magnetization process, repel each other and that if one of the rods is turned around, the ends of the rods will attract one another.* Since, according to accepted terminology, the end of a compass needle or any other magnet that points north is called its *north pole,* we conclude that the magnetic pole of the earth located near its geographical north pole is actually a magnetic south pole, and vice versa. But, again, as in the case of positive and negative electricity, it would be too much trouble to change the existing terminology.

At this time, it is important for us to remember the fact that, unlike positive and negative charges, *magnetic poles always occur in pairs* and that it is impossible to cut a north or south pole from a magnet and carry it away, for if we cut a magnet into two pieces we will get two smaller magnets, since a new pair of poles will originate at the broken ends. The celebrated British physicist, P. A. M. Dirac, who predicted on the basis of purely theoretical considerations the existence of the so-called "positive electrons" (see Chapter 13), had a theory according to which single magnetic poles should be found to exist in nature. However, the existence of these so-called "magnetic monopoles" has not been experimentally verified.

The attractive and repulsive forces between magnetic poles obey a law similar to that of electric charges: *the forces between the magnetic poles are directly proportional to the product of the strengths of the poles* and inversely proportional to the square of the distance between them.* We can also define *a unit of magnetism* (or *the strength of a magnetic pole*) as *the amount of magnetism that repels an equal amount placed one centimeter away with a force of one dyne.*

---

* One can double or triple the strength of the magnetic pole used in such experiments by fastening together several equal small bar magnets.

Electromagnetic Interaction

The possibility of having a continuous flow of electricity led to the study of various interactions between electric currents and magnets. (Stationary electric charges and magnets do not interact at all.) There are several basic laws governing these interactions, all of them discovered early in the nineteenth century. In the year 1820, a Danish physicist, H. C. Oersted (1770-1851), noticed that **an electric current flowing through a wire deflects a magnetic needle placed in its neighborhood in such a way that the needle assumes a position perpendicular to the plane passing through the wire and through the center of the needle** (Fig. 5-5). Oersted's discovery was followed up by two French physi-

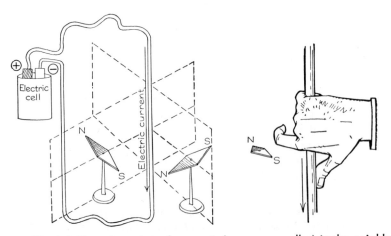

Fig. 5-5. The orientation of magnets (compass needles) in the neighborhood of an electric current. The direction in which the north pole of the needle will point can be found by the following rule: Grab the wire with your right hand so that the thumb is in the direction of the current; the index finger will then indicate the direction of the needle's north pole.

cists, J. B. Biot (1774-1862), and F. Savart (1791-1841), who amended it by the statement that **the forces attempting to orient the needle in this direction are directly proportional to the strength of the current and inversely proportional to the distance of the needle from the wire.** This law provided a simple method for detecting and measuring electric currents by means of a *galvanometer,* the scheme of which is shown in Fig. 5-6. It consists of a coiled wire that can carry an electric current and a magnetic needle placed in the center of the coil in such a way that its normal position (as determined by the suspension wire) is in the plane of the coil. When a current flows through the coil, the forces of electromagnetic interaction attempt to turn the needle into a position perpendicular to the plane of the coil, against the resistance of the twisted suspension wire. Thus, the stronger the current the larger is the angle through which the needle will be turned away from its normal position, and by measuring that angle we can find how strong the current is.

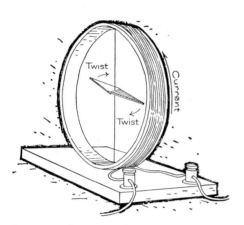

Fig. 5-6. The principle of the galvanometer. The current in the coil deflects the magnetic needle against the resistance of the vertical suspension wire.

Suppose now that instead of a movable magnet and a fixed wire carrying an electric current, we have the reverse situation of a fixed magnet and a movable wire (Fig. 5-7). Since the magnet cannot move but the wire can, electromagnetic interaction will result in the motion of the wire as indicated in the figure. If the direction of the current is reversed or if the magnet is turned upside down, the direction of the force acting on the wire will also be reversed. Experiments of this kind proved that **the force acting on a current-carrying wire placed in the field of a magnet is directed perpendicular to the length**

Fig. 5-7. A movable wire carrying electric current (black arrows) experiences a mechanical force (white arrow) if placed in the neighborhood of a magnet. If the direction of the current is reversed, or if the magnet is turned upside down, the directions of the force will be reversed too.

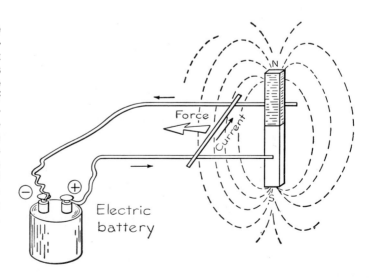

of the wire as well as to the direction of the magnetic field (i.e., the direction that would be assumed by a compass needle in that spot) and is proportional to the strength of the current. The interaction between currents and magnets constitutes the principle of electric motors. In one type of motor the wire is coiled on an *armature* which can rotate in a strong magnetic field. The coiled wire is arranged in such a way that the forces of electromagnetic interaction between the current it carries and the magnetic field tend to turn it by a certain angle. When this turn is accomplished, however, the direction of the current is automatically reversed, and the motion continues indefinitely. The situation is similar to that of a donkey who runs after a carrot suspended a few feet in front of him from a stick attached to his head.

Now we come to a very important modification of the experiment just described. Suppose we change the arrangement from that shown in Fig. 5-7 to that shown in Fig. 5-8 by substituting a galvanometer for the

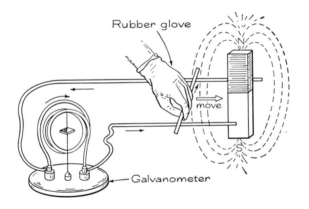

Fig. 5-8. If the wire is forcibly moved in the field of a magnet, an electric current will be induced opposing that motion.

source of the electric current, and, instead of letting the wire move at will, we move it by hand towards or away from the magnet. What will happen? There is in physical science a very general principle known as the *principle of Le Chatelier*, which, in a way, represents the generalization of the mechanical principle of inertia. It states that **whenever we try to impose changes on the existing "status quo" of a system, the "nature of things" will do its best to oppose our action.** To start with, the movable wire was resting on its supports, the galvanometer was showing no current, and everything was nice and quiet. But once we disturb the system by moving the wire towards or away from the magnet, something must happen to prevent us from doing so. What happens is that, as the result of our act, a current is induced in the moving wire, and the direction of that current is such that the current-magnet interaction creates a force opposing the motion of the wire. The fact that **electric currents are always produced (or induced) in any electric conductor moving through a magnetic field** constitutes the principle of all kinds of *dynamos* and *generators* in which electric currents are originated by rotating in strong magnetic fields the wire coils attached to the armatures. Just as the experiments shown in Figs. 5-7 and 5-8 are mutually complementary, electric motors and electric generators are the counterparts of one another. If we rotate the armature a current will be induced in the wire; if we send a current through the wires in the armature, the armature will begin to rotate.

So far we have been talking about the interaction between currents and magnets. What about the interaction between two currents? This case was first studied by the French physicist, A. M. Ampère (1775-1836), who showed that **two wires carrying electric currents which flow in the same direction are attracted to one another, whereas in the case of currents flowing in opposite directions, the attraction changes to repulsion** (Fig. 5-9). This law of the interaction between currents can be

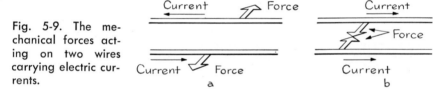

Fig. 5-9. The mechanical forces acting on two wires carrying electric currents.

logically derived from the previously stated laws of electromagnetic interactions. Electric current flowing through one of the wires produces a magnetic field which acts on the current in the second wire, pulling or pushing it away from the first one. In Chapter 14 we will find an interesting application of Ampère's law to a device called the "Perhapsatron," which is being developed for the purpose of producing thermonuclear reactions.

Ampère also found that, **in the case of two parallel wires, a current sent through one of them produces a current of opposite direction in the other** (Fig. 5-10). This *induced current* exists, however, only for the

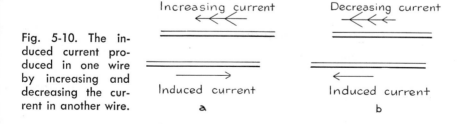

Fig. 5-10. The induced current produced in one wire by increasing and decreasing the current in another wire.

short time during which the current in the first wire is building up from zero to its maximum value. But if we cut off the current in the first wire, another current (in the same direction as that in the first wire) will be induced in the second wire when the first current is dropping down to zero. This law, too, can be derived from what was said above about the interactions of currents and magnets. Indeed, when the current is growing in the first wire, the magnetic field around it becomes stronger and stronger. Thus, the second wire finds itself in a rapidly increasing magnetic field which must have the same effect as if it were moving towards a permanent magnet. The currents induced in one wire by a change of the current in the other play an important role in many practical applications, and we will encounter this phenomenon again later in this chapter when we discuss oscillating circuits. To sum up the previous discussion, we give Table 5-1, which shows all possible electromagnetic interactions.

TABLE 5-1   DIFFERENT TYPES OF ELECTROMAGNETIC INTERACTIONS

Interaction between	*and*	*results in*
Positive electric charge	Positive electric charge	Repulsion
Negative electric charge	Negative electric charge	Repulsion
Positive electric charge	Negative electric charge	Attraction
North magnetic pole	North magnetic pole	Repulsion
South magnetic pole	South magnetic pole	Repulsion
North magnetic pole	South magnetic pole	Attraction
Electric charge	Magnetic pole	No force
Current in fixed wire	Movable magnet	Orientation of the magnet with respect to wire
Current in movable wire	Fixed magnet	Motion of wire with respect to magnet
Moving wire	Fixed magnet	Current induced in wire
Current in fixed wire	Current in movable wire	Attraction or repulsion, depending on the direction of the currents
Current growing or decreasing in a fixed wire	Fixed wire	Current of short duration in second wire

Electrical Conductivity

Just as water flows faster through a pipe when the difference in pressure between the ends of the pipe is larger, electric current depends on the difference in electric potential between the ends of the wire. The law discovered by a German physicist, G. S. Ohm (1787-1854), states that **electric current in a wire is directly proportional to the difference of electric potentials at the two ends, directly proportional to the cross-sectional area of the wire, and inversely proportional to its length.** The situation is quite similar to the case of water flowing through a pipe where the flow is proportional to the pressure difference at the two ends, and for the same pressure difference the flow of water will be less in longer and narrower pipes. On the basis of this law we can define *a unit of electric conductivity as resulting in one unit of current flowing through a unit cross-section when the electric potential drops by one unit per unit length.* If we express electric current and electric potential in practical units of amperes and volts, the unit of electric conductivity will be an "inverse ohm." If we spell out this "inverse ohm" we get the *mho*, which is the proper scientific name for the unit of electrical conductivity. The reason for such a strange name is that one ohm is defined as the unit of electrical resistivity, which is the inverse of electrical conductivity.

In Table 5-2 we list the electrical conductivities of some familiar substances. We see that, as in the case of heat conduction, metals stand at the head of the list, while other materials are rather poor electric conductors (good insulators).

TABLE 5-2   ELECTRICAL CONDUCTIVITIES OF DIFFERENT MATERIALS AND THEIR RATIOS TO CORRESPONDING HEAT CONDUCTIVITIES, FROM TABLE 4-1

Material	Electrical conductivity in inverse ohms (for 18°C)	Ratio of electrical conductivity to heat conductivity
Silver	6.1×10^5	6.3×10^5
Copper	5.6×10^5	6.1×10^5
Gold	4.6×10^5	6.6×10^5
Zinc	1.6×10^4	6.1×10^5
Tin	1.0×10^4	6.7×10^5
Lead	5.4×10^3	6.5×10^5
Maplewood	3×10^{-11}	
Glass	2×10^{-14}	
Hard rubber	1×10^{-18}	

Comparing the figures given in this table with the figures for heat conductivity given in Table 4-1, we notice that in the case of metals, electrical and heat conductivities change proportionally to one another. This is very interesting! Why should two things, so different at first sight as "heat" and "electricity," behave in such a similar way in their passage through metals? The discovery of such unexpected correlations between phenomena belonging to seemingly entirely different branches of physics represents one of the important driving forces in the development of science and helps us to understand the hidden mechanisms of various physical phenomena. In this particular case, the correlation between thermal and electrical conductivities of metals indicates that the two phenomena have a common cause. In both cases we deal with the motion of tiny particles, known as *electrons*, which form an essential part of all material bodies. Whereas in all other substances, electrons are tightly bound within the atoms, in metals a certain fraction of them (about one per atom) are on the loose and can move more or less freely through the material in a way similar to that of air molecules in a tube filled with cotton wool. Thus, when electric tension is applied to the wire, electrons will move along it, constituting an electric current. As was mentioned before, electrons move from cathode to anode i.e., opposite to the conventional direction of the electric current. Along with atoms, these "free electrons" are involved in thermal motion, and the hotter the metal is, the faster they rush around, so that if we heat one end of a metallic bar, the fast-moving electrons from the heated end will diffuse to the other, cooler end of the bar, communicating part of their thermal agitation to the electrons and atoms in this region. This process, constituting the mechanism of the thermal conductivity of metals, is very similar to the migration of electrons under the action of an applied electric tension, and there is no wonder that heat and electrical conductivities go together. The easier it is for the free electrons to shoulder their way through the crowd of atoms forming metallic bodies, the faster they will move along under the action of applied electric tension and the faster they will diffuse from the heated to the cooler regions.

The Nature of the Electromagnetic Field

In considering the mechanical interactions between material bodies, we are accustomed to the fact that such interactions require immediate bodily contact. If we want to move an object, we have to touch it with our hand, or else have a stick to push it or a rope to pull it. On the basis of such views, the famous British physicist, Michael Faraday (1791-1867), to whom science is obligated for many important discoveries in the field of electricity, liked to imagine that what one usually calls "empty space" is actually filled by some peculiar substance, "world ether," which is responsible for all electric and magnetic interactions.

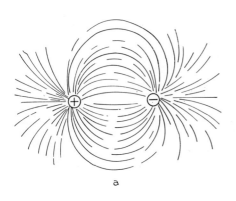

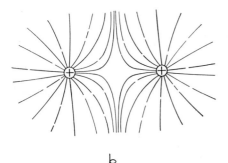

Fig. 5-11. The electric field surrounding (a) two opposite and (b) two identical electric charges.

According to Faraday's conception, the placing of an electric charge on a copper sphere or the magnetization of an iron bar results in certain deformations in the surrounding "world ether" that lead to repulsive or attractive forces between the material bodies. The stress and strain lines in this hypothetical "world ether" were supposed to coincide with the *lines of force* defined by the direction of electric or magnetic forces in the points of the surrounding space. In Fig. 5-11a and b, we see the lines of force in the space around two unlike and two like electric charges. If, following Faraday, we visualize these patterns as being formed by some elastic rubber-like bands, it is easy to get the impression that in the first case the stresses will lead to an attraction and in the second to repulsion. Somewhat more complicated patterns are shown in Fig. 5-12. These photographs represent the lines of force surrounding two magnets when they are oriented

parallel and antiparallel to one another. Here again one may feel that the first case corresponds to repulsion and the second to attraction. Faraday's views were put into mathematical form by his disciple, James Clerk Maxwell (1831-1879), who proved that electromagnetic interaction can be represented by a set of equations that can be interpreted is describing the stresses and strains in some elastic medium.

Although Maxwell's equations represent the basis of today's theory of electricity and magnetism, their interpretation has been radically changed. As will be described in more detail in Chapter 7, Einstein's theory of relativity rejected the notion of an all-penetrating "world ether" as a physical reality and returned to considering emptiness as the basic property of space. On the other hand, Einstein ascribed a physical reality to the *electromagnetic field* itself and considered it to be some peculiar kind of material surrounding electrified and magnetized objects and responsible for the interactions between them. Instead of extending

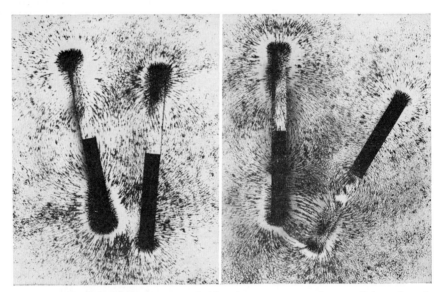

Fig. 5-12. The magnetic fields of two magnets in parallel and anti-parallel positions, shown by the orientation of iron filings. *Photograph by R. Conklin, University of Colorado.*

through entire space, however, this electromagnetic material exists only where electric and magnetic forces are present and is absent in really empty space. Thus, the field around an electrically charged conductor or a magnet should be considered as a jelly-like material surrounding them in the form of a local cloud rather than as local deformations in a jelly-like medium which fills up all of space (see Fig. 7-7).

Electromagnetic Oscillations

If we take two spherical electric conductors and give their surfaces opposite electrical charges, we will have to do work in some way to pull electrons off the surface we charge positively and to force excess electrons onto the surface we charge negatively. If we look to see where this work has gone, we will find that it is stored in the *electric field* which now exists between these two conductors. Suppose we connect these conductors by a piece of wire (Fig. 5-13a). The opposite charges on the spheres will begin to be neutralized by the flow of electric current from one to the other, and as the charge on each sphere becomes less, the electric field between them will also decrease. We may ask, now, what happens to the energy stored in the electric field as the field becomes weaker? The answer is that we can find this missing energy stored in the *magnetic field* that has been created by the current in the connecting wire (Fig. 5-13b). In Fig. 5-13c we see the situation when the charges have been completely neutralized: the electric field has vanished, and all of its energy is now in the magnetic field. There is no difference in charge to keep the current flowing, and if this were all of the story, the current would stop. But Le Chatelier's principle now goes to work to

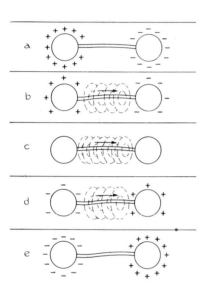

Fig. 5-13. Electromagnetic oscillations between two charged conductors.

maintain the status quo, i.e., to prevent the current from stopping. Hence the magnetic field delivers its stored energy back into the wire to keep the current flowing (Fig. 5-13d), and the charge begins to build up on our spheres in the opposite direction. Finally, when the magnetic field has been reduced to zero, the current stops, and we have (Fig. 5-13e) the same situation we had in the beginning (Fig. 5-13a), except that the sign of the charges has been reversed. Now, of course, the whole cycle will repeat itself in the reverse direction, and again and again, and so on.

This oscillating electric current is analogous to the behavior of a pendulum. We start it by pulling the pendulum aside and giving it potential energy (we give the conductors the energy stored in the electric field). As it swings down, this potential energy is converted into kinetic energy (the energy of the electric field is now in the magnetic field). The pendulum swings over to the other side, and its kinetic energy is again converted to potential energy (the magnetic field has vanished, and its energy appears in the electric field again). And, just as the pendulum's period can be changed by changing its length, the period of electric oscillation in our system can be changed by changing the size of the two spheres or the distance between them.

The pendulum, of course, will not swing forever; it gradually loses its energy by friction. The electrons moving back and forth in our oscillating electrical system encounter resistance, too, in the wire through which they flow, and unless its energy were periodically replenished, it would also come to a stop.

This analogy can be carried a step further. If we suspend our pendulum from a clothesline instead of a rigid support, some of the pendulum's energy will go to moving the clothesline back and forth and will be dissipated in waves traveling out along the line in both directions. Part of the energy of our oscillating electric circuit will in a somewhat similar way go into creating "electromagnetic waves" that radiate out into space. From the point of view described in the previous section, we can say that the "lumps" of jelly-like electromagnetic field material vibrating in the space surrounding the two spheres are torn away and travel freely into the space beyond. Here again, a propagating electromagnetic wave should be visualized as a vibrating lump of electromagnetic field material flying through empty space rather than as the propagation of an elastic deformation in some all-penetrating medium.

The existence of electromagnetic waves, which were predicted by Maxwell's theory, was proved in 1888 by the experiments of the German physicist, H. Hertz (1857-1894), and their practical importance was realized by an Italian engineer, G. Marconi (1874-1937), who established radio communication across the British channel in 1899 and, in 1901, across the Atlantic Ocean.

Electric circuits used in radio and TV transmitters today are just an improvement on the original scheme shown in Fig. 5-13. First of all, in order to store a maximum amount of positive and negative electricity on two conductors, it is important to bring these two conductors as close to one another as possible. Thus, instead of two spheres which can be close to one another at only one point, it is preferable to use two metal plates located close together; such a pair of plates is known as an *electric condenser* (Fig. 5-14). Also, in order to increase the amount of

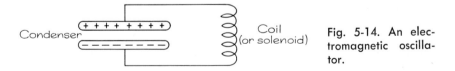

Fig. 5-14. An electromagnetic oscillator.

energy stored in the magnetic field, we use a longer wire and then coil it into what is known as a *solenoid*.

Vacuum Tubes

In early radio equipment the oscillation rapidly died out, and the condenser had to be continually recharged. Modern radio and TV transmitters, however, maintain uninterrupted oscillations by means of an ingenious device based on the passage of "free" electrons through the empty space separating the cathode and anode in a completely evacuated glass tube. We have seen earlier that metallic conductors contain a large number of free electrons which carry electric current and also participate in the heat conduction of metals. Normally these conductivity electrons remain within the metal, being prevented from crossing the surface by forces similar to those of surface tension in liquids. If, however, the metal is heated to a sufficiently high temperature (red hot for most of the metals), some of the conductivity electrons may get sufficiently high thermal energy to cross the surface and to escape into the surrounding space in a process that is quite similar to that of the evaporation of liquids. Thus, if we heat the cathode of a vacuum tube and apply an electric tension between the cathode and the anode, these "evaporated electrons" will fly through the tube and constitute an electric current. The important point is that in such a device *electric current can flow only in one direction*, from the anode to the cathode, since the flow of electrons through the vacuum is always directed from the cathode to the anode. Thus, if we place such a tube into an oscillating electric circuit, only unidirectional impulses will be able to pass through. This so-called *diode vacuum tube* (Fig. 5-15a) was developed by the British engineer,

Fig. 5-15. Two types of vacuum tubes: (a) a diode tube used for the rectification of electric current, and (b) a triode tube used for amplification.

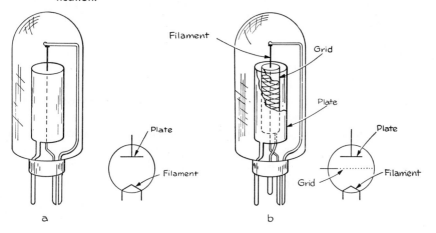

a
b

J. A. Fleming (1849-1945) and is used in many electronic devices for the purpose of rectifying electric currents.

A somewhat more complicated device, developed in 1906 by an American engineer, Lee deForest (1873-   ), and known as a *triode vacuum tube* is shown in Fig. 5-15b. This device consists of two concentric cylinders and a thin wire running along their common axis. The outer cylinder, known as the *plate,* is made of a solid metal sheet, while the inner one, the *grid,* is made of a thin wire screen or a closely spaced helical coil. The central wire (*filament*) is heated by an electric current, and when it is red hot, it begins to emit a large number of electrons. If we apply a positive voltage to the outer cylinder (the plate) and a negative voltage to the filament, electrons will flow from the filament to the plate along the radii of the cylinder just as they do in the diode tube. Suppose, however, that we charge the grid with negative electricity. The electrons coming from the filament will now be repelled by the grid, and, if the field is strong enough, will never reach the plate. Thus, *our tube acts as a faucet* that permits us to control the strong current flowing between the filament and the plate by placing a small charge on the grid. In order to charge the grid to the necessary electric potential, only a very small current is needed.

ELECTRONIC OSCILLATOR

In Fig. 5-16, we show how oscillations in an electric circuit CS (identical with that shown in Fig. 5-14) can be maintained indefinitely by the energy supplied by a battery, B, and regulated by a triode tube, *PGF.* The situation here is rather similar to that of a pendulum in a grandfather's clock driven by the clock's mechanism. Let us start with the situation shown in (a) when the upper plate of the condenser, C, is charged positively so that an increasing electric current begins to flow in the solenoid, S. (The pendulum is in its extreme position on the right from where it begins to move, gaining speed toward the left.) The increasing current in S will induce a current in the nearby solenoid, S',[*] which is connected to the grid and to the filament of the triode tube. If you look at Fig. 5-10 representing Ampère's law of induction, you will find that the induced current must have a direction opposite to the increasing one. However, since the solenoids S and S' are wound in directions opposite to one another, the direction of the current induced in S' will be that shown by the arrow in (a). This current will result in a negative charge on the grid, G, of the triode tube that will prevent the electrons emitted from the filament, F, from passing through the

---

[*] Actually solenoids S and S' have a common axis and are shown separately in Fig. 5-16 just to make the drawing clearer.

tube. Thus, the battery power will be cut off and that part of the oscillation in the main circuit will proceed undisturbed. (The pendulum will swing from the extreme right to the middle position.)

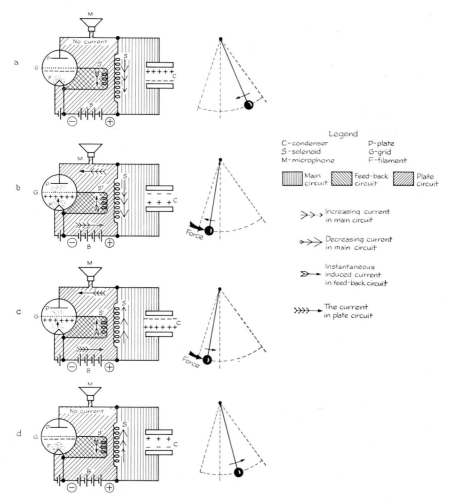

Fig. 5-16. A scheme showing how a battery and a triode tube maintain the oscillations in an electric circuit, CS. The drawings on the right represent analogous phases in the case of a power-driven pendulum.

At the end of the first quarter of the oscillation, the charges on the condenser will vanish, and the current in the solenoid, S, will be at its maximum. During the second quarter (in which the pendulum swings to the left from its middle position), the current in the solenoid, S, will decrease and recharge the condenser, *C*, in the opposite direction. The decreasing current in S will induce a current in S′ directed as shown by the arrow in (b) and will result in a positive charge on the grid. Now the battery, *B*, will be able to drive a current through the tube and the plate circuit, and, as can be seen from (b), the direction of that current in the solenoid, S, will be opposite to that of the original oscillating current. In our pendulum analogy, we would say that a certain force begins to act on the pendulum when it swings too much to the left.

During the third part of the cycle (c), we have an increasing current in S which, however, flows in the opposite direction to the decreasing current of the second quarter. Thus the current induced in S′ will retain its direction and the grid of the tube will remain positively charged. The battery, *B*, will continue to drive the current through the plate circuit and will contribute to the current existing in the solenoid, S. Following our pendulum analogy, we would say that the pendulum is pushed in the direction of its motion when it begins to move to the right.

The fourth quarter of the cycle (d) is trivial. The current in the main circuit is now decreasing in such a way that the grid of the triode tube is again charged negatively, thus cutting off the action of the battery. The pendulum swings to the extreme right in a free fashion, and then the cycle is repeated again.

Summing up the above discussion, we may say that this arrangement permits the battery to supply electric energy to the current in the main circuit during one part of its oscillation and to cut it off during the other, in the same way as the spring (or weights) supply mechanical energy to an oscillating pendulum in a clock. Such an arrangement is usually called a *feed back* since the current in the main circuit "feeds" some energy into the triode tube to charge its grid and thereby causes much more of the energy supplied by the battery to be "fed back" into that circuit. As a result, the amplitude of the electric vibrations in the main circuit, *CS*, will steadily increase until the constant energy supplied by the battery is compensated for by the energy losses in the circuit. These losses are due partially to the electric resistance of the wires (heating) and partially to the emission of energy in the form of electromagnetic waves. To increase the intensity of the electromagnetic waves for the purposes of radio broadcasting, one introduces an antenna (not shown in Fig. 5-16), which is coupled to the solenoid, S, through still another solenoid. The antenna plays a role similar to that of a violin's belly or the sounding board of a grand piano in the case of sound waves. Thus our device will represent a steady source of electromagnetic waves, the frequency of which can be changed by bringing the two plates of the condenser, *C*, closer together or by taking them farther apart.

The frequency of the waves emitted by oscillating electric circuits usually lies in the region of several megacycles (i.e., several million oscillations per second) and is well beyond acoustical frequencies. To make electromagnetic waves transmit the sound of voices or music, one has to *modulate* them by means of a microphone introduced into the circuit.

RADIO AND TV

One of the most familiar applications of an electronic oscillator is in broadcasting sounds (radio) and pictures (TV). In the case of a radio transmitter, the sound of a voice or of music is fed into the transmitter through a microphone and *modulates* the amplitude of its electric oscillations. Since the frequency of audible sound is much lower than the frequency of electric oscillations in the transmitter, the signal radiating from the antenna looks as shown in Fig. 5-17. In the case of TV, a camera

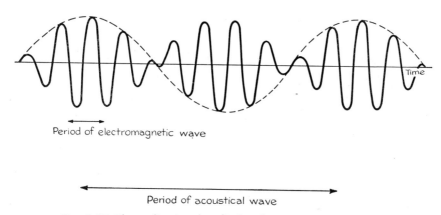

Period of electromagnetic wave

Period of acoustical wave

Fig. 5-17. The radio signal radiating from an antenna.

rapidly scans the scene to be transmitted, and the intensity of light coming from different points of the picture is turned into a modulated radio signal as shown in Fig. 5-18.

The scheme of a receiving radio station is shown in Fig. 5-19. Electromagnetic waves falling on the antenna excite the vibrations in the main circuit because of the induction between two solenoids. These vibrations result in an alternating charge on the grid of the triode tube, which in its turn modulates the current from the battery and makes the loudspeaker emit sound waves. In the case of TV reception, the signal is sent into the TV tube and modulates the intensity of the electron beam that continuously scans a fluorescent screen.

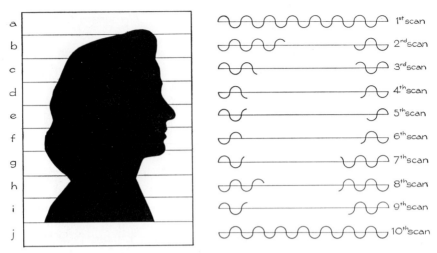

Fig. 5-18. The principle of television. At left is a silhouetted profile showing ten consecutive scannings by a photosensitive cell. At right is the modulated signal sent through radio waves.

RADAR

In the case of radio and TV, one party always wants to talk, to sing, or to be seen, while another party wants to listen or to look. Radar, on the contrary, is strictly a one-sided proposition. The name "radar" stands for

Fig. 5-19. A simple diagram of a radio receiver. C is a variable condenser used for tuning; EM and M are the electromagnet and membrane of a loudspeaker.

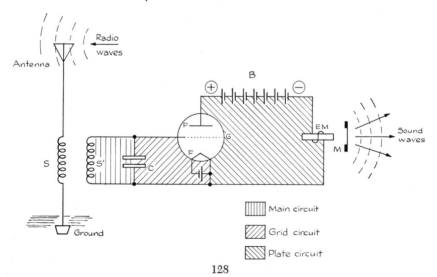

"radio direction and range"* determination, which means that, while the party on one side would like to know about the presence and the exact position of the party on the other side, the party on the other side would much prefer to withhold this information from the party on the first side. This unfriendly attitude exists, for example, between an anti-aircraft

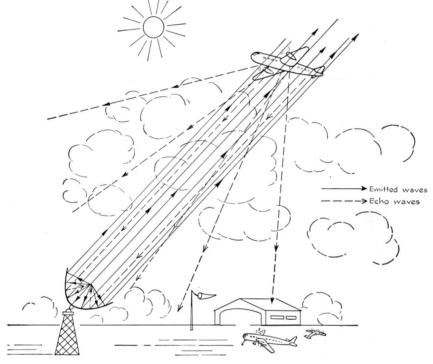

Fig. 5-20. The principle of radar.

battery and a bomber going in for the kill through the dark of night, and between two hostile warships in a foggy sea, where all depends on who is faster on the draw. Since radar was invented and developed during the war, it is only natural that it acquired in its babyhood these militaristic tendencies. However, it is now being used for many peaceful purposes, some of which are: preventing collisions between commercial airplanes and ships; detecting whales, schools of herring (although the whales and herring would protest this purpose being called peaceful), and tropical hurricanes; and the tracking of the target moon by the U. S. Army Signal Corps.

---

* "Range" is a military term for distance.

Radar is essentially a "radio echo" instrument. It consists of a radio transmitter, which sends short pulses of electromagnetic radiation in a narrow beam, and a radio receiver, which catches the echo arising from the reflection of these waves from any object in their way. The direction of the objects is, of course, given by the direction from which the radio echo comes, and the distance (range) can be estimated exactly from the delay in the arrival of the echo. While radio and TV can operate on comparatively long waves, radar equipment must use very short waves (10 to 30 cm), since waves longer than the object to be observed will pass by it without much reflection. The functioning of radar equipment is shown in Fig. 5-20, and Fig. 5-21 shows a comparison of a radar map with an ordinary one.

The same reflector and small antenna serve for both transmitting and

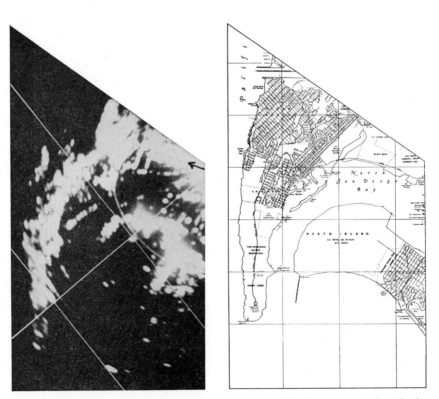

Fig. 5-21. (Left) Radar map of San Diego harbor compared with the corresponding section of the regular city map (right). The small elongated spots on the radar map represent ships. The dark streak on the radar map (indicated by arrow) is the runway of the Municipal Airport. *Courtesy Convair, San Diego, Calif.*

receiving, and automatic electronic switching connects the antenna to the proper circuit at the proper time.

●

Electronic Computers

The simplest and the most ancient computing device is the *abacus,* which was invented by the Arabs many centuries ago and is still being used extensively in some countries. The hand- or motor-driven computers that we find today in many business offices and scientific laboratories represent nothing more than purely technical improvements of the ancient abacus, even though they may look much more complicated and do their work considerably faster. Real progress in the development of fast computing machines began during World War II, mostly due to the ideas conceived by a Hungarian-born American mathematician, John von Neumann.

Von Neumann proposed to build a computer using as a model the human brain, substituting electronic tubes for the individual brain cells, or "neurones." Just as the neurones of the brain are capable of only two states, *excited* and *relaxed,* electronic tubes can be only *on* or *off.* The cogwheels of ordinary mechanical computing machines can handle numerals from 0 to 9 if they are built with ten cogs, but electronic computers handle only two numerals: 0 and 1. This necessitates re-writing all the numbers that are to be given to an electronic computer in the "binary" system, which uses powers of 2 in the way that powers of 10 are used in the decimal system. Thus, while in the decimal system the notation 137 means $1 \times 10^2 + 3 \times 10^1 + 7 \times 10^0$, in the binary system it would mean $1 \times 2^2 + 3 \times 2^1 + 7 \times 2^0$, i.e., only seventeen. To translate the decimal number 137 into the binary system, we must write it as 10001001, which means: $1 \times 2^7 + 0 \times 2^6 + 0 \times 2^5 + 0 \times 2^4 + 1 \times 2^3 + 0 \times 2^2 + 0 \times 2^1 + 1 \times 2^0$, i.e., $128 + 8 + 1$, or one hundred and thirty-seven. Although it looks considerably longer than the same number written in the decimal system, it has the advantage of operating with only two figures. Thus, in the binary system, the multiplication table is reduced to the simple form:

$$0 \times 0 = 0 \qquad 0 \times 1 = 0 \qquad 1 \times 1 = 1$$

which is easy to remember.

The tubes in an electronic computer are arranged in long rows, each one corresponding to the proper binary place; thus the number 137, written as 10001001 in the binary system, will call for the first, fifth, and eighth tubes "on" with the rest of the tubes being "off." The electric connections between the rows of tubes operate similarly to the mechanical connections in any old-fashioned computer, but the entire process runs much much faster. Thus, the veteran computer known as "Maniac" in the Los Alamos Scientific Laboratory (Fig. 5-22) contains 3,000 electron

Fig. 5-22. The Los Alamos electronic computer known as "Maniac." The lower part of the equipment is formed by rows of computing tubes. On the upper shelf is the row of memory tube boxes. The small box at front right contains an abacus to be used in case the electronic equipment fails. Apart from making an important contribution to the development of the H-bomb, this instrument has also made a number of important calculations on various physical, astronomical, and biological problems. *Courtesy Los Alamos Scientific Laboratory.*

tubes, can add two numbers with twelve decimal places each in about two hundred-thousandths of a second, and can multiply or divide the same numbers in less than one-thousandth of a second. At that speed, electronic computers can do in a few days the work that would require a hundred human computers a hundred years to do!

Apart from the long rows of electronic tubes designed for strictly arithmetical operations, electronic computers also have special tubes that serve as a *memory*, in which they store the information and the instructions pertaining to a given problem as well as all the previously obtained numerical results. The presence of an electronic memory makes it possible to "teach" the computers to perform various human tasks, such as, for example, to play chess. Recently the Los Alamos Maniac was taught the elementary rules of chess by his "mathematics teacher," S. Ulam, and is now playing this game "like a 10-year old with average ability who has already played a dozen or two games." It is expected, however, that specially designed electronic chess-playing machines will eventually be able to beat any human world champion.

SIX

LIGHT, VISIBLE

AND INVISIBLE

The study of light is one of the most important parts of physics since, indeed, most of our knowledge concerning the world around us is gained through seeing. We learn about the properties of giant stellar systems by means of light that travels for millions of years through empty space to deliver us its message. We learn about the properties of minute atoms through the light that is emitted by them and that carries in a hidden form important information concerning their internal structure. And, of course, most

134

of the information that we get in our everyday life is also obtained through the medium of light.

Reflection of Light

To demonstrate the basic laws of the propagation of light, we use thin light beams that can be formed by a screen with a small hole or slit in it. To make a light beam visible when we look at it from the side, we may blow tobacco smoke into it or arrange for it to graze obliquely along a white surface. The arrangement shown in Fig. 6-1 is very useful for the

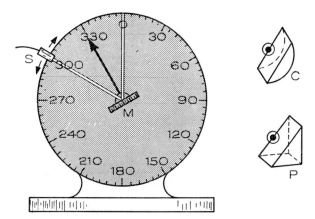

Fig. 6-1. A gadget for the study of the reflection and re-fraction of light. S —light source, M— a mirror, C—a cylinder, P—a prism.

study of the basic laws of the propagation of light. It consists of a vertical disc of frosted glass with the degrees of the angular scale plotted on it and a movable source that emits a thin light beam. At the center of the disc we can attach different devices such as mirrors, prisms, etc. that can also be rotated around the axis. If we use first a flat mirror, we will find that the direction of the reflected beam changes in respect to the mirror with the changing position of the light source. However, no matter how we place them, we will always find that **the incident and the reflected beams of light form equal angles with the surface of the mirror.**

While this rule holds for mirrors and, generally speaking, for all polished surfaces, light reflected from such surfaces as paper or frosted glass is scattered irregularly in all directions. This diffuse reflection of light is due to the fact that non-polished surfaces are coarse, being covered by a network of microscopic irregularities that have the same effect on the reflection of light as the surface of an unkept tennis court has on the direction of bounce of tennis balls.

MIRROR ON THE WALL

The mirrors that hang on walls are usually flat ones and we are all very familiar with them. In Fig. 6-2 we show a scheme depicting how the rays of light reflected from a plane mirror give the impression that there is another similar object placed behind the mirror. But here is a question for those who think they know how a plane mirror works. The person you see in the mirror is very much like you, but there are a few oddities. He parts his hair on the wrong side and his tailor apparently made a mistake in placing the breast pocket on his coat; she wears her wedding ring on the wrong hand (or maybe she is from Europe),

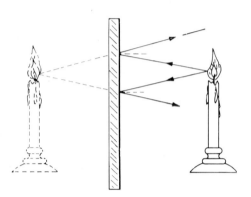

Fig. 6-2. The reflection of light from a plane mirror.

and you are rather sure that an X-ray picture of your mirror image would show your heart on the wrong side. In other words, a mirror turns things right to left and left to right. But, on the other hand, the mirror on the wall does not turn up down and down up! The head is not turned into feet and the feet are not turned into a head. Why? Just to give another example, write T O M on a piece of paper, turn it toward a mirror, and

you will read M O T. But if you write it in Chinese fashion, T O M and look

at it in the mirror, you will not notice any difference. Isn't this strange? Why does the mirror rotate the image around the vertical axis and not around the horizontal one? Is it connected with the vertical direction of the force of terrestrial gravity? Or does it depend on the fact that our two hands are more similar to one another than our head and our feet? Or, maybe it is because we have two eyes located on a line perpendicular to the "head to feet" direction? (By closing one eye, you can easily disprove this latter possibility.)

The answer to this riddle is that the phenomenon *does* depend on the dissimilarity of the upper and lower parts of our body. Suppose you are walking along a street and hear an unexpected sound from behind. You turn around to see what caused it. But there are two ways of looking back, as illustrated in Fig. 6-3. The "normal" way is to turn around the

Fig. 6-3. Two ways of looking backwards.

vertical axis, thus keeping your feet on the ground; another way, which is geometrically just as good, is to stand on your head. The reason that you usually make the first choice is due, of course, to purely anatomical considerations. Returning to our mirror problem, we face a rather similar situation. The person in the mirror faces in the opposite direction, so that to make a comparison between ourselves and our mirror image we have to imagine ourselves turning by 180°. If we do it in the customary way, keeping our feet on the ground, we will find that our right and left hand will not fit those of our image. However, if we do it in the less conventional way and stand on our head, our head and feet will be mixed up instead. We leave it to the reader to apply the same principles to the T O M vs. M O T problem.

Fig. 6-4. The formation of an image in a convex (a) and a concave (b) mirror.

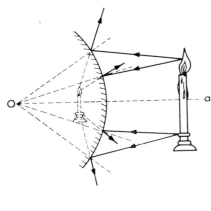

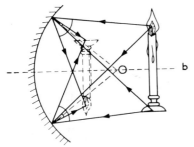

CONVEX AND CONCAVE MIRRORS

If the surface of the mirror is not a plane but has a regular shape such as a segment of a sphere, light rays from a point source will still intersect at a single point (focal point), but the position of this point will depend on the curvature of the surface. Figure 6-4a shows the path of rays in the case of a convex mirror; here as in the case of a plane mirror the reflected rays give the impression that the object is behind the mirror, but in the case shown the image is smaller than the actual object. In the case of a concave mirror (Fig. 6-4b), reflected rays intersect in front of the mirror to produce the so-called "real image," which, in the case shown, is smaller than the original object and in addition is turned upside down. See if you can tell by means of the diagrams how the size and direction of an image in a concave and a convex mirror depend on the distance of the object from the mirror.

It should be noted here that in the case of spherical mirrors the rays intersect in a single point only if the surface of the mirror corresponds to a small part of the complete sphere; otherwise, the focal point becomes somewhat blotted out and the image becomes blurred. This can be avoided, however, by using an elliptical mirror (Fig. 6-5a), since, indeed, it can be proved geometrically that the lines connecting any point of an ellipsoid with two of its foci form exactly equal angles with the perpendicular at that point. Ellipsoidal mirrors are not often used in practice because for any given mirror of that kind there is only one pair of points (the foci) where the object can be placed. If we keep one focus, F_1, in place and move another, F_2, into infinity, the ellipsoid becomes an open paraboloid (Fig. 6-5b). The rays diverging from its focal point become parallel to each other after reflection, and, vice versa, parallel light beams falling on a parabolic mirror along its axis are collected exactly in its focal point.

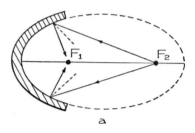

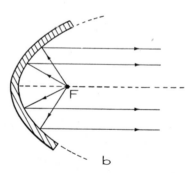

Fig. 6-5. The paths of rays in an elliptical (a) and a parabolic (b) mirror.

This property of parabolic mirrors is widely used in the construction of various light-beam casting devices, such as headlights and searchlights, and in the making of astronomical instruments such as reflecting telescopes (or, simply, "reflectors") for obtaining sharp images of celestial bodies. In Fig. 6-6 we show a photograph of the 200-inch telescope—the largest in the world—at the Palomar Mountain Observatory in California. There are three principal ways that astronomers can observe the images formed by the mirror of a reflecting telescope, as is shown in Fig. 6-7a, b, and c. In all three cases a real image of the celestial object is formed by a large parabolic mirror and is inspected through an eyepiece similar in principle to an ordinary magnifying glass. For photographic work, the eyepiece and the human eye are replaced by a camera, and, in fact, big instruments such as that on Palomar Mountain are used more as "tele-cameras" than as "telescopes."

Refraction of Light

To study the refraction of light, instead of a mirror we may use semi-cylinders made of different transparent materials, which may be glass, plastic, or a thin plastic container filled with some liquid. We will find

Fig. 6-6. The 200-inch reflector of the Palomar Mountain Observatory as seen from the front. The big parabolic mirror is seen in the rear. An astronomer is sitting in the "prime focus cage" looking through an eyepiece at the image. *Courtesy Palomar Mountain Observatory.*

Fig. 6-7. Three ways of viewing the image in a reflecting telescope.

that the light that falls on the flat surface of the semi-cylinder and penetrates into it is refracted, i.e., is bent in a different direction from the original one. The angle formed by the refracted beam with the surface of the semi-cylinder depends on the corresponding angle for the incident beam and also on the material of the semi-cylinder. This is illustrated in the series of drawings given in Fig. 6-8a, b, and c.

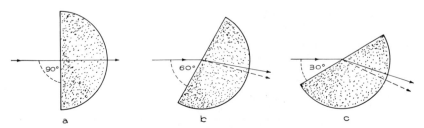

Fig. 6-8. The refraction of light when the incident beams form angles of 90°, 60°, and 30°. Solid and broken lines correspond to red and blue light, respectively.

The law of refraction is somewhat more complicated than the law of reflection, but nevertheless it can be formulated in a comparatively simple way. If we mark on the directions of incident and refracted beams two points, A and C (Fig. 6-9), equidistant from the entrance point, B ($BA = BC$), and draw two perpendiculars from these points to the surface, thus fixing points A' and C', then **the ratio BA'/BC' is independent of the direction of the incident light beam for any given pair of substances** (though it will have different values for different pairs of substances chosen for the experiment). This ratio is known as the *refractive* *index* of Substance II with respect to Substance I. In Table 6-1 we list the refractive indices of a few substances with respect to air, but since air differs very little in this respect from a vacuum, they can also be considered as "correct" refractive indices expressing the optical properties of these materials with respect to empty space. (In the same way the weight of an object measured in the air where Archimedes' law tells us it will be buoyed up slightly by the weight of the displaced air is for all practical purposes the same as its "correct" weight in a vacuum.)

TABLE 6-1   REFRACTIVE INDICES OF DIFFERENT SUBSTANCES (FOR YELLOW LIGHT)

Substance	Refractive index (Yellow light)
Water	1.33
Alcohol	1.36
Glass (flint)	1.65
Diamond	2.42

We see from this table, for example, that air-to-water and air-to-glass refractive indices are 1.33 and 1.65, respectively. What then will be the water-to-glass refractive index? It was found that **the refractive index on the surface between any two substances is equal to the ratio of their individual refractive indices.** Thus, the water-to-glass refractive index is 1.65/1.35 or 1.22.

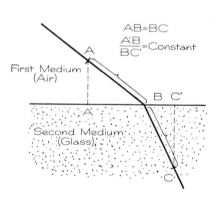

Fig. 6-9. A demonstration of the law of refraction.

If a transparent solid is submerged in a transparent liquid with the same refractive index, it becomes practically invisible since the light rays are not refracted when they pass through the boundary between the two substances. This fact was used by H. G. Wells in his story, "The Invisible Man," which is about a man who managed to make his body transparent by reducing its refractive index to 1. But Wells overlooked, probably intentionally, one essential point: The invisible man would also be blind since the lenses in his eyeballs would not form any image on the retina.

WHY IS LIGHT REFRACTED?

Why do light rays change their direction when they travel from air into water or glass? This question has an important bearing on the problem of the nature of light. Sir Isaac Newton, who, besides his great achievements in mechanics, made many important contributions to optics, believed that a light beam represents a swarm of tiny material particles that are emitted from light sources and fly at high speed through space. He visualized the refraction of light rays entering any material medium as being caused by a certain attractive force (similar to ordinary surface tension forces) acting on the particles of light when they

Fig. 6-10. Newton's and Huygens' explanations of the refraction of light.

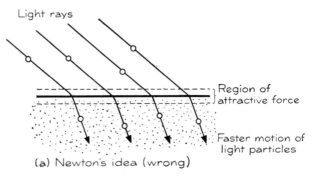

(a) Newton's idea (wrong)

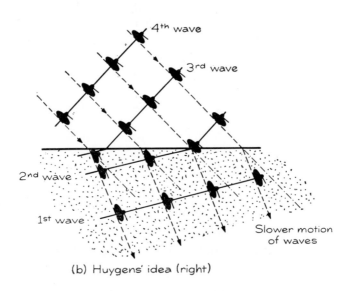

(b) Huygens' idea (right)

cross the surface of a material body (Fig. 6-10a). The denser the material is, he thought, the stronger the force is and, hence, the greater is the refraction. It is important to realize that, according to Newton's views, the velocity of light in substances with a higher refractive index should be larger than the velocity of light in air or in a vacuum, because the force pulling the light particles into the denser materials adds to their velocity.

Newton's views were opposed by the Dutch physicist, Christian Huygens (1629-1695), who believed light to be a wave motion in a certain all-penetrating medium ("world ether") and the propagation of light to be similar to the propagation of sound waves through the air. It is instructive to notice that the explanation of the refraction of light based on Huygens' ideas leads to conclusions concerning light velocity in dense media that are directly opposed to those reached by Newton. To understand it in a simple way, let us substitute for successive waves of light approaching the surface of glass, successive waves of tanks operating in open country such as the North African desert. As the tanks cross a boundary between comparatively good terrain and poor, sandy terrain, their velocity is reduced (Fig. 6-10b). If, after getting into the sandy terrain, individual tank commanders stubbornly maintain their original direction of motion, the advancing line of tanks that entered the sandy terrain earlier will be delayed in their advance in respect to those that enter it later. To make the rows of tanks continue to be at right angles to their direction of advance it becomes necessary to change the course of advance and turn all the tanks somewhat to the right. It is questionable whether this argument would be acceptable to Field Marshal Montgomery (or to General Rommel for that matter), but this is exactly what light waves do. It is easy to conclude from the diagram in Fig. 6-10 that, according to Huygens' view, the refractive index of the second medium with respect to the first is equal to the inverse ratio of the light velocities in them. Thus, the refractive index of glass with respect to water is:

R.I. (water $\longrightarrow$ glass)

$$= \frac{\text{light velocity in water}}{\text{light velocity in glass}}$$

$$= \frac{\text{light velocity in water}}{\text{light velocity in vacuum}} \times \frac{\text{light velocity in vacuum}}{\text{light velocity in glass}}$$

$$= \frac{\text{R.I. (glass)}}{\text{R.I. (water)}}$$

which proves the empirical relation between refractive indices of different substances as stated earlier in the previous section.

Wave Nature of Light

If at the time of the Newton vs. Huygens dispute physicists had known a way of measuring the velocity of light in different substances, the argument could have been settled in the above described simple way. But, since this was not the case, the decision rested on another basic property of wave motion known as the interference of two light beams. We have already described the interference phenomenon in connection with the waves on the surface of a liquid (Figs. 3-6 and 3-7), and the same reasoning can apparently be applied to the interaction of two light waves.

But how can we synchronize the vibrations of two light sources? Well, this can be done with mirrors as was first suggested in 1814 by the French physicist, Augustin Fresnel (1788-1827). Fresnel's idea is illustrated in Fig. 6-11. If we have a source of light S and two mirrors, M^1 and M^2, forming a very small angle θ between them we will have two images, S_1 and S_2, located very close to each other. Since S_1 and S_2 are identical images of the original source S, the light waves coming from them will be perfectly synchronized; in fact these two waves come actually from the single source S. Point P_1 is located on the screen in such a way that the difference between the distances $P_1 S_1$ and $P_1 S_2$ is equal to an integral number of wave lengths. In this case the two light waves will arrive at P_1 *in phase*, and the illumination at this point will be increased. On the other hand, at point P_2, located in such a way that $P_2 S_2 - P_2 S_1$ is equal to an integral number of wave lengths plus one-half, light waves from S_1 and S_2 will arrive *out of phase;* the crest of one of them will always overlap the trough of the other, and as a result the illumination will be zero. We would therefore expect that the screen would be covered by a system of light and dark bands instead of being uniformly illuminated, and that is exactly what happens. This simple experiment proved beyond

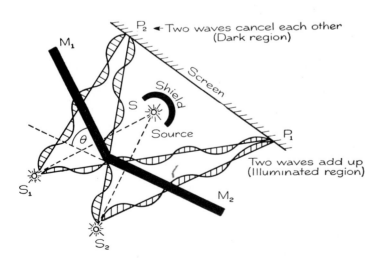

Fig. 6-11. Fresnel's experiment with the interference of two light beams.

any doubt the correctness of Huygens' point of view and also provided a simple method for measuring the wave length of light. As we shall see later, the color of light depends on its wave length, and since light consists of a mixture of different wave lengths, the pattern seen on the screen will be somewhat blurred and will consist of rainbow colors. To eliminate this, we should place a piece of colored glass in front of the source of light, which will absorb all light except that of a single color (i.e., of a single narrow range of wave lengths).

The idea of the interference of water waves, as shown in Fig. 3-8b, can be extended to a very long breakwater with many openings in it. This is analogous to the effect of an optical "grating" on light waves. We can make a "transmission grating" from a piece of glass on which we have scratched a large number of fine parallel grooves. When placed in a beam of light, the glass will transmit (i.e., let pass through) only the light that falls on the smooth unscratched strips between the grooves. A "reflection grating" works in a similar manner by reflecting light from the smooth sides of accurately shaped grooves in the surface of a metal mirror. With modern techniques, we can make gratings of several thousand scratches per millimeter. These optical gratings are a useful substitute for prisms in the study of optical spectra. Since the angular separation between separate beams depends on the wave length, white light falling on such gratings will be broken up into rainbow-colored strips.

The wave nature of light is also revealed when light passes through a very small opening that has dimensions comparable to the wave length of light (i.e., about 0.001 mm). If the opening is much larger than the wave length, light passing through it will make a spot of light the same shape as the opening on a screen placed behind it. However, in the case of a small opening, the light will be scattered (diffracted), and all that will be seen on the screen will be a diffused, luminous spot from which we cannot conclude anything about the shape or size of the opening. This phenomenon, known as "diffraction of light," places a lower limit on the size of small objects that can be seen or photographed by using visible light. In fact, light waves cannot produce a picture of objects that are only the length of a light wave for the same reason that a painter cannot paint a miniature portrait using a 2-inch brush.

Considering light as waves propagating through space, scientists logically assumed that there must be some medium through which these waves propagate. Since light propagates easily through empty space (which is not true in the case of sound), this hypothetical medium was assumed to fill all space and also to penetrate into the interior of all material bodies. It was called "light ether" or "world ether." We have already encountered this notion in a previous chapter in connection with Faraday-Maxwell's view on the nature of electric and magnetic fields, and we have also seen that electromagnetic waves were considered as the propagation of some kind of elastic deformation through this medium. In fact, light waves are electromagnetic waves and differ from radio waves only by their very short wave length.

Lenses and Lens Systems

The phenomenon of refraction of light is used in the construction of optical instruments that are similar in their operation to those based on the laws of reflection. These instruments contain convex and concave lenses which, like convex and concave mirrors, either disperse the incident beam of light, thus forming a virtual image, or collect it into real focus. The paths of light rays in these two kinds of lenses are shown in Fig. 6-12a and b.

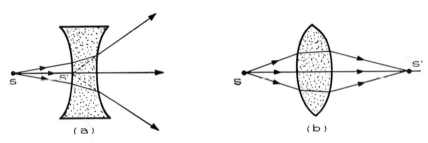

Fig. 6-12. The paths of light rays in a dispersing (a) and a converging (b) lens.

The simplest optical instrument based on the refraction of light is an ordinary magnifying glass (Fig. 6-13) in which the rays of light emitted from various points of the object form its virtual image on the same side of the lens as the object. By combining lenses in various ways, we can build more complicated and more powerful optical instruments. The principle of the telescope (which is the same for Captain Kidd's spyglass through which he searched for treasure-laden merchantmen as for the 36-inch refracting telescope of the Lick Observatory in California, Fig. 6-14) is explained in the diagram in Fig. 6-15. We see from this diagram that the role of the front, or objective, lens *A* is to form a real image *B* of the distant object near the rear end of the telescope tube. The larger this lens *A* is, the brighter and sharper the image *B* is. Notice that the size of the image does not depend on the size of the lens but is entirely determined by the angle α through which the distant object is seen by the naked eye, or, in other words, to the ratio of the size of the object to its distance from us. The role of the rear, or ocular, lens *C* is to turn the divergent beams of light coming from different points of the image into parallel beams again, and, as can be seen from the diagram, these parallel beams form between themselves a larger angle β, thus giving the impression that the object is considerably nearer. The magnifying power of the telescope is defined as the ratio β:α, and, as can be clearly seen from

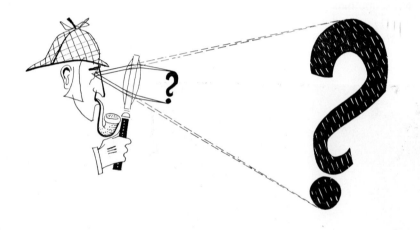

Fig. 6-13. Solving a murder mystery by the use of a simple lens.

the drawing, is equal to the ratio of the distance *AB:BC*. Big telescopes usually have a selection of ocular lenses with different focal distances *BC* that can be used to obtain different magnifications. However, the functioning of the ocular lens depends entirely on the quality of the image formed by the objective lens, and each telescope is only as good as its objective lens. A very useful combination of a "refracting" and a "reflecting" telescope was invented by the German optical designer and manufacturer, B. Schmidt (1879-1935), and carries his name.

In astronomical telescopes, the image is usually seen upside down, but this makes no difference in the study of celestial objects. In terrestrial telescopes, the eyepiece is made of two lenses, the second one serving to reverse the image to its proper position. (Captain Kidd actually would have used one of this type, but Fig. 6-15 shows him using the simpler astronomical telescope, in which the ship would appear upside down.)

As in the case of the telescope, the role of the microscope is to make a small object look large enough for detailed study. Since, in contrast to a telescope, a microscope is used for observing minute objects that are close to us instead of large objects that appear small only because they are distant, the arrangement of lenses is now somewhat different (Fig. 6-16). The objective lens is now quite small while the eyepiece is considerably larger. A real image of the object is formed by the objective lens, *A*, which is near the bottom end of the tube, and this image is viewed through the ocular lens, *C*. Thus, while a telescope makes distant objects look closer, a microscope makes small objects look larger. Magnification is defined in this case, not as the ratio of two angles, but as the ratio of the size of the image to the real size of the object.

Fig. 6-14. The 36-inch refractor of the Lick Observatory at Mount Hamilton, California. *Courtesy Lick Observatory.*

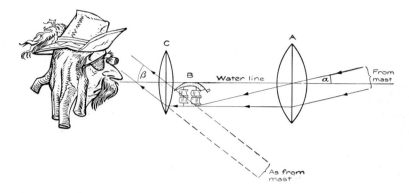

Fig. 6-15. The paths of light rays in an ordinary telescope. Because of the action of the lenses, the angle between the light rays coming from the water line and the mast of the ship is considerably increased.

THE ELECTRON MICROSCOPE

Although the electron microscope does not, properly speaking, belong to the field of optics, its principles are so similar to those of the ordinary microscope that it is suitable to describe it at this time. As we have seen above, the resolving power of the ordinary microscope is limited by the wave length of light, and the images of objects that are comparable to or smaller than that wave length become completely blurred. This limitation is the natural consequence of the wave nature of light, and if

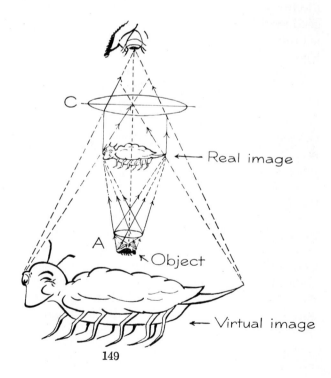

Fig. 6-16. The paths of light rays in a microscope.

149

Newton instead of Huygens had been right in their old dispute on the subject, the construction of better and better optical microscopes would be limited only by purely technical difficulties. But, although we cannot change the nature of light and deprive it of its wave character, we can produce beams of particles that possess all the properties that are necessary for the construction of a microscope with an almost unlimited resolving power.

The substitute for light rays is provided by electronic beams with which we have become already partially acquainted in the discussion of radio engineering. We have learned that heated wires emit streams of electrons in very much the same way as hot filaments in ordinary electric bulbs emit rays of visible light. These electronic beams are similar to the beams of light rays inasmuch as they also propagate along straight lines if not acted upon by any external forces, so that we can observe the shadows of an object placed in their way. Falling on a photographic plate, electronic beams produce blackening in very much the same way as light does, and this fact enables us to use standard photographic methods for their study. But when an electronic beam falls on an ordinary screen such as a piece of white paper, it does not "illuminate" it as visible light does. Therefore, for the purpose of visual observation, we must use fluorescent screens that become luminous under electronic bombardment. Electronic beams show scarcely any diffraction phenomena,* which is good from the point of view of microscope designers. However, they are not subject to refraction and this makes it impossible to use the ordinary lenses that constitute the principal parts of all optical instruments.

But, human ingenuity knows no limits, and it was suggested as early as 1930 that an electronic analogy of an optical lens could be constructed by sending electronic beams through a suitably selected magnetic field. We have learned in the previous chapter that wires carrying electric currents are affected by the presence of magnetic fields. Since electronic beams are nothing but electric currents running through free space instead of through the body of a wire, we would expect that these beams would also be deflected from their original direction of motion if sent through a coil producing a magnetic field. By using these magnetic deflections instead of the deflections caused by refraction, it is possible to construct "magnetic lenses" which focus the electronic beams in the same way as optical lenses focus light rays. From now on the going is easy, since all we have to do is arrange magnetic "lenses" in the same way as optical lenses are arranged in an ordinary microscope. The comparison of the two arrangements is shown in Fig. 6-17. The first commercially produced electronic microscope was designed and constructed for RCA by

---

* Compare, however, Chapter 13.

Dr. V. K. Zworikin and his chief assistant, Dr. James Hillier. Two photographs taken by the electron microscope are shown in Figs. 6-18 and 6-19.

Fig. 6-17. A comparison of an optical microscope (left) with an electron microscope (right). From V. K. Zworikin *et al, Electron Optics and the Electron Microscope* (New York: John Wiley and Sons, 1945).

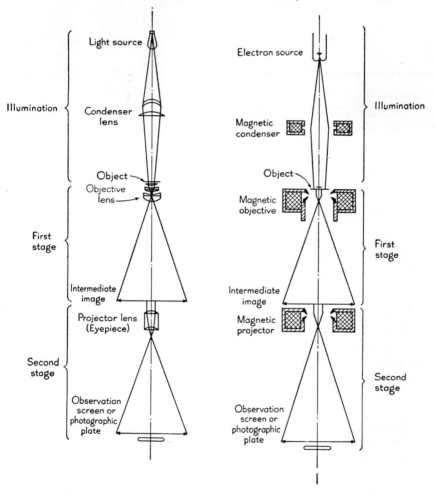

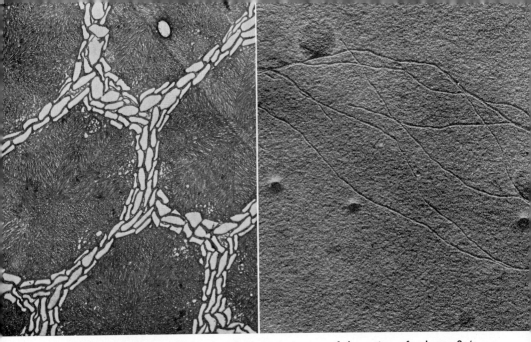

Fig. 6-18 (left). An electronmicrogram of the retina of a butterfly's eye taken by Dr. H. Fernandez-Morán at the Venezuelan Institute of Neurology. The white spaces are the cross-sections of the air-conducting channels. Magnification: about 5,000 times.

Fig. 6-19 (right). An electronmicrogram of the molecules of DNA (see Chapter 11) taken by Dr. Robley Williams at the Virus Institute of the University of California. Magnification: about 500,000 times.

The Eye

Lenses, telescopes, and microscopes are man-made optical gadgets designed to help the human eye see very distant or very small objects. But the eye itself is an optical instrument designed by Mother Nature, the most ingenious of all designers, and it still remains the most versatile optical instrument ever made. The eye (Fig. 6-20) is essentially a double lens system, the first and more important lens being formed by the *cornea* and the second by a deformable, transparent cartridge usually known as the *lens*, though the name, "auxiliary lens," would be more suitable. In the eye disease known as a "cataract," the lens becomes opaque, but vision can be restored by removing the lens and compensating for its loss by a glass spectacle lens outside the eye.

Fig. 6-20. A cross-section of the human eye.

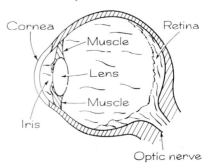

By the combined action of the cornea and the lens, the image of the object at which we look is formed on the back wall of the eyeball, which is covered with a multitude of nerve endings sensitive to light and is known as the *retina*. Muscles supporting the lens can increase its curvature at will so that the eye can be focused on objects located at different distances. There is no ocular musculature to make the lens *less* convex; accommodation appears to depend entirely on squeezing the lens to make it stronger. The normal eye, when paralyzed by atropine, is accommodated for infinity, so a farsighted eye must exert a constant tension even for distant objects, and consequently tires easily. A myopic eye cannot by any muscular effort accommodate for distant objects and hence has a relaxed lens muscle and a blurred image it can do nothing about. In young, normal individuals, the accommodation power of the eye (i.e., its ability to focus at different distances) is very high, and a child can usually accommodate its eyes for clear vision even if the spectacles belonging to a very nearsighted person are put on its nose. With age, the accommodation power of the eye decreases, and its normal focusing abilities very often become defective. This situation, familiar to many readers, is shown in Fig. 6-21a, b, and c. In nearsighted persons, the eye

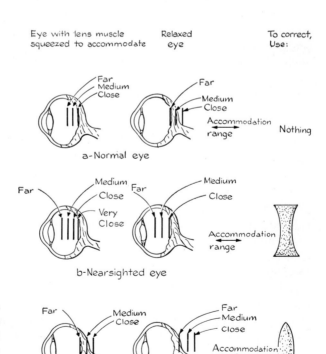

Fig. 6-21. The positions of the images of objects that are at a far, medium, and close distance from normal and abnormal eyes.

lens is curved too much so that the image is formed generally in front of the retina. While the eye can still accommodate for good vision of objects located quite close, it cannot possibly bring to the retina the image of distant objects, and they appear blurred. On the other hand, the eye lens of a farsighted person does not have enough curvature, and the image is formed on the average behind the retina. In this case, the eye can still accommodate for the clear vision of distant objects but fails to do so for objects that are comparatively near. Opticians can help in both cases by prescribing concave spectacles for nearsighted persons and convex spectacles for farsighted ones.

Rainbow Colors

When a rainstorm passes and the sun shines again in the sky, we often see a brightly colored arch against the dark background of the departing clouds opposite to the sun. The rainbow, which according to popular belief promises no more rain, is an optical phenomenon caused by the reflection of sunlight from the raindrops of a vanishing storm. In order for the direction of the rays of sunlight to be practically reversed, the rays must enter the raindrops and be reflected from their inner surfaces as indicated on a greatly exaggerated scale in the drawing in Fig. 6-22. It can be seen from this figure that only those raindrops that are located along the arch forming a certain angle around the point opposite to the sun, which is below the horizon, will reflect the light into the eyes of the observer. This explains the circular shape of the rainbow. But why, instead of being just plain white, does the rainbow break into the brilliance of different colors?

This question was answered by Sir Isaac Newton, who was the first man, in recorded history at least, to produce an "artificial rainbow" and study its properties. Making a pinhole in the window shade of a darkened room and passing the resulting narrow beam of sunlight through a glass prism, Newton observed that instead of a white point image, a rainbow-colored strip was formed on a screen. Modern astronomers have investigated this phenomenon by placing a large glass prism in front of the objective lens of a telescope which is then pointed up at the stars in the night sky. If there were no prism, each star would give a white point image, but with the prism each point image is stretched into a brilliantly colored strip (Plate I). From the point of view of the wave theory of light, the interpretation of this phenomenon comes quite naturally. In fact we have seen in Chapter 3 that, whereas pure musical tones correspond to sound waves with well-defined frequencies or wave lengths, "noise" repre-

Plate I (top). Stellar spectra obtained by placing a large prism in front of a telescope's objective lens. *Photographed at Warner and Swasey Observatory, Case Institute of Technology.*

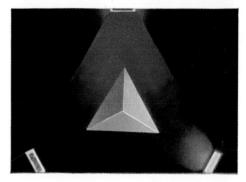

Plate II (middle). The addition of colors. *Photographed by Edward Jenkins, University of California.*

Plate III (bottom). Growing crystals look like rainbows under polarized light. *Photographed by Professor R. W. Wood, Johns Hopkins University.*

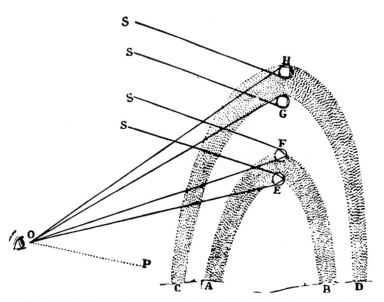

Fig. 6-22. Newton's own explanation of a rainbow: "Suppose now that O is the spectator's eye, and OP a line drawn parallel to the sun's rays and let POE, POF, POG, and POH be angles of 40 degr. 17 min., 42 degr. 2 min., 50 degr. 57 min., and 54 degr. 7 min., respectively, and these angles turned about their common side OP, shall with their other sides OE, OF, OG, and OH describe the verges of two rain-bows AF, BE, and CHDG. For if E, F, G, and H be drops placed any where in the conical superficies described by OE, OF, OG, and OH, and be illuminated by the sun's rays SE, SF, SG, and SH; the angle SEO being equal to the angle POE, or 40 degr. 17 min., shall be the greatest angle in which the most refrangible rays can after one reflection be refracted to the eye, and therefore all the drops in the line OE shall send the most refrangible rays most copiously to the eye, and thereby strike the senses with the deepest violet color in that region." From Newton's Optics. (Reprinted by G. Bell & Sons Ltd., London, 1931.)

sents a mixture of all possible audible frequencies. Similarly, we can say that white or colorless light is a mixture of light waves of all possible frequencies or lengths, and in this sense we can call such light an "optical noise" in the same way as acoustical engineers often call ordinary noise a "white sound."

Light Emission by Hot Bodies

We all know that in order to emit light, material bodies must be heated above a certain temperature. Hot radiators of a room heating system (below 100°C) do not emit any visible light whatever, while the heating

155

units of an electric range (at about 750°C) glow with a faint reddish light that can be seen only if the kitchen is not too brightly illuminated. The filament of an electric bulb (about 2,300°C), which is much hotter than the kitchen range units, emits intense white light, while the light of an electric arc, which is still hotter (3,500°C), is almost uncomfortably intense and possesses a bluish tint. Thus, **the intensity of light that a heated body emits increases as its temperature increases, and the prevailing wave length shifts from the red toward the blue end of the spectrum.** Figure 6-23 shows how the intensity varies with wave length

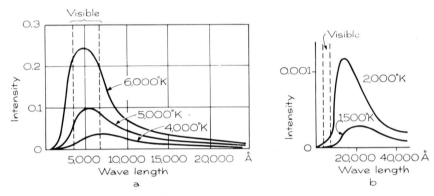

Fig. 6-23. Intensity distribution in the emission of hot bodies at different temperatures. The upper curve in (a) corresponds to the surface temperature of the sun, in which case a large fraction of the total energy falls within the visible part of the spectrum. The upper curve in (b)—notice the difference in scale—shows only a small fraction of visible radiation, which is mostly red. The lower curve in (b) corresponds to a low-temperature emission with all the energy in the infrared region.

at different temperatures. The studies of these curves led to two fundamental laws of thermal radiation that may be formulated in the following way:

Wien's law: **The wave length of maximum intensity is inversely proportional to the temperature of the emitter.**

The Stefan-Boltzmann law: **The total intensity of the emitted radiation** (i.e., the areas of the curves shown in Fig. 6-23) **is proportional to the fourth power of the emitter's temperature.**

Thus, if we could increase by a factor of 2 the temperature of the filament in an electric bulb without melting it, the lamp would become considerably bluer and also 16 times brighter. These two laws of thermal radiation play a very important role in physics, and we will have an opportunity to use them in the following chapters.

INFRARED AND ULTRAVIOLET RADIATION

Just as in acoustical phenomena a *human ear can hear only the sounds* within a certain frequency (or wave length) interval, so the *human eye can see only the light* within narrow limits of frequencies (or wave lengths). Radiation with wave lengths *longer* than that of a red light is known as *infrared radiation*. It is also often called "heat radiation" since it is emitted from hot bodies (such as a room radiator) that are not yet hot enough to be luminous. In fact, heat rays are emitted by all material bodies no matter how low their temperatures are, but, according to the Stefan-Boltzmann law, their intensity falls very rapidly with the temperature.

Ultraviolet radiation has wave lengths *shorter* than the blue-violet end of the spectrum, and this radiation becomes more and more important with the increasing temperature of the emitting body. While the ordinary electric bulb (at 2,300°C) does not emit any ultraviolet radiation to speak of, the sun, which has a surface temperature of about 6,000°C, emits enough ultraviolet radiation to sunburn or tan the exposed parts of the human skin. As an extreme case, there is a star located in the center of the so-called Crab Nebula (see Chapter 18) that has a surface temperature of 500,000°C. At this tremendously high temperature, the prevailing wave length is shifted, according to Wien's law, so far into the short-wave region that only a small fraction of its energy is emitted within the visible range. Most of the remaining energy is radiated in the invisible ultraviolet.

LINE SPECTRA

While the light emitted by hot solid bodies represents a mixture of all wave lengths and is known as a "continuous spectrum," gases behave, in this respect, quite differently. Take a candle and analyze the light from the flame by means of a simple spectroscope (Fig. 6-24). You will see a continuous spectrum which looks about the same as the spectrum of light emitted by a hot solid body. But the fact is that in the case of a candle (or the flame in a fireplace), we do see the light emitted by solid bodies. It can be shown, indeed, that the main portion of light is emitted, not by the hot gas which forms the flame, but by tiny particles of unburned carbon (chimney black) that are heated to high temperatures by the flame gases. If the burning is complete, as it is in the case of a Bunsen gas burner, the flame loses most of its brightness.

If we introduce into the flame of a Bunsen burner a small amount of table salt, we will notice that the flame becomes a brilliant yellow, and if we look at it through a spectroscope, we will see, not a continuous rainbow-colored band, but a single narrow yellow line on a generally dark background. This line is produced by the sodium that is introduced into the flame. In fact, the line always appears when a substance introduced into the flame contains some sodium, and it is never present if

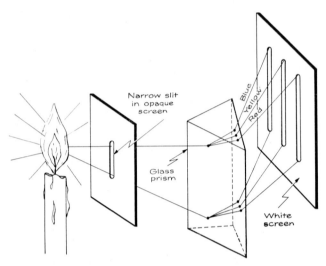

Fig. 6-24. The three lines shown on the screen at right are the particular colors (or wave lengths) of blue, yellow, and red. Each one of the colors present in the light of the flame will produce a similar line on the screen, and the infinite number of wave lengths from the incandescent carbon particles will make a continuous spectrum.

the substance is lacking in that element. If, instead of a sodium compound, we put some lithium salt into the flame, the flame will become a brilliant red, while compounds of copper will give it a greenish tint. Another method of producing line spectra of different gaseous materials consists of subjecting them to an electric discharge, as is done, for example, in luminous advertising signs.

The fact that each chemical element emits a set of spectral lines characteristic only of that particular element is the basis of so-called *spectral analysis,* i.e., the method by which we can observe the spectral lines emitted by a material of unknown chemical constitution and tell of what elements (and in what relative amounts) the substance is composed. Spectral analysis is particularly useful in astronomy for studying the composition of the sun and the stars, since we clearly cannot get a piece of the material from these bodies to analyze by conventional methods in a chemical laboratory.

FRAUNHOFER LINES

We can now continue our experiment with the table salt-colored flame by placing *behind* the flame a strong source of white light. While without the flame the source will produce a bright rainbow-colored continuous spectrum, the introduction of the sodium-contaminated flame between the white light source and the spectroscope will result in the appearance of a narrow black line exactly in the same place where the sodium emission line was previously found. The explanation of this fact is based on the notion of *resonance*, discussed in some detail in previous chapters. If the sodium atoms *emit* light waves of a certain characteristic frequency, they are also apt to *absorb* the waves of this particular frequency when an intense white light passes through them. The best-known example of such absorption lines is provided by the multitude of thin dark lines that cross the continuous spectrum of the sun; these lines were discovered by the German physicist, Joseph Fraunhofer (1787-1826), and are therefore named after him. Fraunhofer lines originate when the white light radiated by the deeper and denser layers of the solar body (the so-called "photosphere") passes through the thin gaseous envelope ("chromosphere") and "reversing layer" of the sun. By observing them, we can make definite conclusions about the chemical composition of the sun. The interesting fact revealed by this method is that, apart from the large predominance of hydrogen and helium gases, the chemical composition of the sun is identical with that of our earth. By using the methods of spectral analysis, astronomers have been able to learn a lot, not only about the sun, but also about the chemical composition of the planetary atmospheres and the outer envelopes of distant stars.

WHY SOLIDS EMIT A CONTINUOUS SPECTRUM

Since each chemical element possesses a characteristic set of spectral lines, we must conclude that this characteristic frequency pattern is directly connected with the properties of atoms. We may visualize the different kinds of atoms as being similar to different kinds of musical instruments; an instrument emits a characteristic *assortment of pure tones* and the atoms of a chemical element emit a characteristic *assortment of "pure colors,"* i.e., sets of spectral lines. When atoms are tightly piled together as in a solid or liquid body, they disturb each other so much that instead of a definite "optical chord," they produce nothing but an "optical noise" caused by the orderless superimposition of all possible frequencies. In fact, this situation is like having several dozen tuning forks shaking in a bag: lots of clinking and squeaking, but no pure tones. On the other hand, in gases the atoms fly freely through space and most of the time are too far from neighboring atoms to be disturbed by them. This gives them a chance to emit their characteristic frequencies between successive collisions.

SPECTRAL LINES AND ATOMIC STRUCTURE

The study of the spectral lines that characterize various elements led to the discovery of a number of amusing regularities that are apparently due to the specific properties of atomic mechanisms responsible for the emission of these lines. In the case of hydrogen, which is the simplest chemical element, the relation between various lines shown in Fig. 6-25 can be expressed by an extremely simple mathematical formula that was discovered in 1885 by the German school teacher, J. J. Balmer, and carries his name. This formula states that the frequencies of the observed lines are exactly proportional to the difference between the inverse square of 2, i.e., $\frac{1}{4}$, and the inverse squares of 3, 4, 5, etc. In fact, calculating these differences, we obtain:

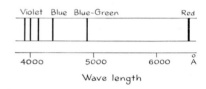

Fig. 6-25. Part of the hydrogen spectrum with the color of different emission lines indicated.

$$\left(\frac{1}{2^2} - \frac{1}{3^2}\right) = \left(\frac{1}{4} - \frac{1}{9}\right) = 0.138889$$

$$\left(\frac{1}{2^2} - \frac{1}{4^2}\right) = \left(\frac{1}{4} - \frac{1}{16}\right) = 0.1875$$

$$\left(\frac{1}{2^2} - \frac{1}{5^2}\right) = \left(\frac{1}{4} - \frac{1}{25}\right) = 0.21$$

$$\left(\frac{1}{2^2} - \frac{1}{6^2}\right) = \left(\frac{1}{4} - \frac{1}{36}\right) = 0.222222$$

etc.

Multiplying these values by 3.28937×10^{15} we obtain:

$$4.5686 \times 10^{14}$$

$$6.1676 \times 10^{14}$$

$$6.9077 \times 10^{14}$$

$$7.3097 \times 10^{14}$$

etc.

which is to be compared with the values:

$$4.5685 \times 10^{14}$$
$$6.1676 \times 10^{14}$$
$$6.9075 \times 10^{14}$$
$$7.3099 \times 10^{14}$$

representing the actually measured frequency of hydrogen's spectral lines. The agreement is good up to the fifth decimal place.

The line spectra of alkali metals, such as lithium, sodium, and potassium are similar to the spectrum of hydrogen, though somewhat distorted, indicating that the structure of these atoms is similar to that of hydrogen. But in other elements, as for example in oxygen or iron, the pattern of spectral lines becomes so very complicated that any mathematical formulation becomes extremely difficult.

For some time after the discovery of characteristic spectral lines and the regularities existing between them, physicists tried to explain these regularities by considering atoms as miniature elastic bodies of various shapes. Thus, a hydrogen atom was considered to be a sphere, a sodium atom an elongated ellipsoid, and an oxygen atom a doughnut with a very small central hole. The physicists hoped that they could calculate the vibration frequencies of these variously shaped bodies and find that they were in agreement with the observed sets of spectral lines. However, all these attempts resulted in a fiasco; the picture of atoms as miniature vibrating bodies was too simple and too naive. A complete understanding of the laws of optical spectra came only much later as the result of exhaustive studies of the inner electric structure of matter.

Color Vision

When we were discussing the functioning of the ear, we saw that its receptive part, the cochlea, is a linear array of resonators ranging in their frequencies from the lowest to the highest limits of audible sound. If a pure musical tone is sounded, only one narrow section of the cochlea will be excited, and we can recognize the tone as a definite musical pitch. In the case of a chord, a trained ear can recognize the separate notes from which it is composed. If the eye were constructed in the same way as the ear, the retina would have to be formed by a large variety of light-sensitive elements, each element responding to only one particular wave length of the visible spectrum. The eye, however, is not so constructed. There are actually only three kinds of light-sensitive elements, and each one of them responds to a rather broad band of wave lengths. If the eye receives monochromatic light with a frequency near the lower limit of sensitivity, only one set of light-sensitive elements of the retina will be excited, and we will get the sensation of color which we call "red." The medium frequency excites the second set of light-sensitive elements, giving us the sensation of "green," while the frequency near the upper limit causes the sensation of "blue" by acting on the third set of light-sensitive elements. If the frequency of the incident monochromatic light is intermediate between the frequencies of red- and green-sensitive elements, both sets are simultaneously excited, and we get the sensation which we call "yellow." However, we can receive the same sensation by using two monochromatic wave lengths, one corresponding to red-sensitive elements and one to green-sensitive ones. Similarly, the overlap of blue and green colors leads to the color sensation known as "cyan," while a red and blue overlap gives the sensation we call "purple."

This effect can be illustrated by this experiment. Three lanterns supplied with red, green, and blue filters throw light on a white pyramid placed in the center between them (Plate II). If the pyramid were placed in such a way that its three sides were facing the three beams its sides would show these three colors. If, however, each side of the pyramid is illuminated by two beams, the mixture of basic colors produces "yellow," "purple," and "cyan." Thus, as far as the eye is concerned, it does not make any difference whether the incident light is "really yellow" or a mixture (or "chord," in acoustical terminology) of green and red colors. Another difference between sound and light perception lies in the fact that whereas sounds of very low and very high frequencies are perceived by the ear as widely different sensations, the far blue end of the optical spectrum gives the same optical sensation as the far red end. From a point of view of color perception, we should draw the visible spectrum not along a line but around the circumference of a circle. It is clear from the preceding discussion that, as far as frequency perception is concerned, the eye is much inferior to the ear. This is probably the reason why various attempts to compose "color symphonies," which would appeal to our senses through the interplay of colors thrown on a screen, have failed.

Although we criticize the eye with respect to its ability to distinguish between different incident wave lengths of light, we should not forget that its main function is to inform us about the position and shapes of objects emitting light. It is true that the human ear can do much better in analyzing the complexity of sound emitted by a symphony orchestra, but, on the other hand, we cannot "hear" the location of the individual musicians on the stage nor the shape of the instruments they are playing!

THE DOPPLER EFFECT

An important phenomenon, both in the case of light waves and of sound waves, is the change of wave length in the light or sound that comes to us from a moving source. This phenomenon is known as the "Doppler effect." If the source of a given frequency moves toward us, the waves coming in our direction will be squeezed and will appear to us shorter than those from a stationary source. In the case of a receding source, the situation is the opposite, and the arriving waves will be longer. How it happens can be easily understood by inspecting the diagram in Fig. 6-26.

In the case of sound, the approaching source will appear to have a higher pitch and the receding source a lower pitch. In the case of a

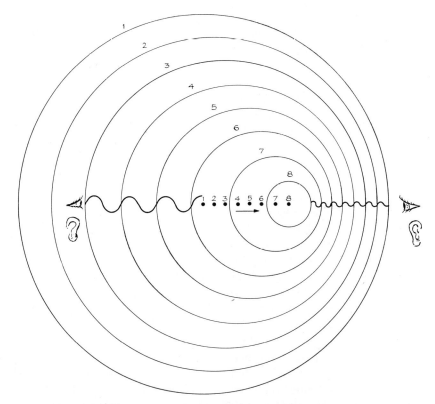

Fig. 6-26. The consecutive positions of spherical waves emitted by a source moving to the right. The positions of the source and the corresponding waves are indicated by the same numbers.

moving light source, we will see violet and red shifts of spectral lines. We can show that the relative change of wave length $\Delta\lambda/\lambda$ due to the Doppler effect equals the ratio of the velocity of the source to the propagation velocity of waves (sound or light velocity). Thus, by measuring the change of wave length, we can easily calculate the velocity of the source. This method is widely used in astronomy for estimating the radial velocities of stars and galaxies from their observed spectra.

The Doppler effect also exists, of course, in the case of a stationary source and a moving observer, and there is a story (not a true one, of course) that the famous American physicist, R. W. Wood, once tried to use this effect in a traffic court as an excuse for going through a red light. The judge, so the story goes, was almost ready to let the famous man go without paying the fine when one of Wood's students, whom he had recently flunked on an examination in optics, proposed that the judge ask the professor to calculate the velocity with which he must have been driving toward the red signal light to see it green. As a result, Wood had to pay a much higher fine for greatly exceeding the speed limit of the city of Baltimore.

Polarization of Light

We have seen in Chapter 3 that there are two possible ways of wave propagation: 1) longitudinal waves in which the motion of individual particles is along the line of propagation, and 2) transverse waves in which the motion is perpendicular to the line of propagation. Which kind of wave motion do we have in the case of light? The important difference between the longitudinal and transverse waves is that the latter can be "polarized." To understand this important notion let us look at a wave in the direction of its propagation as shown in Fig. 6-27. In the case of longitudinal waves (a), the motion of the par-

Fig. 6-27. Cross-section of a wave in the direction of its propagation.

ticles takes place perpendicular to the surface of the paper and will not be noticeable from the direction we are observing it. In the case of transverse waves (b and c), the motion of the particles is in the plane of the paper and easily observable in that projection. We call the transverse wave "natural" or "nonpolarized" if the motion of the particles takes place in all possible directions (b); if the motion is only in one direction (c), the wave is "polarized." The notion of polarization can be clarified by the analogy given in Fig. 6-28. Suppose we have a sieve, made of a set of parallel wires without cross wires, and drop matches on it in such a way that the falling matches remain horizontal but may have different orientations in the horizontal plane. It is clear that only those matches that are parallel

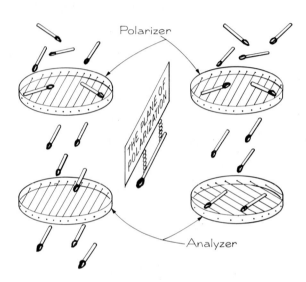

Fig. 6-28. "Polarized matches."

to the sieve wires will pass through. If under this "match polarizer" we place a similar "match analyzer," the "beam of matches" will pass through only if the wires in the lower sieve run parallel to those of the upper sieve. We can extend this analogy to the case of longitudinal waves by dropping the matches in a vertical position. In this case, all the matches will pass through, regardless of the relative positions of the two sieves.

It was found that many crystals have the ability to polarize light waves in such a way that the light is able to pass through a pair of crystals when their "optical axes" (sieve wires in Fig. 6-28) are parallel to one another but is completely stopped when the axes are crossed. This fact shows beyond any doubt that *the vibrations of light waves are perpendicular to the propagation of motion.*

We cannot finish this already overgrown chapter on light without mentioning the phenomenon known as "rotation of the plane of polarization." If we place certain crystal objects in a beam of polarized light between a polarizer and an analyzer, we will notice that the plane of polarization has been rotated, and in order to extinguish the passing light we have to turn the analyzer by a certain angle. Properly speaking, the passing light can be completely extinguished only if we use a monochromatic source, since the rotation of the plane of polarization depends on the wave length of light in very much the same way as it does in the phenomenon of refraction. If we place crystals or other materials, such as certain plastics (crumpled cellophane will do nicely) in the beam of white polarized light, we will observe beautiful rainbow patterns that are very helpful in the study of crystalline structures (Plate III).

SEVEN

MODERN VIEWS ON SPACE, TIME, AND MOTION

In discussing the phenomena of electromagnetism and light, we referred time and again to the notion of "world ether," the hypothetical all-penetrating substance that was supposed to be responsible for long-range electric and magnetic interactions between material bodies as well as for the propagation of light waves across what we usually consider to be empty space. In order to carry out all these functions, "world ether" had to be a solid medium, since only a solid body can be subjected to elastic stresses and since only in a solid medium can transverse elastic waves exist. The idea of a solid material filling the entire space of the universe without, however, offering any resistance to the motion of material bodies passing through it naturally led to grave conceptual difficulties. These difficulties finally culminated in the paradoxical result of an experiment carried out especially for the purpose of detecting the motion of our earth through this hypothetical universal substratum. Since this experiment pertains to the effect of the earth's motion through space on the observed velocity of light, we start with a description of the methods used for measuring that velocity.

Velocity of Light

The first attempt to measure the propagation of light was undertaken by Galileo in a very primitive way. One evening, he and his assistant placed themselves on two distant hills in the neighborhood of Florence, each of them carrying a lantern with a shutter. Galileo's assistant was instructed to open his lantern as soon as he noticed the flash from the one carried by his master. If light was propagating with a finite speed, the flash from the assistant's lantern would have been observed by Galileo with a certain delay. The result of this experiment was, however, completely negative, and we know now very well why. Light propagates so fast that the expected delay in Galileo's experiment must have been about one hundred-thousandth of a second, which is quite unnoticeable to human senses.

The first successful measurement of the velocity of light was carried

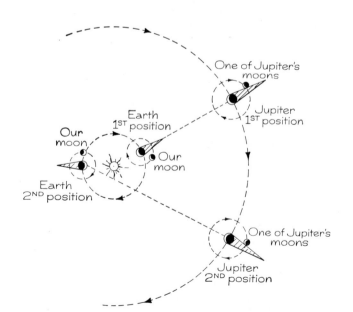

Fig. 7-1. Roemer's method of measuring the velocity of light by observing the eclipses of Jupiter's moons.

out in 1675 by the German astronomer, Roemer, who replaced Galileo's assistant by the moons of the planet Jupiter, thus increasing the distance to be covered by light by a factor of hundreds of millions.* Roemer's method is illustrated in Fig. 7-1, which shows the orbits of the earth, Jupiter, and one of its moons. Moving around the planet, the moons are periodically eclipsed as they enter the broad cone of shadow cast by Jupiter. Studying these eclipses, Roemer noticed that sometimes they took place as much as eight minutes ahead of schedule and sometimes with a delay of eight minutes. He also noticed that the eclipses were early when the earth and Jupiter were on the same side of the sun (1st position) and delayed in the opposite case (2nd position). Ascribing correctly the observed irregularities to the difference of time taken by light to cover the changing distance between the earth and Jupiter, Roemer calculated that light must be propagating through space at a speed of about 300,000 kilometers per second (3×10^{10} cm/sec).

The first laboratory measurement of the speed of light was carried out in 1849 by the French physicist, H. L. Fizeau (1819-1896), whose apparatus is shown in Fig. 7-2. It consists essentially of a pair of cog-

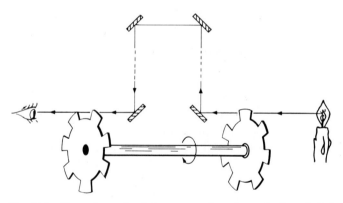

Fig. 7-2. Fizeau's method for measuring the velocity of light.

wheels set at the opposite ends of a long axis. The wheels were positioned in such a way that the cogs of one were opposite the intercog openings of the other, so that a light beam from the source could not be seen by the eye no matter what the position of the wheels. However, if the wheels were set in fast rotation and the speed of this rotation was such that the wheels moved by half the distance between the neighboring

---

* It may be remarked here that Galileo still had a hand in Roemer's measurement of the velocity of light, since it was he who discovered the moons of Jupiter.

cogs during the interval of time taken by light to propagate from one wheel to the other, the light was expected to pass through without being stopped. As the reader must have already noticed, Fizeau utilized here the same principle that is often used nowadays on express highways where the traffic signals at the intersections are set for uninterrupted driving at a legal speed. In order to observe the effect at the speed of a few thousand revolutions per minute, which was about the maximum that Fizeau could achieve, he had to lengthen the path of the light beam by using four mirrors as shown in Fig. 7-2. This direct laboratory measurement gave a value for the speed of light that stood in reasonably good agreement with that obtained by Roemer's astronomical method.

Ether Wind?

If it were true that light waves propagate through a jelly-like "world ether" which fills universal space, we would be able to notice our motion through space by observing the effect of that motion on the velocity of light. In fact, since the earth moves along its orbit at a speed of 30 km/sec, we would experience an "ether wind" blowing in the direction opposite to our motion in the very same way that a speeding motorcyclist experiences a strong "air wind" blowing into his face. Light waves propagating in the direction of that "ether wind" would move faster, being helped by the motion of the medium, while those propagating in the opposite direction would be slowed down. In the year 1887, the American physicist, A. A. Michelson (1852-1931), carried out an experiment that was expected to demonstrate the effect of the earth's motion on the velocity of light as measured on its surface. Instead of measuring the velocity of light in two opposite directions, Michelson found it more convenient to measure it in two mutually perpendicular directions. In order to understand Michelson's scheme, let us consider a Mississippi steamboat running between St. Louis, Missouri, and Memphis, Tennessee, some 300 miles apart. Sailing downstream the boat moves faster since it is helped by the current, while on the way back it is correspondingly retarded. Does the gain in time one way compensate for the loss in time the other? Although it may appear at first sight that it does, this conclusion is not true. Let us do some simple arithmetic, assuming that the boat's speed (in still water) is 30 miles per hour and that the velocity of the stream is 3 miles per hour. Sailing up and downstream, the boat will have the velocities, relative to the shore, of 27 and 33 miles per hour. The time necessary for the round trip will apparently be:

$$\frac{300}{27} + \frac{300}{33} = 11.11 + 9.09 = 20.20 \text{ hours}$$

which is one per cent more than it would be in still water. The closer the velocity of the stream is to the velocity of the boat, the longer is the time necessary for the round trip, and if the two velocities are equal the boat will never return!

Let us consider now the problem of how to move across the stream as it confronts a ferry connecting two ends of a highway at two opposite points across the river (Fig. 7-3). It is clear that when crossing the river

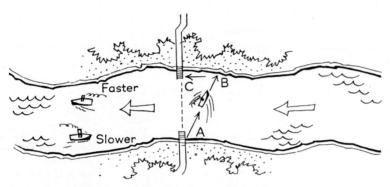

Fig. 7-3. How to propel a ferry across a moving stream.

the ferry must keep its course slightly upstream to compensate for the drift. Thus, while it covers the distance AB in respect to the water, it drifts downstream by the distance BC. Clearly the ratio BC/AB is equal to the ratio of stream and ferry velocities, and we will take it, as in the previous example, to be equal to 1/10. Applying the Pythagorean theorem to the rectangular triangle ABC, we can write:

$$(AC)^2 + \left(AB \, \frac{\text{river velocity}}{\text{boat velocity}} \right)^2 = (AB)^2$$

or:

$$(AB)^2 \left[1 - \left(\frac{\text{river velocity}}{\text{boat velocity}} \right)^2 \right] = (AC)^2$$

Since we have assumed that the ratio of velocities is 1/10, we find from the above formula that:

$$AB = \frac{AC}{\sqrt{1 - \frac{1}{100}}} = 1.005 \times AC$$

Since this result applies equally well to both crossings, the distance, with respect to the water to be covered by our motor launch on a round trip across the river, will also be 0.5 per cent longer and so will be the time needed for the trip. Thus we find that moving across the stream and back also introduces a delay, but this delay is only half as much as the delay connected with sailing up and downstream.

Now substitute the "ether wind" for the river and propagating light waves for the boats and you will have the principle of Michelson's experiment. The details are shown in Fig. 7-4. A light beam from a source,

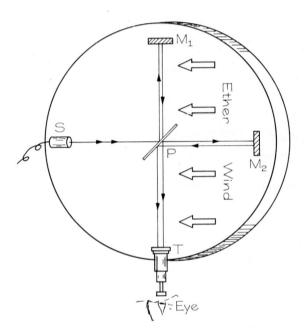

Fig. 7-4. Michelson's apparatus. All instruments were installed on a round marble plate floating in mercury, so that the system could be rotated without shaking. The separate light beams are shown here somewhat apart from one another in order to make the drawing clearer.

S, falls on the glass plate, P, covered with a thin semi-transparent layer of silver which reflects one-half of the beam in the direction of the mirror, M_1, and passes the other half through in the direction of mirror M_2. Being reflected by these mirrors, the beams return back to the plate, P; one-half of the first beam penetrates the thin silver coating on P and continues on to the telescope and the eye at T; one-half of the second beam is reflected into the telescope by the silver layer. Thus, the two beams entering the telescope will have the same intensity and the same phase, so that, according to the considerations in Chapter 6, the field of vision will be brightly illuminated.

However, in the presence of "ether wind" the situation was expected to be rather different. When the apparatus was placed in such a way that the line PM_2 coincided with the direction of the wind or its projection on a horizontal plane, the light waves traveling in this direction would be in the position of a boat sailing up and downstream, whereas the light waves traveling along the line PM_1 would correspond to a ferry moving to and fro across the river. Because of the difference in time delays in the two cases, the light beams would not arrive at the telescope simultaneously, and the ensuing difference in their arrival would result in interference which would reduce the brightness of the field of vision. The ratio of the orbital velocity of the earth, 30 km/sec, to the velocity of light, 300,000 km/sec, is considerably smaller than in the above discussed nautical example. Using the same method of calculation, we find that in this case the two light beams should arrive at the telescope with a relative delay of only 5×10^{-7} per cent of the total travel time. If (which is about right) the distance between the central plate of Michelson's apparatus and the mirrors is 150 cm, the total travel time (plate to mirror and back) is $\frac{300}{3 \times 10^{10}} = 10^{-8}$ sec, so that one light beam should be delayed in respect to the other by 5×10^{-17} sec. Although this is a very short time from our everyday point of view, it is fairly long from the point of view of wave optics. Indeed, during that time interval, light propagates by a distance of $5 \times 10^{-17} \times 3 \times 10^{10} = 1.5 \times 10^{-6}$ cm, which is about 5 per cent of the wave length.

Turning the apparatus by $90°$ and thus exchanging the roles of the mirrors, M_1 and M_2, we would expect the same delay in the opposite direction. Thus the total difference between the two light beams in the first and in the second positions of the apparatus was expected to be 10 per cent of the wave length and should have caused an easily noticeable change in the illumination of the field of vision in the telescope.

However, to his great surprise, and to the surprise of the entire scientific world (at least in the fields of physics and astronomy), Michelson failed to notice any change at all! How could it be? Some scientists suggested that there might be some drag of the "world ether" caused by the moving bulk of the earth so that the resulting velocity of the "ether wind" near the ground is considerably reduced. However, the repetition of Michelson's experiments carried out on top of a mountain and in a high-flying balloon disproved that possibility. A British physicist, G. F. Fitzgerald (1851-1901), tried to interpret the negative result of Michelson's experiment by postulating that all material bodies moving through the "world ether" shrink in the direction of their motion by an amount dependent on their velocity. The effect of this so-called "Fitzgerald's contraction" would be to transform the round table on which Michelson's mirrors were mounted into an ellipse with the shorter axis in the direction of the earth's motion. This would reduce the distance to be traveled by the light beam propagating in the "up and down wind" direction and would enable that light beam to arrive at the telescope simultaneously with the beam that was traveling across the wind. Numerous attempts were made to explain this hypothetical contraction by the change of electric and magnetic forces between the atoms moving through the "world ether," but they never led to any positive result.

CONCEPTUAL FAILURE OF WORLD ETHER NOTION

Michelson's failure to detect the motion of the earth through the "world ether" had the same roots as the failure of contemporary physical theories to formulate the mechanical properties of this hypothetical medium. As we have already discussed earlier in some detail, it was illogical to ascribe to the hypothetical "world ether" the properties of ordinary matter, such as, for example, elasticity or compressibility, since in doing so we would also have to assume that "world ether" possesses some kind of granular structure formed by "sub-atoms." But if, on the other hand, we consider "world ether" to be an absolutely homogeneous substance without any internal structure, there is no logical possibility of talking about the motion of that ether or the motion of objects in respect to it. In fact, when we watch a rotating disc we notice that it rotates by observing the motion of minor marks on its surface, such as scratches or dents. If the surface of the disc is perfectly smooth, with no marks that would catch our eye, we will not be able to tell just by looking at it whether it is moving or not. But, of course, we can touch it with our finger tip and immediately feel whether its surface is at rest or slides under our finger. And if the disc rotates fast enough, we will feel the warmth produced by the friction between the skin of our finger and the moving surface of the disc. But the phenomenon of friction, which informs us about the state of motion of the disc, is again a purely molecular

Fig. 7-5. (a) A wave propagating through a stationary elastic ribbon; (b) a moving wave-shaped rigid ribbon.

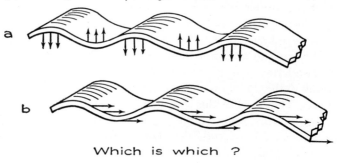

Which is which ?

phenomenon and would be absent in an "absolutely homogeneous" substance.

If we give a little thought to the problem, we can easily persuade ourselves that *it is meaningless to talk about the motion of a continuous medium or the motion in respect to it unless this medium can be considered to be formed by individual discrete particles.* If we had a long ribbon made of an absolutely continuous material and observed a wave propagating along it (Fig. 7-5), it would be meaningless to ask whether (a) it is a regular elastic wave propagating along a stationary ribbon, or (b) a rigid ribbon cut out of a sheet shaped like corrugated iron that is moving bodily from left to right.

So Spoke Einstein

In the year 1905 Albert Einstein (1879-1955), who was at that time working as a patent clerk in Zurich and had just invented a new type of oil pump, looked at Michelson's failure to notice any motion through the "world ether" in a much more radical way than did his contemporaries. Instead of trying to patch up the accumulating difficulties and contradic-

Fig. 7-6. Albert Einstein at the age of 26 delivering his first paper on the theory of relativity. Most theoretical physicists produce their first important contribution to science at about this age.

tions connected with the notion of "world ether," he rejected the notion outright as unsuitable for the description of the physical world and returned to the pre-etherian idea of a completely empty space. Along with the exit of "world ether" from the stage of physics, out went also the notion of "absolute motion" through space which was always associated, though often subconsciously, with the idea of motion with respect to "world ether." If there is no ether filling entire space and serving as a universal reference system for the motion of material bodies, **we can speak only about the motion of one material body relative to another material body, and the basic laws of physics should be the same no matter in which system of reference we are studying them.** Because of this basic postulate stating that there is no such thing as *absolute motion* and that only a *relative motion* of one object in respect to another has a physical meaning, Einstein's theory is commonly known as the *theory of relativity*.

It follows from the above postulate that it should be impossible to detect the motion of one system of reference in respect to another by performing some physical experiment in each of them and then comparing the results. Thus, the grandfather's clock in the captain's cabin on the "Queen Mary" speeding towards New York across the smooth, blue waters of the Atlantic with no storm or choppy sea breaking the uniformity of motion will operate just as well as if it were standing in the sitting room of his home. And the passengers playing ping-pong or billiards on "this sheep will not be able to tell whether their sheep is lying quietly in the Southampton ducks or sailing across the blue Atlantic."* Michelson's experiment had shown that this is also true for light phenomena. A physicist repeating Michelson's experiment in an inside cabin of the ship will not know whether the ship is moving or resting (relative to Great Britain) unless he goes up on deck and sees the gray buildings of dock installations or the limitless expanses of the ocean.

All this is very well. But what about the nature of electromagnetic interactions between material bodies, and what about the light waves propagating through empty, interstellar space? If there is no "world ether" *what* attracts or repels the poles of two magnets, and *what* is oscillating when light or radio waves propagate through the empty space? As has already been hinted in the two previous chapters, the rejection of "world ether" necessitates the introduction of a new physical entity, which is the electromagnetic field itself. *Instead of considering electric and magnetic fields as the stresses in a certain universal substratum, we now ascribe to*

---

* This passage is retained from the original handwritten text to show the amount of work performed by *Mrs. Katharine D. Cram* in typing the manuscript. (As the reader must have noticed, "sheep" means "ship" and "ducks" "docks" in the author's phonetic spelling.)

*them a definite physical reality, in fact, about as much reality as we
ascribe to ordinary material bodies.*

Probably the most important innovation brought by Einstein to our
views concerning electromagnetic and optical phenomena is that we
must ascribe a certain mass to electromagnetic energy as well as to any
other form of energy. Thus, a magnetized iron bar is slightly heavier than
it was before magnetization, the difference being due to the weight of
the magnetic field surrounding it. Similarly, a flashlight sending out a
beam of light gradually loses weight because a certain amount of mass
is being carried away by light waves. According to Einstein's law of the
equivalence of mass and energy, **the mass (in grams) to be ascribed to a
certain amount of energy (in ergs) is equal to that amount of energy
divided by the square of the velocity of light (in cm/sec).** Since the
square of the velocity of light (9×10^{20}) is a very large number, the
mass of various forms of energy is usually very small. Thus, in the case
of an ordinary laboratory magnet, the energy stored in the magnetic field
surrounding it is about 10^6 ergs, which corresponds to a mass of only
$\frac{10^6}{9 \times 10^{20}} = 10^{-15}$ gm. A flashlight with a ten-watt bulb emits 6×10^9 ergs
per minute, so that in each minute of operation the flashlight be-
comes lighter by 7×10^{-12} grams. In astronomical applications, Einstein's law leads to considerably larger masses. For example, the sun
emits 4×10^{11} tons of heat and light per day.

Thus, whereas according to the old-fashioned ideas, electric and magnetic fields were considered as elastic deformations in the all-penetrating
"world ether" (Fig. 7-7a), we now consider them as independent physical
entities that possess a certain mass, have no internal granular structure,
and surround electrically charged and magnetized objects, thinning out
to zero away from them (Fig. 7-7b). Similarly, while classical physics
considered light waves as the propagation of elastic deformations through
the "world ether" filling entire space (Fig. 7-7c), we consider them now
as vibrations taking place within the lumps of a certain physical entity
(i.e., *electromagnetic field*), flying freely through the empty space (Fig.
7-7d).

In other words, the propagation of an electromagnetic wave is more
similar to the wave-like motion of a snake crawling through the grass
and carrying along its body as well as its form of motion than it is to the
waves on the surface of water where only the form of motion but not the
material itself is moving forward.

Einstein's views concerning the close similarity between ordinary
material bodies and electromagnetic fields have found a brilliant confirmation in more recent experimental findings, which have shown that under
certain conditions electromagnetic fields can be transformed into material

particles and vice versa. In fact, as we shall see in Chapter 13, gamma rays, which are short electromagnetic waves emitted by radioactive materials, can be turned into swarms of particles (positive and negative electrons), while, on the other hand, some material particles, such as the so-called neutral pions, can completely vanish by being transformed one-hundred per cent into oscillating electromagnetic fields.

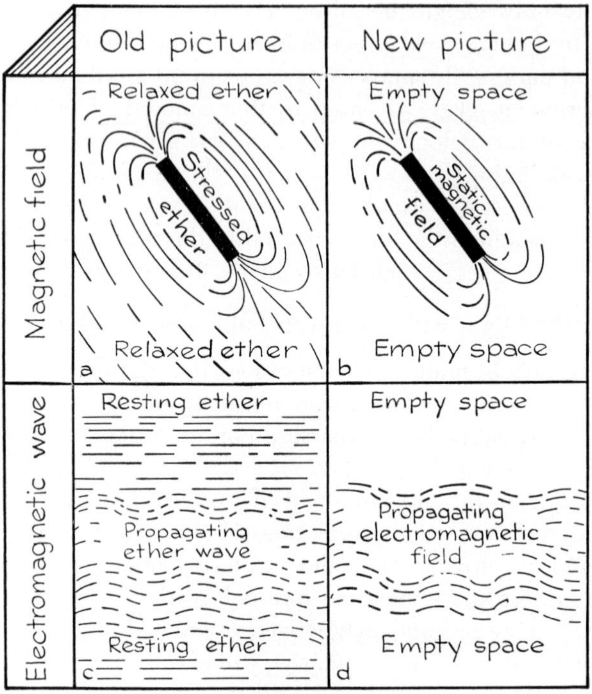

Fig. 7-7. The contrast between the pre-Einsteinian and the post-Einsteinian view of a magnetic field and an electromagnetic wave.

With these new views concerning the propagation of electromagnetic waves, and in particular that of light, we can return to the interpretation of the negative result of Michelson's experiment. There is no conversation now about "ether wind," and the light beams in Michelson's apparatus should be considered as vibrating lumps of electromagnetic fields flying more or less like rubber balls through space and being reflected by the mirrors and the half-silvered plate. As would be in the case with ordinary rubber balls, their arrival at the joining point *T* of Michelson's apparatus will not be influenced at all by the motion of the apparatus, provided this motion is smooth and nonaccelerated. No matter whether Michelson's experiment is performed on the "Queen Mary" lying at anchor at the Southampton docks or sailing towards New York across the Atlantic, or on the earth speeding on its orbit around the sun, or on an interplanetary ship "anchored" in space with respect to fixed stars, it will always show the same negative result.

In a way, the above described new view concerning the nature of light represents a compromise between Newton's idea of a stream of particles moving along the light rays and Huygens' idea of waves propagating through the "world ether." In fact, it combines the best features of both theories.

Relativistic Mechanics

As we have seen in the last section, the difficulties connected with Michelson's experiment have been resolved by abolishing the picture of light waves as propagating through the stationary "world ether" and re-placing it by a picture of a vibrating material substance (electromagnetic field) moving bodily through empty space. However, this change in our way of considering the nature of light was still far from sufficient to straighten out all the difficulties pestering physics at the turn of this century. One trouble arose in connection with the velocity of light emitted by moving sources. If a rifleman sits in a fast-moving jeep and shoots in a forward direction, the velocity of the bullets with respect to the ground will be the sum of the muzzle velocity and the velocity of the jeep (Fig. 7-8a), but bullets shot backwards will fly correspondingly slower (Fig. 7-8b). If we consider light as some kind of vibrating bullets emitted by light sources, we would expect that the velocity of light emitted by an approaching source would be higher than that emitted by a receding source. Abundant astronomical evidence based on the observation of binary stars proves, however, beyond any doubt that this is not the case. A binary star (Fig. 7-8c) is a system of two giant suns rotating around their common center of gravity and is a rather com-mon object in the sky (in fact, about half of all known stars are binaries). Because of its rotation around the common center, each of the stars is moving towards us during one-half of its rotation period and away from us during the other half.

If the velocity of light were affected by the motion of the source, the light from the approaching star would reach us sooner than the light from the receding one, and the difference in the arrival of the two light signals would be quite large. Assuming, for example, that the orbital velocities of the two stars are the same as the orbital velocity of the earth, i.e., 30 km/sec (and they are often larger than that), we find that the light would be accelerated or retarded by 0.01 per cent depending on whether it comes from the approaching or from the receding component of a binary star. Over a distance of one hundred light-years, which is not uncommon for the observed binaries, this seemingly small difference in velocity would result in one week's difference between the arrival of light from these two stars to the earth, and this difference would be reversed every half revolution period. Thus, an astronomer observing a binary star would find himself in the position of a sports fan watching a prize fight on a TV screen which, because of some trouble in transmission during the third round, shows the champion and the challenger with a

Fig. 7-8. The velocity of a bullet is affected by the motion of its source. Is this also true in the case of light?

few minutes difference in phase. Our fan would see the champion *already* resting in his corner while the challenger is *still* shadow boxing in the middle of the arena, and a minute later the champion would go out for the kill while the challenger is *still* being readied by his aids. In the middle of the fourth round the fight would seem to be normal but towards the end of it things would change in the opposite direction, and the surprised sports fan would see the champion deliver his K.O. blow after the challenger was already counted out. Since nothing of this kind has ever been seen by astronomers observing the motion of binary stars, we must conclude that **the velocity of light is not affected by the motion of its source.**

But this means that if **we add to the velocity of light any other velocity we get again the same original velocity of light!** This is paradoxical! It contradicts common sense! Well, said Einstein, if there is a scientifically established paradox you cannot get rid of, all you can do is to rationalize it. And as to the common sense . . . well, the same common sense was once objecting to the idea that the earth is round. If the common sense idea concerning the addition of two velocities does not apply to the velocity of light and the velocity of its source, it must be generally wrong and its common use in everyday life may be justified only by the fact that all the velocities we encounter in ordinary life are much smaller than that of light. Thus, cutting another Gordian knot, Einstein introduced a new and at first sight very fancy law governing the addition of two velocities. If v is the velocity of the jeep and V the muzzle velocity of the bullet shot in the forward direction by the rifleman in the jeep, the velocity of the bullet with respect to the ground will be, not $V + v$, but:

$$\frac{V + v}{1 + \dfrac{V \times v}{c^2}}$$

where c is the velocity of light. If both velocities, V and v, are small compared to the velocity of light, the second term in the denominator is practically zero, and the old "common sense" formula holds. But if either V or v, or both, approaches the velocity of light, c, the situation will be quite different.

Suppose that the velocity of the jeep is 75 per cent of the speed of light and that the muzzle velocity of the rifleman's bullet is the same. According to common sense, the velocity of the bullet with respect to the ground should be 50 per cent above the velocity of light. However, putting $V = 0.75\ c$ and $v = 0.75\ c$ into the above formula, we get only $0.96\ c$, so that the velocity of the bullet with respect to the ground remains less than the speed of light. The reader can easily verify this fact, that no matter how close the two velocities to be added are to the velocity of light, the resulting velocity will never exceed it. In the limiting case, if we make $v = c$, we obtain:

$$\frac{V + c}{1 + \dfrac{V \times c}{c^2}} = \frac{V + c}{1 + \dfrac{V}{c}} = \frac{c(V + c)}{(c + V)} = c$$

This is why the velocity of the source does not add anything to the velocity of light emitted by it. Fantastic as it may look at first sight,

Einstein's law for the addition of two velocities is correct and has been confirmed by direct experiments. It does not agree with common sense conclusions, but we should not forget that common sense conclusions are based on our everyday experience, and neither a jeep traveling with a speed close to that of light nor rifles shooting bullets at that speed can be considered as an "everyday experience"! Thus, Einstein's theory of relativity leads us to the conclusion that **it is impossible to exceed the velocity of light by adding two (or more) velocities no matter how close each of these velocities is to that of light.** The velocity of light, therefore, assumes the role of some kind of *universal speed limit* which cannot be exceeded no matter what we do.

Another way to understand the existence of an upper limit for velocity is to consider the amount of energy that would be necessary to accelerate a material body to the velocity of light. As was discussed in Chapter 2, the kinetic energy of motion in classical mechanics is defined as half of the mass times the square of the velocity. Thus the energy of an object moving with the speed of light would be: $\frac{1}{2}$ mass $\times c^2$. However, according to Einstein's law of the equivalence of mass and energy, we have to revise this conclusion by taking into account the fact that the kinetic energy of motion, as for any other form of energy, possesses a certain mass. Therefore the argument will run as follows: If a mass M moves with the velocity of v, the kinetic energy of motion is $\frac{1}{2} Mv^2$. But, since this kinetic energy possesses the mass $(\frac{1}{2} Mv^2)/c^2$ and since it moves along with the object, there must be an additional kinetic energy:

$$\frac{1}{2} \left(\frac{\frac{1}{2} Mv^2}{c^2} \right) v^2$$

However, this additional kinetic energy has the mass:

$$\frac{1}{2} \left(\frac{\frac{1}{2} Mv^2}{c^2} \right) \frac{v^2}{c^2}$$

and moving with the velocity, v, must give a further contribution,

$$\frac{1}{2} \left[\frac{1}{2} \left(\frac{\frac{1}{2} Mv^2}{c^2} \right) \frac{v^2}{c^2} \right] v^2$$

to the total kinetic energy. But this additional kinetic energy possesses the mass, etc., etc. It can be shown mathematically that this limitless series of rapidly decreasing terms amounts to:

$$M \times c^2 \left(\frac{1}{\sqrt{1 - \dfrac{v^2}{c^2}}} - 1 \right)$$

which represents the correct relativistic expression for the kinetic energy of an object moving with the velocity v. If the velocity, v, approaches the velocity of light, c, the expression under the radical in the above formula tends to zero, so that the kinetic energy of the moving object tends to infinity. Therefore we conclude that **it is impossible to accelerate a material object to the velocity of light (not to mention super-light velocities) because, in order to do this, we would need an infinite amount of energy.**

The above given formula for kinetic energy was confirmed by direct experiments on fast-moving electrons and gives us another aspect of the relativistic postulate that considers the velocity of light as the maximum possible velocity.

Space-Time Transformation

Einstein's new law for the addition of velocities clearly contradicts the classical (common sense) ideas concerning space and time, so that in accepting this new law as experimental fact we are forced to introduce radical changes in our old notions. In his *Principia,* the great Newton wrote:

I. Absolute, true, and mathematical time, of itself, and from its own nature, flows equably without relation to anything external.

II. Absolute space, in its own nature, without relation to anything external, remains always similar and immovable.

According to Einstein's views, however, space and time are more intimately connected with one another than it was supposed before, and, within certain limits, the notion of space may be substituted by the notion of time and vice versa. To make this statement more clear, let us consider a railroad passenger having his meal in the dining car. The waiter serving him will know that the passenger ate his soup, steak, and dessert in the same place, i.e., at the same table in the car. But, from the point of view of a person on the ground, the same passenger consumed the three courses at points along the track separated by many miles (Fig. 7-9a, b, and c). Thus we can make the following trivial statement: **Events taking place in the same place but at different times in a moving system will be considered by a ground observer as taking place at different places.**

Now, following Einstein's idea concerning the reciprocity of space and time, let us replace in the above statement the word "place" by the word "time" and vice versa. The statement will now read: **The events taking place at the same time but in different places in a moving system will be considered by a ground observer as taking place at different times.**

This statement is far from being trivial and means that if, for example, two passengers at the far ends of the diner had their after-dinner cigars lighted simultaneously from the point of view of the dining-car steward, the person standing on the ground will insist that the two cigars were

Fig. 7-9. Events that occur at the same place relative to a moving railroad car will look as if they occurred at different places when observed from the ground (a, b, and c). Events that occur simultaneously for an observer in a moving car will look as though they occurred at different times to an observer on the ground (d and e).

lighted at different times (Fig. 7-9d and e). Since, according to the principle of relativity, neither of the two reference systems should be preferred to the other (the train moves relative to the ground or the ground moves relative to the train) we do not have any reason to take the steward's impression as being true and the ground observer's impression as being wrong, or vice versa.

Why then do we consider the transformation of the time interval (between the soup and the dessert) into the space interval (the distance along the track) as quite natural and the transformation of the space interval (the distance between the two passengers having their cigars lit) into the time interval (between these two events as observed from the track) as paradoxical and very unusual? The reason lies in the fact that in our everyday life we are accustomed to velocities that lie in the lowest brackets of all the physically possible velocities extending from zero to the velocity of light. A race horse can hardly do better than about one-millionth of a per cent of this upper limit of all possible velocities, while a modern supersonic jet plane makes, at best, 0.0003 per cent of it. In comparing space and time intervals, i.e., distance and durations, it is rational to choose the units in which the limiting velocity of light is taken to be one. Thus, if we choose a "year" as the unit of duration, the corresponding unit of length will be a light-year, or 10,000,000,000,000 kilometers, while if we choose a "kilometer" as the unit of length, the unit of time will be 0.000003 sec, which is the time interval necessary for light to cover the distance of one kilometer. We notice that whenever we choose one unit in a "reasonable" way (a "year" or a "kilometer"), the other unit comes out either too large (a light-year) or too short (3 microseconds) from the point of view of our everyday experience. So, in the case of the passenger eating his dinner on the train, a half-hour interval between the soup and the dessert could result in 200,000,000 miles of distance along the track (time × c) if the train were moving at a speed close to that of light, and we are not surprised that the actual difference is only 20 or 30 miles. On the other hand, the distance of, let us say, 30 meters between two passengers lighting their cigars at opposite ends of the railroad car translates into a time interval of only one hundred-millionth of a second (distance ÷ c), and there is no wonder that this is not apparent to our senses.

The transformation of time intervals into space intervals and vice versa can be given a simple geometrical interpretation as was first done by the German mathematician, H. Minkowski, one of the early followers of Einstein's revolutionary ideas. Minkowski proposed that time or duration be considered as the fourth dimension supplementing the three spatial dimensions and that the transformation from one system of reference to another be considered as a rotation of coordinate systems in this four-dimensional space. His basic idea can be understood by considering the diagram shown in Fig. 7-10. In the old system (an observer in the railroad car), the space interval (soup to dessert) and the time interval (1st cigar to 2nd cigar) are both zero. In the rotated coordinate system (corresponding to a moving observer) it is not so, and the two cigar-lightings become non-coincident in time. We notice from this diagram that the appearance of a time interval between two events which were simultaneous in the first system of reference is connected with a shortening of the apparent distance between them as seen from the second system of reference, and, *vice versa*, the appearance of a space interval between two events which were occurring in the same place of the first

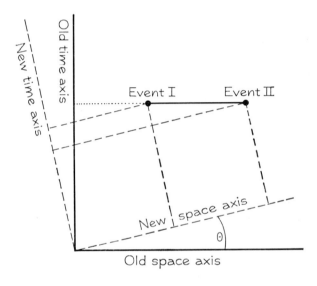

Fig. 7-10. Two events that occur at the same time in the old space-time system occur at different times when the space-time axes are rotated.

system shortens the apparent time interval between them as observed from the second. The first fact gives the correct interpretation of the apparent Fitzgerald's contraction of the moving bodies, while the second makes the time in a moving system flow slower from the point of view of the second system. Of course, both effects are relative, and each of the two observers moving with respect to one another will see the other fellow as somewhat flattened in the direction of his motion and will consider his watch to be slow.

Because both effects become appreciable only when the velocities involved are close to that of light, we do not notice them at all in our everyday snail's pace life. But we can imagine a fictitious situation which would arise if the velocity of light were much smaller and closer to

our everyday experience. This is what happened to the author's good
friend, Mr. Cyril George Henry Tompkins, who, after listening to a
popular lecture on the theory of relativity, was transferred, in his dream,
to a fantastic city in which the velocity of light was only 20 miles per
hour and served as the natural speed limit for its inhabitants.*

At first, when he found himself on the street of this relativistic city,
nothing unusual seemed to be happening around him; even a policeman
standing on the opposite corner looked as policemen usually do. The
hands of the big clock on the tower down the street were pointing almost
to noon and the streets were nearly empty. A single cyclist was coming
slowly down the street and, as he approached, Mr. Tompkins' eyes
opened wide with astonishment. For the bicycle and the young man on
it were unbelievably flattened in the direction of the motion, as if seen
through a cylindrical lens (Fig. 7-11). The clock on the tower struck
twelve, and the cyclist, evidently in a hurry, stepped harder on the
pedals. Mr. Tompkins did not notice that he gained much in speed, but,
as the result of his effort, he flattened still more and went down the
street looking exactly like a picture cut out of cardboard. Mr. Tompkins
felt very proud because he could understand what was happening to the
cyclist—it was simply the contraction of moving bodies. "Evidently
nature's speed limit is quite low here," thought Mr. Tompkins, "that is
why the policeman on the corner looks so lazy; he need not watch for
speeders." In fact, a taxi moving along the street at the moment and
making all the noise in the world could not do much better than the

* From G. Gamow, *Mr. Tompkins in Wonderland* (Cambridge University Press,
Cambridge, England, 1939), by permission of the publishers. Certain slight modifications have been made in order to place Mr. Tompkins' dream city in America rather
than in England.

Fig. 7-11. The bicyclist
seemed to be unbe-
lievably flattened.

cyclist, and was just crawling along. Mr. Tompkins decided to overtake the cyclist, who looked a good sort of fellow, and ask him all about it. Making sure that the policeman was looking the other way, he borrowed somebody's bicycle standing near the curb and sped down the street. He expected that he would be immediately flattened, and was very happy about it as his increasing figure had lately caused him some anxiety. To his great surprise, however, nothing happened to him or to his cycle. On the other hand, the picture around him completely changed. The streets grew shorter, the windows of the shops began to look like narrow slits, and the policeman on the corner became the thinnest man he had ever seen (Fig. 7-12).

"By Jove!" exclaimed Mr. Tompkins excitedly, "I see the trick now. This is where the word relativity comes in. Everything that moves relative to me gets shorter for me, whoever works the pedals!" He was a good cyclist and was doing his best to overtake the young man. But he found that it was not at all easy to get up speed on this bicycle. Although he was working on the pedals as hard as he possibly could, the increase in speed was almost negligible. His legs already began to ache, but still he could not manage to pass a lamp post on the corner much faster than when he started. It looked as if all his efforts to move faster were leading to no result. He understood now very well why the cyclist and the cab he had just met could not do any better, and he remembered the words in the book on relativity which he had read. It was stated that it is impossible to surpass the limiting velocity of light. He noticed, however, that the city blocks became still shorter and the cyclist riding ahead of him did not now look so far away. He overtook the cyclist at the second turning and, when they had been riding side by side for a moment, was surprised to see that he was quite a normal, sporting-looking young

Fig. 7-12. As he speeded up, the city blocks became quite short.

man. "Oh, that must be because we do not move relative to each other," he concluded; and he addressed the young man.

"Excuse me, sir!" he said, "Don't you find it inconvenient to live in a city with such a slow speed limit?"

"Speed limit?" returned the other in surprise, "we don't have any speed limit here. I can get anywhere as fast as I wish, or at least I could if I had a motorcycle instead of this good-for-nothing old bike!"

"But you were moving very slowly when you passed me a moment ago," said Mr. Tompkins. "I noticed you particularly."

"Oh you did, did you?" said the young man, evidently offended. "I suppose you haven't noticed that since you first addressed me we have passed five blocks. Isn't that fast enough for you?"

"But the blocks became so short," argued Mr. Tompkins.

"What difference does it make, anyway, whether we move faster or whether the blocks become shorter? I have to go ten blocks to get to the post office, and if I step harder on the pedals the blocks become shorter and I get there quicker. In fact, here we are," said the young man, getting off his bike.

Mr. Tompkins looked at the post office clock, which showed half-past twelve. "Well!" he remarked triumphantly, "it took you half an hour to go this ten blocks, anyhow—when I saw you first it was exactly noon!"

"And did you *notice* this half hour?" asked his companion. Mr. Tompkins had to agree that it had really seemed to him only a few minutes. Moreover, looking at his wrist watch he saw that it was showing only five minutes past twelve. "Oh!" he said, "is this post office clock fast?" "Of course it is, or your watch is too slow, just because you have been going too fast. What's the matter with you anyway? Did you fall down from the moon?" and the young man went into the post office.

Continuing his journey down the street he finally saw the railway station. A gentleman obviously in his forties got out of the train and began to move towards the exit. He was met by a very old lady, who, to Mr. Tompkins' great surprise, addressed him as "dear Grandfather." This was too much for Mr. Tompkins. Under the excuse of helping with the luggage, he started a conversation.

"Excuse me, if I am intruding into your family affairs," said he, "but are you really the grandfather of this nice old lady? You see, I am a stranger here, and I never . . ." "Oh, I see," said the gentleman, smiling through his moustache. "I suppose you are taking me for the Wandering Jew or something. But the thing is really quite simple. My business requires me to travel quite a lot, and, as I spend most of my life in the train, I naturally grow old much more slowly than my relatives living in the city. I am so glad that I came back in time to see my dear little granddaughter still alive! But excuse me, please, I have to help her into the taxi," and he hurried away leaving Mr. Tompkins alone again with his problems.

The above described relation between the young grandfather and his old granddaughter is, of course, grossly exaggerated, but the fact is that, according to Einstein's theory, such a difference in aging is really expected to occur in the case of relative motion. Thus, if sometime in the future a space ship were to take off from the surface of the earth to visit other planets of the solar system or maybe the planetary systems of other stars of the Milky Way, the pilot and the passengers would be relatively younger upon their return than the people of the same original age who had stayed on the earth. This difference might become quite conspicuous if the space ship were accelerated to velocities close to the velocity of light. It is well known, however, that human organisms cannot stand strong accelerations and that pilots suffer blackout when their plane makes several g's ($g = 981$ cm/sec^2 being the normal acceleration of gravity on the surface of the earth). If we assume that the space ship is traveling with the comfortable acceleration of one g, we find that it takes about a year to approach the velocity of light, when relativistic changes of time rate begin to play any role. (Since a year contains 3×10^7 seconds, the acceleration of 981 cm/sec^2 will raise the velocity to 98 per cent of the speed of light.) For accelerated space trips which last well beyond one year, such as a trip to the nearby star, Sirius, which is 8 light-years away, relativistic time changes begin to be quite appreciable, whereas from the point of view of the inhabitants of the earth the crew of a ship making a round trip to this star comes back only 16 years after the departure; for the crew itself these 16 years will seem only as 9 years. If, instead of to a nearby star, the space ship travels with constant acceleration to the center of our own stellar system of the Milky Way and back, it will return 40,000 years later by the earth's calendar, whereas by its own time reckoning, the trip will take only 30 years.

It is needless to say, however, that the above example, giving a striking demonstration of the relativistic properties of space and time, is completely non-realistic from the practical point of view. Indeed, even the use of atomic energy for the propulsion of space ships will not permit us to travel to distant stars, and the space navigation of the future will be necessarily limited to the much shorter distances within our planetary system, for which the effects of relativistic time changes are of comparatively little importance.

MICROCOSM

RESTLESS MOLECULES

Molecular Hypothesis

Surveying the physical properties of different substances encountered in nature, we find a great deal of variety. Some of the substances are normally solid, melting and turning into gas only at extremely high temperatures. Others are normally gaseous, becoming liquid and freezing only when the temperature drops close to absolute zero. Some liquids are of high fluidity while others are very viscous. Some substances, generally known as metals, possess a high degree of electric and thermal conductivity, while others, the so-called dielectrics, are very good insulators. Some substances are transparent to visible light while others are completely opaque; some possess a high refractive index and some a low one. . . .

We ascribe all these differences between substances to differences in their internal structure and attempt to explain them quantitatively as well as qualitatively as being due to different properties and interactions of the structural elements of matter. We assume that such seemingly homogeneous substances as air, water, or a piece of metal are actually composed of a multitude of extremely small particles known as *molecules*. All molecules of a given pure substance are identical, and the differences in physical properties between various substances are due to the differences between their molecules. There are as many different kinds of molecules as there are different substances, of which there is indeed an enormous number. There are the molecules of oxygen and of mustard gas, the molecules of water, alcohol, and glycerine, the molecules of iron, asbestos, and camphor, the molecules of gelatine, insulin, and fats. . . .

The molecules forming any given material body are held together by so-called *intermolecular forces,* which are determined by the nature of the molecule. These forces resist the tendency of internal thermal agitation (see Chapter 4) to break up the molecular aggregates. If intermolecular forces are strong, molecules will be as rigidly cemented together as the bricks in a garden wall (Fig. 8-1a), and the material will remain solid

Fig. 8-1. The three states of matter.

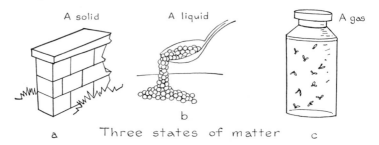

up to very high temperatures. If these forces are comparable to the forces of thermal agitation, they may not be able to hold the molecules rigidly in their places and may permit the molecules to slide more or less freely past each other as if they were grains of fresh Russian caviar (Fig. 8-1b). Thus the substance will keep its volume, but it will take the shape of the container in which it is placed. The viscosity of the liquid will depend on how easily this sliding of molecules can take place, and the substance will become more and more fluid as its temperature and ther-

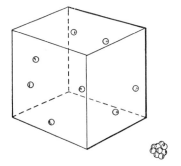

Fig. 8-2. The relative diameters and the distances between molecules in atmospheric air. At the right are the same molecules in liquid air.

mal agitation rise. If the intermolecular forces are very weak, the molecules will fly apart in all directions and the material must be kept in a closed container like a bunch of agile flies in a glass jar (Fig. 8-1c). This picture explains the high compressibility of gases, since compression results only in the reduction of the free space in which the molecules are moving. We can get an idea about the amount of free space between the molecules of a gas by comparing the density of the gas with its density in the liquefied state, when the molecules are packed together. For example, the density of atmospheric air, under normal conditions, is 0.0012 gm/cm³, while the density of liquid air is 0.92 gm/cm³ or 800 times larger. Since, in the liquid state, the distance between the centers of neighboring molecules are approximately equal to their diameters, the distances in the gaseous state must be $\sqrt[3]{800} = 9.3$ times the diameters. This relation is shown in Fig. 8-2.

BROWNIAN MOTION

Although molecules are too small to be seen individually even through the best microscope, their thermal agitation can be noticed by observing the movement of small particles of smoke floating in the air. This phenomenon is called *Brownian motion*, after the British botanist, Robert Brown (1773-1858), who in 1827 observed the irregular motions of plant spores floating in water. Such small particles play the role of an intermediary between our familiar surroundings and the world of molecules, since they are large enough to be observed microscopically but are also sufficiently small to be affected by irregular molecular motion. The situation is similar to that of a pilot in a high flying plane observing a Navy task force in a choppy sea. He cannot, of course, see the waves themselves, and tiny life-rafts that follow every movement of the water are invisible to him; at the other extreme, the big aircraft carriers will seem to float without any disturbance at all. But the medium-sized ships, which he can still see, will show a definite roll, and our pilot will know that the sea is rough. In Fig. 8-3 we show the successive positions of a smoke particle, 1 micron in diameter, dancing its Brownian dance in atmospheric air. The study of the Brownian motion, especially by the

French physicist, Jean Perrin (1870-1920), led to indisputable proof of the reality of the thermal motion of molecules and gave us valuable information concerning the amount of kinetic energy involved in it.

In fact, if we apply statistical methods to the study of the mechanical motion of a large number of particles, we arrive at the so-called *equipartition theorem*, which states that **in the random motion of a large number of interacting particles, the mean kinetic energies of all particles are the same, regardless of their mass.** In other words, more massive particles move correspondingly slower so that the product of their masses by the squares of their velocities remains constant. In our Navy analogy, it means that the tonnage of a ship multiplied by the square of the velocity with which it rolls is the same for all the ships of the task force in the same choppy sea.

Brownian particles 1μ in diameter (μ, the Greek letter "mu," stands for "micron," and $1\mu = 0.001$ mm, or 10^{-6} meter) are observed to move at room temperature with an average velocity of 0.65 cm/sec, and since their mass is about 5×10^{-13} gm, their kinetic energy must be 10^{-13} erg. Thus, this value must also represent the kinetic energy of individual molecules at this temperature.

With an increase of temperature, the intensity of Brownian motion also increases, so that by direct observation of the tiny particles suspended in a gas, or a liquid, we can study how the energy of thermal motion depends on temperature. The results of such experiments performed

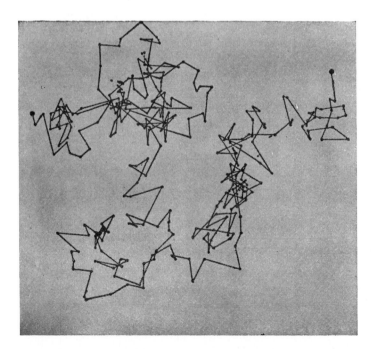

Fig. 8-3. The successive positions of a smoke particle in the air, recorded at one-minute intervals (according to J. Perrin).

between 0°C and 100°C are shown in Fig. 8-4. The observed points are located on a straight line and, extrapolating it in the direction of lower temperatures, we come to the conclusion that Brownian motion must completely stop at −273°C. The graph shown in Fig. 8-4 is identical with that of Fig. 4-4 which represented the volume change of a gas as the

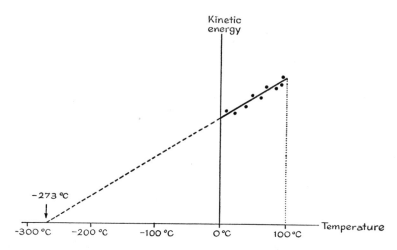

Fig. 8-4. The kinetic energy of Brownian motion measured for temperatures between 0 and 100°C, and extrapolated to lower temperatures.

function of the temperature. Thus we come to the conclusion that **the kinetic energy of thermal motion is directly proportional to the absolute temperature.** Since, as we have seen above, the kinetic energy of a single molecule at room temperature (i.e., about 300°K) is about 10^{-13} erg, the rate of the increase of that energy with temperature must be:

$$\frac{10^{-13}}{300} = 3.3 \times 10^{-16} \text{ erg/°C} = 8 \times 10^{-24} \text{ cal/°C}$$

On the other hand, we know that the amount of heat needed to raise the temperature of 1 gram of air by 1 degree centigrade (the "heat capacity" of air) is 0.16 cal/°C. Thus, by simple division, we find that 1 gram of air must contain about 2×10^{22} molecules,* or, in other words, that 1 air molecule weighs about 5×10^{-23} gm.

Since one gram of liquid air occupies a volume of about one cubic centimeter (as mentioned above, its density is 0.92, i.e., about 1). the

---

* This being, of course, a mixture of nitrogen and oxygen molecules.

volume of a single air molecule must be about $\dfrac{1 \text{ cm}^3}{2 \times 10^{22}} = 5 \times 10^{-23}$ cm³, and its diameter about $\sqrt[3]{5 \times 10^{-23}} = 4 \times 10^{-8}$ cm.

We can also use the above data to estimate the velocity of molecular motion. Since, at room temperature, the kinetic energy of a molecule (i.e., half the product of its mass by the square of its velocity) is about 10^{-13} erg and its mass is about 5×10^{-23} gm, simple arithmetic tells us that the velocity is about 6×10^4 cm/sec or 0.6 km/sec. We summarize these results in Table 8-1, our first acquaintance with figures pertaining to the molecular world.

TABLE 8-1   PROPERTIES
OF AIR MOLECULES

The mass	5×10^{-23} gm
The diameter	4×10^{-8} cm
Velocity (at room temp)	0.6 km/sec

MOLECULAR BEAMS

If we make a small hole in the wall of a vessel containing a considerable amount of gas and the gas escapes out into the surrounding vacuum, the picture will look in general like that of a panicked crowd rushing out of a burning theater. Although the resulting stream of gas will be generally directed away from the opening, individual molecules inside the stream

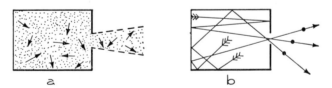

Fig. 8-5. Molecular beams: (a) when the density of the molecules in a vessel is high, gas flows out as a continuous stream; (b) when only a few molecules are present, they get out individually.

will continue to execute their irregular thermal motion, rushing in all directions and constantly colliding with each other (Fig. 8-5a). The motion of the gas streaming into the vacuum can be, in this case, considered as the motion of a continuous material, and it will be subjected to the laws of ordinary aerodynamics governing "gaseous jets." The phenomenon will be, however, rather different if the amount of gas in the container is so small that the molecules have a very small chance of colliding with each other and hence can change their direction of motion only as the result of reflection from the walls of the container. In this case, the molecules will fly out of the container one by one (Fig. 8-5b); the rules of ordinary aerodynamics will no longer be applicable, and the velocity of the outgoing stream will be determined by the thermal velocity of the molecular motion corresponding to the temperature of the gas. These so-called *molecular beams*, in which the individual molecules go their own way and do not interact with the others, are very useful for the study of many molecular properties.

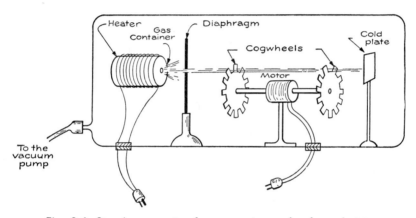

Fig. 8-6. Stern's apparatus for measuring molecular velocities.

Figure 8-6 shows the arrangement used by the German physicist, O. Stern, for the direct measurement of the thermal velocities of the molecules. The arrangement is practically identical with that used by Fizeau for measuring the velocity of light (Fig. 7-2) except that the molecular beam is substituted for the light beam. The source of the beam is a ceramic cylinder heated to the required high temperature by electric current in a wire wound around its surface. Within the cylinder is placed a small piece of some volatile material (sodium or potassium metals in this particular experiment), which give rise to a gas of rather low density and pressure. Individual molecules of the gas fly out through a small opening at the base of the cylinder, and a thin molecular beam is cut out of that divergent stream by a diaphragm. The beam is then passed through a pair of fast-rotating cogwheels and falls on a metal plate cooled by liquid air. The molecules that reach the cold plate stick to it and form a thin layer of metal, the amount of which can be exactly measured later. It was found that the molecular beam passes through both cogwheels at certain definite rotation speeds and is stopped at the intermediate speeds. Using the same arguments as in the case of Fizeau's experiment, we find that the numerical value of the velocity increases in direct proportion to the square root of the absolute temperature of the gas in the cylinder. The value of thermal velocities obtained by this direct method stand in perfect agreement with the values obtained by less direct considerations described in the previous section.

In carrying out his measurements of the velocity of the molecules of a gas at a given temperature, Stern found that the cut-off of the molecular beam caused by the changing speed of the cogwheels does not take place sharply, as it would if all the molecules had exactly the same velocity. In fact, although the main bulk of the molecules move with about the velocity corresponding to the temperature of the gas, there are always present some molecules which move considerably slower or considerably faster than the average. The curve showing the deviations of molecular velocities from the mean value is given in Fig. 8-7. These

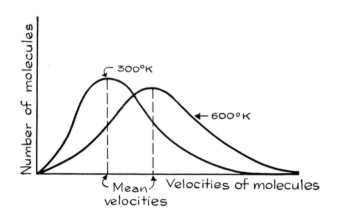

Fig. 8-7. Maxwell's distribution of molecular velocities in a gas at two different temperatures.

deviations result from the statistical nature of molecular motion and the irregularity of molecular collisions which may occasionally almost stop a molecule in its tracks or else send it rushing on with an abnormally high speed. The statistical study of the velocity distribution of the molecules of a gas was carried out in the last century on a purely theoretical basis by the British physicist, J. Clerk Maxwell (mentioned before in Chapter 5), who derived a mathematical expression describing the distribution of molecules of different velocities. The curve obtained by Stern in his experiments stands in excellent agreement with this so-called *Maxwell's distribution* of molecular velocities.

KINETIC THEORY OF GASES

The discussion in previous sections serves as the foundation for an elegant mathematical theory known as *the kinetic theory of gases*. One basic law describing the properties of gases was discussed in Chapter 1 and states that **at a given temperature, the volume of a gas is inversely proportional to the pressure to which it is subjected.** Another basic law of gases was mentioned in Chapter 4 and states that **at a given pressure, the volume of a gas is proportional to the absolute temperature.**[*]

These two laws can be combined into a formula:

$$\text{volume} = A \frac{\text{abs. temperature}}{\text{pressure}}$$

or:

$$\text{pressure} = A \frac{\text{abs. temperature}}{\text{volume}}$$

where A is a constant.

How can we explain this fundamental relation on the basis of the thermal motion of molecules described earlier in this chapter? Consider a closed vessel (Fig. 8-8) containing a certain amount of gas. The molecules of the gas are rushing ceaselessly in all directions, bouncing off the walls and colliding between themselves. The pressure of the gas on the surrounding walls is the result of the continuous bombardment to which the walls are subjected by the onrushing molecules. Suppose we keep the temperature of the gas (i.e., the velocity of its molecules) constant but reduce the volume. It is easy to see that in this case the number of molecules hitting a unit area A of the wall will increase in inverse proportion to the decreasing volume. Since the pressure experienced by the walls is proportional to the total number of impacts they receive per unit time, we have here the ex-

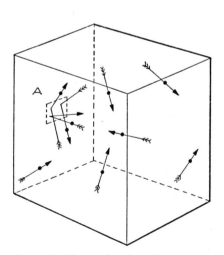

Fig. 8-8. The molecules of gas are reflected from the wall and thereby exert a pressure.

[*] This law should be considered rather as the definition of absolute temperature.

planation of the inverse proportionality between the pressure and the volume of gas.

Now keep the volume constant but increase the temperature and thus speed up the molecular motion. This will have two effects:

1. Since the molecules are moving faster, a larger number of them will collide with the wall area per unit time.

2. The impact of each molecule will be more violent because of its greater speed.

Since the pressure depends on both the number of impacts and the force of each impact and since each effect is proportional to molecular velocity, the combined result is that the pressure will be proportional to the square of that velocity, i.e., to the kinetic energy of molecular motion, or, what is the same, to the absolute temperature of the gas. This is the explanation of the pressure-temperature relationship.

The characteristic features of the thermal motion of gas molecules can be easily demonstrated by means of a gadget originally designed by Thomas B. Brown. The apparatus looks like a flat aquarium formed by two glass plates placed just far enough apart to allow ping-pong balls, which represent the molecules, to be placed between them. At the bottom of the "aquarium" there is a wooden cogwheel that can be driven by an electric motor at different speeds. The motion of this wheel agitates the ping-pong balls and makes them move in an irregular fashion through the space between the bottom and the top of the container. When the wheel rotates very slowly, most of the balls remain at the bottom of the container, and only a few of them are kicked up occasionally (Fig. 8-9a); this represents the model of a liquid with a few molecules evaporating from its surface. If we increase considerably the rotation speed of the wheel, all the ping-pong balls will be thrown up into the air, and our device will represent now a model of a vapor or a gas. If the upper part of the "aquarium" were open, the fastest moving balls would get out of the container, and it would soon become quite empty. However, in the arrangement shown in Fig. 8-9, the container is provided with a movable piston which prevents the ping-pong balls from leaving their enclosure. The balls that hit the piston and are reflected back into the container communicate to the piston a certain amount of mechanical momentum, and the total effect can be described as the gas pressure acting on the piston. Fig. 8-9b, c, and d represents the situation that arises when there are various degrees of agitation of the molecules in our ping-pong gas. In (b) the velocities of the balls are not high enough to overcome the weight of the piston, so the piston hangs in the lowest position permitted by its suspension. In (c) the balls move faster and push the piston up to a level position. In (d) the velocity of the balls is still higher, and the piston is pushed all the way up.

Fig. 8-9. An apparatus originally designed by T. B. Brown for demonstrating the kinetic theory of gases (University of Colorado model). (Top left) The evaporation stage of a liquid; some of the molecules are detached from the original conglomerate. The other three photos correspond to the increasing temperature of a gas (rpm of the agitator's motor). Notice that some of the ping-pong balls' images are smeared, indicating their accidentally higher speed.

a   b

c   d

The above described model is very useful for understanding the fundamental principles of the kinetic theory of gases. In fact, by measuring the velocities of the ping-pong balls and the pressure they exercise on the piston, one can prove quantitatively the fundamental gas law discussed above.

Liquids

While the behavior of molecules in a gas can be described mathematically with very great precision, leading to elegant and simple laws, the picture of molecular motion in liquids is unpleasant and untidy. The molecules forming a liquid can be compared to Japanese beetles caught in abundance in a patented trap, or to the worms in a fisherman's can. They crawl and wiggle around each other, they constantly come to clinches like two inexperienced boxers, and they do not permit a physicist to say anything simple or reasonable about them. We can build simple theories and formulate simple mathematical laws only when things themselves are simple, and the motion of molecules in liquids is certainly not that. Nevertheless. . . .

One of the most important things about liquids is their surface tension, which has already been discussed phenomenologically* in the first chapter of this book. Surface tension arises from the fact that each molecule of a liquid sticks to its immediate neighbors; a container of liquid is something like a barrel filled with shell-less snails. The molecules inside the liquid are pulled by their neighbors that surround them on all sides so that the total force acting on them averages zero. On the other hand, the molecules that are on the surface and have a breath of fresh air from above are pulled only inwards by their neighbors located underneath them. This results in the general tendency of liquids to reduce their free surfaces as much as possible. Since the shape of the surface of least area which will enclose any given volume is that of a sphere, liquids that are not (or only slightly) affected by outside forces, assume the form of spherical or spheroidal drops.

Suppose a liquid is poured into a solid container and accommodates itself to the bottom of the container because of the forces of gravity. The situation will appear as shown in Fig. 8-10 where the molecules of the liquid appear as white spheres and the molecules forming the walls of the container as gray spheres. The molecules of the liquid can choose as neighbors their own kind or those forming the (foreign) wall of the container. If the liquid molecules prefer their own kind and shy away from the container molecules (i.e., if the intermolecular forces are greater

---

* I.e., from the purely observational point of view.

between two molecules of the liquid than they are between one of the liquid molecules and one of the wall molecules), the surface of the liquid will take the shape shown in Fig. 8-10a. If, however, the molecules of the liquid feel differently and prefer to associate with the molecules of the

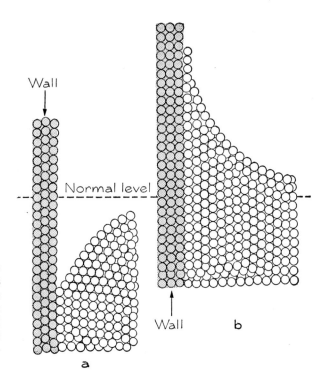

Fig. 8-10. The two different conditions that can exist on the boundary between a liquid and the wall of its container: (a) not wetting, (b) wetting.

container's walls, the situation will be that shown in Fig. 8-10b. This explains the *wetting* versus the *non-wetting* properties of liquids described in Chapter 1.

MONOMOLECULAR LAYERS

If matter were absolutely continuous, we would be able in principle to roll it into sheets of any desired small thickness. However, the molecular structure of matter places a lower limit on the possible thickness of material sheets or layers; they cannot be thinner than the diameter of one single molecule. The most convenient way to produce such layers of minimum thickness is to spread a small quantity of oil over the surface of water. Let us take a long trough-like container filled to the brim with water and place a wire across it as indicated in Fig. 8-11. If we put a drop of oil on the water surface to the left of the wire, it will spread in the form of a thin layer over all the surface and attach itself by intermolecular forces to the rim of the container and to the wire. By moving the wire to the right, we will stretch the layer of oil, and its thickness will gradually diminish. We will find by this direct experiment that this

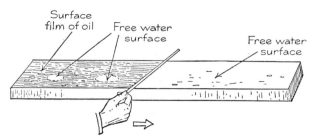

Fig. 8-11. Measuring the diameter of oil molecules.

stretching of the oil layer cannot be carried on indefinitely; at a certain stage the layer breaks up and shows patches of free water surface. Apparently the maximum possible stretching takes place at the stage when the oil layer becomes "monomolecular" and cannot become any thinner. If, for example, the width of the container is 1 cm and the volume of oil dropped on the water surface is 10^{-6} cm³ (corresponding to an oil droplet about 0.1 mm in diameter), we will be unable to stretch the oil film more than a distance of 10 cm. The thickness of the oil film in this case is apparently:

$$\frac{10^{-6} \text{ cm}^3}{1 \text{ cm} \times 10 \text{ cm}} = 10^{-7} \text{ cm}$$

which must represent the diameter of a single oil molecule. Notice that this figure is in approximate agreement with that for the diameter of air molecules as estimated by an entirely different method earlier in this chapter.

DIFFUSION

We come now to the phenomenon of *diffusion*, which takes place in liquids as well as in gases. We have intentionally postponed the discussion of diffusion phenomena in order to enhance the meager subject matter of the physics of liquids. If we drop a lump of sugar into a cup of tea and then do not stir it, it will take a very long time, hours as a matter of fact, until the tea becomes uniformly sweetened. If we *do* wait for a few hours, we will find that the situation is the same as could have been achieved more quickly by using a spoon. How do the molecules of sugar, without being stirred, travel through the liquid? Well, they just shoulder their way through the crowd of water molecules in the cup as the result of thermal agitation. They do not follow any straight path but execute a "random (or drunkard's) walk," illustrated in Fig. 8-12. If a

Fig. 8-12. A "random walk" is a walk in which a person, instead of following a straight line, continuously changes his direction by turning at unpredictable angles.

person takes N steps in one direction and the length of each step is L, then obviously he will cover the distance NL away from the point from which he started. If, however, he changes his direction at random with each step, he does not go that far. It can be shown mathematically in this

Fig. 8-13. The diffusion of sugar. The distances traveled in 10, 20, and 30 min stand in the ratio of 1: $\sqrt{2}$: $\sqrt{3}$, i.e., 1:1.42:1.72.

case that the mean distance traveled away from the original point is only: $\sqrt{N} \times L$. Thus, since the number of steps taken is proportional to time, the distance traveled in a random walk increases only as the square root of time. The situation is illustrated in Fig. 8-13, which shows the diffusion of sugar molecules through the unstirred cup of tea. The phenomenon of diffusion plays an important role in many other processes of physics besides the sweetening of unstirred tea. The principle of the atomic pile (Chapter 14) is based on the diffusion of neutrons through the moderator, and the energy-quanta produced by thermonuclear reactions in the center of the sun (Chapter 19) similarly diffuse slowly through the body of the sun until they can fly off freely into space after reaching the surface.

CRYSTALLINE ARCHITECTURE

When a substance is at a sufficiently low temperature to prevent thermal agitation from shuffling the molecules around, intermolecular forces cement them together into a regular structural pattern. The material becomes solid and assumes a definite crystalline form that reflects the specific properties of its molecules. Inspecting the grains of ordinary table salt through a lens (Fig. 8-14), we will find them to have the shape of regular cubes, while water crystallizes in the shape of long needles of hexagonal symmetry. When ice crystals freeze together, they give rise to intricate figures that are characteristic of snowflakes and the frozen designs on windows in winter. Practically all solids, except some substances such as glass and plastics that should be considered as "super-cooled liquids," possess a crystalline structure, although in many cases we cannot see it directly because the material is composed of a large number of very

Fig. 8-14. When we inspect ordinary table salt through a lens, we find that its crystals possess a regular cubical shape.

small crystals tightly packed together. An ordinary copper wire or a door knob certainly does not look like a crystal but an inspection of its surface under a microscope reveals its microcrystalline nature.

By using modern scientific methods, we can find the exact patterns of molecular arrangements that produce various crystalline forms and associate these patterns with various known properties of corresponding ma-

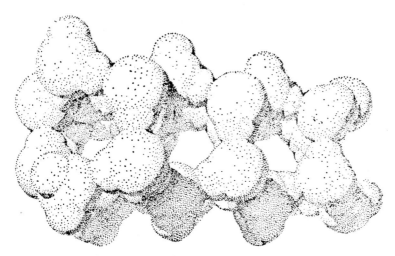

Fig. 8-15. The structure of an ice crystal. From Linus Pauling, *College Chemistry* 2nd ed. (San Francisco: W. H. Freeman and Co., 1955).

terials. In Fig. 8-15 we see the pattern of water molecules frozen together into a crystal of ice. Notice that, owing to the particular nature of this pattern, the molecules are not packed very tightly and there is considerable empty space between them. When the ice melts, the molecules of

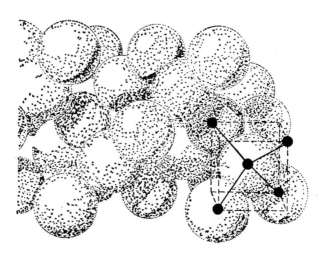

Fig. 8-16. The structure of diamond. After Fig. 7-2, Linus Pauling, *College Chemistry* 2nd ed. (San Francisco: W. H. Freeman and Co., 1955).

water come closer together, and this accounts for the fact that water is denser than ice. Figures 8-16 and 17 show the molecular arrangement in the crystals of *diamond* and *graphite,* which represent two different forms of crystallized carbon. In the diamond crystal, the molecules are packed very tightly together, which accounts for the strength and hardness of the diamond. On the other hand, in graphite the same molecules are bound together rather tightly into thin monomolecular sheets piled quite

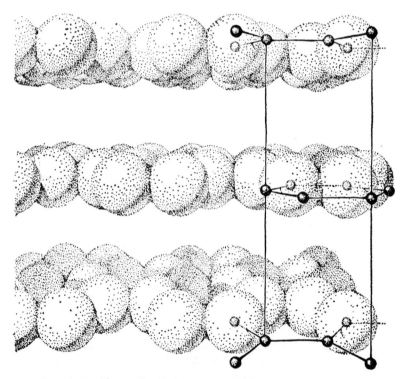

Fig. 8-17. The molecular structure of graphite. From Linus Pauling, *College Chemistry* 2nd ed. (San Francisco: W. H. Freeman and Co., 1955).

loosely on top of each other. The lack of strength between these mono-molecular sheets accounts for the softness of graphite that makes it useful for making pencils and even for lubrication purposes. Figure 8-18 repre-sents the packing of atoms in a crystal of copper. Notice that in this case the atoms are packed considerably tighter than in either ice or a diamond, not to mention graphite. Whereas each water molecule in an ice crystal and each carbon atom in a diamond has four adjacent neighbors to which

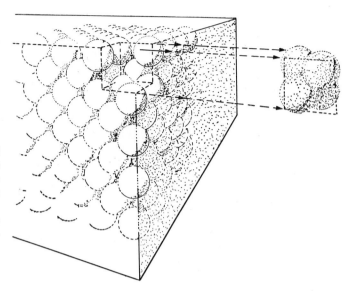

Fig. 8-18. A crystal of copper. Note that the basic unit—four copper atoms—has been pulled out to the right. After Fig. 2-4, Linus Pauling, *College Chemistry* 2nd ed. (San Francisco: W. H. Freeman and Co., 1955).

it is bound by intermolecular forces, the atoms in a copper crystal and in the crystals of most metals are surrounded by twelve close neighbors in an arrangement that is the most efficient geometrically possible for the packing of spheres. This large number of identical neighbors in metallic crystals gives to metals their strength and also accounts for their malleability. When a piece of metal is struck by a hammer, the molecular

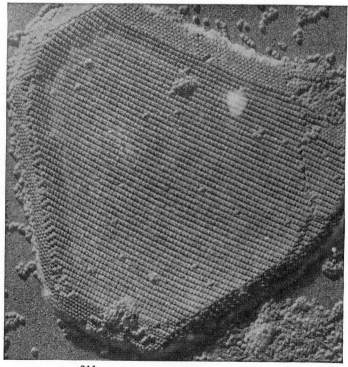

Fig. 8-19. Electron-micrograph of the crystal of a southern bean mosaic virus protein made by L. W. Labaw and R. W. G. Wyckoff. The particles are 250 Ångstroms in diameter. Magnification: 37,500 times.

layers slide relative to one another, and instead of being smashed into splinters, a piece of metal is flattened into a sheet or foil.

The pictures shown above are, naturally, just hand drawings, since these molecules are too small to be observed directly by any kind of microscope. However, in the case of crystals formed by much larger molecules, we can obtain direct photographs of their structure by using an electron microscope, described in Chapter 6. Figure 6-19 shows a crystal of "southern bean mosaic virus protein," which is formed by giant organic molecules that are several hundred times larger in diameter than the molecules of water.

Order vs. Disorder

The facts and the arguments presented earlier in this chapter leave no doubt that what we usually call "heat" is the manifestation of the internal micromotion of the molecules that form all material bodies, and that "temperature" characterizes the intensity of the internal molecular agitation. But, in discussing the phenomenon of heat (Chapter 4), we also spoke of *entropy*, which was interpreted as the "degree of naturality" of various thermal transformations. In all "natural" processes, such as the flow of heat from a hot body to a cooler one or the transformation of mechanical energy into heat (as, for example, in the case of friction), the entropy is increasing. The "unnatural" processes, such as the flow of heat from a cool body to a hot one or the transformation of heat into mechanical energy, never occur spontaneously and are possible only in conjunction with some "natural" processes which compensate for the "unnaturality" of the former ones. The decrease of entropy in an "unnatural" process is always compensated for (or over-compensated for) by the increase of entropy in the accompanying "natural" process, so that the total entropy of the entire system is always going up.

What is the interpretation of entropy from the point of view of the kinetic theory of heat, and what is the physical meaning of the statement that "the entropy can never decrease"? Let us consider a lead bullet flying towards a steel plate with a certain velocity v. In this case we can say that all the molecules forming the material of the bullet are moving towards the target with an equal and parallel velocity, v. (In this argument we disregard, for the sake of simplicity, the velocities of the thermal vibrations of the atoms forming the bullet, which are usually small as compared with a bullet's velocity.) When the bullet hits the steel plate it stops, and the mechanical energy of its motion is transformed into the internal kinetic energy of its molecules. (Again, for the sake of simplicity, we neglect the heating of the steel wall hit by the bullet and assume that the entire kinetic energy of the bullet is transformed into heat within its own body.) With these simplifying assumptions, made only for the purpose of making this discussion less complicated, we find that, while before the impact all the molecules of the bullet had identical velocities v in the same direction, after the impact their velocities are distributed equally in all directions, which is as it should be in random thermal motion. The "organized" motion of the molecules, when all of them were moving in the same direction, is transformed into a "disorganized" (or random) motion within the body of the bullet. The "mechanical energy" of motion is transformed into "heat." This example shows quite clearly that *the transformation of mechanical energy into heat is the same as the transformation of organized motion into disorganized motion.*

Speaking of the transformation of order into disorder, we can quote many authoritative opinions:

1. Every housewife knows that, while it takes a lot of work to keep the house spick and span, all she has to do to get it in disorder is just to sit pretty and do nothing.
2. Every highway commissioner knows that all he has to do to make the roads impassable is to lean back in his chair and discontinue maintenance and repairs.
3. Every army officer knows that to get his troops disorganized requires much less effort than to maintain discipline.

Messy houses, impassable roads, and disorganized groups of men are "natural" states of affairs. Well-kept houses, good roads, and organized teams of men are "unnatural" states and require a lot of organizing activity in order to be maintained.

Since molecules have no feeling of personal responsibility, we should expect that **the natural tendency of any physical system consisting of a large number of individual units is to go from a state of order into a state of disorder.** While the "orderly" translatory motion of the molecules in a bullet goes quite easily into "disorderly" thermal motion as the result of an impact, it is impossible to heat a bullet in a flame and then to arrange things in such a way that all the molecular velocities are turned in the same direction, thus forcing the bullet to take off and fly away at a high speed!

The fact that the "natural" way for heat to flow is from hotter places to cooler ones is explained in the same way. The hotter a body is, the higher is the commotion among its molecules.

Of course, with the anthropomorphic examples given above, we can always reverse the argument by referring to the human brain, consciousness, and initiative, but molecules "ain't human" and, obeying straightforward "low brow" rules, they prefer disorder to order. In this sense,

"mysterious" entropy is simply a measure of the disorder of molecular motion, and the statement that "the entropy always increases" is equivalent to the statement that "all the processes in nature proceed in the direction of increasing molecular disorder." Thus, the second law of thermodynamics is reduced to a statistical argument pertaining to the behavior of the multitude of individual molecules forming material bodies.

Thermodynamics of Life

At first sight it would seem that the second law of thermodynamics fails in the case of living organisms, since the word "organism" itself implies a high degree of order and organization of the molecules forming it. Consider a plant growing from a seed inside a glass box containing soil at the bottom and abundantly supplied by fresh water and air, which brings in the carbon dioxide necessary for building new material for the growing plant. Although both water and carbon dioxide gas possess a very low degree of order, the plant nevertheless manages to organize H, O, and C atoms and to turn these simple substances into highly complex organic compounds such as sugars, proteins, etc. Don't we witness here a case where disorder goes spontaneously into order, with the entropy decreasing in contradiction to the basic rules of thermodynamics? The answer is: No. We have forgotten that, apart from water and a carbon dioxide supply (plus a small amount of some salts from the soil), the plant needs for its growth and development an abundance of sunshine. The sun's rays that are absorbed by the green leaves of the plant bring in the energy necessary for building up complex organic molecules from the simple molecules of H_2O and CO_2; but this is not the point. We are not worried here about the first law of thermodynamics (i.e., conservation of energy), but about its second law, which prohibits any spontaneous decrease of entropy.

During the transformation of H_2O and CO_2 into complex organic molecules, the entropy of the system decreases,[*] and, according to the second law of thermodynamics, we have to look for some related process that results in an equal or larger entropy increase. In fact, we find that, apart from supplying a growing plant with necessary amounts of energy, the sun's rays also take care of the necessary entropy decrease. The point is that when solar radiation arrives at the surface of the earth, it is strongly "diluted" in the sense that, whereas its *prevailing wave length* still corresponds to the temperature of the solar surface (i.e., 6,000°K),

---

[*] The fact that a piece of wood burns spontaneously when set afire proves that (wood) $+ O_2 \rightarrow H_2O + CO_2$ is the *natural* direction of the process.

its *intensity* is not more than that of the radiation emitted by a room-heating radiator. A thermodynamical study of radiant energy indicates that such a dilution of the radiation without a reduction of the prevailing wave length leads to a high entropy *deficiency* or, as we sometimes put it, to the presence of "negative entropy." It is the inflow of this "negative entropy" that permits a plant to grow by organizing the H_2O and CO_2 into more complex organic molecules. The processes of the growing of a plant under the action of the rays of the sun and the subsequent burning of the material so produced in the fireplace can best be described by the following two symbolic equations:

from   from
soil   air   from the sun

$$H_2O + CO_2 + (\text{energy} + \text{entropy deficiency}) \longrightarrow \text{wood} + O_2$$

from
air

$$\text{wood} + O_2 \longrightarrow (\text{energy} + \text{entropy excess}) + H_2O + CO_2$$

The energy, which *is to be conserved,* is absorbed in the first process and liberated in the second. The entropy, which *must always increase,* increases in both processes, since, indeed, the "disappearance of a deficiency" is equivalent to the "appearance of an excess."

The high organization of molecules (negative entropy), obtained by plants from the sun's rays is then passed, along with accumulated energy, to animals, which in this sense are entirely parasitic beings, at least from the point of view of the plants.

NINE

THE BASIC LAWS

OF CHEMISTRY

The Greek Idea

It was already suspected by the ancient Greek philosophers who speculated about the nature of things that *the immense variety of different substances forming the world results from a combination of comparatively few simple elements*. Democritus (fifth century B.C.) believed that there are four elementary substances: air, water, stone, and fire, all formed by a very large number of very small

216

particles called atoms, i.e., "indivisibles" in Greek. The atoms of air were supposed to carry the property of "lightness" and "dryness," the atoms of water the property of "heaviness" and "wetness," the atoms of stone the property of "heaviness" and "dryness," while the atoms of fire were supposed to be very mobile, "slippery, and hot." On the basis of these ideas, the Greek philosophers attempted to explain the various transformations of matter as resulting from the reshuffling of the atoms constituting matter. They believed that the material of a growing plant is composed of water and stone atoms provided by the soil and atoms of fire supplied by the rays of the sun. In modern chemical terminology, the Greek formula for wood would be: SWF. The drying of wood was considered to be the escape from the wood of water atoms, SWF → SF + W, and the burning of wood the decomposition of dry wood into fire atoms (flame) and stone atoms (ashes), SF → F + S. Metals were considered to be the combination of stone atoms with varying amounts of fire atoms, SF_n (the fire atoms were supposedly responsible for metallic

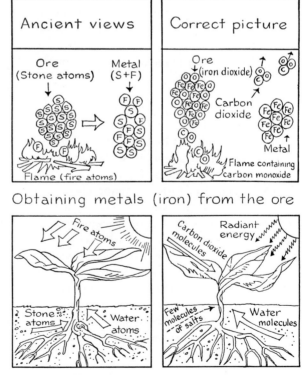

Fig. 9-1. Two wrong vs. two correct views in chemistry.

glitter). Iron was supposed to be rather poor in fire atoms, but gold was considered to have the maximum amount of them. The formation of metals from ores treated in a furnace was thought to result from the union of the stone atoms of the ore and the fire atoms of the flame, $S + nF \rightarrow SF_n$, and it seemed logical to expect that by enriching common metals like iron or copper with fire atoms one should be able to turn them into gold. This point of view, which also prevailed in the Middle Ages, explains the incessant efforts of medieval alchemists to transform common metals into the precious ones.

We know now that these views were quite wrong. The metals themselves and not their ores are elementary substances, and the process that takes place in blast furnaces does not add fire atoms to stoney ores and turn them into metals, but, quite on the contrary, subtracts oxygen from metallic oxides (ores) and thus liberates pure metals. Also, the material of a growing plant is obtained by the carbon dioxide (carbon + oxygen) from the air combining with the water (hydrogen + oxygen) from the soil, while the sun's rays supply only the energy necessary for synthesizing complex organic substances from these simple ingredients. The difference between the ancient and the modern view in chemistry is shown in Fig. 9-1. Although the attempted explanations were completely wrong, the idea of reducing the multitude of chemical substances to combinations of comparatively small numbers of simple elements was basically correct and now lies at the foundation of modern chemistry.

Atomic Weights and Valency

The most important fact concerning the formation of various chemical compounds from elements is contained in the so-called "law of constant proportions," which states that **the relative amounts of different chemical elements needed to form a definite chemical compound always stand in a certain given ratio.** Thus, when we place a mixture of hydrogen and oxygen gases in a thick-walled container and ignite the gases with an electric spark, we produce a rather violent chemical reaction (or explosion) which results in the formation of water. If the original proportions of hydrogen and oxygen are 1:8 by weight, the reaction will be complete and there will be nothing left over of either of the two gases. If, however, there is originally more hydrogen or more oxygen than is specified in the 1:8 proportion, then a corresponding excess of either gas will be left over. (There exists, however, another compound of hydrogen and oxygen known as *hydrogen peroxide* in which the ratio of the two elements is 1:16.)

The law of constant proportions was interpreted by the British chemist,

John Dalton (1766-1844), as being due to atom-to-atom union in the formation of chemical compounds. To explain the above described facts concerning water and hydrogen peroxide, one can assume that the weight ratio of the atoms of hydrogen and oxygen is 1:16 and that there is one atom of hydrogen per each atom of oxygen in hydrogen peroxide, while there are two hydrogen atoms per each oxygen atom in the case of water. Therefore, writing H for a hydrogen atom and O for an oxygen atom, and using a subindex to denote the number of atoms of each kind, we can express the chemical composition of these two substances as:

water molecule = H_2O
hydrogen peroxide molecule = HO (or H_2O_2, as it can be shown to be by other methods)

The second way of writing the expression for hydrogen peroxide indicates that this molecule has one oxygen atom too many in comparison with the much more common compound, water. And, indeed, hydrogen peroxide is an unstable substance that decomposes spontaneously according to the equation:

$$H_2O_2 \longrightarrow H_2O + O$$

The free oxygen atoms that are liberated in this reaction possess strong oxidative properties, which make H_2O_2 useful in various bleaching processes, not the least of which is the turning of a dark-haired girl into a platinum blonde.

Similarly, the union of carbon and oxygen may result either in carbon dioxide, CO_2, or, in the case of burning with an unsufficient supply of oxygen, in carbon monoxide, CO. In contrast to hydrogen peroxide, CO molecules lack one oxygen atom and are anxious to rob that extra oxygen atom from any other molecule which does not hold it strongly enough. The ratio by weight of carbon to oxygen in carbon monoxide is 3:4, which can also be written as 12:16. Since the atomic weight of oxygen was established as 16 (i.e., it weighs 16 times as much as a hydrogen atom, which for the present we can consider to be of unit weight), the atomic weight of carbon must be 12. Carbon also unites with hydrogen, giving rise to a gas known as methane or "marsh gas." The ratio of hydrogen to carbon in methane is 1:3 or 4:12, and, since 12 is the weight of one carbon atom, the formula of methane must be CH_4. Let us now consider a slightly more complicated example presented by an analysis of ethyl alcohol, which is 52.2 per cent carbon, 34.8 per cent oxygen, and 13.0 per cent hydrogen. By noticing that the ratio $\frac{52.2}{34.8}$ is 1.50 while the ratio of the atomic weights of carbon and oxygen is only 0.75, we can conclude that there must be two carbon atoms for each oxygen atom. If there were only one hydrogen atom for each oxygen atom, the ratio of corresponding percentages would have to be $\frac{1}{16} = 0.0625$, but the ratio is actually $\frac{13.0}{34.8}$ $= 0.375$, i.e., six times larger. Therefore there must be 6 hydrogen atoms per each oxygen atom, and the formula for ethyl alcohol is C_2OH_6.

The ability of atoms to unite with one or more other atoms is known as *chemical valency* and can be represented in an elementary way by drawing on each atom a number of hooks that can be coupled with the hooks of other atoms. In the examples so far considered, we have ascribed to hydrogen atoms a valency of 1, to oxygen 2, and to carbon 4. The way atoms are then bound into molecules (the so-called "structural formula" of the molecule) is shown in Table 9-1.

TABLE 9-1 MOLECULAR STRUCTURE OF VARIOUS COMPOUNDS

Water		H—O—H
Hydrogen peroxide		H—O—O—H
Carbon dioxide		O=C=O
Carbon monoxide		=C=O
Methane		H—C—H (with H above and below)
Ethyl alcohol		H—C—C—O—H (with H's)
Hydrogen gas		H—H
Oxygen gas		O=O
Ozone		triangular O structure

Valence "hooks" can also act between identical atoms and bind them into "diatomic" or "triatomic" molecules of a simple chemical substance, as indicated in the lower part of Table 9-1. Similar relations can be found for other chemical elements and for more complicated chemical compounds.

In speaking about chemical valency, we must mention six very peculiar elements known as *argon, helium, krypton, neon, radon,* and *xenon* which do not possess any chemical valency whatsoever. The atoms of these elements despise any chemical intimacy and prefer to remain alone; they do not even form pairs between themselves as other atoms often do, so their molecules are always "monatomic." Closely connected with this chemical inertness is the fact that all these six substances are gases and liquefy only at very low temperatures. Using the self-apparent analogy, we call these elements *noble gases,* or, sometimes, *rare gases,* since, indeed, they all are rather rare on the earth.* As everybody knows, helium is used for filling balloons and dirigibles to avoid fires, while neon, which emits a brilliant red light when subjected to an electric discharge, is used for making luminous signs for advertising purposes.

The List of Elements

As we have seen above, none of the four elements considered basic by the ancient Greek philosophers turned out to be actually elementary. On

TABLE 9-2   PRINCIPAL ELEMENTS KNOWN TO MEDIEVAL ALCHEMISTS

Name	Medieval alchemic notations*	Notations used by Dalton (1808)	Modern notations introduced by Berzelius (1814)
Arsenic	♎	Ⓐ	As
Copper	♀	Ⓒ	Cu
Gold	☉	Ⓖ	Au
Hydrogen		⊙	H
Iron	♂	Ⓘ	Fe
Lead	♄	Ⓛ	Pb
Mercury	☿	⊛	Hg
Oxygen		○	O
Silver	☽	Ⓢ	Ag
Sulfur	♁	⊕	S

* Hydrogen and oxygen were unknown to medieval alchemists.

* As we shall see in the third part of this book, the rarity of noble gases on the earth is due to the peculiar circumstances of the formation of our planet. In the cosmos in general, i.e., in the sun, stars, interstellar material, and the large planets, Jupiter and Saturn, they are not rarer than any other element. In fact, the lightest of them, helium, forms about half of all the matter of the universe.

the other hand, the work of medieval alchemists and later generations of chemists led to the discovery of truly elementary chemical substances, the number of which increased all the time. In Table 9-2 is a list of the principal chemical elements known to the medieval alchemists, with the symbols used for them during various periods in the development of chemical science.

Today, the number of chemical elements forming the matter of the

TABLE 9-3 LIST OF CHEMICAL ELEMENTS

Name	Symbol	Description	At. wt.	Name	Symbol	Description	At. wt.
Actinium	Ac		(227)	Mercury	Hg	White liquid metal	200.61
Aluminum	Al	White metal	26.98				
[*Americium*]	Am		(243)	Molybdenum	Mo	White metal	95.95
Antimony	Sb	Gray solid	121.76	Neodymium	Nd	Yellow metal	144.27
Argon	A	Colorless gas	39.94	Neon	Ne	Colorless gas	20.18
Arsenic	As	Gray solid	74.91	[*Neptunium*]	Np		(237)
[*Astatine*]	At		(210)	Nickel	Ni	White metal	58.69
Barium	Ba	White metal	137.36	Niobium	Nb	Gray metal	92.91
[*Berkelium*]	Bk		(245)	Nitrogen	N	Colorless gas	14.008
Beryllium	Be	White metal	9.01	Osmium	Os	White metal	190.2
Bismuth	Bi	White metal	209.00	Oxygen	O	Colorless gas	16
Boron	B	Black solid	10.82	Palladium	Pd	White metal	106.7
Bromine	Br	Brown liquid	79.92	Phosphorus	P	Red or white solid	30.98
Cadmium	Cd	White metal	112.41				
Calcium	Ca	White metal	40.08	Platinum	Pt	White metal	195.23
[*Californium*]	Cf		(246)	[*Plutonium*]	Pu	Metal	(242)
Carbon	C	Transparent crystal or black solid	12.01	Polonium	Po	Metal	210
				Potassium	K	White metal	39.10
				Praseodymium	Pr	Yellow metal	140.92
Cerium	Ce	Gray metal	140.13	[*Promethium*]	Pm		(145)
Cesium	Cs	White metal	132.91	*Protactinium*	Pa		231
Chlorine	Cl	Greenish gas	35.46	Radium	Ra	White metal	226.05
Chromium	Cr	White metal	52.01	Radon	Rn	Colorless gas	222
Cobalt	Co	Gray metal	58.94	Rhenium	Re	Metal	186.31
Copper	Cu	Reddish metal	63.54	Rhodium	Rh	White metal	102.91
[*Curium*]	Cm		(243)	Rubidium	Rb	White metal	85.48
Dysprosium	Dy		162.46	Ruthenium	Ru	Gray metal	101.1
[*Einsteinium*]	E		(253)	Samarium	Sm	Gray metal	150.43
Erbium	Er		167.2	Scandium	Sc	Metal	44.96
Europium	Eu		152.0	Selenium	Se	Red or gray solid	78.96
[*Fermium*]	Fm		(255)				
Fluorine	F	Yellowish gas	19.00	Silicon	Si	Gray metalloid	28.09
[*Francium*]	Fr		(223)	Silver	Ag	White metal	107.88
Gadolinium	Gd		156.9	Sodium	Na	White metal	22.99
Gallium	Ga	Gray solid	69.72	Strontium	Sr	White metal	87.63
Germanium	Ge	Gray metal	72.60	Sulfur	S	Yellow solid	32.07
Gold	Au	Yellow metal	197.0	Tantalum	Ta	Metal	180.95
Hafnium	Hf	White metal	178.6	[*Technetium*]	Tc		(99)
Helium	He	Colorless gas	4.003	Tellurium	Te	Gray metal	127.61
Holmium	Ho		164.94	Terbium	Tb	Metal	158.93
Hydrogen	H	Colorless gas	1.008	Thallium	Tl	Gray metal	204.39
Indium	In	White metal	114.76	*Thorium*	Th	Gray metal	232.05
Iodine	I	Black solid	126.91	Thulium	Tm	Metal	168.94
Iridium	Ir	White metal	192.2	Tin	Sn	White metal	118.70
Iron	Fe	White metal	55.85	Titanium	Ti	White metal	47.90
Krypton	Kr	Colorless gas	83.80	Tungsten	W	Metal	183.92
Lanthanum	La	White metal	138.92	*Uranium*	U	Gray metal	238.07
Lead	Pb	Gray metal	207.21	Vanadium	V	Gray metal	50.95
Lithium	Li	White metal	6.94	Xenon	Xe	Colorless gas	131.3
Lutetium	Lu		174.99	Ytterbium	Yb	Metal	173.04
Magnesium	Mg	Gray metal	24.32	Yttrium	Y	Metal	88.92
Manganese	Mn	Gray metal	54.94	Zinc	Zn	White metal	65.38
[*Mendelevium*]	Mv		(256)	Zirconium	Zr	Metal	91.22

universe has grown to 88, and 13 more, normally non-existent in nature, have been added by synthesizing them artificially in atomic piles. Various combinations of these elements give rise to the many thousands of different compounds that are listed in comprehensive chemical handbooks. Table 9-3 gives a complete list of the 101 elements known today* along with a short description of their properties and their atomic weights. The unstable elements found in nature (natural radioactive elements) are shown in italics, while the unstable elements that are non-existent in nature but are produced in an artificial way are shown in bracketed italics.

Out of the 101 elements listed in the table, eleven are gases, two are liquids, and the remaining eighty-eight are solids. This does not have, however, any fundamental significance since the disjunction between the three states is made specifically for the normal (for us) temperature. We find in the table many familiar names such as carbon, iron, silver, and gold and numerous ones such as gadolinium, samarium, and yttrium which the reader has probably never heard of before. To memorize the names of all the elements, which sometime may be useful, one should play a rather exciting game. The person who starts the game names, without, of course, looking at the table, the first element in alphabetical sequence. The next in line must name the following element in alphabetical sequence and so on, round and round. Naturally, some elements will be missed, and the person who recalls the name of the by-passed elements when his turn comes gets as many points as there have been elements called since the omissions. The game can be modified by using the alphabetical order based not on the English names of the elements but rather on their chemical symbols.

The Periodic Law

While the arrangement of chemical elements in alphabetical order is convenient for inventory purposes or for the game described in the previous section, it is more reasonable to arrange them in the order of increasing atomic weights. In doing so, we find rather remarkable regularities which have led chemists to a rational classification of the elements. Using the data presented in Table 9-3 and arranging the elements in order of increasing atomic weights,† we obtain the following sequence: H, **He**, Li, Be, B, C, N, O, F, **Ne**, Na, Mg, Al, Si, P, S, Cl, **A**, K, Ca, Sc,

---

* It is very likely that by the time this book appears a few more unstable elements beyond the atomic number 101 will be produced.

† The careful student will notice that K, Ni, and I are out of order, but, as it was found later, the sequence of chemical properties has priority over atomic weights.

Ti, V, Cr, Mn, Fe, Co, Ni, Cu, Zn, Ga, Ge, As, Se, Br, **Kr**, Rb, Sr, Y, Zr, Nb, Mo, Tc, Ru, Rh, Pd, Ag, Cd, In, Sn, Sb, Te, I, **Xe**, Cs, Ba, La, etc. We notice, first of all, that there is a remarkable regularity in the distribution of noble gases, shown in heavy type, through the sequence: there is only one element preceding **He**, 7 elements between **He** and **Ne**, another 7 elements between **Ne** and **A**, 17 elements between **A** and **Kr**, and another 17 elements between **Kr** and **Xe**. Finally, there are 31 elements between **Xe** and **Rn**, which is the heaviest known noble gas.

The elements immediately following the noble gases, lithium, sodium, potassium, rubidium, and cesium, are physically and chemically very similar to each other. They are all light, silvery-white metals with high chemical activity. If we drop a small piece of any of these elements in water, it will undergo a violent chemical reaction of the type:

$$Li + H_2O \longrightarrow LiOH + H$$
$$Na + H_2O \longrightarrow NaOH + H$$
$$\text{etc.}$$

liberating hydrogen and forming the corresponding "hydroxide" with water (structural formula, Li—O—H, etc.). The hydrogen liberated in this reaction often becomes ignited and produces a flame which takes on the characteristic color of the vaporized metal (yellow for sodium, red for potassium, etc.), Uniting with hydrogen and oxygen, these elements form "hydrates" and "oxides" of the type LiH (Li—H), Li_2O (Li—O—Li), etc., showing that their valency is 1. These elements are commonly known in chemistry as *alkali metals*.

The second neighbors to the right of the noble gases, beryllium, magnesium, calcium, strontium, barium, and radium, also form a homologous group known as *alkali-earth metals*. As their name indicates, they are similar to the alkali metals, but, as a rule, they are much harder and less reactive. Reacting with water, they produce compounds of the type: $Ca(OH)_2$ (H—O—Ca—O—H), while uniting with hydrogen and oxygen they give rise to compounds such as CaH_2(H—Ca—H) and CaO (Ca=O), which indicates that their valency is 2. Similarly, we find that the third group to the right, boron, aluminum, etc., possesses a valency of 3 as demonstrated by such compounds as boron oxide, B_2O_3(O=B—O—B=O), and aluminum hydroxide, $Al(OH)_3$.

Now if we look at the elements standing to the left of the noble gases, we will find that they are very similar to each other, but as different from metals as they could possibly be. This group comprises fluorine, chlorine, bromine, iodine, and astatine, and they are known as the *halogens*. They have a strong affinity for both alkali and alkali-earth metals, with which they form such compounds as NaCl (ordinary table salt) and $CaBr_2$, indicating that they possess a single valency. The second neighbors to the left of the noble gases, oxygen, sulfur, etc., are also in some ways similar to each other and possess a valency of 2.

The existence of homologous groups and of a certain periodicity in the chemical properties of elements arranged in the order of increasing atomic weights was noticed by several chemists during the nineteenth century, but the most important step of actually arranging the elements into a periodic table was made in 1869 by the Russian chemist, Dmitri Mendeleev (1834-1907). In his studies, Mendeleev was handicapped by the fact that in his time the list of known chemical elements was rather incomplete and, in particular, the existence of the noble gases was not even suspected. From the sequence given above, Sc, Ga, Ge, Tc, and Rh were missing, making the sequence quite irregular except for the first two periods. Driven by a deep belief that there *must be* a regular periodicity in the natural sequence of elements, Mendeleev made the bold hypothesis that the deviations from the expected periodicity in his list were due to the failure of contemporary chemistry to have discovered some of the elements existing in nature. Thus, in constructing his table, he left a number of empty spaces to be filled in later by future discoveries. He gave to the "missing elements" names formed by adding the prefixes "eka" or "dvi," meaning "first" and "second" in Sanskrit, to the names of neighboring homologous elements. In certain instances he also reversed the atomic-weight order of elements in order to comply with the demands of the regular periodicity of their chemical properties. Using his table, shaky as it was, he was able to predict the physical and chemical properties of 6 "missing elements" on the basis of the known properties of

TABLE 9-4

Mendeleev's prediction for eka-silicon (Es) (*1871*)	*Winkler's data for germanium (Ge)* (*Discovered in 1886*)
Atomic weight will be about 72	Atomic weight is 72.6
Will be obtained from EsO_2 or K_2EsF_6 by reduction with Na	Was obtained from K_2GeF_6 by reduction with Na
Will be a dark gray metal with high melting point and density about 5.5	Is a gray metal with melting point 958°C and density 5.36
On heating, Es will form the oxide EsO_2 with high melting point and density 4.7	Reacts with oxygen forming GeO_2 with melting point 1,100°C and density 4.7
The sulfide EsS_2 will be insoluble in water but soluble in ammonium sulfide	GeS_2 is insoluble in water but readily soluble in ammonium sulfide

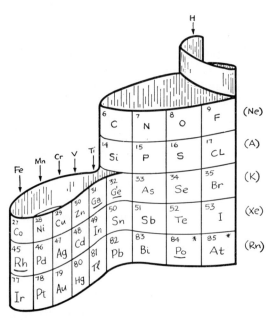

Fig. 9-2. The periodic system of the elements represented on a wound ribbon. The lower diagram on the opposite page shows the other side of the second loop. At present the ribbon is cut at atomic number 101 (mendelevium). An asterisk indicates that the element is unstable (radioactive), and an asterisk in parenthesis indicates the presence of a radioactive isotope in the normally stable element. The properties of the underlined elements were predicted by Mendeleev.

their alleged neighbors. He called these elements eka-boron, eka-aluminum, eka-silicon, eka-manganese, dvi-manganese, and eka-tantalum. His predictions turned out to be in excellent agreement with the actually observed properties of the "missing elements" when they were finally found and named: scandium, gallium, germanium, technetium,* rhenium, and polonium. Just as an example, we give in Table 9-4 the comparison of Mendeleev's predictions of the properties of his hypothetical element, "eka-silicon," with the actually observed properties of this element, which was found 15 years later by a German chemist, Winkler, and given the name germanium.

Pretty good for a prediction at this state in the development of chemistry!

By enumerating the elements from 1 (for hydrogen) and up as they come in the periodic system of elements, we obtain what is known as the *atomic numbers* of the elements. Thus, the atomic number of carbon is 6, that of mercury is 80, and that of mendelevium, 101. The atomic

---

* Technetium, an unstable element normally non-existent in nature, was produced only recently in atomic piles.

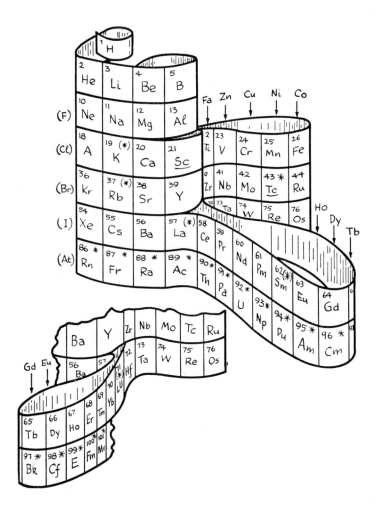

numbers of the six noble gases that form important landmarks of chemical periodicity are: 2, 10, 18, 36, 54, and 86. It is convenient to represent the periodic system of elements by a three-dimensional spiral structure that is shown in Fig. 9-2. The backbone of the structure is the column containing the noble gases running all the way from He down to Rn. The next column to the right contains the alkali metals, with hydrogen placed at the top because its chemical properties are similar to those of the alkali metals. To the left and around the corner from the noble gas column is the one containing the halogens. The first two periods, from He to F and from Ne to Cl, contain 8 elements each and fall neatly into this scheme, but the next period contains 18 elements and constitutes a problem. While, on the basis of chemical properties, there seems to be no doubt that the 3 elements that follow A (K, Ca, and Sc) must be placed under the 3 corresponding elements (Na, Mg, and Al) of the previous period and that those preceding Kr (As, Se, and Br) should be under those preceding A (P, S, and Cl), we do not seem to have places for the remaining 11 elements (Ti to Ge). To dispose of this difficulty we place Ti and Ge, which both resemble Si, under that element and make an extra loop to accommodate the remaining 9 elements (V to Ga). The same situation arises in the next and in all of the following periods so that the extra loop perpetuates itself all the way to the end of the known sequence of elements. In the beginning of the fifth period we encounter further trouble of the same kind and are forced to build another extra loop to accommodate 14 extra elements (Ce to Lu), known as the *rare earths*. The sixth and last period runs in the same way with most of the natural and artificial radioactive elements forming a loop under that formed by the rare earths.

Things become quite complicated, and Dmitri Ivanovich Mendeleev would probably be horrified by the looks of it, but that's how it is. Nevertheless, in spite of the complexity of the diagram (which reflects the complexity of the internal structure of the atom), the periodic system of elements in Fig. 9-2 gives a very good representation of the properties of the different elements.

INORGANIC

FAMILY ALBUM

In the present chapter, we will describe the properties of the most important chemical compounds, natural and man-made, which we encounter in our daily life. They are formed mostly by the elements of the first two or three periods of the Mendeleevian table. Since there is a rapid decrease in the natural abundance of elements with their increasing atomic weight, the heavier elements become prominent only when they possess some particularly useful property, such as the attractive glitter of gold, the high melting point of tungsten, or the ability of uranium to maintain nuclear chain reactions. For the purpose of this survey, we will use the unfolded and partially shrunken periodic table of elements shown in Fig. 10-1, which is less elegant but more handy than that shown in Fig. 9-2. In this table we have distinctly marked categories of chemical elements. The (all white) column of noble gases on the extreme right is bordered by the column of the five typical halogens (dotted squares). On the left, we

Fig. 10-1. A simplified periodic table of the elements.

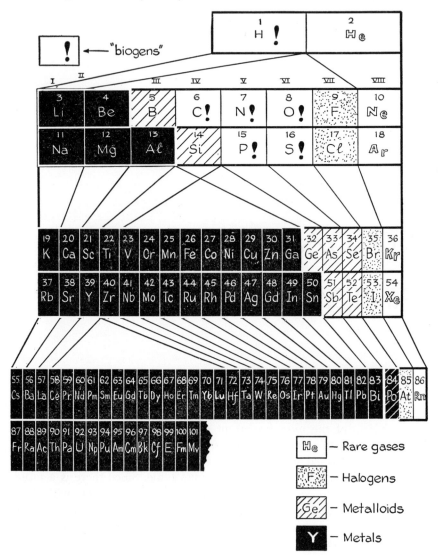

have the (black squares) metals; out of the 101 elements, 76 are metals! Bordering the metals on the right are the substances known as *metalloids* (shown in squares with diagonals), which are not full-fledged metals but do show some metallic properties. This leaves the six elements, *hydrogen, carbon, nitrogen, oxygen, phosphorus,* and *sulfur*, which form a very distinguished group that are the principal participants in the structure of living matter. It would be appropriate to call these six elements **Biogens**.

Water

We will start our survey of chemical compounds with the liquid formed by the union of hydrogen and oxygen gases, commonly known as water. Having lost its honorary and ancient position as a member of the "Quadrumvirate of Elements," water remains, nevertheless, the most important chemical compound on the surface of the earth. It fills the seas and oceans, floats in the form of clouds in the sky, and is even sometimes violently ejected from somewhere deep under the surface of the earth. Water constitutes 75 per cent of the total weight of living organisms, and without it life would be completely impossible. Engineers use water as the intermediary for the transfer of energy from fuel to the moving parts of steam engines, and house-wives use it to transport heat from the kitchen stove to the vegetables that are to be cooked. Chemists carry on most of their studies of different reactions in water solutions, and water is an integral part of many large-scale technological processes.

Both physically and chemically water is a very unusual substance, with properties widely different from those we would expect for a substance that results from the union of hydrogen and oxygen. On the basis of the periodic system of elements, we would expect the properties of water, i.e. H_2O, to fall in line with the properties of H_2S, H_2Se, and H_2Te,

Fig. 10-2. The change of boiling and freezing points along a sequence of homologous substances.

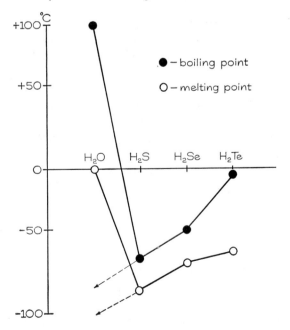

since oxygen, sulfur, selenium, and tellurium belong to the same column in that system. A glance at Fig. 10-2, which shows the melting and boiling points of these four substances, proves right away that this is not the case. If water were an ordinary substance, it would be in the state of vapor at room temperature, it would become liquid only at about −80°C, and it would turn into ice only at about −100°C! The fact that ice remains solid until its temperature rises 100 degrees above the point where it should have melted and that water remains liquid for 180 degrees above the point at which it should begin to boil indicates that abnormally strong intermolecular forces exist between its molecules. This property of water (shared, to a lesser degree, by only two other substances: ammonia, H_3N, and hydrogen fluoride, HF) is due to the ability of the hydrogen atom, although attached to oxygen in a water molecule, nevertheless to establish further contact with the oxygen atoms of neighboring water molecules. This so-called *hydrogen bonding* by normally monovalent hydrogen atoms—which is an illegal characteristic from the point of view of conventional chemistry—plays an important role in the properties of water (see Fig. 8-16 showing the crystalline structure of ice) and also, as we shall see later, in the properties of complex organic molecules that constitute the backbone of living matter. This abnormally strong bonding between water molecules is also responsible for the fact that water is an excellent solvent for a large number of different substances and a very useful medium for carrying out a large variety of chemical reactions.

More about Halogens

We have already mentioned the halogens ("salt makers" in Greek) in connection with the periodic system of elements, and we will now give a little more information about this important group of substances.

Fluorine, the lightest of the halogens, is the most chemically active of all the elements. It is a yellow gas and will attack even gold and platinum; inflammable materials such as wood ignite spontaneously when a stream of fluorine gas touches them. In nature, fluorine occurs in minerals such as "fluorite" (CaF_2), from which its name is derived. It combines with hydrogen to form *hydrogen fluoride*, HF, the water solution of which is called *hydrofluoric acid*. Although not an outstandingly strong acid, it has the ability to attack silicon dioxide according to the reaction:

$$SiO_2 + 4HF \longrightarrow SiF_4 + 2H_2O$$

Since SiO_2 is the main constituent of glass, hydrofluoric acid must be kept in containers made of wax, lead, or plastics. This property of HF to destroy SiO_2 makes it widely used to etch markings and designs on glass.

Chlorine is a greenish-yellow gas with a sharp irritating odor. It is very effective in killing bacteria and is extensively used in sterilizing drinking water and the water in swimming pools. Like fluorine, it unites with hydrogen to form a gas, hydrogen chloride, HCl, which, when dissolved in water, leads to a strong acid known as *hydrochloric acid*. The most familiar compound of chlorine is, of course, table salt, NaCl. "Bleaching powder," CaCl(ClO), is another fairly common one.

Bromine is a reddish brown liquid with a strong, unpleasant odor. Its principal compounds are *sodium and potassium bromides,* NaBr and KBr, which are used in medicine, and *silver bromide,* AgBr, used in photography.

Iodine is an almost black crystalline solid which, when warmed, gives off a beautiful blue-violet vapor. Iodine is used as an antiseptic, in photography, and in many branches of the chemical industry.

Nitrogen Compounds

The element on the left of oxygen in the periodic system is nitrogen, which, together with oxygen, constitutes the main part of the terrestrial atmosphere (78 per cent N, 21 per cent O) and participates with it on an equal basis in the constitution of living matter. Nowadays, nitrogen is mostly "mined from the air" by the ingenious process invented by the German chemist, Fritz Haber, during the First World War when Germany badly needed nitrogen compounds for the production of high explosives. Haber's method, which is called the "fixation" of atmospheric nitrogen, involves the direct combination of nitrogen and hydrogen under high pressure and in the presence of a *catalyst,* i.e., a substance that accelerates the reaction but is not consumed by it.* Uniting with hydrogen according to the formula:

$$N_2 + 3H_2 \longrightarrow 2NH_3$$

atmospheric nitrogen gives rise to an unpleasant smelling gas known as *ammonia.* Reacting with atmospheric air under the influence of another

---

* The notion of a catalyst may be made clearer by the following story: An old Arab died and left to his three sons a small herd of camels which represented all his earthly possessions. According to his will, the eldest son was to receive one-half the property, the next son one-third, and the youngest son one-ninth. However, when they counted the camels in the herd they found there were 17, which number could not be divided according to their father's wish. They were helped, however, by an old wise man who loaned them his camel, the only one he had, in order to solve the division process. From the temporary total of 18 camels, the eldest took one-half, i.e., 9, the second son took one-third, i.e., 6, and the youngest one took one-ninth, i.e., 2. Thus they received altogether 17 camels and the one which was left over was returned with thanks to the old man. Clearly, this camel acted as a "catalyst."

catalyst, ammonia is turned into *nitric acid*, HNO_3, according to the equation:

$$12NH_3 + 21O_2 = 8HNO_3 + 4NO + 14H_2O$$

Nitric acid is a very useful product and finds application in many different industries but is mostly used in the production of gunpowder and high explosives.

Black gunpowder is a mixture of fine grains of sulfur, carbon, and potassium nitrate, which is commonly known as saltpeter. When the mixture is ignited, carbon and sulfur react with the saltpeter, rob its molecules of oxygen atoms, and turn the mixture into carbon (mono- or di-) oxide, sulfur dioxide, and nitrogen. This process can be considered as an "internal burning" of carbon and proceeds considerably faster than the burning of a piece of coal in the air where the oxygen is supplied only to the surface of the burning material. If we ignite a small amount of gunpowder piled on a table, the powder will produce an impressive flash but not much noise and no damaging shock wave, since the reaction does not take place fast enough for that. If the powder is placed in the barrel of a rifle or a cannon, however, it will liberate the hot, gaseous products of the reaction fast enough to communicate to the projectile a high muzzle velocity. If the powder is confined on all sides, as in a powder keg, it will produce an explosion, but a comparatively mild one, since most of its internal energy will be liberated after the walls of the container are broken and its burning content is flying out.

The "internal burning" can be considerably accelerated if the reaction can be made to proceed, not between the individual grains, but within each individual molecule of the material used. Substances whose molecules can burn "inside themselves" are known as "high explosives." A typical example of a high explosive is trinitrotoluene, or simply TNT:

As seen from this picture, a molecule of TNT contains 7 atoms of carbon and 6 atoms of oxygen kept apart by the intervening atoms of nitrogen. When TNT is heated or shaken by a violent impact (delivered by the fuse which sets it off), the NO_2 groups in its molecules begin to vibrate and one of the O atoms located on the periphery may come close to one of the C atoms forming the core. In this case, the valance bonds holding C and O apart will snap and the molecule will break up into simpler molecules of carbon, carbon monoxide, water, and free nitrogen:

$$2C_7H_5(NO_2)_3 \longrightarrow 3N_2 + 5H_2O + 7CO + 7C$$

This intramolecular reaction goes extremely fast and is completed before the walls containing the material give way. The result is a fast, concentrated push that produces a shock wave in the surrounding air and sends the fragments of the original container at high speed in all directions.

Sulfur and Its Compounds

The element immediately under oxygen in the periodic table is a yellow solid known as *sulfur*. We have already mentioned *hydrogen sulfide*, H_2S, which is an analogue of water but, because of the absence of strong hydrogen bonding, is normally a gas with the very unpleasant smell of rotten eggs. When burned in the air, sulfur gives rise to the gas, sulfur dioxide, SO_2, which is not any more pleasant and has the characteristic choking odor of an old-fashioned sulfur match. Immense amounts of both gases are ejected from underground during volcanic eruptions, those proverbial ventilation vents of the underground world. In fact, according to Dante's *Divina Comedia*, Hell boasted the possession of several lakes of molten sulfur which served as swimming pools for the sinners. In the reaction:

$$2H_2S + SO_2 \longrightarrow 3S + 2H_2O$$

volcanic gases give rise to pure sulfur which is then deposited, along with clay, gypsum, and limestone, on the slopes of the volcanic cones. Large surface deposits of this kind, containing about 20 per cent pure sulfur, are found in Sicily where this material is mined and collected into huge piles. When a portion of sulfur is ignited, the heat from the burning slowly melts the rest of the mass, and the molten sulfur flows away from its rocky impurities and is collected for industrial uses. In the United States, large deposits of sulfur are found in certain sections of Louisiana and Texas. Since, however, neither of these states possess the volcanic nature of Sicily, their sulfur must have been produced by the volcanic activity of long-past epochs, and, in fact, their sulfur deposits are now buried a thousand feet under thick layers of sand, clay, and rocks.

Sulfur is a yellow solid that crystallizes in two different forms, Fig. 10-3, known as *orthorhombic* and *monoclinic* sulfur. At 113°C it melts, forming a straw-colored liquid. Neither pure sulfur nor either of its two bad-smelling, gaseous compounds can be put to any very important practical use. However, when dissolved in water, sulfur dioxide gives rise to *sulfurous acid*, $SO_2 + H_2O \rightarrow H_2SO_3$, which, through further oxidation, goes over into *sulfuric acid*, H_2SO_4. The latter substance is extremely useful in many walks of industrial life. About one-third of the total production of sulfuric acid is used in various processes connected with the preparation of agricultural fertilizers, about one-fifth in the preparation of various drugs, and about one-tenth in the oil industry. The rest is used in the coal and steel industries and in the manufacturing of paints, textiles, high explosives, etc.

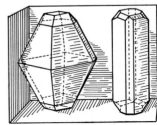

Orthorhombic Monoclinic Sulfur

Fig. 10-3. Crystals of orthorhombic and monoclinic sulfur. After Fig. 14-1, Linus Pauling, *College Chemistry* 2nd ed. (San Francisco: W. H. Freeman and Co., 1955).

Thus, except for the last item on the list, the "hellish" element, sulfur, is now working for good causes.

Phosphorus and Its Compounds

Phosphorus is the neighbor of sulfur in the periodic table and its successful competitor in the making of matches. Standing immediately under nitrogen, it has analogous chemical properties with that element and, uniting with hydrogen, forms the gas known as *phosphine*, PH_3, which is, in many respects, similar to ammonia, NH_3. It also gives rise to *phosphoric acid*, H_3PO_4, which differs from nitric acid by only one extra molecule of water.

Pure phosphorus exists in two different forms depending on the internal arrangement of its atoms: white phosphorus, a soft, waxy, colorless material, and red phosphorus, a more stable form of the molecular arrangement. White phosphorus is extremely inflammable and ignites at a temperature of only 40°C, while red phosphorus does not catch fire below 240°C. White phosphorus is very poisonous, causing necrosis of the bones (lethal dose 0.15 gm), while red phosphorus is quite harmless. These facts show how the properties of materials formed by the same kind of atoms depend on how these atoms are put together.

Silicon, the King of Rocks

Silicon, in its union with oxygen, is the main component of the rocks that form the crust of the earth, as is shown in Table 10-1.

TABLE 10-1 COMPOSITION (BY WEIGHT) OF THE EARTH'S CRUST

Oxygen	46.5%	Calcium	3.5%
Silicon	28%	Sodium	3%
Aluminum	8%	Potassium	2.5%
Iron	5%	Magnesium	2.2%
		Others	1.2%

Elemental silicon, which is not encountered in nature but can be obtained from different silicate minerals, is a brittle, steel-gray metalloid that crystallizes in a tetrahedral system that is identical with that of a diamond shown in Fig. 8-16. It is, however, not so hard as the diamond because the intermolecular forces between silicon atoms are much weaker than those between the atoms of carbon.

The most important compound of silicon is *silicon oxide*, SiO_2, encountered in nature in the form of quartz crystals. The elementary unit of these crystals is a silicon atom surrounded tetrahedrally by four oxygen atoms, Fig. 10-4.

Since each O atom is shared by two Si atoms, there is, on the average, two O atoms per one silicion atom as required by the chemical formula. For one structural unit we may write: $Si(\frac{1}{2}O)_4$. Thus the entire structure is held together by Si—O bonds, which, being very strong, make quartz a very hard material. The way in which individual tetrahedra are connected together in the quartz crystal insures that, in spite of the great structural strength of the entire framework, there is plenty of empty space between the individual atoms.

In many minerals, a certain fraction of the silicon atoms are replaced by atoms of aluminum, which is the next most important element in rock structure. Since, however, the valence of aluminum is only 3 and not 4, as in the case of silicon, the tetrahedral crystalline structure can be maintained only if each aluminum atom replacing a silicon atom is accompanied by an atom of some monovalent element such as sodium or potassium. This extra atom is not attached to the aluminum atom by any valence bond which is used for making the connection with the neighboring silicon atom, but is held in place because of the rigidity of the entire crystalline framework. In the well-known mineral, *feldspar,* one out of each four silicon atoms is replaced by an aluminum atom with the addition of one sodium or potassium atom. Thus the formula of one kind of feldspar is $KAlSi_3O_8$, and its crystalline structure looks very much like that of quartz with extra atoms of potassium located in the empty spaces between the tetrahedrons.

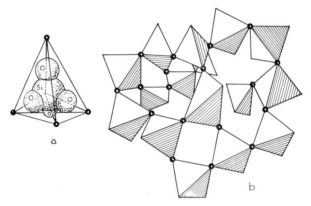

Fig. 10-4. The crystal structure of SiO_2: (a) showing the elementary tetrahedron formed by one silicon and four oxygen atoms, and (b) showing the way these tetrahedra form a complex structure in which each tetrahedron has a common corner with another. After Fig. 26-4, Linus Pauling, *College Chemistry* 2nd ed. (San Francisco: W. H. Freeman and Co., 1955).

In some cases, SiO_4 tetrahedrons assume another arrangement in which, instead of forming a space framework, they are arranged in plane mono-molecular layers piled loosely upon each other. In these cases, which are similar to the diamond and graphite situation illustrated earlier in Fig. 8-17, minerals are obtained that are soft and that can easily be split into thin layers. *Talc,* $Mg_3Si_4O_{10}(OH)_2$; *kaolinite* (a constituent of clay) $Al_2Si_2O_5(OH)_4$; and common *mica,* $KAl_3Si_3O_{10}(OH)_2$ are examples of these so-called "layer materials."

Finally there are cases in which tetrahedra are arranged in long chains, which give the crystals a fibrous structure. The familiar example is *asbestos,* which has the chemical constitution:

$$Mg_6Si_4O_{11}(OH)_6 \cdot H_2O$$

We cannot finish the section on silicon without mentioning *glass*. Glass is not a chemical compound but a mixture of different silicates in a form that is called a "super-cooled liquid." When the molten mixture of silicates is cooled below its freezing point, it does not crystallize but becomes more and more viscous, finally hardening into a brittle solid. Apparently the molecules of the silicates lose their mobility too fast to take the regular positions found in crystals and stick to each other on a catch-as-catch-can principle. Of course it is all a question of terminology, but glass can better be described as the limiting case of very viscous fluid than as a regular solid. It is closer in structure to frozen caviar than to a carefully built garden wall!

ELEVEN

THE CHEMISTRY
OF LIFE

Organic Compounds of Carbon

Carbon is the most interesting chemical element because, apart from its participation in the structure of a
number of trivial inorganic compounds such as *carbon
tetrachloride* and *carborundum,* it plays a principal part
in the structure of the often very complex molecules that
constitute living organisms. The importance of carbon in
the structure of living matter arises from the ability of its

atoms, unshared by the atoms of any other element, to form long chains of this type, —C—C—C—C—, that serve as charm bracelets to which all kinds of different atomic groups can be attached. If all the valences of such a carbon chain are used to hold hydrogen atoms, we get the substances known as *hydrocarbons,* two of which are here shown along with their names.

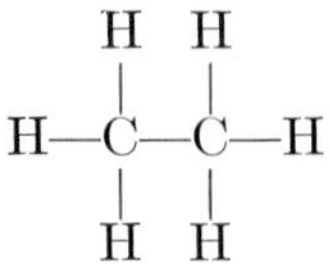

$$\begin{array}{cc} H & H \\ | & | \\ H-C-C-H \\ | & | \\ H & H \end{array}$$

ethane

$$\begin{array}{cccccc} H & H & H & H & H & H \\ | & | & | & | & | & | \\ H-C-C-C-C-C-C-H \\ | & | & | & | & | & | \\ H & H & H & H & H & H \end{array}$$

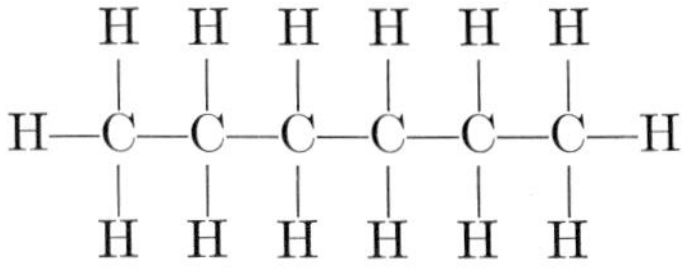

hexane

Between ethane and hexane are the following hydrocarbons, in the order of their increasing complexity: *propane,* C_3H_8; *butane,* C_4H_{10}; and *pentane,* C_5H_{12}. At room temperature *methane* and *ethane* are gases; somewhat longer carbon chain hydrocarbons are liquids of increasing viscosity. *Gasoline* is a mixture of hydrocarbons from about C_6H_{14} (hexane) to $C_{10}H_{22}$ (decane); *fuel oil* a mixture from $C_{15}H_{32}$ to $C_{18}H_{38}$; *lubricating oil,* from $C_{16}H_{34}$ to $C_{20}H_{42}$. Still longer chains begin to act like solids: *greases* run from $C_{18}H_{38}$ and up; *paraffin wax* contains still longer chains.

Often, instead of forming linear chains, carbon atoms make a ring, as, for example, in the case of *benzene,* C_6H_6.

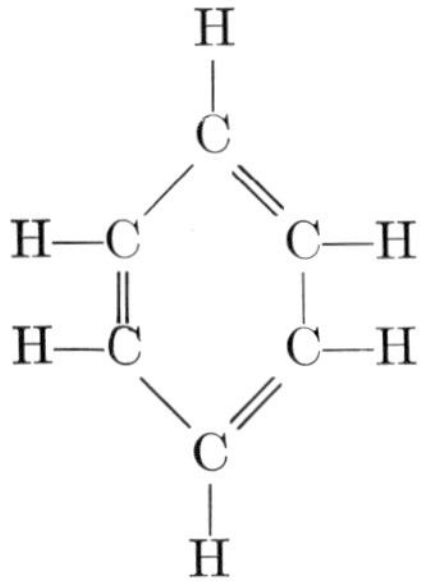

benzene

The benzene rings contain alternately single and double bonds, and sometimes two or more rings fuse together, as in *naphthalene*.

naphthalene

There are also peculiar types of rings, such as the *pyrimidine ring* and the *purine ring*, in which some of the carbon atoms are replaced by atoms of nitrogen, and these substances cannot, of course, be properly called pure hydrocarbons.

pyrimidine ring   purine ring

By replacing the hydrogen atoms adorning the skeletal carbon chains and rings by various atomic groups, we obtain different types of organic compounds. Thus the substitution of —O—H for an —H leads to various *alcohols,* of which the most familiar are *methyl* and *ethyl alcohol.*

methyl alcohol   ethyl alcohol

The binding of two hydrocarbons by an oxygen atom, which replaces one hydrogen atom in each of them, gives rise to *ethers,* of which the most familiar one is an ordinary or *diethyl ether,* not to be confused with the "world ether" that was supposed to be the carrier of light waves.

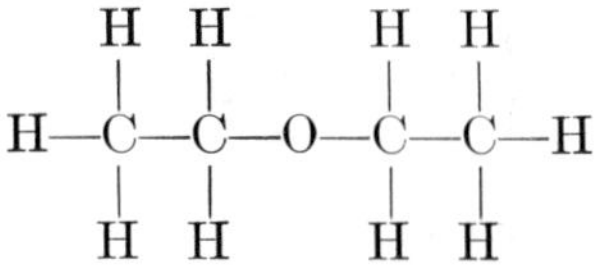

$$\begin{array}{ccccc} \text{H} & \text{H} & & \text{H} & \text{H} \\ | & | & & | & | \\ \text{H—C—C—O—C—C—H} \\ | & | & & | & | \\ \text{H} & \text{H} & & \text{H} & \text{H} \end{array}$$

diethyl ether

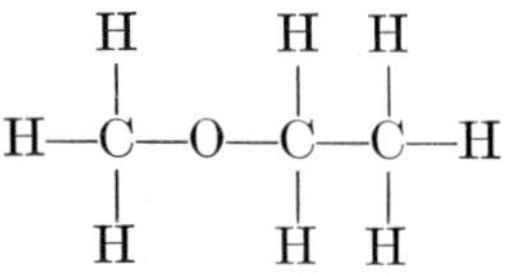

$$\begin{array}{ccccc} \text{H} & & \text{H} & \text{H} \\ | & & | & | \\ \text{H—C—O—C—C—H} \\ | & & | & | \\ \text{H} & & \text{H} & \text{H} \end{array}$$

methyl-ethyl ether

Replacing two hydrogen atoms attached to the same carbon atom by a single oxygen atom, we get *aldehydes* or *ketones*, depending on whether the carbon atom is in the middle or at the end of the chain. A typical ketone is *acetone*, which is used in the manufacture of lacquers and many plastics, such as photographic film, because of its solvent properties.

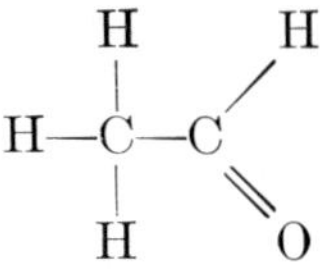

acetaldehyde

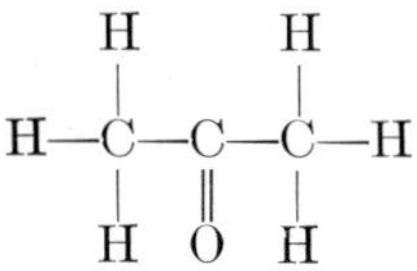

acetone
(dimethyl ketone)

Organic acids are characterized by one or more —COOH groups replacing hydrogens in the carbon skeletons. A typical organic acid is *acetic acid*, found in vinegar.

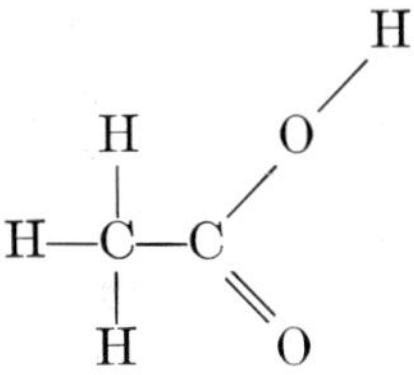

acetic acid

Alcohols and organic acids can be made to react; the —OH from the alcohol and the end —H from the acid join to form a water molecule, and the main parts of the alcohol and acid combine to form an *ester*. Simple esters such as *ethyl acetate* and *butyl acetate* are manufactured for use as solvents, and more complex esters existing in nature are largely responsible for the smell of flowers and the flavor of fruits.

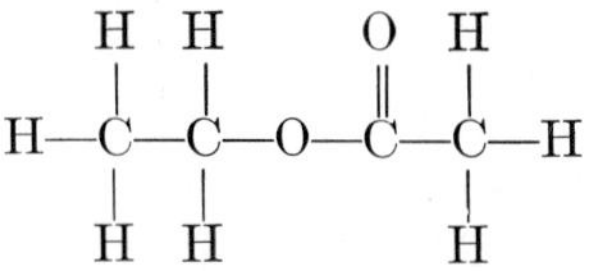

ethyl acetate

Carbohydrates, or *sugars* (also called *polysaccharides* when their molecules are very large), are the substances described by the general formula $C_x(H_2O)_y$, which indicates that the proportions of hydrogen and oxygen atoms in these compounds are the same as in a single water molecule. These are the substances primarily synthesized by plants under the action of the rays of the sun. The structural formula of *dextrose,* or fruit sugar, is:

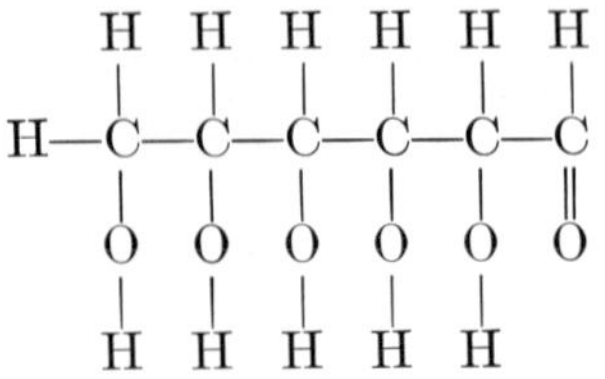

$$
\begin{array}{ccccccc}
& H & H & H & H & H & H \\
& | & | & | & | & | & | \\
H- & C- & C- & C- & C- & C- & C \\
& | & | & | & | & | & \| \\
& O & O & O & O & O & O \\
& | & | & | & | & | & \\
& H & H & H & H & H & \\
\end{array}
$$

dextrose

Finally, there are very important organic compounds known as *amines,* which are combinations of various hydrocarbons and ammonia. Examples of two amines are *methyl amine* and *aniline.*

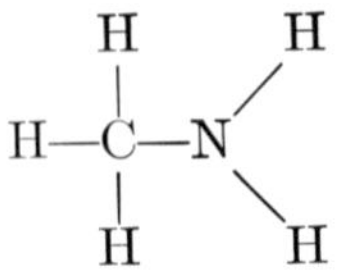

methyl amine

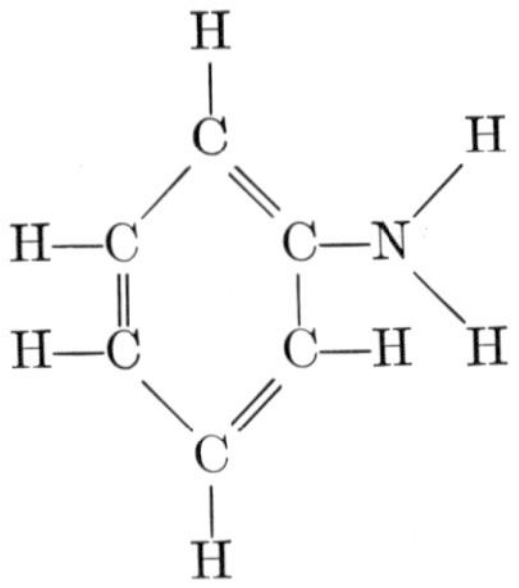

aniline

Vitamins

We have listed various organic compounds above and classified them according to the geometrical features of their structure. However, the effect of these substances on the organism into which they are introduced cannot be predicted merely on the basis of their composition but depends essentially on their specific interactions with the great variety of more complex chemical compounds that form the organism in question. Thus, we cannot deduce from the structural formulas of methyl alcohol and ethyl alcohol, as given on p. 242, that the first substance is poisonous and causes blindness and death, and that the second induces in a person a gay mood but imperils his (or her) driving.

Every organism produces a large variety of simple organic substances for its own uses and obtains others through food. If the food is deficient in certain organic compounds necessary for the proper functioning of the organism, sickness and sometimes even death may follow. The organic compounds that have to be present in small quantities in food apart from the regular diet of proteins, fats, and starches are known as *vitamins*. It should be kept in mind that the list of essential vitamins depends on the organism in question. Thus, simple organisms like molds can themselves produce all the organic compounds which are needed for their life, and they do not require any vitamins at all. Higher organisms, however, have lost the ability to be self-sufficient and always need some help from without. Depending on what they do and what they do not produce within their own systems, their vitamin requirements may be widely different; for example, while *vitamin C* is very essential for human beings, it is not at all necessary for rats, which synthesize it themselves.

However, since we all are human, a few words should be said about the vitamins required by "Homo sapiens." There are more than a dozen vitamins necessary for man and we will give a few of the most important examples.

Vitamin A is a fat-soluble substance present in fish-liver oils, dairy products, egg yolks, and many vegetables. Its lack brings on a scaly inflammation of the eyes and skin and a lowered ability to resist infections. Since it is a necessary part of the "visual purple," a chemical necessary for seeing at low light intensities, a vitamin A deficiency can lead to "night blindness."

Vitamin B_1, or *thiamine*, is soluble in water and thus may be lost in cooking. It is plentiful in yeast, nuts, meat, and the bran, or outer covering, of grains. A B_1 deficiency causes beri-beri, a serious nerve disorder with many complications. It is prevalent in the Orient, where the diet is largely rice that has had the bran polished off.

Vitamin C is found in citrus fruits, tomatoes, and some green vegetables. Its structural formula is:

vitamin C

Without vitamin C, the unpleasant and often fatal disease, scurvy, develops. In scurvy there is anemia and swelling and bleeding from the skin and mucous membranes, especially the gums. British sailors were given a ration of lime juice to prevent scurvy, which has given them the nickname "limey."

Vitamin D is necessary for the proper development and maintenance of bones and teeth. It is found in fish-liver oils, egg yolks and liver. Human beings can produce it in their skin, when the skin is exposed to sunshine or ultraviolet radiation. For other details concerning the vitamins, we refer the reader to special books on the subject.

Proteins

The comparatively simple organic compounds described in previous sections represent some of the elementary components of a complicated chemical machine which we call a living organism. But none of the compounds taken separately shows any manifestation of life, just as a single cogwheel in the mechanism of a clock or a single electronic tube in a TV set does not show time or a Hopalong Cassidy program.

The 64-thousand-dollar question is: "How are all these components put together in a living organism so as to carry out the complicated set of functions characterizing the phenomenon of life?" The study of living organisms leads to the conclusion that the most important substances participating in their structure and functioning are the complex organic compounds known as *proteins*. The molecular weight of protein molecules ranges from tens of thousands to many millions, thus dwarfing even the largest molecules ordinarily encountered in inorganic or organic chemistry. However, a closer inspection reveals that *this apparent complexity of protein molecules can be reduced to comparatively simple laws of structural regularity*. When proteins are heated in a water solution, they break up into relatively simple molecules known as *amino acids*. In the previous section we have seen that *amines* can be obtained by replacing hydrogen atoms attached to carbohydrates by NH_2 groups and that *acids* result from the replacement of hydrogen atoms by COOH groups. Thus, an amino acid (i.e., amine and acid) is a molecule in which both replacements are made. If, for example, we take an ethane molecule, C_2H_6, and replace one of the hydrogen atoms attached to the carbon chain on the right side by an amino group, NH_2, and another by an acid group, COOH, we will get the amino acid known as *alanine*:

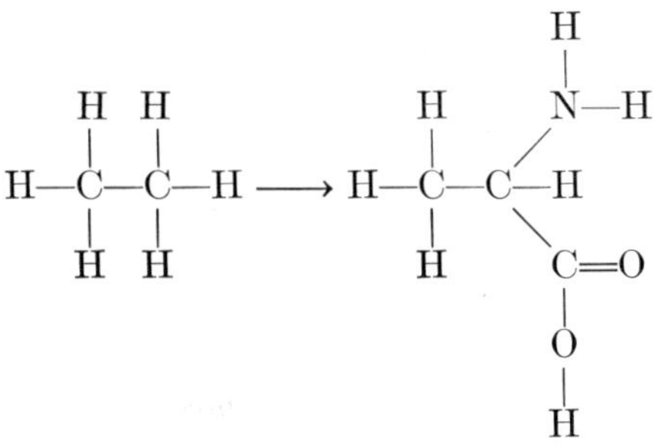

$$\begin{array}{ccc}
\overset{\displaystyle H \quad H}{\underset{\displaystyle H \quad H}{H-C-C-H}} & \longrightarrow & H-\overset{\displaystyle H}{\underset{\displaystyle H}{C}}-C
\end{array}$$

ethane   alanine

According to their definition we can prepare practically unlimited numbers of amino acids by attaching one amino and one acid group to any of the organic molecules; indeed, a skillful organic chemist can synthesize in his laboratory hundreds of different amino acids. But, the fact is that *protein molecules break up into a total of only 20 different amino acids.*[*] Furthermore, although in principle the amino and the acid groups can be attached to different carbon atoms in the molecule, *all amino acids constituting proteins have both the amino and the acid groups attached to the same carbon atom.*

The structural formulas of the 3 amino acids that we will be mostly concerned with are:

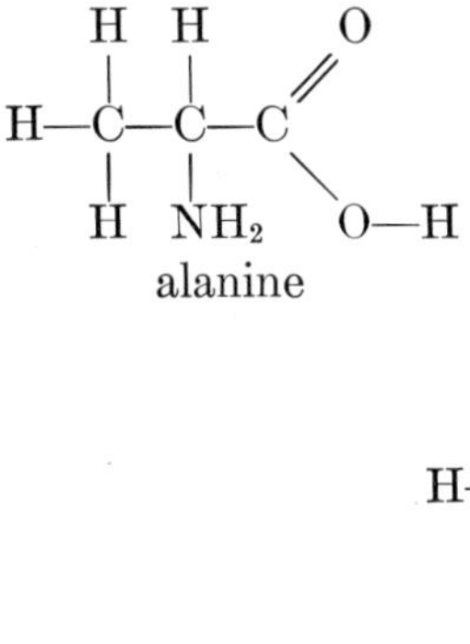

alanine 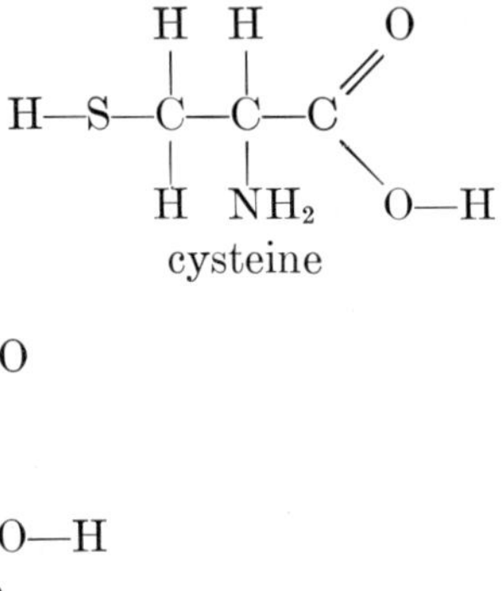   cysteine

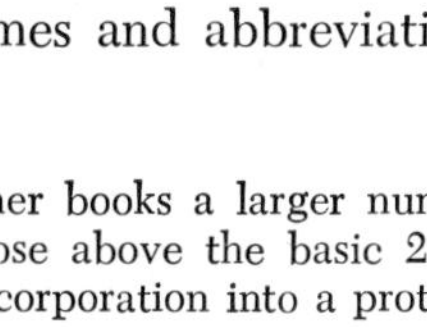

glycine

Table 11-1 gives the names and abbreviations of the 20 amino acids that form the proteins.

---

[*] The reader may find in other books a larger number of amino acids listed, but it seems almost certain that those above the basic 20 are derived from them by a secondary reaction after their incorporation into a protein molecule.

TABLE 11-1   THE 20 AMINO ACIDS THAT FORM THE PROTEINS

Name	Abbreviation	Name	Abbreviation
Alanine	Ala	Leucine	Leu
Arginine	Arg	Lysine	Lys
Asparagine	Asp	Methionine	Meth
Aspartic acid	Aspn	Phenylalanine	Phe
Cysteine	Cys	Proline	Pro
Glutamine	Glun	Serine	Ser
Glutamic acid	Glu	Threonine	Thr
Glycine	Gly	Tryptophan	Try
Histidine	His	Tyrosine	Tyr
Isoleucine	Ileu	Valine	Val

Early in this century, the studies of a German chemist, Emil Fischer (1852-1919), proved that protein molecules are formed by linear sequences of amino acids which are hooked together through their amino and acid groups by so-called *peptide bonds*. These peptide bonds are formed by the removal of —O—H from one of the amino acids and of —H from its adjacent neighbor. This leads to the formation of a free water molecule and of a peptide bridge,

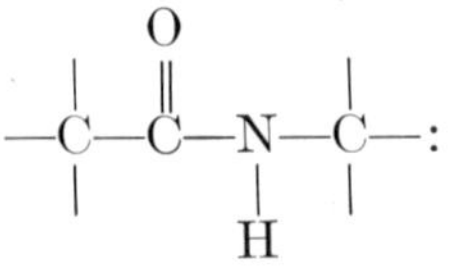

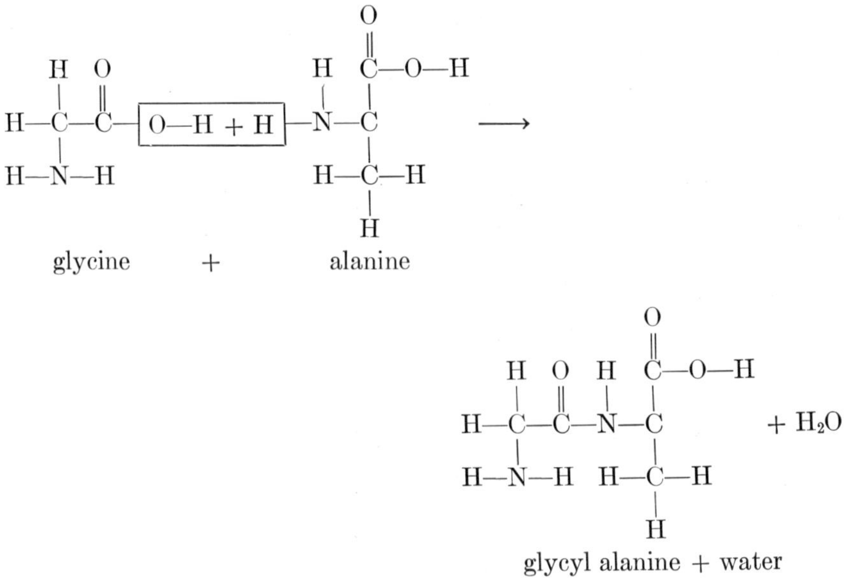

glycine   +   alanine

glycyl alanine + water

When proteins are heated in a water solution, the process is reversed: a water molecule is added to each peptide bridge, breaking it up into separate amino and acid groups, and the long protein molecule falls apart into a large number of individual amino acids.

Since all proteins are constructed from the same 20 amino acids, the difference in their biological functions must lie in the order in which different acids follow each other in the linear sequence. The situation is similar to that existing in any language where the meaning of a sentence is determined by the order in which different letters of the alphabet follow each other. If we reduce the English alphabet to twenty letters, or rather to 19 letters and "space," by writing "i" in place of "j" and "y," "k" in place of "q," etc. and assign each letter to one of the amino acids in Table 11-1, each sentence in English will correspond to a certain protein and vice versa. But, of course, since only a negligible fraction of all possible sequences of letters makes any sense in the English language and since only a very small fraction of all possible sequences of amino acids corresponds to existing proteins, the chance that we can find a sequence which would make sense both in English and in protein language is practically nil!

PROTEIN GEOMETRY

As we mentioned before, amino acids forming the proteins are obtained from hydrocarbons by replacing two hydrogen atoms attached to the same carbon by one amino, $-NH_2$, and one acid, $-COOH$, group. Thus, generally speaking, the four valences of that carbon atom, known as the *α-carbon,* are used to hold *four different chemical groups,* as, for example, CH_3, H, NO_2, and COOH in the case of *alanine.* (The only exception is presented by *glycine,* the simplest of all amino acids, in which there are two H's attached to the α-carbon). The three-dimensional configurations of this type can exist in two different forms that are *mirror images* of one another, as can be easily proved by using our right and left hand for constructing a schematic model of an amino acid. If we consider the palm as the main body (or "residue") of the molecule and place an amino group on the thumb, an acid group on the index finger, and a hydrogen atom on the middle finger, as shown in Fig. 11-1, we will get two different mirror symmetrical configurations on the right and left hand. The corresponding organic molecules are known as *dextro* (right) and *levo* (left) configurations.

Substances whose molecules can exist in two mirror symmetrical configurations have the property of rotating the plane of polarization of polarized light when only one of the configurations is present, the dextro and levo configurations rotating the plane in opposite directions. In a mixture containing equal amounts of both forms, they will cancel each other out, and there will be no rotation.

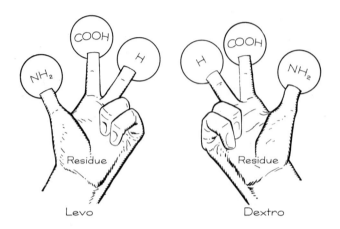

Fig. 11-1. Levo- and dextro-amino acids demonstrated by using the left and right hands.

Synthetically produced organic molecules contain equal amounts of the dextro and levo forms, so these will not rotate the plane of polarization. However, if we send a beam of polarized light through a water solution of ordinary naturally grown sugar, we will find that the plane of polarization turns in a way which corresponds to the right-hand mirror symmetry, and we will get the same result whether the sugar was produced from sugar cane or from beets or whether it came from Puerto Rico, South America, Europe, or Asia.

We find that a solution of any one of the 20 amino acids (except glycine, which does not possess any mirror symmetry) obtained by breaking up protein molecules rotates the plane of polarized light in a way which corresponds to the molecules of the left-hand symmetry. And this is always true no matter whether the protein comes from a cow, a fly, a rose bush, an amoeba, or a colony of influenza virus.* The fact that nature always selects for its work the molecules of one definite mirror symmetry, while the same substances synthesized artificially in a biochemical laboratory are always obtained as a fifty-fifty mixture of dextro and levo varieties, is extremely interesting. It suggests the possibility of another living world, a mirror image of our own formed by dextro amino acids, levo sugars, etc. If the two worlds coexisted, the animals and plants in one of them would be indigestible and probably poisonous to

---

* A possible exception to this rule is presented by *antibiotics* such as penicillin, which contain a certain percentage of dextro amino acids. This is thought (although it is not certain) to make these molds poisonous to all bacteria, and it accounts for their use in modern medicine.

those in the other. We may speculate that both such worlds existed during the early stages of the evolution of life until one of them took the upper hand and won the battle for existence.

Since all amino acids forming the proteins possess left-handed spatial symmetry, the entire chain should have a tendency to coil into the shape of a corkscrew. And, indeed, Linus Pauling (1901-   ) and R. B. Corey (1897-   ) have shown that the most typical configuration of protein molecules is the so-called *helix* (Fig. 11-2), which has 3.6 amino acids per turn, or about 18 amino acids per 5 turns. Fibrous proteins, such as those in hair or muscular tissues, are formed by extensive helical molecular chains, which, in their turn, are twisted about one another to form long fibers possessing a structure similar to that of rope. In the proteins responsible for carrying out various biochemical tasks, the chains are folded and tangled together into more or less spherical bodies known as globular proteins. The *hemoglobin* of the blood and *ovalbumin* of the white of an egg are examples of such globular proteins. An increase of temperature and the action of certain chemicals cause globular proteins to uncoil into long wavy threads that result in a notable increase in the

Fig. 11-2. Linus Pauling with his model of a protein molecule (the white balls are hydrogen atoms).

viscosity of the substance in question (*coagulation*). The hardening of the white of a cooked egg represents a typical example of such a process.

PRODUCTIVE PROTEINS

The most important part played by protein molecules in any living organism lies in the production of a multitude of various organic substances that are essential for the growth, well-being, and reproduction of these organisms. There are, for instance, three different kinds of proteins, known as *digestive enzymes* (trypsin, amylase, and lipase), produced in the cells lining the walls of the digestive tract that break up the crude food into amino acids, sugars, and the so-called fatty acids. These disintegrated products are carried by the bloodstream to all the cells constituting the organism, and when they arrive at their destination they are attacked by teams of twelve specific proteins known as *respiratory enzymes* (hexokinase, oxisomerase, zymohexase, etc.), which operate within each cell. Sugars and fats are oxidized by using the air that is brought by the same bloodstream from the lungs, and the energy liberated in the process is partially used to build new proteins from amino acids and is partially deposited in the molecules of a substance known as *adenosinetriphosphate* (called ATP for short), which, as was shown by F. Lipmann (1899-   ), serves as a storage battery in the internal economy of living organisms. Whenever energy is needed, be it for the work of the muscles, the propagation of sensory impulses along the nerve fibers, the functioning of the brain cells, or the operation of a firefly's flashlight, ATP is always at hand to supply the necessary amounts of it.

A large variety of protein molecules is produced by special glands located in different parts of the body, and these molecules are secreted into the bloodstream to be used wherever and whenever they are needed. To this class of the so-called *protein hormones* belong such substances as *prolactin* (a catalyst in the production of milk); *insulin* (controls the utilization of sugar); *adrenocorticotropin* (stimulates the adrenal cortex); *oxytocin* (causes the contraction of the muscles of the uterus); *vasopressin* (controls blood pressure), etc.

Fig. 11-3. The proteins oxytocin and vasopressin.

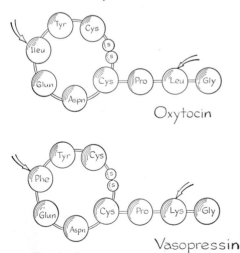

Oxytocin

Vasopressin

Many of these proteins have been studied in detail and their chemical constitutions and structural formulas are exactly known. The structural formulas of oxytocin and vasopressin were obtained by the American biochemist, D. de Vigneaud. Notice that each of these two substances consists of nine amino acids and that they differ from each other only in the third and the eighth position. Thus, these two proteins stand in the same relation to one another as the two English sentences:

"war is on"

and

"wag is in"

By changing only two letters, we obtain a significant difference in the meaning of the sentence and in the functioning of the protein!

As you can see from Fig. 11-3, in both oxytocin and vasopressin, the chain of amino acids is not linear but forms a loop because of the —S—S— linkage between two *cysteines*. This phenomenon is common to all proteins containing cysteine groups and is due to the fact that, since the —S—S— linkage is stronger than two —S—H linkages, two cysteines that

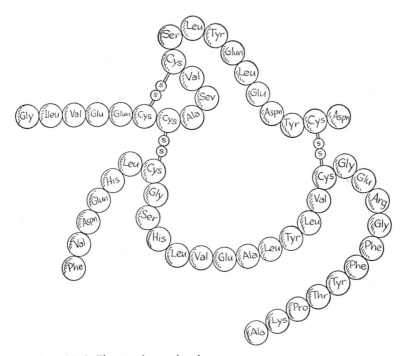

Fig. 11-4. The insulin molecule.

may stand far apart in the linear sequence will usually adhere to each other and form what is called *cystine* by liberating H_2 and forming an —S—S— linkage. This characteristic looping of long protein molecules may be of great significance in their biological activity. Another example of looping produced by the formation of —S—S— linkages is the molecule of insulin, which contains altogether 51 amino acids (Fig. 11-4). The structure of this molecule was recently analyzed by F. Sanger in England. For the sake of simplicity, this diagram does not show the structure of individual amino acids, and only the peptide bonds and —S—S— linkages between them are indicated.

STRUCTURAL PROTEINS

The formation of —S—S— linkages between cysteines becomes of paramount importance in the molecules of *keratin,* the protein constituting hair, furs, wool, nails, horns, hoofs, etc. About 10 per cent of all amino acids forming keratin are cysteines, so the formation of —S—S— linkages goes far and wide. The long protein molecules are lined up alongside each other and are bound together by numerous cross-linkages that give these substances their characteristic elasticity and strength. However, if a keratin fiber such as a human hair is forcibly coiled into a curl and subjected to heat of over 200°F, the strained original —S—S— bridges snap and new ones are formed. Thus, after cooling, the hair remains permanently in a coiled shape. The new "cold wave" method substitutes for the heat treatment, which is often damaging to the hair, certain chemicals or lotions that have the ability to break keratin's —S—S— linkages without a rise in temperature.

DYNAMIC PROTEINS

One of the outstanding attributes of animal life is the ability to move. In the case of simple organisms such as the amoeba, the motion is achieved by slow contraction and relaxation of the cytoplasm of the cells. Higher organisms possess for this purpose highly specialized muscular tissues which set the bones of the skeleton into motion. In 1868, the German biochemist, W. Kühne, found that the fibers of muscular tissues contain a specific protein to which he gave the name *myosin,* and seven decades later, a Hungarian-born biochemist, A. Szent-Györgyi, discovered another important muscular protein which he named *actin.* It seems, in fact, that the remarkable ability of muscles to contract and to relax is due to the binary structure of muscular tissues. The hypothetical units composed of actin and myosin molecules received the name *actomyosin*.

As mentioned above, the principal energy source in any living organism is provided by the so-called ATP molecules in which the energy liberated in the oxidation of food products is stored. This is particularly true for the work of muscles, as demonstrated in the following simple experiment performed by Szent-Györgyi some years ago. An isolated muscle fiber from the hind leg of a frog or a rabbit was stretched and washed for some time in a stream of water to remove all soluble compounds, so that only the insoluble actomyosin threads were left. After this process, the fiber looks like a long thin thread. When the fiber was subjected to the action of an 0.2 per cent water solution of ATP, it began to shrink rapidly and in a few seconds became shorter by a factor of 3. Within a few minutes, the fiber contracted to one-fifth of its original length. Measuring the force exerted by the fiber in this contraction, we find that, per unit of cross-section, the force is the same as in the case of a muscle in living animals. This leaves no doubt that ATP molecules act as the agents that cause the contraction of muscular tissues.

The experiment was repeated with an "artificial muscular tissue" formed by taking chemically pure actomyosin and stretching it into the form of a fiber. When this artificial muscle fiber was acted upon by the ATP solution, it shrank and became thicker just as natural muscle fiber does.

Knowing the results of the above described experiments, we can go on to speculate about the mechanical nature of muscular contraction. You will recall that a heated double-stranded metallic ribbon made from materials with different thermal expansion coefficients will bend. If the ribbon is long enough, it will coil up and considerably reduce its length and increase its width. A similar result ensues when a double-stranded ribbon formed by a layer of hygroscopic material (i.e., a material which readily absorbs moisture) such as wood and a non-hygroscopic material such as metal is subjected to increased humidity. In fact, even ordinary plywood, made from thin layers of wood in which the directions of the grain in alternate layers run perpendicular to one another, becomes badly warped from humidity. It may be that the action of ATP on the double-stranded molecular chains of actomyosin is of the same general nature.

But this kind of speculation remains so far only speculation and much more work remains to be done by combining chemical, physical, and visual (electromicroscopic) studies of muscle tissues. In Fig. 11-5 is a beautiful photograph of a cluster of muscle fibers from the wing muscles of a bumble bee. The rounded bodies on both sides of the fibers are the so-called *mitochondria,* which are the centers where the energy-carrying ATP molecules are produced by the teams of enzymes.

Fig. 11-5. Dr. A. Szent-Györgyi pointing to an electronmicrogram of the actomyosin fibers in the flight muscles of a bumble bee. The dark rounded bodies are the mitochondria where the ATP necessary for muscular contraction is produced. Linear magnification of muscle fibers: 26,000 times; linear reduction of Dr. Szent-Györgyi: 8 times. Photograph by Delbert E. Philpott, Institute of Muscular Research. M.B.L., Woods Hole, Mass.

Genetic Material

If we compare a living organism to a large industrial country, we can consider individual cells to be the factories that carry out specialized tasks for the benefit of the entire community. The productive proteins that operate within individual cells or that are sometimes secreted into the bloodstream to be carried to different parts of the organism can in this case be compared to the workers who are employed in the individual factories or who travel from place to place to carry out their specific assignments. But what is the coordinating agent which shapes the protein working teams and directs their activity in such a variety of different ways? What causes a fertilized egg to develop either into a man or into a mosquito or into an oak tree or into a bread mold? Detailed studies of living cells indicate that the organizing centers of their growth and development are the *chromosomes,* the tiny threadlike bodies that are found within the cellular nucleus. In fact, the cellular nucleus can be compared to the manager's office in the individual factories and the chromosomes to the file cabinets in which all the production plans and blueprints are stored. This analogy is represented graphically in Fig. 11-6.

The main constituent of chromosomes is a substance known as *deoxyribonucleic acid,* or DNA for short. In spite of its fundamental importance for the functioning of living organisms, DNA is present in them in very minute quantities, and whereas proteins represent the major fraction of the total dry weight of an organism (apart from the bones, fat, etc.), the total amount of DNA in the body of a man is only about one teaspoonful. It is just about the same ratio as that of the weight of all the machinery in a plant to the weight of the blueprints and other documents in the manager's office. During recent years our knowledge of the chemical nature of DNA has progressed to such an extent that we can write the structural formula of a DNA molecule with the same degree of certainty that we can for the molecules of alcohol or TNT.

Like protein molecules, the molecules of DNA are long chains formed by the repetition of a small number of different and comparatively simple chemical compounds. But whereas protein sequences involve 20

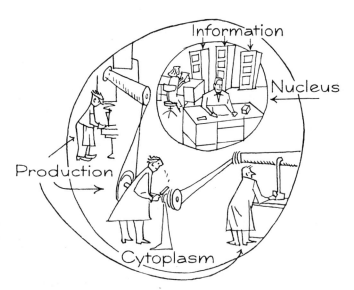

Fig. 11-6. The cell as analogous to a factory.

different amino acids, there are only 4 different units involved in the structure of DNA. These constituent units of DNA are known as *nucleotides* and carry the names *adenine, thymine, guanine,* and *cytosine*. Their structural formulas are shown below united in the polynucleotide chain.

Two of them are formed by a single ring and are known as *pyramidines* while the other two have a double ring and are called *purines*. Each nucleotide possesses a sugar-phosphate group that plays a role similar to that of the amino acid groups in binding nucleotides into long chains (Fig. 11-7). The finding of the Austrian-born American biochemist,

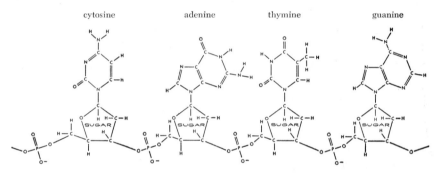

Fig. 11-7. The structural formulas of four basic nucleotides (cytosine, adenine, thymine, and guanine) united into the so-called polynucleotide chain.

E. Chargaff, that the number of adenines in each DNA sample is equal to the number of thymines and that the same ratio also holds for the guanine-cytosine pairs suggests that these molecules are paired, giving to a DNA molecule a double-stranded character. A complete model of a DNA molecule was constructed in 1953 by a young British crystallophysicist, F. Crick, and a still younger American biologist, J. Watson, and is shown schematically in Fig. 11-8. It resembles, in a way, a rope ladder the steps of which are formed by 1 purine and 1 pyrimidine bound together by a double hydrogen bond. These "steps" are held together by two "ropes" formed by alternating sugar and phosphate molecules, and the entire structure is twisted around its axis, forming a helix with a repetition period of ten steps. A corpulent version of a DNA molecule, built by the author using an atomic kit, is shown in Fig. 11-9.

The importance of Watson's and Crick's model of the DNA molecule lies in the possibility it provides for understanding the replication process of chromosomes, a process that secures the transfer of complete hereditary information from the parents to the progeny. Just as the specificity of any given protein molecule is determined by the order in which the various amino acids are arranged in the linear sequence, hereditary information carried by a DNA molecule must depend on the arrangement of the four different nucleotides. The total combined length of the stretched-out DNA molecules that are coiled inside the nucleus of a cell is about 3 cm, which involves a sequence of about a hundred million nucleotides. The order of the nucleotides in this sequence must carry, in a coded form, the complete information about all the major and minor hereditary properties of the given organism. Actually, each DNA molecule carries the hereditary information in two copies, since, due to the adeninethymine and guanine-cytosine pairing, the order of nucleotides in the second strand is uniquely determined by their order in the first one. According to Crick and Watson, the process of cellular division is preceded by the lengthwise splitting of DNA molecules into two single strands. Following, or probably during, this splitting, each half of the original molecule develops again into a double-stranded form by catching free nucleotides present in the surrounding medium. Thus, after the completion of the process, we have two identical DNA molecules which are then distributed between the nuclei of the two daughter cells. According to this picture, occasional mistakes in the rebuilding of the split DNA molecules account for the well-known phenomena of *mutations*.

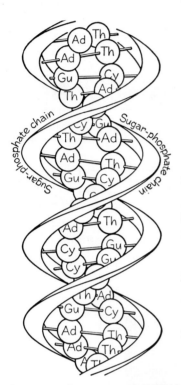

Fig. 11-8. The structure of DNA according to Watson and Crick.

HOW HEREDITY MAY WORK

We come now to one of the most fundamental questions in the study of living matter. Since the DNA molecule represents a long sequence made up of only four different nucleotides,* the hereditary information which it carries can depend only on *the way in which these nucleotides are arranged in a linear sequence.* Using, for the sake of simplicity, the names *hearts, diamonds, spades,* and *clubs* instead of the more complicated chemical names of the four nucleotides given above, we may say that the DNA molecule is equivalent to a long sequence of aces of four different suits. Thus, the sequence:

may carry the instructions for a living cell to develop into a chrysanthemum, while the sequence:

may make a frog out of it. We have mentioned before that the DNA threads in a single cell contain about 100,000,000 nucleotides, which, in

---

* We speak only about one strand of the DNA molecule since any other strand is uniquely determined by the first one.

Fig. 11-9. The section of the DNA molecule that carries hereditary information in all living organisms. The white hemispheres are atoms of hydrogen. The other spheres represent atoms of oxygen, nitrogen, phosphorus, etc. The actual length of a DNA molecule may be thousands of times that shown in the photograph.

our playing card analogy, would correspond to a sequence of cards several thousand miles long. This sequence must serve as a "template" that determines the order of the amino acids in the protein molecules of the enzymes which carry out all the biochemical work in the organism. We have said above that protein molecules are formed by sequences of 20 different amino acids, and can, in this sense, be compared with long sentences written by means of an abridged twenty-letter alphabet. How is it possible that the order in which 20 different amino acids (or letters) are arranged into a sequence is *uniquely determined* by a sequence formed by only 4 different nucleotides? A possible answer to this problem, suggested by the author of this book several years ago, goes this way.

Suppose we play a "simplified poker game" in which each player gets only three cards, and all cards are only the aces of the four different suits. How many different hands can a player have? First of all he can get four different "flushes": 3 hearts, 3 diamonds, 3 spades, or 3 clubs. Then he can have "pairs," such as 2 hearts and 1 spade, or 2 spades and 1 club. There are altogether 12 different combinations of that kind, since the suit of the pair can be selected out of four possibilities, while the extra card can be chosen only from the three remaining ones. The lowest hand is a "bust" with all three cards different, and there are 4 different possibilities in this case (no hearts, no diamonds, etc.). Thus, our hypothetical poker player may have any one of 20 different triplets of cards, which is exactly equal to the number of different amino acids forming a long protein molecule.

Suppose now that, because of their chemical structure, the molecules of the 20 amino acids have a certain affinity for various triplets of nucleotides. Thus, proline may be attracted by the combination of one alanine and a pair of guanines, while asparagine may have a special liking for a triplet of cytosines. This would solve the problem of the translation of one sequence into the other. For example, the protein built at the beginning of the chrysanthemum's sequence of nucleotides might look this way:

There is a considerable amount of evidence that the synthesis of protein molecules on the nucleic acid template proceeds along this line, although the details are still far from being clear. For example, it has not yet been possible to establish a definite one-to-one correlation between the twenty different triplets of nucleotides and the twenty amino acids which they capture in the process of protein synthesis.

TWELVE

THE ELECTRIC NATURE
OF MATTER

Positive and Negative Ions

As was mentioned before, pure distilled water is a very poor conductor of electricity. However, if we dissolve in water a small amount of some acid or salt, its electrical conductivity becomes quite appreciable and increases in direct proportion to the amount of the dissolved substance. In contrast to the case of metallic conductors, the passage of electric current through water solutions is associated with certain chemical phenomena, the nature of which depends on the particular solute used. If we pass an electric current through a solution of nitric acid (HNO_3), small gas bubbles will be formed on both electrodes and will gradually rise to the surface. We can collect these gases in two long inverted glass cylinders that are placed about the electrodes and that are originally completely filled with water (Fig. 12-1a). When

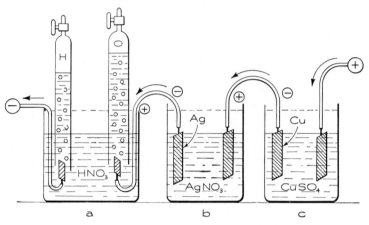

Fig. 12-1. The electrolysis of water solutions of nitric acid (a), silver nitrate (b), and copper sulfate (c) by the same current.

we analyze the nature of the gas liberated on the negative electrode, we find it to be hydrogen; in fact, if we open the valve at the top of the glass cylinder placed above this electrode, we can ignite the gas streaming out from it, and in the process of burning, the hydrogen will unite with atmospheric oxygen and form water vapor. The gas that is collected in the cylinder placed above the positive electrode is oxygen; if we open the valve at the top of that cylinder and place a burning match into the stream of outcoming gas, it will flare up more intensely because of the additional oxygen supply.

Thus, the passage of electric current decomposes water into its two elementary constituents, hydrogen and oxygen. How does this happen, and why should it require something dissolved in the water to get things going? In explaining this phenomenon, which is known as *electrolysis*, we assume that the molecules of nitric acid dissolved in the water break up into two parts that carry opposite electric charges: the atoms of hydrogen, which carry a certain amount of positive electricity, and the remaining NO_3 groups, which carry an equal amount of negative electricity. The positively and negatively charged atoms and atomic groups are known as positive and negative *ions,* and we write H^+ for a positively charged hydrogen atom and $(NO_3)^-$ for a negatively charged NO_3 group. In the molecules of pure nitric acid, the two kinds of ions are held together by the attraction between their opposite electric charges (we should actually write $H^+(NO_3)^-$ instead of HNO_3), but when the acid is dissolved in water, some of the molecules break up (dissociate) into free positive ions of hydrogen, H^+, and free negative ions, $(NO_3)^-$ (Fig. 12-2). When an electric tension is applied to the solution by plac-

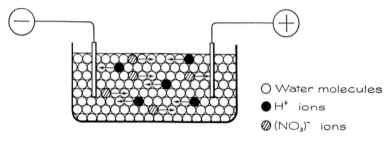

O Water molecules

● H^+ ions

◐ $(NO_3)^-$ ions

Fig. 12-2. Electrically charged ions, H^+ and $(NO_3)^-$, in a water solution of nitric acid "shouldering" their way to corresponding electrodes.

ing into it two electrodes connected with a source of direct current (DC), the positive ions of hydrogen are attracted to the negative electrode (cathode) and the negative ions of NO_3 are attracted to the positive electrode (anode). As the result of the ionic motion caused by these attractions, an electric current flows through the water solution, a current that would have been impossible in pure water. When the traveling ions H^+ and $(NO_3)^-$ arrive at their respective electrodes, they release their electric charges into the metal; hydrogen rises to the surface in the form of tiny bubbles, while the neutral NO_3 reacts with water according to the equation $2NO_3 + H_2O \rightarrow 2HNO_3 + O$, liberating free oxygen and regenerating the original molecules of nitric acid. Thus, the passage of electric current through the water resulted in nothing more than the breaking up of the water molecules into their hydrogen and oxygen components.

If, instead of using nitric acid, we use one of its salts (in which hydrogen is replaced by a metal that does not react with water), the metal will be deposited on the surface of the negative electrode. When, for example, we pass an electric current through a solution of silver nitrate, $AgNO_3$ (Fig. 12-lb) we will notice that after a while the cathode will be covered with a thin layer of silver. This method of coating surfaces with thin layers of various metals is known as *electroplating* and has many useful and practical applications. Just as in the case of nitric acid, the electrolytic process in the silver nitrate solution is due to the fact that the molecules of this salt break up into two oppositely charged ions, Ag^+ and $(NO_3)^-$, which are driven in opposite directions by the applied electric tension.

The Laws of Faraday

Michael Faraday, whose name was already mentioned in connection with the theory of electric and magnetic fields, was the first to investigate in detail the laws of electrolytic processes. He found first of all that, for each given salt solution, the amount of material deposited at the electrodes is directly proportional to the strength of the electric current and to its duration, or, in other words, that **the amount of material deposited on the electrodes is directly proportional to the total amount of electricity which had passed through the solution.** From this *first law of Faraday,* we conclude that each ion of a given chemical substance carries a well-defined electric charge.

In his further studies, Faraday investigated the relative amounts of electric charge carried by ions of different chemical substances. To compare these amounts, he passed an electric current consecutively through the solutions of several different substances, such as nitric acid, silver nitrate, and copper sulfate, as is shown in Fig. 12-1a, b, and c. In the case of nitric acid a certain amount of hydrogen gas was liberated on the cathode, while a certain amount of silver was deposited on the cathode in the case of the silver nitrate solution. Faraday measured the amounts of hydrogen and silver produced in these experiments and found that the ratio of the weight of deposited silver to the weight of liberated hydrogen is 107.02, which is exactly equal to the ratio of the atomic weight of silver to the atomic weight of hydrogen. Thus, he concluded that the same number of atoms of Ag and H had been deposited and that *one ion of silver carries exactly the same electric charge as one ion of hydrogen.* It would be premature, however, to conclude that *all* ions carry the same electric charge. In fact, comparing the amount of silver liberated in the electrolysis of silver nitrate with that of copper liberated by the same electric current flowing for the same length of time in the electrolysis of copper sulfate, we find that the weight ratio of silver to copper is 3.40 instead of the 1.70 (107.9:63.5) that would correspond to one atom of silver per atom of copper. Notice, however, that 1.70 is exactly one-half of 3.40, and if we write the observed ratio in the form $(2 \times 107.9):63.5$, we conclude that *one ion of copper carries twice as much electricity as one ion of silver.* Comparing these facts with the structural formulas of the corresponding compounds:

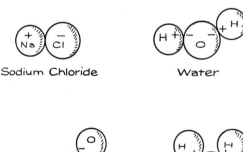

we notice that the amount of electricity carried by the ions of different elements is directely correlated with their chemical valence. And, in fact, in the electrolysis of $AlCl_3$ where Al possesses a triple valency, the Al ions are found to carry a triple charge. This constitutes the *second law of Faraday* which states that **the ions of the elements which have a chemical valence of two, three, and more with respect to hydrogen carry two, three, etc. times the amount of electric charge that a hydrogen ion does.**

THE ELECTRIC NATURE OF CHEMICAL BONDS

The laws of electrolysis give us a simple electric interpretation of the chemical bonds between the atoms. Apparently, because of their inner nature, some atoms "prefer" to be electrically charged either positively (like hydrogen and copper) or negatively (like oxygen and chlorine), while some others (all noble gases) "prefer" to remain neutral. The electric charge carried by different ions is always equal to, or is an integral multiple of, a certain elementary amount of electricity (i.e., the charge carried by a hydrogen ion), and the amount of this charge, along with its sign, helps to determine the location of any given element in the periodic system. Thus, instead of the "valence hooks" used in a previous chapter, we can now use a picture based on electrostatic interaction.

Fig. 12-3. Examples of chemical bonds caused by the attraction between the electric charges of ions.

Several examples of this view of chemical bonding are shown in Fig. 12-3.

Faraday's discovery of the fact that an electric charge is always an integral multiple of a certain elementary amount of electricity played as important a role in the study of the electric properties of matter as did the atomic hypothesis of Dalton in the study of its chemical properties. The numerical value of the elementary electric charge can be obtained by dividing the total amount of electricity passed

Sodium Chloride   Water

Silver nitrate   Methane

through the solution by the number of monovalent atoms deposited on the electrode. Thus if we maintain a current of 10 amperes for one hour in the electrolysis of water, the total amount of hydrogen liberated at the cathode will be 0.376 gm. Since by definition one ampere corresponds to a flow of one coulomb per second, the total amount of electricity which passed through the water is 36,000 coulombs. On the other hand, the number of hydrogen atoms in 0.376 gm of hydrogen is 2.245×10^{23}. The amount of electric charge per hydrogen ion is, therefore, 1.60×10^{-19} coulombs. This is the smallest amount of electricity that can exist in nature.

The Passage of Electricity through Gases

The next step in the study of the electric nature of matter was made by another famous Britisher named J. J. Thomson (1856-1940) (Fig. 12-4). While Michael Faraday studied the passage of electric current through liquids, J. J. (as he was known to his colleagues and his students) later concentrated his attention on the electrical conductivity of gases.

When we walk in the evening along the downtown streets of a modern city, we observe the bright display of neon (bright red) and helium (pale green) advertising signs. Modern offices and homes are illuminated by what are known as fluorescent light tubes. In all these cases we deal

Fig. 12-4. Sir J. J. Thomson (left), the discoverer of the electron, and Lord Rutherford, the discoverer of the nucleus, discuss some administrative problems in the courtyard of Cavendish Laboratory, Cambridge, England, 1929.

with the passage of high-tension electric current through a rarefied gas— the phenomenon that was the object of the lifelong studies of J. J. Thomson. As in the case of liquids, the current passing through a gas is due to the motion of positive and negative ions driven in opposite directions by an applied electric field. But, whereas the positive gas ions are similar to those encountered in the electrolysis of liquids (being the positively charged atoms of the substance in question), the negative ions in this case were found to have an entirely different nature. They carry the same electric charge as the ordinary monovalent negative ions, such as chlorine ions, for example, but their mass is much, much smaller than that of any atom. To study these, at that time, mysterious particles Thomson, in 1897, devised an instrument shown schematically in Fig. 12-5. It consisted of a

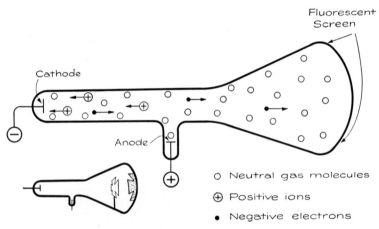

Fig. 12-5. The passage of electric current through rarefied gas.

glass tube containing highly rarefied gas with a cathode placed at one end of it and an anode located in an extension on the side. Because of this arrangement, the negative ions, which form the "cathode-rays" that move from left to right in the drawing, miss the anode and fly into the right side of the tube. The tube broadens here, and its flat rear end is covered with a layer of fluorescent material which becomes luminous when bombarded by fast-moving particles. This original tube constructed by Thomson at the turn of the century is very similar to a modern TV tube where the image of pirouetting ballerinas or sweating prize fighters is also due to the fluorescence produced by a scanning electron beam. But, in those pioneering days of what we now call "electronics" one was satisfied with much simpler shows; placing a metal cross in the way of the beam, Thomson observed that it cast a shadow on the fluorescent screen, indicating that the particles in question were moving along straight lines, similar to light rays.

THE CHARGE-TO-MASS RATIO OF AN ELECTRON

Thomson's next task was to study the deflection of the beam caused by electric and magnetic fields applied along its path. Indeed, since the beam was formed by a swarm of negatively charged particles, it should be deflected towards the positive pole of the condenser that produces the electric field shown in Fig. 12-6a. On the other hand, since a beam of charged particles is equivalent to an electric current, it should be deflected by a magnetic field directed perpendicularly to its track (Fig. 12-6b) according to the second law of electromagnetic interactions as formulated in Chapter 5.

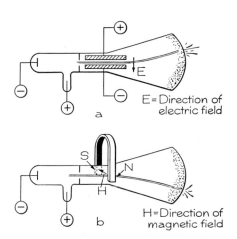

E = Direction of electric field

H = Direction of magnetic field

Fig. 12-6. J. J. Thomson's method of measuring the velocity and the mass of electrons: (a) the electric deflection of an electron beam and (b) the magnetic deflection of such a beam.

The deflection of a particle will depend, of course, on how much force is applied to it. For a charged particle in an electric field, the force depends only on the particle's charge and on the strength of the field. For a magnetic field, however, the situation is different; in Chapter 5 we learned that a magnetic field has no effect on a stationary charge but that it does exert a force on an electric current, which is nothing more than a stream of *moving* charges. Hence the deflection in this case will depend on the strength of the magnetic field, the charge on the moving particle, and also on its velocity.

By combining the two experiments shown in Fig. 12-6a and b, Thomson was able to get valuable information about his little negatively charged particles, which he named "electrons." Unfortunately, however, he was not able to solve his equations to determine their electric charges, because the deflections of the electron beams depend also on the mass of the electrons, which he did not know. His experiments did give him, though, the "charge-to-mass ratio" for the electron, which he determined to be 1.76×10^{-8} coulombs per gram.

THE CHARGE AND MASS OF AN ELECTRON

This work of Thomson's paved the way for the work of the celebrated American physicist, Robert A. Millikan* (1868-1953), who directly measured the charge of the electron by means of a very ingenious experiment illustrated in Fig. 12-7. The apparatus consisted of a glass vessel filled with air, inside of which a vertical electric field was maintained by means of two charged condenser plates. A cloud of tiny oil droplets was injected into the container by means of an atomizer (which has nothing to do with atoms, but rather with perfumes). This cloud of oil droplets was illuminated by a beam of ultraviolet rays emitted (along with visible light) by an ordinary electric arc. Ultraviolet rays are known to eject electrons from the surface of the materials on which they fall, thus inducing a positive electric surface charge. The tiny oil droplets in Millikan's experiment were expected to carry only a few elementary electric charges, changing their charge in jumps once in a while.

Using a microscope (symbolized by a lens in Fig. 12-7), Millikan would pick up a single oil particle and try to stabilize it in mid-air by applying to the condenser plates the potential that would produce an upward electric force equal to the force of gravity acting on the particle. In doing so, he noticed that, while for a certain period of time the particle would hang motionless in the air, as the legendary coffin of Mohammed, sudden changes of its charge would take place now and then, and a new adjustment of the electric field was necessary. Knowing in each case the strength of the electric field between the plates of the condenser and the weight of the particle, Millikan was able to measure the variable electric charge of his oil droplets. It turned out that the charges he measured that way were all multiples of a certain quantity

---

* There is a standard joke among physicists that the name Millikan should be interpreted as a thousandth of a "kan" (as in millimeter), where "one kan" is a unit of scientific ability (as in: I can).

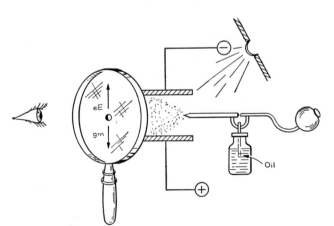

Fig. 12-7. A schematic arrangement of Millikan's experiment for measuring elementary charge.

which was apparently the elementary electric charge, or the charge of an electron. Numerically he found that the value of this elementary charge is 1.6×10^{-19} coulomb, which is in complete agreement with the value of the elementary charge as obtained from the experiments with electrolysis.

From Thomson's charge-to-mass ratio and a direct knowledge of the charge on an electron, the mass of an electron can be computed to be:

$$\frac{1.6 \times 10^{-19}}{1.76 \times 10^{8}} = 9.1 \times 10^{-28} \text{ grams} = \frac{\text{mass of H atom}}{1840}$$

The discovery of the electron as representing a free electric charge and the possibility of its extraction from the neutral atoms was the first indication that *atoms are not the indivisible particles their Greek name implies but complex mechanical systems composed of positively and negatively charged parts.* The positive ions were interpreted as having a *deficiency* of one or more electrons, whereas negative ions were considered as atoms having an *excess* of electrons.

Anode Rays and Isotopes

While the study of cathode rays in Thomson's tube led to the discovery of electrons, *anode rays*, which move in the opposite direction and are formed by a stream of positively charged gas ions, were also very helpful for the understanding of the inner nature of the atom. The mass and electric charge of anode rays can be analyzed by deflecting them in electric and magnetic fields in an arrangement similar to that shown in Fig. 12-6a and b; in fact, that is how J. J. Thomson proved that they are streams of positive gas ions. But the further study of these rays by another British physicist, F. W. Aston (1877-1945), led to results which were quite unexpected. In measuring the mass of the particles forming anode rays in a tube filled with neon, Aston expected to confirm the chemical value of the atomic weight of neon, which was known to be 20.183. However, instead of this value he got only 19.999, which was considerably lower and well beyond the limits of a possible experimental error. This discrepancy was explained when Aston noticed that the beam of neon anode rays passing through the magnetic (or electric) field was not deflected as a single beam but was split into three branches (Fig. 12-8). The particles in the main branch, which contained 90.5 per cent of all the ions, had a mass value of 19.999, but there were also two other fainter branches, one containing 9.2 per cent of the particles and another the remaining 0.3 per cent. Since both of these branches were deflected less by the fields than the main branch, Aston concluded that these beams are formed by somewhat more massive particles, and, performing the exact measurement, found for the values: 21.998 and 20.999.

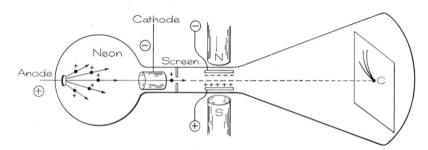

Fig. 12-8. The apparatus of J. J. Thomson that led to the discovery of isotopes. Positive ions of neon were accelerated by an electric field and formed a thin beam after passing through a slit in a screen. The beam was deflected by a combined electric and magnetic field and fell on the fluorescent screen at the far right end of the tube. If all Ne ions had the same mass, though different velocities, the line on the screen would be in the shape of a parabola. But there were three different parabolas corresponding to the masses 20, 21, and 22.

This was quite remarkable! Here were *three kinds of neon atoms, identical in chemical nature and optical spectra, but different in mass.* On top of this, *all three mass values obtained by Aston were almost exactly integral numbers* (20, 21, and 22). Ordinary neon, then, was actually a *mixture* of three neons, and the chemical atomic weight was just an average atomic weight of this mixture (indeed: $20 \times 90.5 + 21 \times 0.3 + 22 \times 9.2 = 20.18 \times 100$). The three different types of neon discovered by Aston were called *isotopes* of this element, which means in Greek "same place" and refers to the fact that all three neons occupy the same place in the periodic system of the elements. We usually denote the isotopes by placing an index indicating the mass at the upper right corner of the symbol of the element in question; thus Ne^{20}, Ne^{21}, and Ne^{22} will be three neon isotopes, while Ne refers to their natural mixture.

Further studies by Aston and his followers have shown that practically every element represents a mixture of several isotopes. While in some cases (as in hydrogen and oxygen) one isotope accounts for almost a hundred per cent of the material, in many other cases (as in chlorine and zinc) different isotopes have comparable abundances. The isotopic composition of some of the chemical elements is shown in Table 12-1.

TABLE 12-1

Atomic Number	Name	Isotopic composition with percentage shown in parentheses
1	Hydrogen	1 (99.985); 2 (0.015)
6	Carbon	12 (98.9); 13 (1.1)
7	Nitrogen	14 (99.64); 15 (0.36)
8	Oxygen	16 (99.76); 17 (0.04); 18 (0.20)
17	Chlorine	35 (75.4); 37 (24.6)
30	Zinc	64 (48.89); 66 (27.81); 67 (4.07); 68 (18.61); 70 (0.62)
48	Cadmium	106 (1.215); 108 (0.875); 110 (12.39); 111 (12.75); 112 (24.07); 113 (12.26); 114 (28.86); 116 (7.58)
80	Mercury	196 (0.15); 198 (10.02); 199 (16.84); 200 (23.13); 201 (13.21); 202 (28.80); 204 (6.85)

The remarkable fact that we notice from this table is that *while the atomic weight of chemical elements is not necessarily an integral number, the weight of individual isotopes is always very close to an integer.* This fact bolstered an important hypothesis that was first proposed a century ago by the British chemist, William Prout, who considered all elements to be some kind of condensation of a single primary element: hydrogen. Prout's hypothesis, proposed very early in the development of scientific chemistry and based on the assumption of the unity of matter borrowed from medieval alchemy, was rejected by his contemporaries, who argued that the atomic weights of chlorine and mercury are far from being integral. Only after Aston's discovery of isotopes was Prout's idea reinstated in its own right, and it became one of the cornerstones of the modern theory of the internal structure of matter.

Thomson's Atomic Model

On the basis of his experiments, J. J. Thomson proposed a model of internal atomic structure (Fig. 12-9) according to which atoms consisted of a positively charged substance (positive electric fluid) distributed uniformly over the entire body of the atom, with negative electrons imbedded in this continuous positive charge like seeds in a watermelon.

Since electrons repel each other but are, on the other hand, attracted to the center of the positive charge, they were supposed to assume certain stable positions inside the body of the atom. If this distribution were disturbed by some external force, such as, for example, a violent collision between two atoms in a hot gas, the electrons were supposed to start vibrating around their equilibrium positions, emitting light waves of corresponding frequencies.

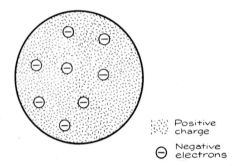

Fig. 12-9. J. J. Thomson's atomic model showing negative electrons floating inside a positive electric "fluid."

Many calculations were made in an attempt to correlate the emission frequencies of electrons in Thomson's atom with the actually observed frequencies of light emitted by different elements, but there was no success. After a number of futile efforts, it became rather clear that although Thomson's model considered an atom to be a complex system formed by positive and negative electric charges rather than an elementary indivisible body and represented a considerable progress towards the truth, it was not yet the truth itself.

Rutherford's Atomic Model

The honor of giving the first correct description of the distribution of positive and negative charges within the atom belongs to a New Zealand-born physicist, Ernest Rutherford (1871-1937) (Fig. 12-4), who was later elevated to the rank of Lord Rutherford of Nelson for his important scientific achievements. Young Rutherford entered physics during that crucial period of its development when the phenomenon of natural radioactivity had just been discovered, and he was the first to realize that radioactive phenomena represent a spontaneous disintegration of heavy unstable atoms.

Radioactive elements emit three different kinds of rays: high frequency electromagnetic waves known as γ-*rays*, beams of fast-moving electrons known as β-*rays*, and the so-called α-*rays*, which were shown by Rutherford to be streams of very fast-moving helium ions. Rutherford realized that very important information about the inner structure of atoms can be obtained by the study of violent collisions between onrushing α-particles and the atoms of various materials forming the target. This started him on a series of epoch-making "atomic bombardment" experiments that revealed the true nature of the atom and led ultimately to the present atomic energy developments. The experimental arrangement used by Rutherford in his studies was exceedingly simple (Fig. 12-10): a speck

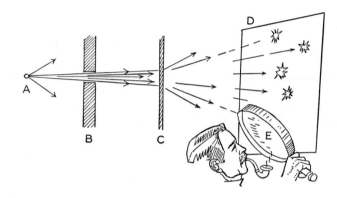

Fig. 12-10. The arrangement used by Rutherford in his "atomic bombardment" experiments.

of α-emitting radioactive material at the end of a pin *A*, a heavy lead diaphragm *B* that cuts out a thin beam of α-rays, the material under investigation in the form of a piece of thin foil *C*, a fluorescent screen *D*, and a microscope *E* to observe the tiny flashes of light, or scintillations, originating when an α-particle hits the screen (and, unavoidably, his pipe). Before the material to be studied was inserted between the diaphragm and the fluorescent screen, scintillations were observed only in a small, sharply defined area immediately opposite the opening of the diaphragm. The introduction of the foil into the path of the α-rays, however, caused a considerable scattering of the original beam with many of the α-particles being deflected by quite large angles, and some of them even being thrown almost directly backwards. Counting, through a microscope, the number of scintillations observed in different directions with respect to the original beam, Rutherford was able to construct a curve giving the relative scattering intensity as the function of the

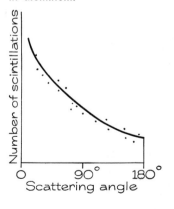

Fig. 12-11. The number of scattered α-particles depends on the angle of scattering in the case of α-rays in aluminum.

angle. One of these curves, pertaining to the scattering of radium α-particles in aluminum, is shown in Fig. 12-11.

Comparing the results of these experiments with the scattering that was theoretically expected on the basis of J. J. Thomson's atomic model, Rutherford noticed at once that something was drastically wrong. In fact, if the positive charge, and most of the atomic mass associated with it, were uniformly distributed through the entire volume of the atom, the collisions between the α-particles of the beam and the atoms of the target could not possibly deflect the incident particles by more than just a few degrees. In order to produce a sufficiently strong electrostatic repulsion between the positive charge of the bombarded atom and the positive charge of the incident α-particle, *all positive charges, along with most of the atomic mass, had to be concentrated in a very small central region of the colliding particles*, a region which Rutherford named *atomic nucleus* (Fig. 12-12). But, if all the positive charge of an atom is concen-

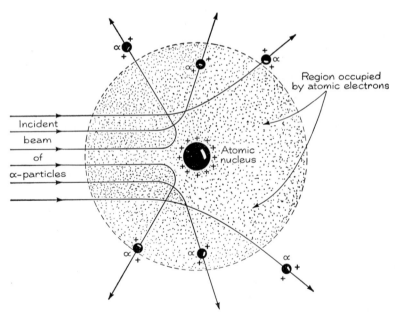

Fig. 12-12. The deflection of α-particles due to the positive charge of the atomic nucleus.

trated in its very center, the main body of the atom must be formed by nothing more than a swarm of negatively charged electrons moving freely through space. In order not to fall into the central nucleus under the action of the forces of electrostatic attraction, the electrons must be rotating very rapidly around the center of the system. Thus, in one bold stroke Rutherford transformed the static "watermelon model" of J. J. Thomson into a dynamic "planetary model" in which the nucleus plays the role of the sun and the electrons correspond to the individual planets of the solar system (Fig. 12-13).

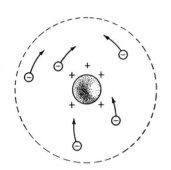

Fig. 12-13. Rutherford's model of the atom.

The strong concentration of atomic mass and positive charge in the very center of the atom not only made possible the explanation of the large scattering angles observed by Rutherford in his experiments but also led to a simple quantitative expression for the number of α-particles scattered in different directions. Since the electrons forming the outer body of the atom are very much lighter than the central nucleus, their role in a collision between two atoms can be completely disregarded, and the scattering problem is reduced to a collision between two mass points that repel each other with a force inversely proportional to the square of the distance. In the case of attractive forces, such as we have when planets rotate around the sun and electrons rotate around an atomic nucleus, the inverse square law of interaction leads to elliptical motion, but repulsive inverse square forces lead to hyperbolic trajectories. A comparatively simple mathematical calculation (which is, however, too complicated to reproduce here) leads to the conclusion that the number of incident particles that are scattered by a certain angle θ must be inversely proportional to the fourth power of the "sine" of $\frac{1}{2}\theta$, a conclusion which stood in perfect agreement with the results of Rutherford's original experiments shown in Fig. 12-11.

NUCLEAR CHARGE AND ATOMIC NUMBER

Rutherford's scattering experiments not only led to the discovery of the existence of the atomic nucleus but also made it possible to measure the amount of positive electric charge carried by it. H. Geiger (1882-   ) and E. Marsden found that the larger the charge of the nucleus, the larger is the repulsive force acting on the incident α-particle, and the larger will be the deflection of that particle from its original path. Thus, by comparing the scattering in different materials of α-particles emitted by the same source, the amount of positive electric charge carried by atomic nuclei could be estimated. These experiments resulted in the extremely important finding that **the nuclear charge of any given element expressed in units of elementary electric charge is exactly equal to its atomic number, which defines its position in the periodic system.** Since, in the normal state, atoms are electrically neutral, the above statement also means that **the atomic number of any given element represents the number of electrons rotating around the nucleus of its atom.** Thus, the simplest of all atoms, the atom of hydrogen, consists of a nucleus carrying a single positive charge and a single electron rotating around it. A neutral helium atom has a doubly charged nucleus and a system of two planetary electrons. If it loses both of these electrons it becomes an α-particle, which is nothing more than a bare helium nucleus. The atom of oxygen has eight planetary electrons, the atom of iron twenty-six, and so on up to the heaviest natural element, uranium, the atoms of which consist of a massive, heavily charged nucleus and a system of ninety-two planetary electrons. Thus, the atomic number, that mysterious number of classical chemistry, received a simple physical interpretation in the light of newly discovered atomic models.

The Electronic Theory of Metals

In the course of this chapter we have discussed the passage of an electric current through liquid solutions of acids and salts and through rarefied gases. In the first case, the current was due to the motion of positively and negatively charged ions, such as Ag^+ and $(NO_3)^-$, shouldering their way through the crowd of water molecules (Fig. 12-2). In the second case, we dealt with positively charged ions flying in one direction and free negative charges, or electrons, flying in the opposite direction (Fig. 12-5). But what happens when an electric current passes through solids, and why are some solids (all of them classed as metals) rather good conductors of electricity while the rest of them, known as insulators, hardly pass any electric current at all? Since in solid materials all atoms and molecules are rigidly held in fixed positions and cannot move freely as they do in gaseous or liquid materials, the passage of electricity through solids cannot be due to the motion of charged atoms or atomic groups. Thus, the only active electric carrier can be an electron, which, being much smaller than the atoms and molecules forming the crystalline lattice of a solid, should be able to pass between big atoms as easily as a small speedboat can pass through a heavily crowded anchorage of bulky merchantmen. Indeed, this is exactly what takes place in metallic conductors. The high electrical conductivity of these substances is inseparately connected with the presence of a large number of free mobile electrons that rush restlessly to and fro through the rigid crystalline lattices (Fig. 12-14). We have seen in Chapter 8 that in metals the atoms are packed considerably tighter than in other substances, and this, among other things, accounts for the relatively high density of metals. As

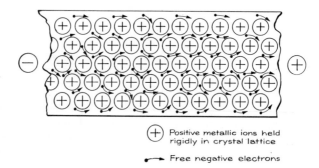

Fig. 12-14. The motion of free electrons explains the passage of electric current through metals.

⊕ Positive metallic ions held rigidly in crystal lattice

•⟶ Free negative electrons

the result of such close packing and squeezing of metallic atoms, some of their structural electrons (about one electron per each atom) get detached from the main atomic body and travel at random through the metallic crystal lattice.

In the case of non-metals such as sulfur (atomic number = 16), each atom holds tightly all of its 16 electrons, and the application of an electric field can cause nothing more than a slight deformation (electric polarization) of the atoms forming the crystal lattice. On the other hand, in the case of aluminum only 12 out of its 13 electrons are retained in each atom while the thirteenth "black sheep" electron is detached from the basic structure and is free to move wherever the applied electric tension urges it to go. Since in metals the transport of electricity is due entirely to the motion of negative electric charges, the direction of the actual physical motion is opposite to the direction conventionally ascribed to the current; *the current that "flows" in a wire from the positive to the negative electric pole is actually carried by electrons that move from the negative pole towards the positive one.* We have here the same mix-up in terminology as we do in terrestrial magnetism, where we find that the north magnetic pole of the earth is located near its south geographical pole and vice versa.

ELECTRICAL CONDUCTIVITY VS. HEAT CONDUCTIVITY

In discussing the electrical conductivity of different metals in Chapter 5, we found a significant parallelism between electrical and heat conductivities. As was demonstrated by Table 5-2, electrical conductivities of different metals are directly proportional to their heat conductivities. This fact clearly indicates that the two phenomena are closely related to each other, and, indeed, the electron theory of metals ascribes their heat conduction to the *diffusion of free electrons* from the heated end of a metallic object to the cooler end. Since the electrons in a metal can move between the atoms forming its lattice with the greatest of ease, the increased thermal agitation existing at the heated end of a metallic object spreads out very quickly towards its cooler end, in contrast to the case of insulators where all electrons are bound to their atoms and thermal agitation propagates through the material only via the interactions between neighboring vibrating molecules.

The electron theory of metals leads to a rather simple mathematical formula for the coefficients of electrical and thermal conductivities. The formula expresses these coefficients through the mass and charge of electrons, their velocity within the metal, and the distance they travel between two collisions with the atoms forming the lattice (the so-called "mean free path"). It turns out first of all that for a given temperature the coefficients of both electrical and thermal conductivities must be proportional to the number of free electrons in the metal in question, from which it follows that **the ratio of thermal and electrical conductivities must be the same for different metals at a given temperature** (the relation which we already mentioned in Chapter 5). Theoretical studies of the motion of free electrons through metals lead further to the conclusion that **the ratio of thermal and electrical conductivities must increase in direct proportion to the absolute temperature of the conductor** and that the coefficient of proportionality must be equal to 3 times the square of the ratio of "Boltzmann's constant" * to the charge of an electron.

These two statements concerning the relation between the thermal and electrical conductivities of metals constitute the so-called *Wiedeman-Franz law* which was found empirically long before the electron theory of metals was formulated. Table 12-2 shows how well this law holds for different metals at widely different temperatures.

The expected numerical value of this ratio calculated from the electron theory of metals turns out to be 2.7×10^{-13}, in good agreement with the empirical values listed in the table. The agreement between the observed and the theoretically predicted correlation between the thermal and electrical conductivities of metals and the absolute temperature is a typical example of how theoretical assumptions about the internal structure of matter increase our understanding of empirically established relations between several, at first sight, unrelated phenomena.

---

* The coefficient of proportionality between the thermal energy of particles and the absolute temperature.

TABLE 12-2   THE RATIOS OF THERMAL AND ELECTRICAL CONDUCTIVITIES
FOR DIFFERENT METALS DIVIDED BY THE CORRESPONDING
ABSOLUTE TEMPERATURES

(All numbers given in the table have to be multiplied by 10^{-13})

Temp	*Copper*	*Lead*	*Metal* *Silver*	*Tin*	*Zinc*
−100°C (173°abs.)	2.39	2.61	2.52	2.76	2.63
0°C (273°abs.)	2.53	2.78	2.56	2.74	2.70
100°C (373°abs.)	2.55	2.76	2.61	2.74	2.56

THERMO-IONIC EMISSION

As we have seen in Chapter 5, the principle of modern electronic tubes is based on the fact that red-hot metallic surfaces emit large numbers of free electrons. This phenomenon (first investigated by the British physicist, Richardson, and sometimes called the "Richardson Effect") is easily explained by the electron theory of metals and is, in a way, similar to the evaporation of liquids. Just as in the case of liquids, where the molecules are normally prevented from crossing the surface by mutual cohesive forces (surface tension forces), free electrons are held inside the metal by electric attraction to the positive ions forming the lattice. But, at sufficiently high temperatures, the kinetic energy of a small fraction of free electrons inside the metal becomes sufficiently high to overcome this surface barrier, and these electrons fly freely into space, to the great delight of physicists and radio-engineers. The temperature at which the "evaporation" of electrons begins to be perceptible depends on the strength of the electric forces holding them in and is different for different metals. As in liquids, where the evaporation process goes easily in ether and alcohol, less easily in water, and quite slowly in heavy oils, we observe different rates of electron evaporation from different metals (fast for cesium, slower for tungsten, and quite slowly for platinum).

Semiconductors

Some materials cannot be classified as either insulators or good conductors; thermal agitation of the atoms can knock loose a few electrons and permit the material to be slightly conductive. Such materials (many of them the "metalloids" of Chapter 10) are known as *semiconductors*. A small amount of the proper kind of impurity in the crystalline structure of a semiconductor may, however, make it enormously more conductive. The three pictures in Fig. 12-15 explain how and why the presence of foreign atoms in the originally completely regular lattice may lead to such a large increase of electrical conductivity.

In Fig. 12-15a we see a pure silicon crystal in which each atom of

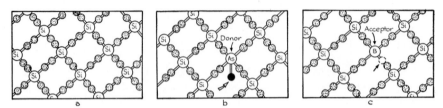

Fig. 12-15. The impurities in the crystalline structure of a semiconductor make the semiconductor very conductive.

silicon, having a chemical valence 4, is connected with four of its neighbors by four electron bonds (it is the same crystal structure as that of a diamond, shown in Fig. 8-16, but is drawn in a plane for the sake of simplicity). Diagram (b) shows the situation that arises when one atom of silicon is replaced by an atom of arsenic, which has a valence of 5. The four valence electrons of the As atom form connections (bonds) with the four neighboring Si atoms, while the fifth "black sheep" electron is left unemployed and free to travel from place to place. The impurity atoms that give rise to free electrons in this way are known as *donors*. A reverse situation occurs when the Si atom is replaced by a trivalent atom of boron (c). In this case there will be a vacant place, or an *electron hole,* that breaks up the spotless regularity of the silicon crystal lattice. The impurity atoms that give rise to such "holes" are known as *acceptors*. A hole formed near a foreign atom present in the lattice may be filled up by an electron originally belonging to one of the neighboring silicon atoms, but in filling this hole the electron will leave a hole at the place where it was originally located. If this hole is filled by another neighboring electron, a new hole will move one step farther out (Fig. 12-16). Thus, we can visualize the hole of that type as an "object" that is moving through the crystal, carrying a deficiency of negative charge, or, what is the same, a positive electric charge. Semiconductors that contain donor atoms and free electrons are known as *n-type* semiconductors, while those with acceptor atoms and holes are called *p-type* semiconductors (*n* and *p* stand for a negative and positive charge of electric carriers). The electrical conductivity of n-type semiconductors is determined by the number of free electrons per unit valence and the ease with which they move through the crystal lattice, while in the case of p-type semiconductors it depends on the number and mobility of the holes.

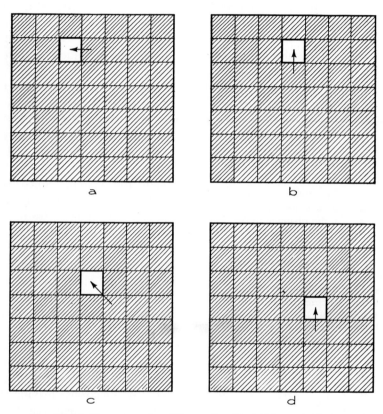

Fig. 12-16. The successive fillings of a "hole" by neighboring electrons (represented by shaded squares) make the "hole" move to the right and downwards.

CRYSTAL RECTIFIERS

Suppose now that we put into contact two crystals: an n-type crystal containing free electrons and a p-type crystal containing electron holes (Fig. 12-17a). Some of the electrons from the n-region will diffuse into the p-region, while some holes from the p-region will diffuse into the n-region. Thus the n-type crystal will become slightly positively charged while the p-type crystal will carry an equal negative charge. Between these opposite charges on both sides of the interface (known as an "n-p-junction") there will be an electric force of attraction which will prevent further diffusion, and the situation will be stabilized with a certain number of holes in the n-type crystal and an equal number of electrons in the p-type crystal. It must be remembered, however, that when free electrons and electron holes exist side by side in a given material, they can be mutually "annihilated" by a free electron filling a hole. In order to compensate for the losses due to this annihilation process, a small number of electrons and holes will continue to diffuse in opposite directions through the n-p-junction.

Let us see what happens now if we apply an electric tension at the two ends of our crystal pair. If the positive pole of a battery is connected with the p-type crystal and the negative pole with the n-type crystal (Fig. 12-17b), there will be a force driving the holes to the right and the electrons to the left, and an electric current will begin to flow through the system. Since both crystals are now being invaded by holes and electrons crossing the border, the rate of mutual annihilation on both sides of the n-p-junction will increase considerably, and more holes and electrons will have to be produced on both sides. These new electrons for the n-type crystal will be supplied by electrons pouring through the wire from the negative pole of the battery, while new holes will be produced by electrons leaving the p-type crystal on their way to the positive pole of the battery.

Fig. 12-17. The motion of electrons and holes across a p-n-junction. (a) In the absence of an electric field, some electrons get into the p-type crystal and some holes into the n-type crystal. (b) If the field is directed from the p-type to the n-type crystal, a continuous electric current will flow through the junction. (c) If the direction of the field is reversed, no current will flow.

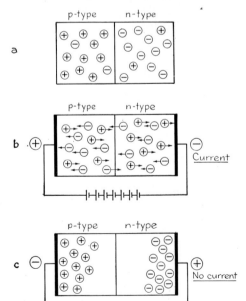

If, on the other hand, we reverse the direction of the electric potential the situation will be quite different (Fig. 12-17c). Now the electrons and the holes will be pulled in opposite directions, leaving a "no-man's land" at the n-p-junction. It is clear that under these conditions no current can flow through our double crystal. Thus we see that our device will conduct electric current in one direction but not in the opposite one. This property of one-way electric conductivity of n-p-junctions permits us to use pairs of n-type and p-type crystals for rectifying alternating current instead of the more complicated electronic tubes described in Chapter 5.

Transistors

We can also use a combination of n- and p-type crystals to carry out the functions of a triode tube described in Chapter 5. Such an arrangement is known as a *transistor* (invented in 1949 by J. Bardeen and W. H. Brattain, and developed in collaboration with W. Shockley), and is shown in Fig. 12-18. It consists of a p-type crystal placed between two

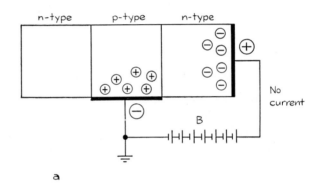

a

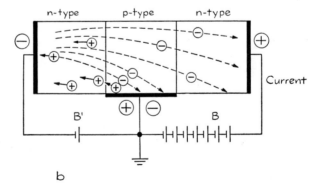

Fig. 12-18. A transistor, involving two n-type crystals and one p-type crystal placed between them.

b

n-type crystals. If we apply to the middle and to the right crystal an electric tension from the battery B in the way shown in Fig. 12-18a, the situation will be identical with that shown in Fig. 12-17c, and no current will flow through the system. Things will change, however, if a small electric tension from the battery B' is applied to the central and to the left crystal in the way shown in Fig. 12-18b. In this case the situation is similar to that shown in Fig. 12-17b, and a current will start to flow through the n-p-junction on the left. However, many electrons entering into the p-type crystal will continue across it and enter into the n-type crystal on the right, thus permitting a current from the battery B to flow through the right n-p-junction. The situation is quite similar to that existing in a triode tube, and the crystal on the left plays the role of the filament, while the middle crystal and the crystal on the right play the role of grid and plate. The principal advantage of transistors over vacuum tubes lies in the fact that the controlled flow of electrons takes place entirely *within solid material.* Thus it is not necessary to use a large amount of power to keep a filament red hot to "boil" electrons off into space. This, in addition to their simplicity, sturdiness, and small size, is rapidly causing transistors to take the place of old-fashioned vacuum tubes in many fields of electronics.

SOLAR AND RADIOACTIVE BATTERIES

The properties of the n-p-junction between two crystals can also be used for the direct transformation into electric energy of both solar radiation and the rays emitted by radioactive materials. The point is that when radiation is absorbed in the material of a semiconducting crystal, it knocks off some electrons from the atoms to which they belong, thus increasing the number of free electrons and electron holes. This increased number of electric carriers disturbs the electrostatic balance at the interface between the n- and p-type crystals and causes an electric current to run from the crystal containing acceptors to the crystal containing donors. A workable solar battery of this kind was recently developed in the laboratories of the Bell Telephone Company. It consists of a silicon crystal with a slight arsenical contamination (donor) through its entire body, except for a thin upper p-type layer (one ten-thousandth of an inch thick), which is contaminated by boron and serves as an acceptor. The sun's rays that fall on the upper surface of this device are absorbed in the material of the crystal, produce extra electrons and extra electron holes, and stimulate an electron potential of about one-half volt. This device has about a 20 per cent efficiency, as compared with only a few per cent efficiency of all previously proposed devices, and it produces a power of about 0.01 watt per cm^2 off its surface. A battery with a working surface of 10 square meters (about 100 square feet) installed on the roof of a house will produce a power of 100 watts, which, when stored in ordinary electric batteries, is sufficient to operate a 100-watt electric bulb at night for the same number of hours that the sun was shining during the day. Because of the present high cost of producing the elements of a solar battery, it would be highly irrational to use it for the purpose of saving on the electric bill, but such batteries will undoubtedly find many useful applications, one of which may be the production of power for running the electric equipment in experimental satellite vehicles.

The principle of the solar battery can be used also for the direct transformation of α-, β-, and γ-rays emitted by radioactive materials, such as fission products (see Chapter 14), into the energy of electric current. If such a device can be constructed with an efficiency comparable to that of the solar battery, the fission products that result from the operation of plutonium-producing piles and various nuclear power reactors could be used to run small household gadgets and devices employed in many other walks of life.

THIRTEEN

ATOMIC MECHANISMS

Ultraviolet Catastrophe

In discussing the properties of light (Chapter 6), we have seen that the radiation emitted by heated bodies represents a mixture of all different wave lengths. An increase in temperature ($T_{abs.}$) results in a rapid increase in the total amount of emitted radiant energy ($\sim T_{abs.}^{4}$) and in the shortening of the prevailing wave length ($\sim T_{abs.}^{-1}$). Comparing the curves showing the distribution of energy at different wave lengths of radiation for various temperatures (Fig. 6-23) with the curves showing the distribution of energy (or velocities) in the molecules of a gas (Fig. 8-7), we can not help noticing a certain analogy between them: in both cases, the curves show a well-defined maximum which shifts its position with the change of temperature.

During the last decade of the nineteenth century, a British physicist (and astronomer), Sir James Jeans (1877-1946), made an attempt to treat the problem of the distribution of energy between different wave lengths of radiant energy in the same statistical way as was done by Maxwell in the case of the distribution of energy between different molecules of a gas (Chapter 8). To do this, he considered the radiant energy of different wave lengths enclosed in a cube, the walls of which are made of ideal mirrors reflecting a full hundred per cent of any radiation falling on them. Of course, this so-called "Jeans's cube" is just an abstraction (since there are no such mirrors) and can be used only for the purpose of purely theoretical arguments; but in physics, we very often use idealized models of this sort.

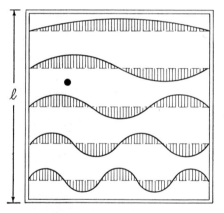

Fig. 13-1. A cross-section of "Jeans's cube," showing the different waves that can exist inside it. Only the waves propagating in a horizontal direction are shown here. The black dot is a tiny coal dust particle.

In Fig. 13-1, we give a schematic picture of Jeans's cube and various waves that can exist within it. The situation is similar to that of the sound waves that can exist inside a cubical enclosure with perfectly reflecting walls. The longest wave has a wave length twice the length of the side l of the cube, and the next possible wave lengths are: 1, $\frac{2}{3}$, $\frac{1}{2}$, $\frac{2}{5}$, etc. of l. We also assume that the box contains one or more "coal dust particles" that are introduced here to permit the exchange of energy between the different modes of vibrations existing in the box. (These particles are supposed to absorb the energy from the vibrations of one wave length and to re-emit it at a different wave length.)

We can now draw an analogy between the different vibrations within the Jeans cube and the molecules of gas contained in a similar cubical enclosure. Just as in the case of the gas where the total available kinetic energy can be distributed in various ways between individual molecules, the total available radiant energy within Jeans's cube can be distributed in various ways between the vibrations of different wave lengths. In Chapter 8, we formulated *the law of equipartition of energy,* according to which all the molecules of gas share equally in the distribution of the total available energy, so that the mean energy of each molecule is simply equal to the total amount of energy divided by the number of molecules in the box. The same kind of statistical considerations led to the conclusion that the total radiant energy in the Jeans cube should be equally distributed between the vibrations of all different wave lengths. But here came a very serious difficulty! Whereas the number of molecules forming a gas, though very large, is still finite, *the number of possible vibrations in Jeans's box is infinite,* since we can continue the above given sequence of possible wave lengths beyond any limit. Thus, if the equipartition law holds in this case, as it certainly should, each individual vibration would get an infinitely small share of the total energy. Since, on the other hand, the sequence of wave lengths continues indefinitely in the direction of shorter and shorter wave lengths, *all the available energy will be concentrated in the region of infinitely short waves.* Thus, if we fill Jeans's cube with red light, it should rapidly become violet, ultraviolet, then turn into X-rays, into gamma rays (such as are emitted by radioactive substances), and so on beyond any limit. What happens to radiant energy in the idealized case of Jeans's cube must also hold for the radiation in all practical cases, and the light emitted by red-hot pieces of coal in the fireplace should be turned into deadly gamma rays even before it leaves the grate! Or, at least, that is what would happen if the laws of classical physics were applicable to radiant energy. This "Jeans's paradox," also known as the "ultraviolet catastrophe," gave a terrible blow to the self-satisfied classical physics of the nineteenth century and catapulted it into an entirely new field of thought and experience—now known as *quantum theory*—unprecedented in the history of physics. Though conceptually difficult, the quantum theory is not insurmountable, even without extensive mathematics; and it is hoped that before finishing this chapter, the reader will acquire a general idea of what it is all about.

The Birth of the Energy Quantum

Just before the close of the last century, in Christmas week, 1899, at a meeting of the German Physical Society in Berlin the young (at that time) German physicist Max Planck (1858-1947) presented his views on how to save the world from the perils of Jeans's ultraviolet catastrophe. His proposal was as paradoxical as Jeans's paradox itself, but it certainly was helpful. In a way, Planck's proposal can be considered as the extension of Democritus' atomic hypothesis concerning the atomic structure of matter to the problem of radiant energy. Following

Democritus, who insisted that matter cannot be sub-divided into arbitrarily small portions and that one atom is the smallest possible amount of matter, Max Planck assumed that *there must exist a smallest portion of energy,* and he gave these smallest portions of energy the name *energy quanta.* According to this revolutionary view, the bright rays of the sun that pour into a room through the windows or the soft light that radiates from a table lamp *do not represent a continuous flow of light waves, but rather a stream of individual "energy packages" or "light quanta"* (Fig. 13-2). To each kind of radiation corresponds a definite amount of energy

Fig. 13-2. The old and the new picture of sunlight coming through the window: (a) old view of light beam as formed by continuous wave trains, *the amplitude* of which increases with the intensity of light; (b) new view of light beam as formed by individual vibrating "light quanta," *the number* of which determines the intensity of light. Both the wave length and the size of the quanta are strongly exaggerated; they are actually only about one micron.

which can be carried in one package, and it is just as nonsensical to talk about three-quarters of a quantum of green light as it is to talk about three-quarters of an atom of copper. Planck assumed that the light quanta of different types of radiation carry different amounts of energy and that **the amount of energy of a light quantum is inversely proportional to the wave length of the radiation, or (what is the same) directly proportional to its frequency.** Writing ν (vibrations/second) for the frequency of the radiation and E for the energy of the light quantum, we can express Planck's assumption in the form:

$$E = h \times \nu$$

where h is the coefficient of proportionality known as *Planck's constant* or the *quantum constant.*

How does Planck's assumption of light quanta help to remove the perils of Jeans's ultraviolet catastrophe? To understand this, in considering the problem of equipartition of energy between vibrations of different wave lengths, let us further assume, as Planck did, that the shorter the wave length (i.e., the higher the frequency) the larger is the *minimum amount of energy* that can be involved in this particular vibration. The situation is represented in Fig. 13-3 where the minimum amount of energy that can be carried by any particular vibration is represented by the shaded area and, according to Planck's assumption, decreases in inverse proportion to the wave length in question. This difference in the demands between the long wave and the short wave radiations makes quite a difference in the application of the equipartition principle. If, for example, six dollars have to be distributed among six persons, none of whom presents any minimum demand, the fairest distribution would be to give one dollar to each of them. Suppose, however, that Mr. A would take no less than $1.00, Mr. B no less than $2.00, and so on up to Mr. F, who would accept no less than $6.00. It would certainly be unfair to give all six dollars to Mr. F and deprive everyone else of any share. It would not be fair either to give $5.00 to Mr. E (his minimum demand) and the remaining $1.00 to Mr. A. Clearly, the most reasonable distribution of the total money available would be to give $1.00 to Mr. A, $2.00 to Mr. B, $3.00 to Mr. C., and to deprive the Messrs. D, E, and F of any share because of their unreasonably high demands.

Well, this is exactly what Max Planck did in the problem of distributing the total available energy among vibrations with different wave lengths existing in an enclosure of a given size. The vibrations with extremely short wave lengths (i.e., with very high frequencies), which presented unreasonably high demands, were denied any share, or rather their demands were satisfied only to a very small degree. The bulk of available energy was distributed among less demanding long wave vibrations, so

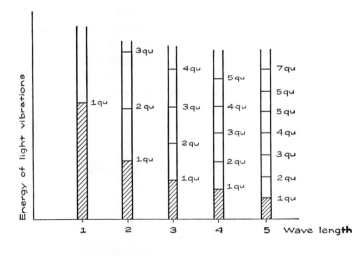

Fig. 13-3. The minimum energy (shaded areas) that can be carried, according to Planck's assumption, by light waves of different lengths. The higher energy marks (2 qu, 3 qu, etc.) represent the possible multiples of the minimum amount.

that instead of looking like the original Jeans curve the distribution curve obtained by Planck took a much more reasonable shape, with the main bulk of energy being given to certain intermediate wave lengths (Fig. 13-4). Further studies of this problem permitted Planck to derive purely mathematically the two thermal radiation laws of Wien and Stefan-Boltzmann mentioned in Chapter 6.

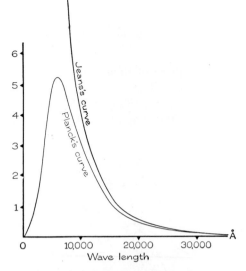

Fig. 13-4. Jeans's curve and Planck's curve representing the dependence of energy on the wave length.

THE PUZZLE OF THE PHOTOELECTRIC EFFECT

A few years after Max Planck introduced the notion of light quanta in order to circumvent the difficulties of Jeans's ultraviolet catastrophe, a new and, in a way, a much more persuasive argument for the existence of these packages of radiant energy was put forward by Albert Einstein. Einstein based his argument on the laws of the *photoelectric effect,* i.e., the ability of various materials to emit free electrons when irradiated by visible or ultraviolet light.* An elementary arrangement for the demonstration of the photoelectric effect is shown in Fig. 13-5. If a metallic plate, *P,* attached to an electroscope is irradiated by ultraviolet rays produced by an electric arc, *E.A.,* the leaves, *L* and *L′,* of the electroscope will gradually separate, indicating the presence of an electric charge. A classical test based on the use of a hard rubber stick (or a galosh) and a woolen cloth (or a fox tail) indicates that this charge has a positive sign, so we conclude that the phenomenon must be due to the emission of (negative) electrons from the surface of the plate. More careful experiments in which we use monochromatic light rays of different wave lengths and also measure the number and the velocities of electrons ejected from the surface of the disc lead to the following empirical rules:

A. For a given wave length of incident light, the number of electrons produced in the photo effect is directly proportional to the intensity of the light, while the velocity of these electrons remains the same.

B. In the case of varying wave length of incident light, the velocity of photo-electrons increases with the decreasing wave length of light, and the relation between these two quantities can be represented graphically by a straight line if we plot the kinetic energy of electrons (i.e., the

---

* This phenomenon has been mentioned before (Chapter 7) in connection with Millikan's method of measuring the elementary electric charge.

square of their velocity) against the inverse wave length (frequency) of light (Fig. 13-6).

Using different metals as the material of the plate, we get different lines in the diagram of Fig. 13-6, but in all cases the lines run parallel and

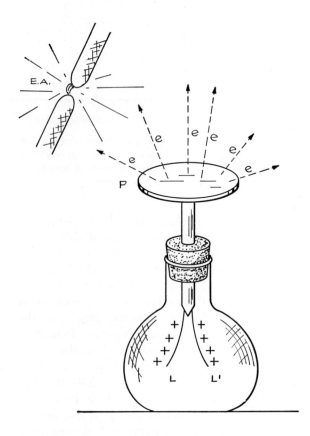

Fig. 13-5. The photoelectric effect experiment.

show only horizontal displacement with respect to each other. In each particular case, no electron emission takes place until the wave length of incident light becomes smaller than a certain threshold (1,980 Å for Pt, 2,640 Å for Ag, 7,100 Å for K, etc.) or, what is the same, until the frequency of the incident light becomes larger than a certain threshold (1.5×10^{15}, 1.1×10^{15}, and 4.2×10^{14} vibrations per second for the metals mentioned above).

These two simple laws of the photoelectric effect presented almost insurmountable difficulties for the understanding of light from the point of view of classical theory. According to the classical point of view, a propagating light wave is essentially a variable electromagnetic field, and the strength of electric and magnetic forces in this field increases with the increasing intensity of light. If the ejection of electrons from the metallic surfaces exposed to light is due to the action of the electric forces of the incident light wave, then the velocity with which these electrons are ejected must increase with the increasing intensity of light, just as in the case when ocean waves sweep up onto the shore bathers are thrown off their feet more violently by big waves than by small ones. However, this

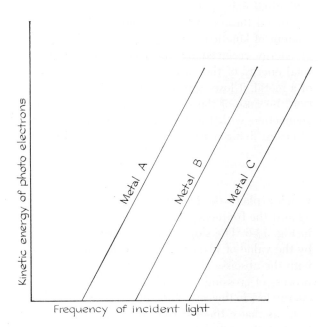

Fig. 13-6. The kinetic energy of photo electrons vs. the inverse wave length (frequency) of light for 3 different metals.

quite natural conclusion does not fit the experimental facts since, as we have seen above, the increase of the intensity of the incident light *increases the number* of ejected electrons *but does not affect their velocity at all.*

EINSTEIN'S LIGHT QUANTA

In his classical paper on this subject, published in 1905, Einstein indicated that the observed laws of the photoelectric effect can be understood if, following the original proposal of Max Planck, one assumes that *light propagates through space in the form of individual energy packages, and that, on encountering an electron, such a light quantum communicates to the electron its entire energy.*

This revolutionary assumption explains quite naturally the observed fact that the increase of the intensity of light leads to the increase of the number of photo-electrons, but not of their energy. More intense light means that more light quanta of the same kind will fall on the surface per second, and, since a single light quantum can eject one and only one electron, the number of electrons must increase correspondingly. On the other hand, by decreasing the wave length of incident light we increase the frequency and, consequently, the amount of energy carried by each individual light quantum, so that in each collision with a free electron in the metal these quanta will communicate to it a correspondingly larger amount of kinetic energy. According to Einstein's hypothesis, the amount of energy received by an electron from the light quantum equals the total energy of the latter, i.e., $h\nu$. When the electron crosses the surface of a metal, it loses a certain amount of energy, W, known as "work function" because of the surface forces which have been discussed already in connection with the Richardson effect. Thus, the energy of the photo-electrons flying out from the surface must be given by the expression:

$$E = h\nu - W$$

which explains the fact that by plotting the energy of the photo-electron against the frequency of incident light we obtain the straight lines shown in Fig. 13-6. The slope of these lines is always the same since it is given by the value of Planck's constant, h, while the intersections of these lines with the abscissa show the amounts of energy W lost by electrons in the process of crossing the surface. Indeed, it turns out that the value of this energy loss in the case of the photo effect on various metallic surfaces is the same as that estimated from the study of thermal electron emission from hot metallic surfaces.

THE COMPTON EFFECT

The Planck-Einstein picture of individual energy packages, or light quanta, forming a beam of light and colliding with the electrons within matter intrigued the mind of an American physicist, Arthur Compton (Fig. 13-7), who, being of a very realistic disposition, liked to visualize collisions between light quanta and electrons as similar to those between ivory balls on a billiard table. He argued that, in spite of the fact that the electrons forming the planetary system of an atom are bound to the central nucleus by attractive electric forces, these electrons would behave exactly as if they were completely free if the light quanta which hit them carry sufficiently large amounts of energy. Suppose that a black ball (electron) is resting on a billiard table and is bound by a string to a nail driven into the table's surface and that a player, who does not see the string, is trying to put it into the corner pocket by hitting it with a white ball (light quantum) (Fig. 13-8). If the player sends his ball with a comparatively small velocity, the string will hold during the impact and nothing good will come from this attempt. If the white ball moves somewhat faster the string may break, but in doing so it will cause enough

Fig. 13-7. Dr. Arthur Compton, who conceived the idea that the interaction between a photon and an electron is analogous to a collision between two elastic balls. The recoiled photon has less energy and a correspondingly larger wave length, as is shown schematically in the picture.

disturbance to send the black ball in a completely wrong direction. If, however, the kinetic energy of the white ball exceeds, by a large factor, the strength of the string that holds the black ball, the presence of the string will make practically no difference, and the result of the collision between the two balls will be the same as if the black ball were completely unbound.

Compton knew that the binding energy of the outer electrons in an atom is comparable to the energy of the quanta of visible light. Thus, in order to make the impact overpoweringly strong, he selected for his experiments the energy-rich quanta of high frequency X-rays. The result of a collision between X-ray quanta and (practically) free electrons can be indeed treated very much in the same way as a collision between two billiard balls. In the case of an almost head-on collision, the black ball (electron) will be thrown at high speed in the direction of the impact, while the white ball (X-ray quantum) will lose a large fraction of its energy. In the case of a side hit, the white ball will lose less energy

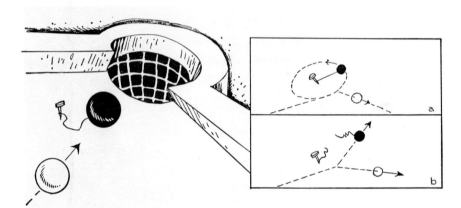

Fig. 13-8. A tied-up billiard ball (black) is hit by a moving ball (white). If the white ball moves slowly (a), the effect of the string will be essential, but if it moves fast (b), the result of the collision will be the same as if the black ball were not tied at all.

and will suffer a smaller deflection from its original trajectory. In the case of a mere touch, the white ball will proceed practically without deflection and will lose only a small fraction of its original energy. In the language of light quanta, this behavior means that in the process of scattering, *the quanta of X-rays deflected by large angles will have a smaller amount of energy and, consequently, a larger wave length.* The experiments carried out by Compton confirmed, in every detail, the theoretical expectations and thus gave additional support to the hypothesis of the quantum nature of radiant energy.

BOHR'S QUANTUM ORBITS

When Rutherford (at that time just plain Ernest Rutherford and not yet Sir Ernest or Lord Rutherford of Nelson) was at the University of Manchester performing his epoch-making experiments that demonstrated the existence of the atomic nucleus, a young Danish physicist named

Niels Bohr (1886-   ) (Fig. 13-9) came to work with him on the theoretical aspects of the atomic structure problem. Bohr was highly impressed by Rutherford's new atomic model in which the electrons revolved around the central nucleus, in very much the same way as the planets revolve around the sun, but he could not understand how such a motion could be at all possible in an atom. While the planets of the

Fig. 13-9. Prof. Niels Bohr taking his wife for a ride on a motorcycle owned by the author, Copenhagen, 1931.

solar system are electrically neutral, atomic electrons are heavily charged with negative electricity (in fact, there is not much more to an electron than its electric charge!). It was well known from the theory of electricity that oscillating or revolving electric charges always emit electromagnetic waves. The emission of electromagnetic waves must result in the loss of energy by the emitting particle, so that the electrons in the Rutherford model were bound to spiral towards the central nucleus and fall into it when all of their kinetic energy was spent on radiation.

Bohr calculated that the emission of electromagnetic waves (which in the case of the atom corresponds to light waves of different lengths) would cause the electrons forming an atomic system to lose all their energy and fall into the nucleus within one hundred-millionth of a second! Thus, on the basis of conventional mechanics and electrodynamics, the planetary system of electrons revolving around the atomic nucleus as visualized by Rutherford could not exist for more than an extremely short period of time. This was in direct contradiction of the fact that atoms *do exist permanently* and do not show any tendency to collapse. How could it possibly be? Bohr's solution of this conflict between the conclusions of conventional mechanics and the facts of nature was straightforward and just: *Since nature cannot be wrong, conventional mechanics must be wrong, at least when applied to the motion of electrons within an atom.* In making this revolutionary statement concerning the motion of electrons within an atom, Bohr followed the precedent established by Planck and Einstein, who had some time before declared that the good old Huygens light waves were not what they were supposed to be according to the conventional views, but rather a bunch of individual oscillating light quanta.

It is always much easier to say that something is wrong than to find a way to make it right, and Bohr's criticism of conventional mechanics in the case of atomic electrons would be of no value whatsoever if he could not show the way out of the difficulty. The way he proposed was so odd and unconventional that he kept the manuscript locked in his desk for almost two years before he decided to send it in for publication. When this epoch-making paper finally appeared in the year 1913, it sent out a shock wave of amazement through the world of contemporary physics!

Defying the well-established laws of classical mechanics and electrodynamics, Bohr stated that in the case of the motion of electrons within an atom the following postulatory rules must strictly hold:

I. From all the mechanically possible circular and elliptical orbits of electrons moving around the atomic nucleus, only a few highly restricted orbits are "permitted," and the selection of these "permitted" orbits is to be carried out according to specially established rules.

II. Circling along these orbits around the nucleus, the electrons are "prohibited" from emitting any electromagnetic waves, even though conventional electrodynamics says they should.

III. Electrons may "jump" from one orbit to another, in which case the energy difference between the two states of motion is emitted in the form of a single Planck-Einsteinian light quantum.

The whole thing sounded quite incredible, but it *did* permit Bohr to interpret the regularities of spectra emitted by various atoms and to construct a consistent theory of internal atomic structure. We will limit our discussion here to the case of the hydrogen atom which contains a single electron revolving around the nucleus. Bohr's original restrictions concerning the motion of the electron in a hydrogen atom pertained strictly to the case of circular motion and demanded that *the "permitted" orbits be only those whose radii were* 2^2, 3^2, 4^2, 5^2, *etc. larger than a certain minimum radius:* r_0. The set of these "permitted" orbits is shown in Fig. 13-10.

Since, according to Bohr's postulate, *the radii of permitted orbits increase as the squares of the integers,* we can conclude from the regular laws of mechanics (or, rather, from what is left of these laws) that *the energy of motion along these orbits decreases as the inverse squares of the integers.*

Now, according to the second of Bohr's postulates, an electron does not emit any radiation while moving along a given orbit but does so when it "jumps" from one orbit to another. Consider, for example, the "jump" of an electron from the third orbit to the second one. Since the corresponding energies are proportional to $\dfrac{1}{3^2} = \dfrac{1}{9}$ and $\dfrac{1}{2^2} = \dfrac{1}{4}$, the energy difference liberated in this jump must be proportional to $\left(\dfrac{1}{4} - \dfrac{1}{9}\right)$. In the case of a "jump" taking place from the fourth, fifth, etc. orbits to the second one, the corresponding energy differences are expected to be proportional to $\left(\dfrac{1}{4} - \dfrac{1}{16}\right)$, $\left(\dfrac{1}{4} - \dfrac{1}{25}\right)$, etc.

Remembering that, according to Bohr's third postulate, the energy liberated in such a jump is transformed directly into a single light quantum and that, according to the Planck-Einstein hypothesis, the energy of a light quantum is proportional to its frequency (i.e., $E = h\nu$), we conclude that *the frequencies of light emitted by a hydrogen atom must be proportional to* $\left(\dfrac{1}{4} - \dfrac{1}{n^2}\right)$ *where n is an integer. But, this is exactly the mysterious "Balmer formula" for the hydrogen spectrum that was discussed in Chapter 6.*

Now let us try to be reasonable! Does this highly artificial picture of light emission by a hydrogen atom really make any sense? Haven't Bohr's three postulates been specially adjusted so as to lead in the end to the

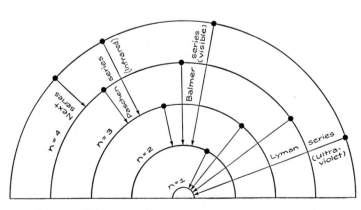

Fig. 13-10. Different series of spectral lines originating in the electron transitions in a hydrogen atom. (The radii of the orbits are not to scale.)

empirically established Balmer's formula? Certainly they were! But this is exactly how a new theory is usually introduced in physics. Newton introduced the notion of universal gravity in order to interpret the observed circular motion of the moon around the earth and the planets around the sun; Dalton introduced the notion of atoms to interpret the observed laws of chemical proportions; and in the very same way Bohr introduced his three postulates pertaining to electron motion in an atom and light emission by "jump" processes in order to interpret the observed laws of atomic line spectra. However, the criterion for the validity of any new theory in physics is not only that this theory should give a correct interpretation of the previous observations but that it also *predict* things which can be later confirmed by direct experiment. In this respect, Bohr's theory of atomic structure came out with flying banners. As we have said above, the theory was constructed in order to interpret Balmer's formula, and this was achieved by ascribing the lines of the Balmer series to the fact that electrons "jump" from various higher orbits to the *second orbit* in the hydrogen atom. But what kind of spectral lines will we get if the electron jumps from the higher orbits to the *first or to the third orbit* in the hydrogen atom? Clearly, in this case the corresponding frequencies should be proportional by $\left(\dfrac{1}{1} - \dfrac{1}{n^2}\right)$ and $\left(\dfrac{1}{9} - \dfrac{1}{n^2}\right)$, respectively. Spectral lines corresponding to the first type of jump (i.e., to the first orbit) were expected to be located in the ultraviolet part of the spectrum and were, in fact, found there by an English spectroscopist, Lyman. The line corresponding to "jumps" to the third orbit have rather low frequencies and were expected to lie in the infrared region where they were actually found by the German spectroscopist, Paschen. The fact that Bohr's atomic model, constructed especially in order to explain the Balmer series alone, leads to further conclusions that were later verified by experiment makes it a *really good theory.*

ELLIPTICAL QUANTUM ORBITS

Bohr's paper in which the notion of quantum orbits of atomic electrons was first introduced caused a cataclysm of publications all over the world, and within a few years the quantum theory of atomic structure developed into one of the most important branches of physics. The first step in this development was the generalization of Bohr's idea of circular quantum orbits in a hydrogen atom for the case of elongated elliptical orbits. This extension of Bohr's scheme was carried out by the German physicist, A. Sommerfeld, and is illustrated in Fig. 13-11. While retaining, unchanged, the first of Bohr's orbits, Sommerfeld added one elliptical orbit to Bohr's second orbit, two elliptical orbits to Bohr's third orbit, etc. Although the elliptical orbits added by Sommerfeld had different geometrical shapes, they nevertheless corresponded to almost the same energies as Bohr's circular orbits (same energy for 2 and 2′, for 3, 3′, and 3″, etc.), so that Bohr's original explanation of the lines of the Balmer series in hydrogen remained unchanged.

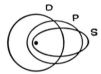

Fig. 13-11. The circular and elliptical quantum orbits in a hydrogen atom, according to Sommerfeld. (The letters represent spectroscopic notations of various types of orbits.)

The purpose of the modification introduced by Sommerfeld was to allow more freedom in choosing the "permitted" orbits in more complicated atoms that contain more than one electron. It was known that for sodium or potassium, for example, the lines of the emission spectrum form a series very similar to the Balmer series of hydrogen, but that in the spectrum each line consists of several closely spaced components called the "multiplicity structure." Sommerfeld explained this multiplicity structure of spectral lines as being due to the fact that, in the presence of other electrons, the energy of elliptical orbits becomes slightly different from that of the circular ones, which results in a corresponding change in the frequencies of light quanta emitted during the electron jumps from one of these orbits to the other.

THE PAULI PRINCIPLE

Since we are now acquainted with all the possible orbital motions of atomic electrons that are permitted by the Bohr-Sommerfeld rules, we can tackle the question of what the combined internal motion looks like in atoms that contain many electrons. Since atomic electrons have a tendency to jump from higher orbits to lower ones, emitting their excess energy in the form of light quanta, the normal state of any atom would be the state in which all atomic electrons move in a "ring around the rosy" along the first of Bohr's orbits. With atoms of increasing atomic number, this ring would become more and more crowded because it would have to accommodate more electrons and also because its radius would become smaller and smaller owing to the stronger electric attraction exercised by the central nucleus.

If this were true, the size of atoms would decrease rapidly with atomic number, and an atom of lead, for example, would be much smaller than one of aluminum. Experiment tells us that this is not so; although atomic volumes show periodic variations, they remain essentially the same throughout the periodic system of the elements. To avoid this congestion of electrons on the innermost orbit, a new postulatory restriction was apparently necessary, and it was introduced by the physicist, W. Pauli. According to what is known as the "Pauli principle," * **any given quantum orbit in an atom can be occupied by no more than two electrons.** Electrons are known to rotate rapidly around their axis like little spinning tops, and the Pauli principle permits two electrons to move along the same orbit only under the condition that they spin in opposite directions.

Electron Shells and Periodic Systems

We are now in a position to find the pattern of electron motion in atoms of elements with various atomic numbers. The element immediately following hydrogen in the periodic system is helium, the atom of which contains two electrons. If these two electrons spin in opposite directions, both can be accommodated on the first (circular) Bohr's orbit, as shown in Fig. 13-12a.

The next element is lithium, with three atomic electrons. Since no place is available on the first Bohr's orbit, the third electron has to be placed on the next higher energy shelf, i.e., either on the second Bohr's circular orbit or on the corresponding elliptical (Sommerfeld's) orbit. A

---

* Called the "exclusion principle" by Pauli himself.

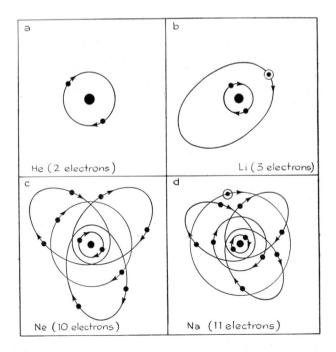

a
He (2 electrons)

b
Li (3 electrons)

c
Ne (10 electrons)

d
Na (11 electrons)

Fig. 13-12. How the electron shells in more and more complex atoms are filled. As the atomic number increases, the electron shells shrink, because of the increased nuclear electric charge, so that the size of the atoms remains on the average constant. Electrons forming the beginning of a new shell are indicated with a circle around them.

detailed analysis of this situation indicates that there are three elliptical orbits of this type, which are identical in shape and in energy but are oriented in space in three different ways, and that the energy of motion along these elliptic orbits is slightly lower than that for the second circular orbit. Thus, the normal state of the lithium atom will be as shown in Fig. 13-12b.

As we proceed along the natural sequence of elements, more and more electrons are placed on the second set of orbits until we reach neon, the tenth element of the periodic system. In neon, eight electrons are accommodated on the second shelf, and the pattern of electron motion within the atom looks as shown in Fig. 13-12c. This shelf of energy or, as physicists call it, "electron shell," is completely occupied, and if there are more electrons, they should be placed on the third shelf (or shell). Thus, the atom of the eleventh element of the periodic system, sodium, will have two completed electron shells (with 2 and 8 electrons, respectively) and one extra electron that is to be accommodated on the third energy shelf (Fig. 13-12d).

An atom of sodium is, in a way, similar to an atom of lithium, since in both cases there is one extra electron moving outside of a previously completed electron shell; this similarity accounts for the similarity of their chemical properties and also of their optical spectra. It goes without saying that the prototype of sodium and lithium atoms is the hydrogen atom itself.

The element following sodium is magnesium, which has two extra

Fig. 13-13. A model showing the orbits of the 92 electrons in a uranium atom.

electrons beyond the completed shell that give it chemical properties similar to those of beryllium. It is followed by aluminum with 3 outer electrons that make this atom chemically similar to boron, and so on until we come to argon. Argon has 18 electrons: 2 in the first shell, 8 in the second, and 8 in the third, which is a very stable configuration. The next element is potassium, which has one extra electron beyond the outer shell of argon and is the fourth member of the H, Li, Na sequence of chemically similar elements.

We see from the above discourse that the combination of the Bohr-Sommerfeld notion of quantum orbits and Pauli's principle concerning the orbital cohabitance of atomic electrons leads to a simple and complete explanation of the periodic properties of the elements in Mendeleev's table. The exhaustive studies of this problem carried out by Bohr and Coster give us an understanding of even such complicated features of the periodic table as the longer (18 step) periods for higher atomic numbers and the existence in it of abnormal "loops" (Fig. 9-2). They also give us a quite reasonable explanation of the observed variation of atomic volume with atomic number. The average constancy of atomic volume is due to the fact that as the number of atomic electrons increases, the previously formed shells shrink in size while the new shells are being formed around them, thus keeping the total volume about the same. For heavy elements containing many atomic electrons, the orbital structure of the atom becomes very complicated, as in the case of uranium shown in Fig. 13-13.

EXPLANATION OF CHEMICAL VALENCE

This view of atomic shell structure gives us a simple explanation of the nature of the chemical valence of different elements. We can show, on the basis of the quantum theory, that atoms which have an almost completed shell have a tendency to take in extra electrons in order to finish this shell and that atoms which have just the beginning of a new electron shell have a tendency to get rid of these extra electrons. For example, chlorine (atomic number 17) has 2 electrons in the first shell, 8 in the second, and 7 in the third, which makes the outer shell short one electron. On the other hand, a sodium atom (atomic number 11) has 2 electrons in the first shell, 8 in the second, and only 1 electron as the beginning of the third shell. Under these circumstances, when a chlorine atom encounters a sodium atom, it "adopts" the latter's lonely outer electron and becomes Cl^-, while the sodium atom becomes Na^+. The two ions are now held together by electrostatic forces and form a stable molecule of table salt. Similarly, an oxygen atom that has two electrons missing from its outer

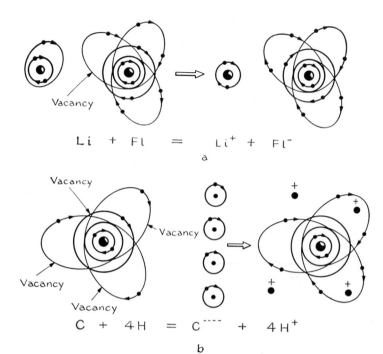

$$\text{Li} \quad + \quad \text{Fl} \quad = \quad \text{Li}^{+} \quad + \quad \text{Fl}^{-}$$

a

Fig. 13-14. The formation of (a) lithium fluoride (single valence of Fl) and (b) methane (quadruple valence of C).

$$\text{C} \quad + \quad 4\,\text{H} \quad = \quad \text{C}^{----} \quad + \quad 4\,\text{H}^{+}$$

b

shell (atomic number $= 8 = 2 + 6$) tends to adopt two electrons from some other atom and can thus bind two monovalent atoms (H, Na, K, etc.) or one bivalent atom such as magnesium (atomic number $= 12 = 2 + 8 + 2$), which has two electrons to lend. Some examples of chemical binding of this kind are shown in Fig. 13-14. It also becomes clear why the noble gases, which have all their shells completed and have no electrons to give or to take, are chemically inert.

De Broglie Waves

Although Bohr's theory of atomic structure was immensely successful in explaining a large number of known facts concerning atoms and their properties, the three fundamental postulates underlying his theory remained quite inexplicable for a long period of time. The first step in the understanding of the hidden meaning of Bohr's discrete quantum orbits was made by a Frenchman, Louis de Broglie, who tried to draw an analogy between the set of discrete energy levels that characterize the inner state of atoms and the discrete sets of mechanical vibrations that are observed in the case of violin strings, organ pipes, etc. "Could it not be," de Broglie asked himself, "that optical properties of atoms are due to some kind of standing waves enclosed within their tiny bodies?" As a result of these considerations, de Broglie came out with his hypothesis that *the motion of electrons within the atom is "guided" by a peculiar kind of waves which he called "pilot waves."* According to these, to say the least, unconventional views, each electron circling around an atomic nucleus must be considered as being accompanied by a wave that runs around and around the electronic orbit. If this is true, the only orbits that would be possible are those whose lengths are an integral multiple of the wave length of the corresponding de Broglie wave. And, indeed, assuming that **the wave length of the "pilot wave" accompanying an electron is inversely proportional to its velocity,** de Broglie was able to show that the first, second, third, etc. of Bohr's orbits in a hydrogen atom have circumferences equal to 1, 2, 3, etc. wave lengths, corresponding to the electrons moving along them (Fig. 13-15). Thus, with one bold stroke, de Broglie reduced the mysterious quantum orbit conditions introduced by Bohr to the more familiar conditions encountered in the case of violin strings, organ pipes, drum membranes, etc.

But, if electrons are really accompanied by these mysterious de Broglie waves while moving along the circular orbits within an atom, the same must be true for the free flight of electrons as observed in free electron beams. And, if the motion of electrons in the beams is "piloted" by some

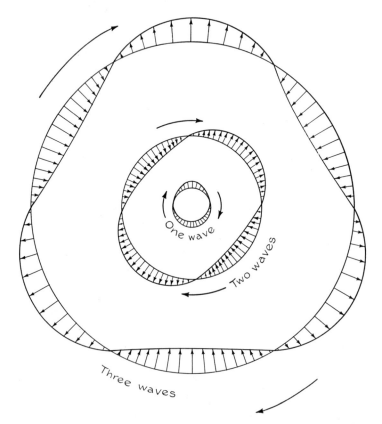

Fig. 13-15. De Broglie's waves corresponding to the first three orbits of Bohr's atom.

kind of waves, we should be able to observe the phenomena of *interference* and *diffraction* of electron beams in the same way that we observe these phenomena in beams of light. In order to get a numerical agreement between his idea of standing "pilot waves" and Bohr's picture of quantum orbits, de Broglie had to assume that **the length of the waves is equal to Planck's quantum constant *h* divided by the momentum (the product of mass *m* and velocity *v*) of the moving particle:**

$$\lambda = \frac{h}{m \times v}$$

For the electron beams used in laboratories, this wave length comes out to be much shorter than that of ordinary visible light and is comparable, in fact, with the wave lengths of X-rays, i.e., about 10^{-8} cm. Thus, it would be futile to try to observe the diffraction of electron beams by

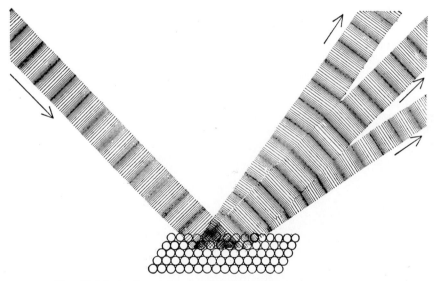

Fig. 13-16. An X-ray beam being reflected by the molecular layers in a crystal lattice. Courtesy *Scientific American*.

using ordinary optical diffraction gratings. We should instead employ a method similar to that used in studying X-ray spectra. To examine X-ray spectra, physicists use a "crystal spectrograph" that was developed by the British physicists, W. H. and W. L. Bragg (father and son), and is shown in Fig. 13-16. A beam from an X-ray tube (left) falls on the surface of a crystal and is reflected successively from the molecular layers that form the crystalline surface. Depending on the angle, the wavelets reflected from different layers may be "in phase" with each other or "out of phase," thus leading to the intensification or to the reduction of the intensity of the reflected beam.

Two American physicists, C. J. Davisson and L. H. Germer, used a similar arrangement in their experiments on electron diffraction, the only difference being that the beam of X-rays was replaced by a beam of electrons, which was accelerated by passing it through an electric field between two grids. The result of Davisson and Germer's experiment gratified their expectations, and they have obtained a genuine diffraction pattern of an electron beam (Fig. 13-17) with the wave length corresponding exactly to the value predicted by the de Broglie theory.

A few years later, a German physicist, O. Stern, repeated the experiments of Davisson and Germer by using a molecular beam of sodium atoms (Fig. 13-18) instead of an electron beam and found that the diffraction phenomenon exists in that case, too. Thus, it became quite evident that in material particles as small as atoms and electrons, the basic ideas of classical Newtonian mechanics should be radically changed by introducing the notion of "pilot waves" guiding material particles in their motion. An intricate mathematical method for handling this kind of problem was worked out by an Austrian physicist, E. Schroedinger,

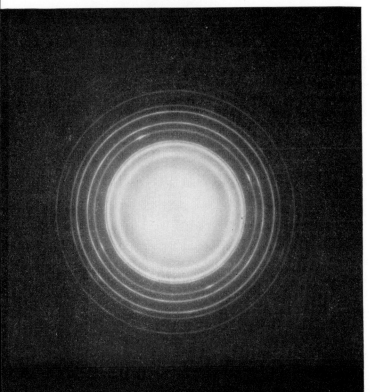

Fig. 13-17. The diffraction pattern of an electron beam. *Courtesy RCA Laboratories, Princeton, N. J.*

and it represents the subject matter of an important but rather difficult branch of modern theoretical physics known as *wave mechanics.*

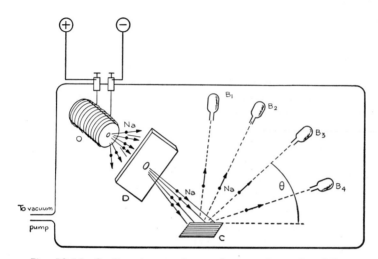

Fig. 13-18. O. Stern's experiment demonstrating the diffraction of a molecular beam. A beam of sodium atoms from the oven, O, is passed through a diaphragm, D, and falls on a crystal, C. The atoms reflected from the crystal in different directions are collected in bottles, B_1, B_2, B_3, etc., and their amounts are measured. The results show a strong maximum in the direction required by the ordinary law of reflection, and a number of secondary maxima corresponding to a diffraction pattern.

THE UNCERTAINTY PRINCIPLE

Now things seemed to be going from bad to worse. First, we had Bohr's "quantized orbits" that looked like railroad tracks along which the electrons were running around the atomic nucleus. Then these tracks were replaced by mysterious "pilot waves" that were supposed to provide "guidance" for the electrons in their orbital motion. It all seemed to be against common sense, but, on the other hand, these developments of the quantum theory provided us with the most exact and most detailed explanation (or description) of the properties of atoms—their spectra, their magnetic fields, their chemical affinities, etc. How could it be? How could an, at the first sight, nonsensical picture lead to so many positive results? Here we have to repeat what was already said in Chapter 7 in connection with Einstein's theory of relativity. Modern physics extends its horizons far beyond the everyday experience upon which all the "common sense" ideas of classical physics were based, and we are thus bound to find striking deviations from our conventional way of thinking and must be prepared to encounter facts that sound quite paradoxical to our ordinary common sense. In the case of the theory of relativity, the revolution of thought was brought about by the realization that space and time are not the independent entities they were always believed to be, but are the parts of a unified space-time continuum. In the quantum theory we encounter a nonconventional concept of *the minimum amount of energy,* which, being of no importance in the large-scale phenomena of everyday life, leads to revolutionary changes in our basic ideas concerning motion in tiny atomic mechanisms.

Let us start with a very simple example. Suppose we want to measure the temperature of a cup of coffee but all we have is a large thermometer hanging on the wall. Clearly, the thermometer will be inadequate for our purpose because when we put it into the cup it will take so much heat from the coffee that the temperature shown will be considerably less than that which we want to measure. We can get a much better result if we use a small thermometer that will show the temperature of the coffee and take only a very small fraction of its heat content. The smaller the thermometer we use for this measurement, the smaller is the disturbance caused by the measurement. In the limiting case when the thermometer is "infinitely small," the temperature of the coffee in the cup will not be affected at all by the fact that the measurement was carried out. The common sense concept of classical physics was that this is always the case in whatever physical measurements we are carrying out, so that we can always compute the disturbing effect of whatever gadget is used for the measurement of some physical quantity and get the exact value we want. This statement certainly applies to all large-scale measurements carried out in any scientific or engineering laboratory, but it fails when we try to stretch it to such tiny mechanical systems as the electrons revolving around the nucleus of the atom. Since, according to Max Planck and his followers, the energy has "atomic structure," *we cannot reduce the amount of energy involved in the measurement below one quantum,* and making exact measurements of the motion of electrons within an atom is just as impossible as measuring the temperature of a demitasse of coffee by using a bulky bathtub thermometer! But, whereas we can always get a smaller thermometer, it is absolutely impossible to get less than one quantum of energy.

A detailed analysis of the situation indicates that *the existence of the minimum portions of energy prohibits us from describing the motion of atomic particles in the conventional way by giving their successive positions and velocities.* Both of these quantities can be known only within certain limits, which, although negligibly small for the large-scale object, become of paramount importance within tiny atomic mechanisms. This uncertainty in the knowledge of the coordinate x and the velocity v of a particle can be expressed mathematically by writing $x \pm \Delta x$ and $v \pm \Delta v$, which means that all we can say is that the value of the coordinate lies somewhere between $x - \Delta x$ and $x + \Delta x$, and that the value of the velocity lies somewhere between $v - \Delta v$ and $v + \Delta v$. The German physicist, W. Heisenberg, has shown that the quantities Δx and Δv are subject to the relation:

$$\Delta x \times \Delta v = \frac{h}{m}$$

where m is the mass of the particle and h the quantum constant which has the numerical value 6.77×10^{-27}. The smaller m is the more restricting is Heisenberg's uncertainty relation. If we apply it, for example, to a particle weighing one milligram (10^{-3} gm), we find that:

$$\Delta x \times \Delta v = 10^{-24}$$

which may mean that if the uncertainty of the position is ± 0.000000000001 cm, the uncertainty of the velocity is ± 0.000000000001 cm/sec. Clearly, such small uncertainties are of no importance! However, using for m the mass of an electron (10^{-27} gm), we obtain:

$$\Delta x \times \Delta v = 1$$

which indicates that there may be an uncertainty of ± 1 cm in the position and ± 1 cm/sec in the velocity. These uncertainties are large enough to make the classical picture of the orbital motion of atomic electrons completely invalid. De Broglie's "pilot waves" give us a new way of describing the motion of atomic particles in which, instead of speaking about their trajectories, we *speak only about the probability of finding the particle in one or another location in space*. In fact, *the intensity of these waves gives us directly this probability*.

Anti-Particles

Up until about a quarter of a century ago, physicists recognized only two kinds of elementary particles from which matter was supposedly built. They were *protons*, the relatively massive particles carrying a positive electric charge, and the much lighter negatively charged *electrons*. But this simple picture was distorted in 1929 by a British physicist,

P. A. M. Dirac (Fig. 13-19), who was at that time busy trying to reconcile the basic principles of the quantum theory with those of Einstein's theory of relativity. On the basis of very abstract theoretical considerations, Dirac came to the conclusion that, apart from the "ordinary" electrons which rotate around atomic nuclei or fly through vacuum tubes, there must also exist an incalculable multitude of "extraordinary" electrons distributed uniformly throughout what one usually calls empty space.

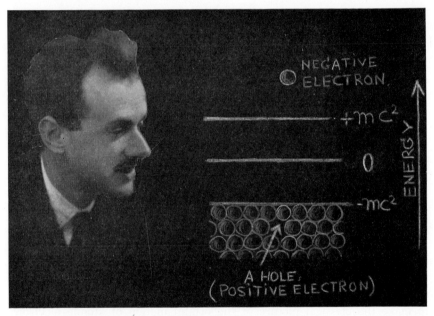

Fig. 13-19. Dr. P. A. M. Dirac, who conceived the idea that "empty space" is actually tightly packed with electrons of negative mass that are inaccessible to any physical observation. We can observe an electron only when it is raised into the region of positive energy (above on the right). The removal of an electron from the continuous distribution forms a "hole" (below on the right) which represents a "positive" electron.

Although, according to Dirac's views, each unit volume of vacuum is packed to capacity with these "extraordinary" electrons, their presence escapes any possible experimental detection. The "ordinary" electrons studied by physicists and utilized by radio engineers are those few excess particles that cause an "overflow" of "Dirac's ocean" (Fig. 13-19, right), which is formed by the "extraordinary" particles, and they thus can be observed individually. If there is no such "overflow" nothing can be observed, and we call the space empty. The nearest simple analogy that may serve to clarify these rather unorthodox views is that of a deep-water fish who never rises to the surface of the ocean. Of course, fish in general do not possess much in the way of brains, but even if they were as intelligent as modern theoretical physicists they would find it difficult to conceive of the idea of a surrounding medium of water provided this medium is completely uniform and (as it is in the case of "Dirac's ocean") frictionless. In a similar way, Dirac's ocean surrounding us on all sides and extending into infinity in all directions remains unobservable to us. In a sense, Dirac's theory brings us back to the old-fashioned idea of the "all-penetrating world ether," but in an entirely new fashion.

In addition to having the property of not being observable by any physical means, these "extraordinary" electrons possess, according to Dirac, a "negative inertial mass," which means that when they are pushed in one direction by any physical force they move in exactly the opposite direction. (Because of an apparent analogy, the author used to call these particles "donkey electrons.") Of course, for a conventional physicist the idea of a "negative mass" seems just as nonsensical as the idea of a vacuum tightly packed by extraordinary electrons, and during the first couple of years after its publication, Dirac's paper was subjected to all kinds of criticism. The criticism stopped abruptly in 1931, however, when an American physicist, Carl Anderson, confirmed by direct observation the existence of the new particles predicted by Dirac's theory.

We have said above that, because of their uniform distribution, the "extraordinary" electrons forming Dirac's ocean are invisible to observation, but what happens if one of these particles is absent, leaving in its place an empty "hole"? (Fig. 13-19.) This "hole" in the uniform distribution of negatively charged particles represents the *lack of a negative charge,* which is equivalent to the *presence of a positive charge.* Thus, the electrical instruments used in our physical laboratories would register this "hole" as a positively charged particle with the same numerical value of charge as an ordinary electron, but with the opposite sign. The reader will recall that the notion of "holes" in the uniform distribution of electrons in semi-conductors led to a successful explanation of their properties (Chapter 12). But, whereas in that case the notion of a "hole" can be readily visualized on the basis of an ordinary picture of the electric nature of matter, Dirac's "holes" belong to a much more abstract physical picture.

It is also easy to see that when experimentalists study the motion of such a "hole" under the action of any external physical force, they will ascribe to it an ordinary positive mass. Returning to our intelligent deep-water fish, imagine that it observes a series of air bubbles rising to the surface from a sunken submarine. Being accustomed to seeing objects in the water moving downward and sinking toward the bottom under the action of the forces of gravity, our fish would be surprised to see these silvery spheres move in the opposite direction; if our fish were intelligent enough, he might be inclined to ascribe to these unusual rising objects a "negative mass." For Dirac's ocean of "extraordinary" negative electrons possessing a negative mass, we conclude that a "hole" in this distribution must possess a mass opposite to that of the particles forming it, i.e., a

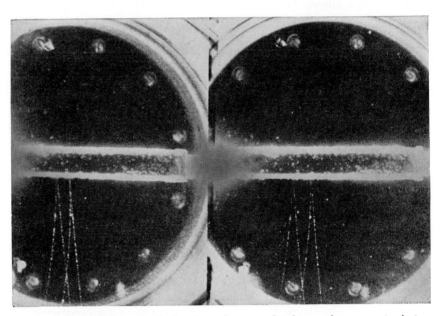

Fig. 13-20. A cloud chamber photograph of two electron pairs being produced in a metal plate by cosmic rays. *Photo by Dr. Carl Anderson, California Institute of Technology.*

positive mass. Thus, through *double negation*, we find that the *"holes"* in *Dirac's ocean must behave as ordinary particles carrying a positive electron charge and a positive mass.* They are called *anti-electrons, positive electrons,* or simply *positrons.*

From what has been said, we can conclude that in order to form a positron we have to remove a negative electron from its place in Dirac's ocean. But when this electron is removed from the uniform distribution of the negative electric charge, it becomes observable as an ordinary negatively charged particle. Thus, *the positive and negative electrons always must be formed in pairs.* We often call this process *"the creation"* *of an electron pair,* which is not quite correct because the pairs of electrons are not created from nothing, but are formed at the expense of the energy spent in carrying out the process of their formation. According to Einstein's famous law of the equivalence of mass and energy $\left(E = Mc^2 \text{ or } M = \dfrac{E}{c^2} \right)$,the energy necessary to produce two electronic masses is equivalent to 1 million electron-volts. Thus, if we irradiate matter with gamma rays of this and higher energies, we should be able to induce the formation of pairs of positive and negative electrons. The electron pairs discovered by Anderson were produced in atmospheric air, and also in metal plates placed in a detecting cloud chamber, by the high-energy gamma radiation that forms the so-called cosmic rays which fall on the earth from interstellar space (Fig. 13-20). Following this discovery, physicists learned to produce electron pairs by irradiating different materials by the high-energy gamma rays that are emitted by natural radioactive substances.

The opposite of the "creation" of an electron pair is the "annihilation" of a positive electron in a collision with an ordinary negative electron. According to the above described picture, the annihilation process occurs when an ordinary negative electron, which moves "above the rim" of the completely filled Dirac's ocean, finds a "hole" in the distribution and falls into it. In this process the two individual particles disappear, giving rise to gamma radiation with a total energy equivalent to the vanished mass radiating from the place of encounter. Dirac's original theory of "holes" not only predicted the existence of positive electrons before their experimental discovery but also gave an excellent mathematical apparatus for calculating the probabilities of the formation of electron pairs under different circumstances, as well as the probability of their annihilation in casual encounter. All the predictions of this theory stand in perfect agreement with experimental evidence.

FOURTEEN

NUCLEAR PHYSICS

The Discovery of Radioactivity

As is the case with so many other discoveries, the discovery of the phenomenon of radioactivity was purely accidental. It was discovered in 1896 by a French physicist, A. H. Becquerel (1852-1908), who was interested at that time in the phenomenon of fluorescence, i.e., the ability of certain substances to transform the ultraviolet radiation that falls on them into visible light. In one of the drawers of his desk Becquerel kept a collection of various minerals that he was going to use for his studies, but because of other pressing matters, the collection remained untouched for a considerable period of time. It happened that in the drawer there were also several unopened boxes of photographic plates, and one day Becquerel took one of the boxes in order to photograph something or other. When he developed the plates he was disappointed to find that they were badly fogged, as if previously exposed to light. A check on other boxes showed that they were in the same poor condition, which was difficult to understand since all the boxes were sealed and the plates inside were wrapped in thick black paper. What could be the cause of this mishap? Could it have something to do with one of the minerals in the drawer? Being of an inquisitive mind, Becquerel investigated the situation and was able to trace the guilt to a piece of uranium ore labeled "Pitchblende from Bohemia." The reader must take into account, of course, that at that time the name "uranium" was not in vogue as it is today, and that, in fact, only a very few people, even among scientists, had ever heard about that comparatively rare and not very useful chemical element. But the ability of a uranium compound to fog photographic plates through a thick cardboard box and a layer of black paper rapidly brought this obscure element to a prominent position in physics.

The existence of penetrating radiation that could pass through layers of ordinarily opaque materials as if they were made of clear glass was a recognized fact at the time of Becquerel's discovery. In fact, only a year earlier (1895) a German physicist, Wilhelm Roentgen (1845-1923), discovered what are now known as X-rays, which can penetrate equally well through cardboard, black paper, or the human body. Although special high-tension equipment is required to produce X-rays, the radiation discovered by Becquerel was flowing quite steadily and without any external excitation from the piece of uranium ore resting in his desk. What could be the origin of this unusual radiation? Why was it specifically associated with the element *uranium* and, as found by further studies, with two other heavy elements known as *thorium* and *actinium?*

The early studies of the newly discovered phenomenon, which was called "radioactivity," showed that the emission of mysterious radiation was completely unaffected by physical or chemical conditions. We can stick a radioactive element into a very hot flame or drop it into liquid air without the slightest effect on the intensity of the mysterious radiation it emits. No matter whether we have pure metallic uranium, or its oxide, which is contained in pitchblende, the radiation flows out at a rate proportional to the amount of uranium in the sample. These facts ruled out any possibility of ascribing the phenomenon of radioactivity to any kind of chemical properties of this element, and led the early investigators to the conclusion that *the phenomenon of radioactivity is the intrinsic property of the atoms of these peculiar elements and that its cause must be deeply rooted in the atomic interior.*

ALPHA, BETA, AND GAMMA RAYS

In order to study the nature of the newly discovered radiation, Becquerel arranged the following very simple experiment. He placed a small amount of uranium in a deep hole made in a lead block (Fig. 14-1), so

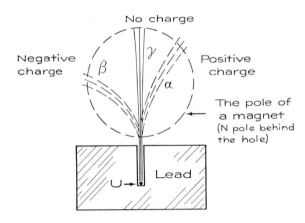

Fig. 14-1. Becquerel's experiment demonstrating the existence of alpha, beta, and gamma rays.

that only a thin beam of radiation emerged from the groove. He also placed a magnet over the block in such a way that the magnetic lines of force were running perpendicular to the direction of the emerging beam. Under these conditions, we could expect three different results:

If the radiation emitted by uranium is formed by short electromagnetic waves similar to X-rays, no deflection should take place.

If, on the other hand, the radiation were formed by fast-moving electric particles, like the cathode and anode rays in J. J. Thomson's tube, the beam should be deflected to the left in the case of a negative charge and to the right in the case of a positive one.

In Becquerel's experiment all three things happened, and the original beam emerging from the hole split into three parts. The part that consisted of particles carrying a positive charge was named α-rays and was later proved (by Rutherford) to be a stream of doubly ionized helium atoms, i.e., a stream of helium nuclei. The part consisting of negatively charged particles, which turned out to be ordinary electrons, was named β-rays, whereas the undeflected beam formed by short-wave electromagnetic radiation similar to X-rays received the name of γ-rays.

MADAME CURIE AND RADIUM

The discovery of Becquerel attracted the attention of Polish-born Marie Curie (1867-1934) (Fig. 14-2), the wife of the French physicist,

Pierre Curie. She suspected that the radioactivity of uranium ores might, to a large extent, be due to some other chemical element which, being much more active than uranium, is however present in uranium ores in very small quantities. Being an experienced and laborious chemist, Madame Curie decided to try to separate this unknown element from uranium ores by a painstaking method known as "chemical fractioning," through the maze of which Madame Curie was led by the "Theseus' Thread" of the radiation emitted by the atoms of this mysterious element. Carload upon carload of "Pitchblende from Bohemia" went through Madame Curie's chemical kitchen where careful processing took place, and only the fractions of material emitting radiation were retained. Finally, after years of exhausting work, this herculean job culminated in brilliant success: Madame Curie obtained a few milligrams of a pure element that was a million times more active than uranium itself. She christened this new element "radium," and its number in the periodic system of elements was 88.

Fig. 14-2. Madame Curie as pictured on a Polish postage stamp. **Courtesy** *Johns Hopkins Magazine.*

The discovery of radium, however, did not deprive uranium of its role as the paternal element in this family of radioactive substances, although for almost half a century its position was overshadowed by the glory of radium. Uranium was mentioned comparatively rarely on the pages of scientific periodicals until it made the headlines in all the newspapers of the world after the detonation of the so-called atomic bomb.

The Families of Radioactive Elements

Radioactivity, observed by Becquerel in uranium and its compounds, turned out to be a composite effect that was due to the presence of a large number of radioactive elements, including radium and uranium themselves. In fact, the studies by the British physicist, Soddy, and his famous collaborator, Rutherford, have shown that this mixture contained over a dozen individual elements, which were given such peculiar names as: uranium X_1 and uranium X_2, ionium, radium emanation, radium A, B, C, D, and E, and finally polonium (or radium F), which was discovered by Madame Curie and named by her after her native country. *The puzzling process of the radioactivity of heavy elements was interpreted by Rutherford to be the result of the transformation of unstable chemical elements into one another in fulfillment of the dreams of the medieval alchemists. The α- and β-particles associated with radioactive transformation were shown to be the fragments of atomic nuclei ejected during the breaking-up process.*

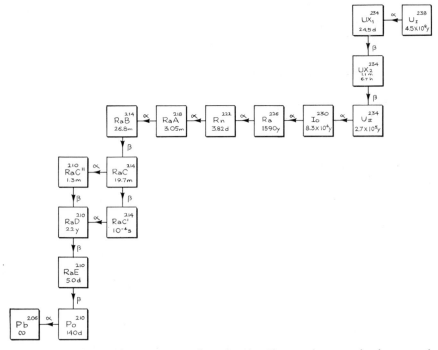

Fig. 14-3. The uranium-radium family. The numbers at the bottom of the squares give the halflife periods in years (y), days (d), hours (h), minutes (m), and seconds (s). Notice the forking (αβ or βα) at RaC.

In the so-called uranium family, which also includes radium, uranium plays the role of the head of the family, and, being very long-lived, produces numerous children, grandchildren, great grandchildren, etc. The genealogy of the uranium family is shown in Fig. 14-3. An atom of

UI, the father of the family (atomic number 92, atomic weight 238), emits an α-particle and is transformed into the atom of so-called UX_1. Since the α-particle carried away two units of electric charge and four units of mass, UX_1 has an atomic number of only 90 and an atomic weight of 234. The next step in the family tree is the emission of an electron (β-particle) by UX_1 which turns it into a UX_2 atom with atomic number 91 (because a *negative* electric charge was emitted) and the same atomic weight, 234 (because the mass of the emitted electron is negligibly small). The next step is the emission of another β-particle by UX_2 which turns it into UII with the same atomic number as UI, but four units of mass lighter. The following α-emission leads to ionium (atomic number 90, atomic weight 230), etc., etc. After seven α-emissions and six β-emissions, we arrive at a polonium atom, which emits an eighth α-particle and turns into an atom of lead (Pb) with atomic number $92 - 8 \times 2 + 6 \times 1 = 82$, and atomic weight $238 - 8 \times 4 = 206$. The nuclei of Pb^{206} are stable and no further radioactive transformations take place.

Genealogically speaking, the thorium and actinium families are very similar to that of uranium and terminate with stable lead isotopes Pb^{208}, and Pb^{207}, respectively. It may also be mentioned that, apart from these radioactive families, which include the heaviest elements of the periodic system and are transformed by a series of intermittent α- and β-decays into isotopes of lead, there are also a few lighter elements that go through a one-step transformation. These include samarium (Sm^{148}), which emits α-rays and turns into stable Nd^{144}, and two β-emitters, potassium (K^{40}) and rubidium (Rb^{87}), which turn into stable isotopes of calcium (Ca^{40}) and strontium (Sr^{87}).

DECAY ENERGIES

The velocities of α-particles emitted by various radioactive elements range from 0.98×10^9 cm/sec for samarium 148 up to 2.06×10^9 cm/sec for ThC′, which corresponds to kinetic energies of from 3.2 to 14.2×10^{-6} erg. The energies of β-particles and γ-quanta are somewhat smaller but of the same general order of magnitude. These energies are considerably higher than the energies encountered in ordinary physical phenomena. For example, the kinetic energy of thermal motion, even at such a high temperature as 6,000°K (surface temperature of the sun), is only 1.25×10^{-12} erg., i.e., several million times smaller than the energies involved in radioactive decay.

In speaking about the energies liberated in radioactive transformations, nuclear physicists customarily use a special unit known as one *electron-volt*. This unit is defined as *the energy gained by a particle carrying one elementary electric charge* (no matter whether it is an electron or any singly-charged positive or negative ion) *when it is accelerated by an electric field with a potential difference of one volt.* Thus, the electrons accelerated in J. J. Thomson's tube, with 5,000 volts applied between the anode and cathode, acquire by this definition the energy of 5,000 electron-volts, or 5 kilo-electron-volts. On the other hand, the energy of a doubly-charged oxygen ion, O^{++}, accelerated by the same electric field, will be 10 kilo-electron-volts, since the electric force acting on the ions and consequently the work done by it is twice as large. Remembering the value of an elementary electric charge (1.6×10^{-19} coulombs or 4.80×10^{-10} cgs units) and the definition of a volt ($\frac{1}{300}$ cgs units), we find that *one electron-volt of energy is equal to 1.6×10^{-12} erg.*

Half Lifetimes

As was mentioned above, the process of radioactive decay is ascribed to some kind of intrinsic instability of the atomic nuclei of certain chemical elements (especially those near the end of the periodic table), which results from time to time in a violent break-up and the ejection from the nucleus of either an α-particle or an electron. The nuclei of different radioactive elements possess widely varying degrees of internal instability.

While in some cases (such as uranium) radioactive atoms may remain perfectly stable for billions of years before breaking up, in other cases (such as RaC′) they can hardly exist longer than a small fraction of a second. The break-up process of unstable nuclei is a purely statistical process, and we can speak of the "mean lifetime" of any given elements in just about the same sense as insurance companies speak of the mean life expectancy of the human population. The difference is, however, that, whereas in the case of human beings and other animals the chance of decaying (i.e., dying) remains fairly low up to a certain age and becomes high only when the person grows old, radioactive atoms have the same chance of breaking up no matter how long it has been since they were formed (by the decay of the previous element in the family). Since radioactive atoms begin to die out at the very moment of their birth, the decrease of their number with time is different from the corresponding decrease of the number of living individuals (Fig. 14-4a and b). In the latter case, the curve of surviving individuals runs first almost horizontally and becomes steep later only when the organism begins to wear out, but the radioactive decay curve is steep all the time.

The number of decaying radioactive atoms is proportional to the number of atoms available, but is quite independent of the initial age of these atoms.

The situation resembles that existing on a battlefield where any of the soldiers can be killed with equal chances any day of the campaign, while the cases of natural death, which depend on the soldier's age, are of very small importance. The time period during which the initial number is reduced to one-half is known as the "halflife period" of the element. At the end of twice that period only a quarter of the original amount

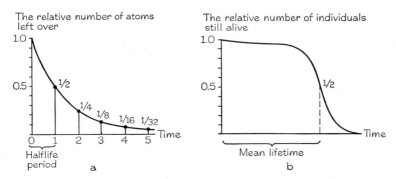

Fig. 14-4. A comparison of the survival curve for radioactive atoms and for living individuals.

will be left; at the end of three halflife periods only one-eighth will be left, etc.

As we have seen above, various elements possess widely different lifetimes (Fig. 14-3). While the halflife of U^{238} is 4.5 billion years, which accounts for its presence in nature in spite of the fact that all atoms of both stable and unstable elements were formed about five billion years ago, the halflife of radium is only 1,620 years, and the 200 mg of radium separated in 1898 by Marie and Pierre Curie now weighs only 195 mg. The short-lived atoms of RaC′ exist, on the average, for only 0.0001 sec between the moment they are formed by β-emission of RaC and their transformation into RaD atoms.

URANIUM-LEAD DATING

The decay of radioactive elements and its complete independence of physical and chemical conditions gives us an extremely valuable method for estimating the ages of old geological formations. Suppose we pick up a rock from a shelf in a geological museum that is marked as belonging to the late Jurassic era, that is, to the period of the earth's history when gigantic lizards were the kings of the animal world. Geologists can tell approximately how long ago this era was by studying the thicknesses of various prehistoric deposits and by comparing them with the estimated rates of the formation of sedimentary layers (see Chapter 16), but the data obtained by this method are rather inexact. A much more exact and reliable method, based on the study of the radioactive properties of igneous rocks, was proposed by Joly and Rutherford in 1913 and soon became universally accepted in historical geology. We have seen above that uranium is the father of all other radioactive elements belonging to its family and that the final product of all these disintegrations is a stable isotope of lead, Pb^{206}.

The igneous rock of the Jurassic era that now rests quietly on a museum shelf must have been formed as a result of some violent volcanic eruption of the past when molten material from the earth's interior was forced up through a crack in the solid crust and flowed down the volcanic slopes, spreading horror and panic among the dinosaurs, tyrannosaurs, and other saurs living in the neighborhood. The erupted molten material soon solidified into rock that did not change essentially for millions of years. But, if that piece of rock had a small amount of uranium imbedded in it, as rocks often do, the uranium would decay steadily, and the lead resulting from that decay would be deposited at the same spot. The longer the time since the solidification of the rock, the larger would be the relative amount of the deposited lead with respect to the left-over uranium. Thus, by measuring the uranium-to-lead ratio in various igneous rocks, we can obtain very exact information concerning the time of their origin and the age of the geological deposits in which they were found. These data are used in giving the time scale in the geological chart in Fig. 16-4.

Similar studies can be carried out by using the rubidium inclusions in old rocks and measuring the ratio of left-over rubidium to the deposited strontium. This method has an advantage over the uranium-lead method because we deal here with a single transformation instead of the long sequence of transformations in the uranium family. In fact, one of the members of the uranium family is a gas (radium emanation or radon) and could partially diffuse away from its place of their formation, thus leading to an underestimation of the age of the rocks.

CARBON DATING

Apart from the above mentioned natural radioactive elements, which are presumably as old as the universe itself, we find on the earth a number of radioactive elements that are being continuously produced in the terrestrial atmosphere by cosmic ray bombardment. Among these, the most interesting is the heavy isotope of carbon, C^{14}, which is produced from atmospheric nitrogen by a high-energy neutron impact (N^{14} + neutron → C^{14} + proton) and incorporated into the molecules of atmospheric carbon dioxide. Since plants use atmospheric carbon dioxide for their growth, radioactive carbon is incorporated into each plant's body, making all plants slightly radioactive throughout their life.

As soon as a tree is cut or falls down, and all of the metabolic processes stop in its body, however, no new supply of C^{14} is available, and the amount of radioactive carbon in the wood gradually decreases as time goes on. Since the halflife of C^{14} is 5,700 years, the decay will last for many millennia, and by measuring the ratio of C^{14} to C^{12} in old samples of wood we are able to estimate rather exactly the dates of origin. The studies in this direction were originated by an American physicist, W. Libby (1908-), and are playing the same role in the exact dating of ancient human history as the measurement of the uranium-lead ratio in the dating of the history of our globe. The measurement of C^{14} radioactivity in old samples of wood is a very delicate matter since it is usually much weaker than the radioactivity of the background surrounding the object (the experimenter himself has a higher C^{14} concentration than the piece of wood he is studying) and cosmic rays. Thus, the sample under investigation must be heavily shielded, and a very sensitive Geiger counter must be used. In Fig. 14-5 we give a few examples of the measured and expected concentrations of radioactive carbon in various wooden objects of known age. Using these data and measuring the C^{14} concentration in wooden objects of unknown age, we can easily estimate their ages. Some examples of such estimates are given in Table 14-1.

TABLE 14-1

1. Lake mud from Knock nac ran, Ireland.   Age: 11,310 ± 720
2. Wood from the bottom deposits of Lake Kickapoo, Illinois.   Age: 13,842 ± 780
3. Charcoal from Lascaux Cave near Les Eyzies, France.   Age: 15,516 ± 900
4. Wood from the woody layer at the bottom of the sand and
gravel deposit at Dyer, Indiana.   Age: 18,500 ± 500

TRITIUM DATING

Another interesting method of dating by the use of radioactive materials, which was also worked out by W. Libby, utilizes the radioactivity of tritium, i.e., the heavy unstable isotope of hydrogen with atomic weight 3. Tritium is also produced in the terrestrial atmosphere under the action of cosmic radiation and is precipitated to the surface by rains. However, tritium's halflife is only 12.5 years, so that all age measurements involving this isotope can be carried out only for comparatively recent dates. It seems that the most interesting application of the tritium dating method is in the study of the movements of water masses, both in ocean currents and in underground waters, since by taking samples of water from different locations and from different depths, we can tell

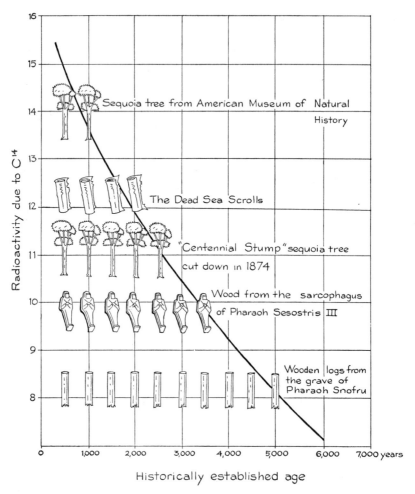

Fig. 14-5. The radioactivity, due to C^{14}, of various old objects as the function of their age, measured by Dr. W. Libby. Each symbol represents 500 years of age.

by their tritium content how long ago this water came down in the form of rain.

Samples of old water are more difficult to collect than samples of old wood, and Libby resolved this problem by analyzing the tritium content in the wine of different vintages, originating in different countries. The unpleasant part of this task is that an entire case of a fine wine has to be

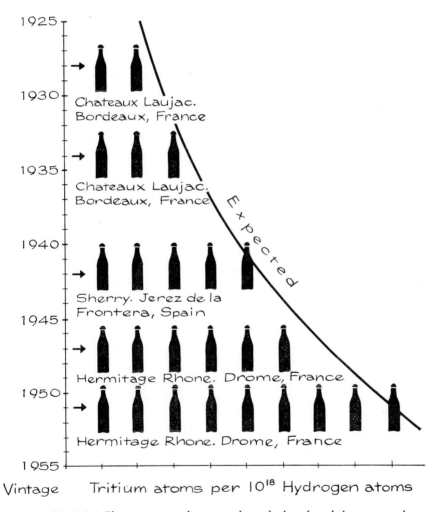

Fig. 14-6. The agreement between the calculated and the expected relationship of radioactivity vs. age in various wines.

used for each measurement and is rendered undrinkable in the process. But the agreement with the expected tritium content was in all cases excellent, as demonstrated in Fig. 14-6.

Splitting of Atomic Nuclei

After Rutherford became completely persuaded that the radioactive decay of heavy elements is due to the intrinsic instability of their atomic nuclei, his thought turned to the possibility of producing the artificial decay of lighter and normally stable nuclei by subjecting them to strong external forces. True enough, it was well known at that time that the rates of radioactive decay are not influenced at all by high temperatures or by chemical interactions, but this could be simply because the energies involved in thermal and chemical phenomena are much too small as compared with the energies involved in the nuclear disintegration phenomena. While the kinetic energy of thermal motion (at a few thousand degrees) as well as the chemical energy of molecular binding are of the order of magnitude of only 10^{-12} erg (see Chapter 8), the energies involved in radioactive decay are of the order of 10^{-6} erg, i.e., a million times higher. Thus, in order to have any hope of a positive outcome, the light stable nuclei must be subjected to a much stronger external agent than just a high temperature or a chemical force, and the bombardment of light nuclei by high-energy particles ejected from the unstable heavy nuclei was the natural solution of the problem.

Following this line of reasoning, Rutherford directed a beam of α-particles emanating from a small piece of radium against a thin layer of nitrogen gas and observed, to his complete satisfaction, that besides the α-particles that passed the layer and were partially scattered in all directions, there were also a few high-energy protons (i.e., the nuclei of hydrogen) that were presumably produced in the collisions between the onrushing α-projectiles and the nuclei of nitrogen atoms. The energy measurements of the protons produced in this experiment indicated that the α-particles that penetrated the nitrogen nuclei and ejected the protons could not get out themselves and must have been detained by the nuclei. The capture of an α-particle followed by the ejection of a proton increases the atomic number of the nucleus in question by one unit ($+2 - 1 = +1$) and its mass by three units ($+4 - 1 = +3$), transforming the original nitrogen atom $_7N^{14}$ into an atom $_8O^{17}$ of the heavier isotope of oxygen. We can express this reaction by the "alchemical" formula:

$$_7N^{14} + _2He^4 \longrightarrow _8O^{17} + _1H^1$$

Following this original success, Rutherford was able to produce the artificial transformation of other light elements such as aluminum, but the yield of protons produced by α-bombardment rapidly decreased with the increasing atomic number of the target material, and he was not able to observe any ejected protons for elements heavier than argon (atomic number 18).

PHOTOGRAPHING NUCLEAR TRANSFORMATIONS

The study of nuclear transformations was considerably facilitated by the ingenious invention of still another Cavendish physicist, C. T. R. Wilson.* This device, known as the "Wilson chamber" or "cloud chamber," permits us to obtain a snapshot showing the tracks of individual nuclear projectiles heading for their targets and also the tracks of various fragments formed in the collision. It is based on the fact that whenever an electrically charged fast-moving particle passes through the air (or any other gas), it produces ionization along its track. If the air through which these particles pass is saturated with water vapor, the ions so produced serve as the centers of condensation for tiny water droplets, and we see long thin tracks of fog stretching along the particles' trajectories. The scheme of a cloud chamber is shown in Fig. 14-7. It consists of a metal cylinder, C, with a transparent glass top, G, and a piston, P, the upper surface of which is painted black. The air between the piston and the glass top is initially almost saturated with water vapor and is brightly illuminated by a light source, S, through a side window, W. Suppose now that we have a small amount of radioactive material on the end of a needle, N, which is placed near the opening, O.

The particles that are ejected by the radioactive atoms will fly through the chamber ionizing the air along their paths. However, since the air is not quite saturated with water vapor, no condensation occurs, and the positive and negative ions produced by the passing particles recombine rapidly into neutral molecules. Suppose, however, that the piston is pulled rapidly down for a certain distance. The expansion of the air enclosed between the piston and the glass top will lower the air's temperature and will cause the condensation of water vapor in the very same way that clouds are formed as a result of rising streams of humid air in the terrestrial atmosphere. But, since the condensation of water vapor is considerably helped by the presence of ions produced by the charged particles passing through the chamber at this moment, the fog formation will take place along the particles' tracks, and thin, long streaks of fog will

Fig. 14-7. A cloud chamber.

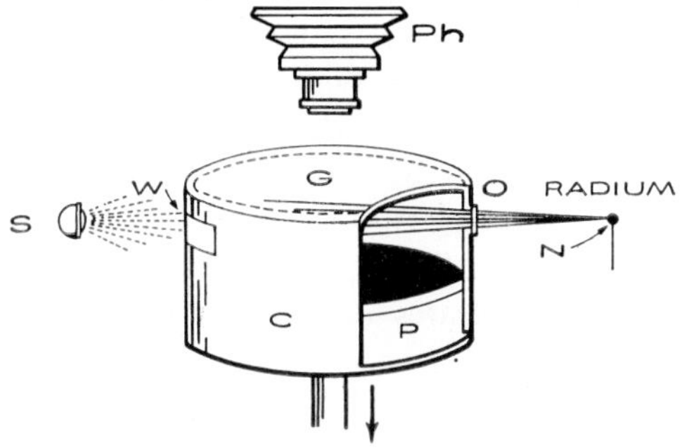

---

* "A brilliant star is C. T. R.," so goes a Cambridge physics students' song.

stand out clearly against the black background in the beam of illuminating light. This picture can be viewed directly by looking through the glass top or photographed by a camera, *Ph.*

Figure 14-8 is a classical cloud chamber photograph taken in 1925 by

Fig. 14-8. The first cloud chamber photograph, taken by Blackett, of nuclear disintegration. The long thin track at upper left is that of a proton that has been ejected from a nitrogen hit by an α-particle. The short thicker track, at upper right, is that of an oxygen nucleus formed in the collision. All other α-particles shown on the photograph lost their energy before they had a chance to hit a nucleus.

P. T. M. Blackett that shows the collision of an incident α-particle with the nucleus of a nitrogen atom in the air which fills the chamber. The long thin track going almost backwards is that of a proton ejected in that collision. It can be easily recognized as a proton track because protons are 4 times lighter than α-particles and carry only one-half as much electric charge; therefore they produce fewer ions per unit length of their path than α-particles. The short heavy track belongs to the nucleus $_8O^{17}$ formed in the process of collision.

FIRST ATOM SMASHERS

Since the only massive projectiles emitted by the nuclei of natural radioactive elements are α-particles, i.e., the nuclei of helium, it was desirable to develop a method for the artificial production of beams formed by other atomic projectiles, particularly beams of high-energy protons. According to the theoretical considerations of the author of this book (Fig. 14-9, right), the ease with which a bombarding particle penetrates into the structure of a bombarded atomic nucleus depends on the atomic number (i.e., the nuclear electric charge) of the element in question. The larger the atomic number, the stronger is the electric repulsive force opposing the approach of α-particles to the nucleus and, consequently, the smaller are the chances of a demolishing collision.

Fig. 14-9. Sir John Cockcroft (left) and the author discuss the possibility of breaking up the atomic nucleus by using artificially accelerated protons (Cambridge, England, 1929).

Since protons carry only one-half of the electric charge carried by an α-particle, they were expected to be much better as atomic projectiles and to be able to smash atomic nuclei of light elements even when moving with only one Mev of energy. Rutherford asked John Cockcroft (Fig. 14-9, left) to construct a high-tension machine that would accelerate protons to the energy of one million electron-volts, and, within a couple of years, the first "atom smasher" was constructed by Cockcroft and his associate, E. T. S. Walton. Directing the beam of 1-Mev protons at a lithium target, Cockcroft and Walton observed the first nuclear transformation caused by artificially accelerated projectiles. The alchemical formula of this reaction is:

$$_3\text{Li}^7 + {}_1\text{H}^1 \longrightarrow 2{}_2\text{He}^4$$

The two α-particles resulting from the collision between the onrushing proton and the target, a lithium nucleus, are clearly seen in Fig. 14-10. If we use boron instead of lithium as the target, the reaction will be:

$$_5\text{B}^{11} + {}_1\text{H}^1 \longrightarrow 3{}_2\text{He}^4$$

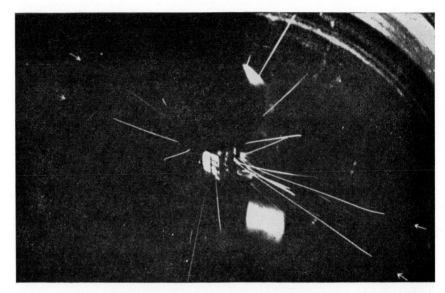

Fig. 14-10. A cloud chamber photograph, after P. Dee and E. T. S. Walton, of the breaking up of the lithium nucleus under the impact of an artificially accelerated proton. The two pairs of (diagonally opposite) tracks, indicated by arrows, correspond to two pairs of α-particles that resulted from the break-up of two lithium nuclei.

and the three α-particles formed in this collision fly apart as shown in Fig. 14-11.

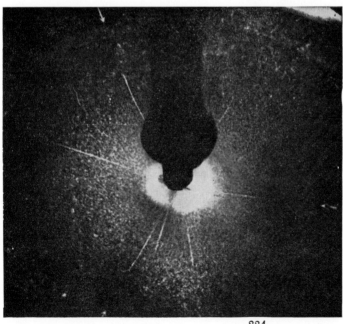

Fig. 14-11. A cloud chamber photograph, after P. Dee and C. Gilbert, of three α-particles (arrows) resulting from the break-up of a boron nucleus under the impact of an artificially accelerated proton.

THE "VAN DE GRAAFF"

Cockcroft and Walton's atom smasher, which was based on the electric transformer principle, gave rise to a series of ingenious devices for producing high-tension beams of atomic projectiles. The *electrostatic atom smasher* constructed by R. Van de Graaff (1901-   ) and usually called by his name, is based on a classical principle of electrostatics, according to which an electric charge communicated to a spherical conductor is distributed entirely on its surface. Thus, if we take a hollow spherical conductor with a small hole in its surface, insert through this hole a small charged conductor attached to a glass stick, and touch the inside surface of the sphere (Fig. 14-12a), the charge will spread out to the surface of the big sphere.

Repeating the operation many times, we will be able to communicate to the large conductor any desirable amount of electricity and raise its electric potential as high as desired (or, at least, until the sparks start jumping between the conductor and the surrounding walls).

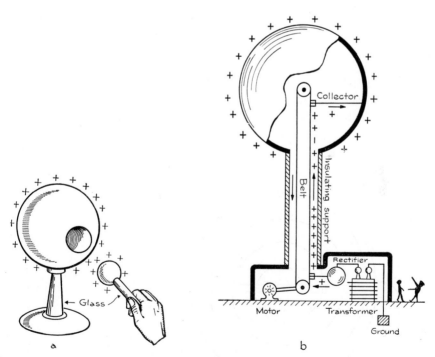

Fig. 14-12. The principle (a) and the actual scheme (b) of Van de Graaff's high-tension machine.

In the Van de Graaff atom smasher (Fig. 14-12b), the small charged ball is replaced by a continuously running belt that collects electric charges from a source at the base and deposits them on the interior surface of the large metallic sphere. The high electric potential developed in this process is applied to one end of an accelerating tube in which the ions of different elements are speeded up to energies of many millions of electron-volts.

THE CYCLOTRON

Another popular atom smasher, invented by E. O. Lawrence (1901-   ), is based on an entirely different principle and utilizes the multiple acceleration of charged particles moving along a circle in a magnetic field. The principle of the cyclotron is shown in Fig. 14-13. It consists essentially of a circular metal chamber cut into halves, C_1 and C_2, and placed between the poles of a very strong electromagnet. The half chambers, C_1 and C_2, are connected with a source of alternating high electric potential, AC, so that the electric field along the slit separating them periodically changes its direction. The ions of the element to be used as atomic projectiles are injected in the center of the box, I, at a comparatively low velocity, and their trajectories are bent into small circles by the field of the magnet. The gimmick of the cyclotron is that, for a given magnetic field, the period of revolution of an electrically charged particle along its circular trajectory is independent of the velocity with which that particle

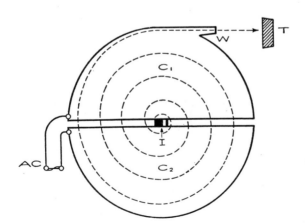

Fig. 14-13. The principle of the cyclotron.

is moving. Since the increase in the radius of the path and the length of the circular trajectory is exactly proportional to the increase in velocity, the time necessary for one revolution remains the same.

If things are arranged in such a way that the period of revolution of the ions injected into the field of the magnet is equal to the period of alternating tension produced by the *AC* source, the particles arriving at the boundary between the two half chambers, C_1 and C_2, will be subject each time to an electric force acting in the same direction that the particles are moving. Thus, each time the ion passes through that boundary it will be given additional acceleration and its velocity will gradually increase. Gathering speed, the ions will move along an unwinding spiral trajectory and will finally be ejected through the window, W, in the direction of the target, T. The largest existing cyclotron is in the radiation laboratory of the University of California. It has an accelerating circular box 60 inches in diameter and produces artificial α-beams with an energy of 40 Mev (4.5 times higher than that of the fastest natural α-particles). With this atom smasher, it was possible to cause the artificial transformation of all elements up to the heaviest ones. The synchrotron in the Insti-

Fig. 14-14. The large synchrotron at the Institute of Nuclear Studies, University of Chicago.

tute of Nuclear Studies at the University of Chicago is pictured in Fig. 14-14. A proton-synchrotron combines a high-frequency electric field, such as that employed in a cyclotron, with a low-frequency magnetic field to accelerate charged particles.

DISCOVERY OF NEUTRONS

In the year 1930, a German physicist, W. Bothe, noticed that the bombardment of beryllium by natural α-particles from polonium gave rise to very peculiar radiation of very high penetrating power. Bothe believed that the radiation he discovered was formed by high-energy γ-quanta, and it was only two years later that Rutherford's collaborator, J. Chadwick, proved that the mysterious radiation is actually nothing more than a fast-moving beam of material particles that have the same mass as protons but carry no electric charge. These new particles received the name of *neutrons,* and the reaction by which they were produced in Bothe's original experiments can be written as:

$$_4\mathrm{Be}^9 + {}_2\mathrm{He}^4 \longrightarrow {}_6\mathrm{C}^{12} + {}_0\mathrm{n}^1$$

with ordinary carbon as the reaction product. Neutrons can be considered as an electric modification of protons ("chargeless protons") and do, in fact, decay spontaneously into protons within 12 minutes through the emission of an electron:

$$_0\mathrm{n}^1 \longrightarrow {}_1\mathrm{p}^1 + \mathrm{e}^-$$

The collective name for neutrons and protons is *nucleon;* neutrons are neutral nucleons while protons are nucleons carrying a positive elementary charge. Being deprived of the electric charge, neutrons are not subject to electric repulsive forces when they approach the nucleus and can penetrate into heavily charged nuclei, such as those of mercury or lead, with the greatest of ease. Because of this fact, neutrons are ideal atomic projectiles, but the trouble was (before the discovery of nuclear fission) that in order to produce a beam of neutrons one had to kick them out from the nuclei of some other element by bombarding the nuclei with charged projectiles (as in the Be reaction above).

Constitution of Atomic Nuclei

It was mentioned in Chapter 12 that the integral values of the atomic weight of the isotopes of different elements strongly suggests that their atomic nuclei are formed by polymerization of the nuclei of hydrogen atoms, i.e., protons. But if the nuclei of heavier elements were formed exclusively by proton aggregates, they would have a much larger electric charge than that actually observed. For example, the nucleus of oxygen has the mass of 16 protons but carries only 8 elementary units of positive charge. It follows that 8 of the 16 hydrogen nuclei that combine to form a nucleus of oxygen have lost their positive charge, i.e., have turned into neutrons. Thus, the composition of an oxygen nucleus can be written as:

$$_8O^{16} = 8 \text{ protons} + 8 \text{ neutrons}$$

Similarly we may write for the composition of iron and U^{238} nuclei:

$$_{26}Fe^{56} = 26 \text{ protons} + 30 \text{ neutrons}$$

and:

$$_{92}U^{238} = 92 \text{ protons} + 146 \text{ neutrons}$$

We notice that, whereas the lighter nuclei are about fifty-fifty protons and neutrons, the number of neutrons in the nuclei of heavier elements considerably exceeds the number of protons. This is due to the fact that nuclear protons repel each other because they are positively charged, so that if there are very many protons, extra neutrons are required to hold the entire structure together.

NUCLEAR FORCES

Since the protons that form atomic nuclei repel each other by electric forces and since there is no electric interaction at all between the neutrons and between the neutrons and the protons, there clearly must be some attractive forces of a non-electric nature that hold the nucleus together. These attractive forces are known as *nuclear forces* and were shown to act between the nucleons, irrespective of whether they are protons or neutrons. They also differ from the electric forces in their dependence on the distance between the interacting particles. Whereas electric forces decrease comparatively slowly with increasing distance (Fig. 14-15a), nuclear forces are very strong when the two nucleons are almost in contact and suddenly become zero when the distance is only slightly increased (Fig. 14-15b). In this sense they are similar to the cohesive forces caused by molecular interaction in the case of "sticky" substances; two pieces of modeling clay do not show even a slight mutual attraction when brought very close together, but they will stick tightly when put into the direct contact.

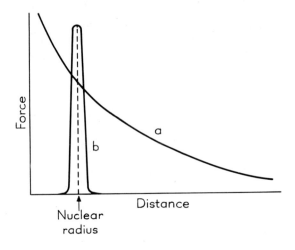

Fig. 14-15. "Long-range" forces, such as coulomb attractive and repulsive forces (a), decrease slowly with distance, while "short-range" forces (b) act only when two bodies are in contact.

NUCLEAR POTENTIAL BARRIER

When a positively charged nuclear projectile, such as a proton or an α-particle, approaches an atomic nucleus, it is acted upon by electrostatic repulsive forces and cannot come into direct contact with the nucleus unless its kinetic energy is large enough to overcome this repulsion. However, as soon as the contact is achieved, nuclear attractive forces take hold of the approaching particle and pull it into the nucleus. Thus, plotting the potential energy of a (positively) charged particle in the neighborhood of an atomic nucleus, we obtain the curve shown in Fig. 14-16.

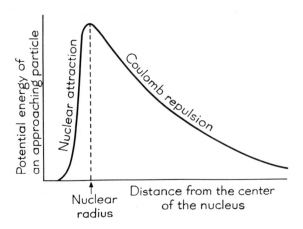

Fig. 14-16. The potential energy of a positively charged particle (α-particle, proton, etc.) in the neighborhood of an atomic nucleus.

This curve represents a "potential barrier" for the penetration of incident positively charged particles into the nucleus, as well as for the escape of such particles from the nucleus.

According to classical mechanics, the incoming or outgoing nuclear particles can pass the potential barrier only if their kinetic energy is larger than the maximum height of the barrier. Experimental evidence shows, however, that this is definitely not so. An example is represented by a uranium nucleus, which has a radius of 9×10^{-13} cm and is surrounded by a potential barrier 27 Mev high. Since the α-particles that escape from uranium in the process of its natural decay have an energy of only 4 Mev, it is difficult to understand how they get out across the barrier at all.

The explanation of this apparent paradox was given in 1928 by the author and also, independently, by R. Gurney and E. Condon. It is based on the partial analogy between the mechanical motion of material particles and the propagation of waves. It turns out, in fact, that the wave mechanics of a particle permit it to do things that would be completely prohibited in classical mechanics. Consider, for example, the case of a ball with a mass of 10 grams rolling with a velocity of one meter per second (10^2 cm/sec) along the flat surface of a table. The kinetic energy of the ball is $\frac{1}{2} \times 10 \times (10^2)^2 = 5 \times 10^4$ erg. Suppose now that we place a wooden barrier (Fig. 14-17) 8 cm high on the table in the way of the ball. Would the ball cross the barrier or not? At the top of the barrier the potential energy of the ball would be $981 \times 10 \times 8 = 7.9 \times 10^4$ erg (where 981 stands for the acceleration of gravity), which is more than the initial amount of the kinetic energy of the ball. According to classical mechanics, this would mean that the ball will never be able to cross the barrier but will roll back after climbing about two-thirds of its total height.

According to wave mechanics, the situation is different, and there is

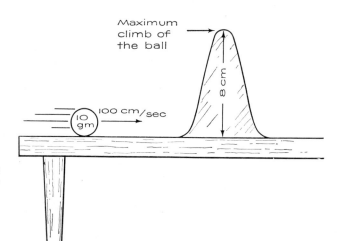

Fig. 14-17. A large scale analogy to the nuclear potential barrier.

always a possibility that the ball will get through, even though in many cases such a possibility may be extremely small. For the above described case, the chances that the ball will roll over the barrier are 1 in $10^{10^{24}}$ * which is zero from any practical point of view. But, as the mass of the moving particle and the geometrical dimensions of the entire system become smaller, the probability of (classically prohibited) penetration across the barrier becomes more favorable. Consider, for example, the case of a uranium nucleus where the height of the potential barrier is 27 Mev, whereas the energy of the escaping α-particle is only 4 Mev. Using wave mechanics, we can calculate that the chances of getting through are about 1 in 10^{38}. But an α-particle imprisoned within the barrier surrounding the U-nucleus makes many escape attempts every second. Indeed, since its velocity is about 10^9 cm/sec and since the size of its "prison" (U-nucleus) is of the order of 10^{-12} cm, it hits the surrounding potential walls 10^{21} times per second. With the probability of 10^{-38} per hit to escape, the imprisoned α-particles must stay in the nucleus for about 1.5×10^{17} seconds or about 5 billion years. And, indeed, as we have seen above, the mean lifetime of this nucleus is 4.5 billion years.

The wave mechanical penetration of nuclear particles through barriers that would be completely prohibitive from the point of view of classical mechanics is known as the "tunnel effect" and is of paramount importance in many nuclear transformation processes. Without the wave mechanical "tunnel effect" there would be no natural radioactive elements, the artificial transformation of elements would have been considerably more difficult, and, above all, we would not have the benefit of the so-called "thermonuclear reactions" that, as we shall see later (Chapter 18), supply the energy to our sun and to the other stars.

NUCLEAR "DROPLET MODEL"

The radical difference between the forces holding together the atom as a whole and those holding together its nucleus results in a large difference in their structures. We have seen in Chapter 13 that the distances between the electrons forming the outer body of the atom are very large as compared with electronic diameters, so that the electronic envelope of an atom is, in a way, like a gaseous atmosphere surrounding its nucleus. With an increasing atomic number and a corresponding increase in the number of electrons in this "atmosphere," atomic electrons come closer together, so that the over-all size of the atom remains, on the average, about the same. In the case of atomic nuclei the situation is entirely different, since the nucleons forming it are packed closely together in very much the same way as the molecules in a liquid. It

---

* Meaning 10 to the power 10^{24} which is a number with 10^{24} decimal places.

follows that, just as in the case of an incompressible fluid, the volume of an atomic nucleus is in direct proportion to the atomic weight, so that the nuclear radius must be proportional to the cube root of that weight. Exact measurements of nuclear diameters confirm this expectation. Thus we can consider the atomic nuclei of different elements to be tiny droplets of a universal *nuclear fluid* formed by a mixture of protons and neutrons. The density of this nuclear fluid exceeds, by a factor of 10^{14}, the density of water, and a jigger filled with it would weigh five billion tons! Like any other fluid, nuclear fluid must manifest "surface tension," since the individual nucleons will be prevented from crossing its surface by the attractive nuclear forces of other nucleons. But just as the density of nuclear fluid is tremendously higher than that of any ordinary fluid, so also is its surface tension. If we form a soap film on a staple-shaped wire with a piece of straight wire placed across it, we can counteract the pull caused by the surface tension forces by the weight of 70 mg per centimeter of length of the cross wire. If we could do the same experiment with a "nuclear soap film," the pull would be able to support ten billion tons per each centimeter of length!

EXPLANATION OF NATURAL RADIOACTIVITY

As we discussed before, atomic nuclei of very heavy elements are intrinsically unstable and emit α- and β-particles. The reason for this instability lies in the presence of a strong electric repulsion between the positively charged protons that form the nucleus. In fact, beyond a certain number of protons in the nucleus, the cohesive nuclear forces become unable to counteract the repulsion between the nuclear electric charges, and small pieces of the nucleus begin to chip off. Since a pair of protons coupled with a pair of neutrons in an α-particle is a particularly stable structural element in the nuclear interior, it is α-particles that are thrown out by the unstable heavy nuclei of radioactive elements.

The emission of electrons (β-rays) is the consequence of the emission of a sequence of α-particles and can be understood by considering the change of the relative number of neutrons and protons resulting from such an emission. Let us take, for example, an α-decay sequence leading from uranium II to RaB:

$$U_{II} \xrightarrow{\ \alpha\ } Io \xrightarrow{\ \alpha\ } Ra \xrightarrow{\ \alpha\ } RaEm \xrightarrow{\ \alpha\ } RaA \xrightarrow{\ \alpha\ } RaB$$

Calculating the number of neutrons and protons in the nuclei in question, we find that the neutron-to-proton ratios are: 1.54; 1.56; 1.57; 1.58; 1.60; 1.61; and are increasing all the time as the α-decay goes on. For each nucleus there is a certain optimum ratio of the relative number of neutrons and protons, and, if this ratio is exceeded, one of the neutrons must turn into a proton and emit an electron. In the above example, this ratio is exceeded when RaB is formed, as the result of which RaB begins to emit electrons, turning into RaC and then again into RaC′. For these two nuclei, the neutron-to-proton ratios are lowered to 1.58 and 1.55, and the nucleus becomes again stable with respect to β-decay. Thus, the next transformation is bound to be an α-decay, and, indeed, the nucleus of RaC′ emits a fast α-particle which turns it into RaD. The increased neutron-proton ratio caused by this α-decay leads again to the possibility of two successive β-transformations which result in the formation of RaE and RaF (or polonium). Finally, the α-decay of polonium turns it into the nucleus of Pb^{206}, which is stable both with respect to α- and β-transformations and thus terminates the long sequence of radioactive decay.

Nuclear Fission

As was mentioned before, neutrons are the ideal projectiles for nuclear bombardment because they have no electrical charge and thus suffer no repulsion in their approach to atomic nuclei. Following the discovery of neutrons, many new types of artificial nuclear transformations have been investigated. In some cases the impact of a neutron may result in the ejection of a proton or an α-particle, as in the reactions:

$$_7N^{14} + {_0}n^1 \longrightarrow {_6}C^{14} + {_1}H^1$$

$$_7N^{14} + {_0}n^1 \longrightarrow {_5}B^{11} + {_2}He^4$$

In some cases the incident neutron can eject another neutron without being captured itself:

$$_6C^{12} + {_0}n^1 \longrightarrow {_6}C^{11} + 2{_0}n^1$$

whereas in other cases the incident neutron can be captured by the nucleus with the release of excess energy in the form of a γ-quantum. The latter process, known as the *radiative capture* of neutrons, is of particular importance for heavy nuclear targets, since in this case the ejection of protons and α-particles is strongly hindered by the "outgoing" potential barrier surrounding the nucleus. The radiative capture of the neutron leads to the formation of a heavier isotope of the bombarded element. Sometimes these isotopes are stable so that no further nuclear transformation takes place:

$$_8O^{16} + {_0}n^1 \longrightarrow {_8}O^{17} + \gamma$$

whereas in some other cases the radiative capture of a neutron leads to a β-emission:

$$_{47}\text{Ag}^{109} + {}_0\text{n}^1 \longrightarrow {}_{47}\text{Ag}^{110} + \gamma$$

$$_{47}\text{Ag}^{110} \longrightarrow {}_{48}\text{Cd}^{110} + e^-$$

which is necessary to re-establish the proper neutron-to-proton ratio.

In the year 1939, a German radio-chemist, Otto Hahn, with his co-worker, Fritz Strassman, studied the effect of the neutron bombardment of uranium atoms, expecting to observe the formation of uranium isotopes with atomic weights higher than that of ordinary uranium, i.e., 238. To his great surprise (Fig. 14-18), Hahn found that the sample of uranium

Fig. 14-18. Dr. Otto Hahn, who discovered that the uranium nucleus (right) when subjected to neutron bombardment breaks up into two nearly equal fragments.

bombarded by neutrons contained radioactive atoms of a much lighter element, barium. The mystery of this discovery was soon cleared up by two German physicists, Lise Meitner and Otto Frisch, who suggested that in Hahn and Strassman's experiments the nuclei of U^{238} were split by incident neutrons into two nearly equal parts:

$$_{92}\text{U}^{238} + {}_0\text{n} \longrightarrow {}_{56}\text{Ba}^{144} + {}_{36}\text{K}^{94}$$

Since the barium and krypton atoms produced in this process possessed excess neutrons, as compared with ordinary stable atoms of the same atomic weight ($_{60}Nd^{144}$ and $_{40}Zr^{94}$), these so-called *fission products* emitted negative electrons, making them strongly radioactive. Frisch and Meitner's interpretation of Hahn and Strassman's experimental finding as the splitting of the uranium nucleus into two nearly equal parts opened new vistas in the field of nuclear physics. Instead of just "chipping off" small pieces of the bombarded nucleus, as was the case in all previous experiments, here was a real breakup of the central body of the atom, the *fission* of a large droplet of the nuclear fluid into two half-size droplets. Instead of just the few million electron-volts of energy observed in previous experiments on artificial nuclear transformations, uranium fission liberates 200 Mev per atom!

The detailed theoretical studies of the process of nuclear fission were carried out by Niels Bohr and John Wheeler (1911-) and published in the September 1939 issue of the *Physical Review*. This was the first and last comprehensive article on the theory of nuclear fission that appeared as "open literature" before the "security curtain" was drawn tight on that subject. According to Bohr and Wheeler, the fission of heavy nuclei resulting from the impact of a neutron is a resolution of a conflict between the opposing tendencies of nuclear (attractive) and coulomb (repulsive) forces acting in the atomic nucleus. In fact, if we imagine an atomic nucleus as an electrically charged droplet of nuclear fluid (Fig. 14-19a), we will find that in the case of any excitation (Fig. 14-19b) transforming its initial spherical shape into a more or less elongated ellipsoid (Fig. 14-19c) there will be two kinds of forces acting on it:

1. The forces of nuclear surface tension attempting to restore the nucleus to its original spherical shape (the same as in the case of a deformed spherical droplet of water or mercury).

Fig. 14-19. What happens when the nucleus breaks up in the fission process.

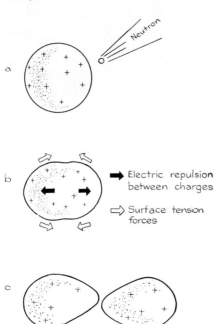

2. Coulomb repulsive forces between the electric charges on the oppo-site ends of the ellipsoid attempting to break up the nucleus into two halves.

With a nuclear droplet model we can show that for the lighter nuclei the surface tension forces have the upper hand, but that for the heavier nuclei the coulombic forces become more and more important. Thus, we would expect that in the case of very heavy nuclei the comparatively small deformation caused by the force of a neutron impact may result in a breakup (fission) of the original nuclear droplet into two halves (Fig. 14-19d).

FISSION NEUTRONS

In spite of the fact that each of the two fragments produced in the fission of a uranium nucleus carries about 100 Mev of energy, these fragments are quite ineffective in producing further fission processes; this is due to the fact that the fission fragments carry a very high electric charge and are consequently strongly repelled by the other uranium nuclei with which they may collide. Thus, the discovery of uranium fission would not contribute anything to the problem of the large-scale libera-tion of nuclear energy if it were not for a secondary process that was found to accompany nuclear fission. It was discovered that apart from the two large fragments of the original nucleus, there are always several extra neutrons emitted in the breakup. In the case of U^{235} the average number of "fission neutrons" formed is 2.5 per uranium nucleus. These fission neutrons formed in the breakup of one uranium nucleus may collide with the surrounding uranium nuclei and produce more fission and still more fission neutrons. And, if the conditions are favorable, the breeding of fission neutrons goes *crescendo* as does the breeding of

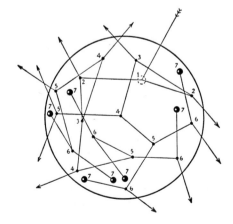

Fig. 14-20. A nuclear chain reac-tion developing in a supercritical piece of fissionable material with a "branching ratio" equal to 2. The reaction is started at 1 by a single neutron from the outside. After seven successive generations, seven neutrons remain inside the volume and eleven are lost through the surface.

Fig. 14-21. Enrico Fermi looking at the plaque on the wall of the University of Chicago Stadium (Stagg Field) which reads: "On December 2, 1942, man achieved here the first self-sustaining chain reaction and thereby initiated the controlled release of nuclear energy."

rabbits on a rabbit farm or of fruit flies in a genetics laboratory. Thus, we get a *branching chain reaction* (Fig. 14-20), and in practically no time all the nuclei of uranium in a given piece of this material break up with the liberation of a tremendous amount of energy.

FISSIONABLE URANIUM-235

As was mentioned above, natural uranium represents a mixture of two isotopes, U^{238} and U^{235}, that are present in the relative amounts of 99.3 and 0.7 per cent respectively. The study of these two isotopes under the influence of neutron bombardment had shown that the rarer isotope U^{235} is much more fissionable than the more abundant U^{238}. Indeed, whereas U^{238} nuclei do not break up unless the bombarding neutron has energy above 1.2 Mev, U^{235} nuclei can be broken up by neutrons moving with much smaller velocities, and, in fact, the breaking up probability increases with the decreasing velocity of incident neutrons. Thus, the strong dilution of the active U^{235} isotope by the inactive U^{238} makes natural uranium just as useless for carrying out nuclear chain reactions as soaking wet logs are for building a campfire. Indeed, most of the fission neutrons ejected in the breakup of U^{235} nuclei in natural uranium will be captured by the much more abundant U^{238} nuclei with the emission of γ-radiation and thus will be taken out of the game.

Accordingly, in the early stages of nuclear energy development ("Manhattan Project"), much effort was spent on the separation of the active U^{235} from the inactive U^{238}. Since the isotopes of a given element possess identical chemical properties, ordinary chemical separation methods could not be used in this case. The problem was finally solved by the development of the so-called "diffusion separation" method, which was based on the fact that the lighter atoms of U^{235} (and their various chemical compounds) diffuse faster through semi-permeable membranes than do the heavier U^{238} atoms, and large amounts of "fissionable" uranium were obtained in this way.

FERMI-PILE AND PLUTONIUM

A good boy scout is supposed to be able to build a campfire even if the wood is soaking wet. This role of a good boy scout in the nuclear energy project was played by the Italian-American physicist, Enrico Fermi (Fig. 14-21), who actually made the "wet" uranium logs "burn." He was able to do so by utilizing the fact mentioned above, that the effectiveness of fission neutrons in producing the fission of U^{235} nuclei increases quite considerably when they are slowed down. If such slowing down of fission neutrons could be achieved, the presence of inactive U^{238} would not make much difference. To slow down the original fission neutrons it was necessary to mix natural uranium with a large amount of carbon in the form of graphite. A large "pile" of graphite bricks with small pieces of natural uranium included in the structure (Figs. 14-22 and 14-23) was constructed in great secrecy under the grandstand of the University of Chicago Stadium, and on December 2, 1941, Professor A. Compton wired to Dr. Vannevar Bush in Washington, D. C.: "The Italian navigator has landed. The natives are friendly." In the secret language of the Manhattan Project this meant: "The Fermi-pile works successfully. Nuclear chain reaction is achieved."

In the Fermi-pile, the fission chain reaction could be maintained in natural uranium, but the natural uranium was so highly diluted by carbon that high efficiency in energy production could not be achieved. Owing to the presence of inactive U^{238}, the chain reaction in the pile could not possibly develop into an efficient explosion, nor could it be very useful as a power source. So what good was the Fermi-pile, except for demonstrating the purely scientific principle of the possibility of a self-maintaining nuclear reaction? Of course, the demonstration of a purely scientific principle is always of very great importance, but the Fermi-pile was built at great expense in the midst of a perilous war when all expenditures were supposed to be judged on the basis of their military usefulness.

The Fermi-pile stood this acid test. Although the energy released in the fission of U^{235} nuclei could not be utilized and was literally sent down the drain by means of the water-cooling system, a new fissionable

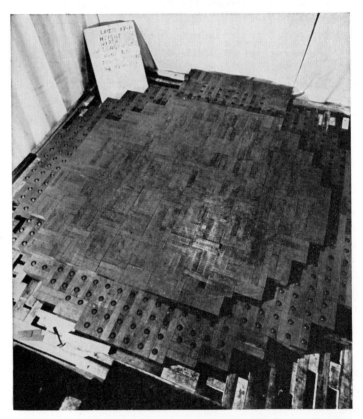

Fig. 14-22. The only photograph made during the construction of the first nuclear reactor (Fermi-pile) made in November, 1942. Here the nineteenth layer of graphite bricks is being added. The eighteenth layer (almost covered up) is formed by graphite blocks containing uranium metal and uranium oxide (the layers of "live" and "dead" graphite blocks were alternated). The pile became critical on December 2, 1942, after 57 layers had been laid down. *Courtesy Argonne National Laboratory.*

element was produced inside the pile during its operation. The neutrons that were not used in the maintenance of the chain reaction in U^{235} nuclei were captured by U^{238} nuclei, producing the heavier isotope:

$$_{92}U^{238} + {}_0n^1 \longrightarrow {}_{92}U^{239} + \gamma$$

Fig. 14-23. A sketch of the first nuclear reactor (Fermi-pile) constructed in a squash court under the west stands of Chicago University's Stagg Field in 1942. *Courtesy U.S. Army Engineers.*

Having an excess of neutrons, the nuclei of $_{92}U^{239}$ underwent two successive β-transformations, giving rise to elements with atomic numbers 93 and 94. These two elements, which do not exist in nature but have been produced artificially by human genius, were given the names *neptunium* and *plutonium*. The reactions following the neutron capture by U^{238} can be written:

$$_{92}U^{239} \longrightarrow {}_{93}Np^{239} + e^-$$
$$_{93}Np^{239} \longrightarrow {}_{94}Pu^{239} + e^-$$

Being chemically different from uranium, the plutonium produced in the Fermi-pile can be separated and purified with much less effort than it takes to separate a light uranium isotope from the heavy one, and this element turned out to be even more fissionable than U^{235}. In fact, whereas U^{235} gives rise to 2.5 fission neutrons, the corresponding figure for Pu^{239} is 2.9 fission neutrons.

CRITICAL SIZE

When a single fission process occurs inside a given sample of pure U^{235} or Pu^{239}, several fission neutrons are ejected from the point where the nuclear breakup took place. The average distance a fission neutron must travel through the material in order to run into another nucleus is about 10 cm, so that if the size of the sample in question is less than that, most of the fission neutrons will cross the surface of the sample and fly away before they have a chance to cause another fission and produce more neutrons. Thus, no progressive chain reaction can develop if the sample of fissionable material is too small. Going to larger and larger samples, we find that more and more fission neutrons produced

351

in the interior have a chance to produce another fission by colliding with a nucleus before they escape through the surface, and for samples of a very large size only a small fraction of the neutrons produced in them has a chance to reach the surface before colliding with one of the nuclei. The size of the sample of a given fissionable material for which the percentage of neutrons giving rise to subsequent fission processes is high enough to secure a progressive chain reaction is known as the *critical size* for that particular material. Since the number of neutrons per fission is larger in the case of plutonium than in the case of uranium-235, the critical size of plutonium samples is smaller than that of uranium-235 samples because the former can afford larger losses of neutrons through its surface.

NUCLEAR REACTORS

As we have just seen, a sample of fissionable material smaller than the "critical size" is unable to carry on a nuclear chain reaction. If the size of the sample is *exactly critical,* the number of neutrons produced in each generation is the same as that produced in the previous one, resulting in steady nuclear energy liberation. The original Fermi-pile and its later modifications maintain nuclear reactions at the critical size level. It must be mentioned in this connection that the conditions of "criticality" are extremely unstable: a small deviation in one direction will result in the rapid extinction of fission neutrons and the cut-off of the nuclear chain reaction, whereas a deviation in another direction will lead to a

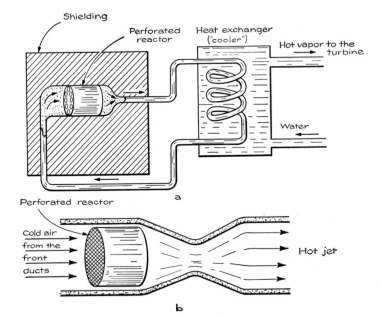

Fig. 14-24. Two types of nuclear reactors for propulsion purposes: (a) a closed-cycle reactor and (b) an open-cycle reactor.

rapid multiplication of the fisson neutrons and the melting of the entire structure. Thus, the important problem in maintaining a steady chain reaction is that of regulating the rate of neutron production and of keeping the chain reaction from "dying out" or "running away." This is achieved by using "control rods" made from neutron-absorbing materials (such as boron) which are automatically pushed in or pulled out from narrow channels drilled through the reacting fissionable material as soon

Fig. 14-25. A modern commercially produced nuclear reactor can be operated with complete safety in a normal-sized laboratory room. *Courtesy Aerojet General Nucleonic.*

as the rate of neutron production drops below or exceeds the desired level.

We have already mentioned that Fermi-piles are unsuitable for purposes of nuclear power production because of the high dilution of uranium by carbon; they should be considered rather as "alchemical plants" in which plutonium is produced. For the purpose of nuclear power production, we use the controlled nuclear chain reactions in pure fissionable materials, such as U^{235} or Pu^{239}, which can be run at quite high temperatures. In the so-called "swimming pool" reactor, in which several cylindrical containers filled with pure fissionable material are placed at the bottom of a large water tank, the water circulating through the tank carries away the heat produced in the fission process and also protects the observer from the deadly nuclear radiation. The color of the water turns blue as a result of the so-called Cherenkoff's radiation produced in water by high-energy electrons.

In Fig. 14-24a and b we give the schemes of two different types of *nuclear power reactors*. In both cases the block of fissionable material is perforated by long cylindrical channels for the passage of the "working fluid" that receives and carries out the heat produced in the fission process. Scheme (a) is known as a "closed-cycle nuclear reactor" since in it the working fluid (a molten light metal) is continuously circulating between the reactor and the "cooler," where the heat is used to produce water vapor for the operation of an ordinary steam turbine. This type of nuclear power reactor is installed, for example, in the "Nautilus," the first nuclear-powered submarine of the U.S. Navy. Fig. 14-24b is an "open-cycle nuclear reactor" which is likely to become very useful for the propulsion of nuclear-powered jet planes. In this type of power reactor the air coming in through the intake ducts in front of the airplane is heated to a high temperature while passing through the reactor and is ejected, in the form of a fast jet, through the nozzle at the rear. Figure 14-25 shows a small nuclear reactor that can be used for scientific and commercial purposes.

FISSION BOMBS

If the sample of fissionable material exceeds the critical mass, the number of fission neutrons and the rate of energy production will increase exponentially with time, and the process will acquire an explosive nature. The principle of the fission bomb, or the "atomic bomb" as it is commonly called, consists of building up (assembling) a highly supercritical mass of fissionable material in such a short time period that the nuclear energy liberation that starts at the beginning of the assembly period does not develop to any important degree before the assembly job is finished. This

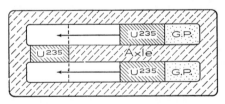

Fig. 14-26. The principle of the gun-type atomic bomb. The ignition of gunpowder (G.P.) shoots a U-235 cylinder along the axle and places it around another part of U-235, which forms the left end of the axle.

can be accomplished in a simple way by inserting one subcritical piece of fissionable material into another subcritical piece as indicated in Fig. 14-26. In order to perform the assembly process fast enough, we must shoot one of the pieces at a high speed from a gun muzzle, which earned for this assembly method the name of "gun gadget." There are also other more ingenious methods of bringing a given amount of fissionable material to supercritical size.

The energy liberation in the explosion of nuclear bombs is measured, according to established convention, in units known as "kilotons" and "megatons," which refer to the weight of TNT (ordinary high explosive) that liberates the same amount of energy. One kiloton, i.e., the energy liberated in the explosion of one thousand tons of TNT, equals 5×10^{19} erg or about 10^{12} calories. We are postponing the discussion of the so-called "fusion bomb," or "hydrogen bomb," to Chapter 19, where a general discussion of thermonuclear reactions will be given.

Biological Effects of Nuclear Radiations

In connection with the world-wide development of atomic industry and the possibility of atomic warfare, it is very important to know the degree of harm that penetrating high-energy radiations can cause to a human organism. When a fast-moving nuclear particle or a high-energy γ-ray quantum passes through a material body, it produces a certain amount of ionization by knocking electrons from the atoms that it encounters on its way. If the ionized atoms belong to some complex organic molecules, such as a protein or a nucleic acid, the molecule might be broken up, and even a small percentage of such breakups would lead to the disruption of the proper functioning of the biological system and result in the death of the organism. Thus, the biological effects of penetrating radiations can be measured by the degree of ionization they produce when passing through matter. An accepted unit is known as the *roentgen,* which is defined as the dose of radiation that produces 1.6×10^{12} ions in one gram of atmospheric air. Remembering that one gram of air contains 4×10^{22} atoms, we find that the dose of one roentgen corresponds to the ionization of 4×10^{-9} per cent of all available atoms. In the case of living tissues, the number of ions produced by one roentgen is of the same order of magnitude.

In considering radiation damage to a living organism, we should distinguish between two types of damage:

1. *Pathological damage* to the organism exposed to radiation, which, being sufficiently severe, could lead to the death of that organism.

2. *Genetical damage* to the reproductive organs that might not affect

the exposed organisms themselves but could do a lot of harm to successive generations. A comparatively weak but continuous irradiation of the entire population could even lead to its complete extinction at some future date.

Pathological damage to individuals requires comparatively large radiation doses and, with the exception of atomic warfare, can be expected only in the case of serious accidents in atomic industry. A lethal dose of radiation is considered to be about 800 roentgens, which, when delivered over the entire body, leads to inevitable death. Smaller doses of one hundred roentgens or less may produce delayed but still lethal effects such as the development of leukemia and cancer. It is usually assumed that small radiation doses such as a few roentgens per week (the accepted tolerance limit in atomic industry) are quite harmless since living matter is continuously regenerated at a rate that compensates for the damaged material. This may not be quite true, however, since statistics show that the mean life of radiologists is 5 years shorter than that of all other members of the medical profession, even though they take all possible measures to minimize the amount of radiation received by their bodies.

Of much more importance are the effects of radiation on the reproductive organs since these effects are definitely cumulative, and 100 roentgens distributed over a period of many years are just as harmful as the same dose delivered all at once in one minute. Passing through the genetic cells, nuclear radiations (as well as ordinary X-rays) affect the DNA molecules that form the chromosomes of the cellular nuclei (see Chapter 11) and cause changes that may manifest themselves as *mutations* in the progeny. Mutations, except for perhaps one in many millions, are admittedly harmful, and, since they are passed down from generation to generation by the hereditary mechanism, they will lead sooner or later to the death of one of the descendants. Thus, while in the process of Darwinian evolution, which was based on the struggle for existence and survival of the fittest, the few beneficial mutations led to a slow improvement of the species, in a balanced human society where the life of each individual is carefully preserved, mutations are apt to do a lot of harm. Under normal conditions, we are all subject to natural mutations that are caused to a large extent by the thermal vibrational motion of organic molecules and also by the radioactivity of the ground and by cosmic rays. The total amount of natural radiation received by a person from the date of conception till the age of 40 (ninety per cent of the children in the U.S. are born to parents below 40 years of age) is known to be about 4.4 roentgens. This figure is almost doubled if we take into account the additional dose (4 roentgens) received by an average person during his life from dental and medical X-rays, shoe-fitting X-ray machines, etc.

Compared with these natural and medical doses received by an average person in the course of a lifetime, the "atomic age supplement," caused at the present time exclusively by bomb tests, is rather small. The radioactive fallout over the continental United States in the course of the last few years accounts for about 0.01 roentgens per year, which would give a cumulative effect of only 0.4 roentgens over a period of 40 years. This is equivalent to a 10 per cent increase in cosmic ray intensity and has a much smaller effect than is caused by the difference in elevation between Denver and New York.

Mesons and Hyperons

In the year 1932 a Japanese physicist, Hidekei Yukawa (known as "Headache" Yukawa to students who struggle with his mathematics), suggested that the nuclear forces acting between protons and neutrons may be due to the presence of a new type of particle that serves as a "nuclear glue" holding the atomic nuclei together. According to Yukawa's theoretical considerations, the new particles must have a mass intermediate between that of protons and that of electrons, so they received the name *mesons* (from the Greek *mesos* meaning "between").

Five years after the introduction of these purely hypothetical particles for the explanation of nuclear forces, they were actually observed in cosmic rays by an American physicist, Carl Anderson. The so-called "primary cosmic rays" bombarding the atmosphere of our planet are formed by streams of extremely high-energy protons and a few other heavier positively charged nuclei that are probably accelerated by electromagnetic fields in interstellar space. The energies of these primary cosmic particles range from comparatively low values to thousands of billions of electron-volts. Colliding with the nuclei of atmospheric oxygen and nitrogen at the outer fringes of the atmosphere, these primary cosmic ray particles produce various kinds of penetrating radiations, including high-energy γ-quanta and streams of negative and positive electrons; in fact, as was mentioned above, positive electrons were first discovered in cosmic rays. Observing the tracks formed by cosmic ray particles in a vertical cloud chamber placed between the poles of a strong magnet, Anderson noticed that the trajectories of some of the particles, both positively and negatively charged, were bent by a magnetic field more than would be expected in the case of fast protons but considerably less than should be the case with electrons. From the observed magnetic deflection, Anderson estimated that this new kind of particle is about 200 times heavier than an electron, in agreement with Yukawa's theoretical prediction. These particles were first called "heavy electrons," but the name was later changed to "mesons."

Later studies by the British physicist, Powell, have shown that there are actually two kinds of mesons, heavier ones called π-mesons or *pions*, and lighter ones known as μ-mesons or *muons*. Both pions and muons

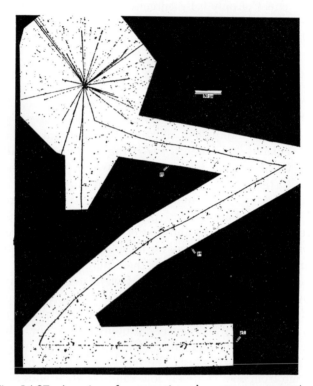

Fig. 14-27. A series of consecutive elementary events. A cosmic ray proton hits an atomic nucleus (upper left) in a photographic emulsion and produces a burst of many different fragments (the so-called "cosmic ray star"). One of the particles, a heavy meson (or pion), travels a long way and, at the right edge of the photo, breaks up into a light meson (or muon) and a neutrino, the trajectory of which does not show on the photo. The muon travels to the lower left corner and breaks up in turn into two neutrinos (their tracks do not show) and an electron, which travels to the right. *Photograph by Dr. E. Pickup, National Research Council, Ottawa, Canada.*

can carry either a positive or a negative electric charge (π^+, π^-, μ^+, μ^-), and in addition there also exist neutral pions (π^0). All of these new particles, as well as the positive and negative cosmic ray electrons (e^+, e^-), are genetically related to each other and form a sequence somewhat similar to the sequence of the radioactive elements. It is now established that the primary high-energy (positive) protons entering the outer fringes of the atmosphere give rise to neutral and charged pions. Neutral pions possess a very short lifetime (about 10^{-16} sec) and, in spite of their high velocity, break up into two γ-quanta:

$$\pi^0 \longrightarrow \gamma + \gamma'$$

before reaching the surface of the earth. The charged pions (both positive and negative) live somewhat longer (10^{-8} sec), but still most of them break up high in the atmosphere according to the equation:

$$\pi^\pm \longrightarrow \mu^\pm + \text{neutrino}$$

Finally the moon breaks up into an electron and two neutrinos according to the formula:

$$\mu^\pm \longrightarrow e^\pm + 2 \text{ neutrinos}$$

The mean lifetime of muons is comparatively long (10^{-6} sec), and many of them reach the surface of the earth and permit themselves to be photographed in ordinary cloud chambers. Since cloud chamber equipment is too bulky and heavy to be sent up in balloons, cosmic ray researchers have developed a new method for photographing the tracks of cosmic particles at high altitudes. Instead of using the ionizing properties of fast charged particles passing through humid air, the new method is based on the fact that these particles affect the grains through which they pass when they travel through a fine-grained photographic emulsion. When the photographic plate is developed, it shows dark streaks that correspond to the trajectories followed by the particles. A very rare photograph of this kind showing the formation of a pion resulting from the collision of a primary cosmic ray particle with a composite nucleus and the subsequent decay of this pion into a muon and an electron is shown in Fig. 14-27. Apart from mesons, which have a mass intermediate between those of an electron and a proton, recent studies of cosmic rays have discovered particles that are heavier than protons and are known under the collective name *hyperons*. The general properties of mesons and hyperons are summarized in Table 14-2. The study of these particles and of their interrelation with each other is, at the present time, the most interesting and most important field of exploration in physics.

THE MYSTERIOUS NEUTRINO

The early studies of radioactive β-decay (the emission of an electron by an unstable atomic nucleus) led to the conclusion that there is something wrong with the energy balance involved. While the α-particles emitted by a given radioactive element always carry a well-defined

TABLE 14-2 THE PROPERTIES OF THE ELEMENTARY PARTICLES OF MATTER

(Bold type indicates the particles known before 1930)

Name and symbol	Mass (in electron masses)	Mean lifetime (in seconds)	Decay scheme
Xi $\Xi^\pm$	2585	10^{-10}	$\Lambda_0 + \pi^\pm$
Sigma $\Sigma^\pm$	2330	10^{-10}	$n + \pi^\pm$
Lambda Λ^0	2182	2.7×10^{-10}	$p + \pi^-$ or $n + \pi^+$
Neutron n	1838.6	10^3	$p^\pm + e^\mp + \nu$
Proton $p^\pm$	1836.1	stable	
K-meson $K^\pm$	966.5	10^{-8}	$\pi^\pm + \pi^0 + \pi^0$ etc.
K-meson K^0	965	10^{-10}	$\pi^0 + \pi^0$ or $\pi^+ + \pi^-$
Pion $\pi^\pm$	273.2	2.6×10^{-8}	$\mu^\pm + \nu$
Pion π^0	264.2	10^{-16}	two gamma rays
Muon $\mu^\pm$	206.7	2.2×10^{-6}	$e^\pm + 2\nu$
Electron $e^\pm$	1	stable	
Neutrino ν	0	stable	

amount of energy characteristic of that particular element, β-particles show a wide energy spread ranging from almost zero to rather high energy values. Since the total energy liberation in the transformation of one atomic nucleus into another is expected to be the same for all nuclei of a given kind, it was suspected that there must be another particle coming out of the nucleus along with the electron that carries the missing balance of energy. This hypothetical particle, which must be electrically neutral and must have a mass that is much smaller than even the mass of an electron (we still do not know how small this mass is), received the name *neutrino,* which means "little neutral" in Italian.

The absence of electric charge and the extremely small mass allow neutrinos to penetrate thick material layers with the greatest of ease; a thick concrete wall is just as ineffective in stopping a beam of neutrinos as a chicken wire fence is in stopping a swarm of mosquitos. The neutrinos that are produced in quantities near the center of the sun in the process of nuclear energy production (see Chapter 19) pierce its entire body and fly away as if there were nothing there at all. It has been estimated theoretically that in order to stop effectively a beam of neutrinos we would need a shield several light-years thick!

In spite of the almost incredible ability of neutrinos to make their "getaway," physicists managed in 1955 to stop a few of them, thus finding unquestionable proof of their existence. F. Reines and C. Cowen of the Los Alamos Scientific Laboratory used for this purpose the collision process between neutrinos and the nuclei of hydrogen atoms (protons) in which the neutrino was expended to produce a positive electron and to transform the proton into a neutron:

$$p + neutrino \longrightarrow n + e^+$$

These two scientists built a giant particle counter that registers neutrons as well as electrons and placed it near one of the nuclear piles at the Savannah River Nuclear Energy Project. The nuclear reactions taking place in the operating pile produce a tremendous number of neutrinos that stream out through a heavy shielding which holds back all other nuclear radiations. Although the chance of a neutrino hitting a proton and producing the above-mentioned reaction is only 1 out of 10^{30}, some of these reactions do actually take place, resulting in the simultaneous appearance of a neutron and the accompanying positive electron. Thus, the uncatchable neutrino was finally caught and joined the company of well-established elementary particles.

ANTI-PROTONS AND ANTI-NEUTRONS

Ever since the experimental confirmation of Dirac's theory of anti-electrons, physicists have been interested in finding the *anti-protons* that should be the particles of proton mass carrying a negative electric charge, i.e., *negative protons*. Since a proton is 1,840 times heavier than an electron, its formation would require a correspondingly higher input of energy. It was expected that a pair of negative and positive protons should be formed when matter is bombarded by atomic projectiles carrying not less than 4.4 billion electron-volts of energy. With this task in mind, the Radiation Laboratory of the University of California in Berkeley and the Brookhaven National Laboratory on Long Island, New York, started construction of the gigantic electron accelerators—*Bevatron* on the West Coast (Fig. 14-28) and *Cosmatron* on the East Coast—that were supposed to speed up atomic projectiles to the energies necessary for the proton-pair production. The race was won by the West Coast physicists who announced in October, 1955, that they had observed negative protons being ejected from targets bombarded by 6.2 Bev (billion electron-volt) atomic projectiles. As is usual in this kind of complicated experimental

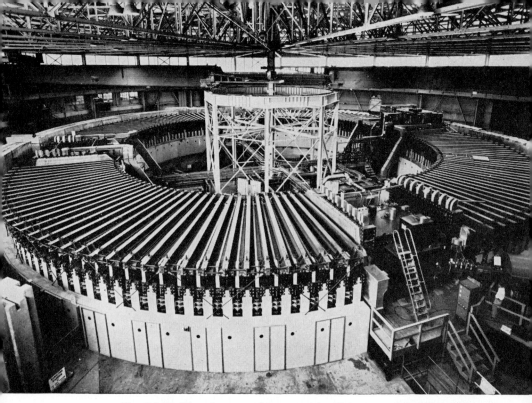

Fig. 14-28. The giant accelerator at the University of California known as the Bevatron. It was this machine that first enabled scientists to detect anti-protons and anti-neutrons. *Courtesy Radiation Laboratory of the University of California.*

research, the work was done by a team, in this case of four people: O. Chamberlain, E. Segré, C. Wiegand, and T. Ypsilantis.

The main difficulty in observing the negative protons formed in the bombarded target was that these protons were expected to be accompanied by tens of thousands of other particles (heavy mesons) also formed during the impact. Thus, the negative protons had to be filtered out and separated from all the other accompanying particles. This was achieved by means of a complicated "labyrinth" formed by magnetic fields, narrow slits, etc. through which only the particles possessing the expected properties of anti-protons could pass. When the swarm of particles coming from the target (located in the bombarding beam of the Bevatron) was passed through this "labyrinth," only the negative protons were expected to come out through its opposite end. When the machine was set into operation, the four experimentalists were gratified to observe the fast particles coming out at a rate of about one every six minutes from its rear opening. As further tests have shown, the particles were genuine negative protons formed in the bombarded target by the high-energy Bevatron beam. Their mass was found to have a value of 1,840 electron masses, which is known to be the mass of an ordinary positive proton.

Just as the artificially produced positive electrons get annihilated in passing through ordinary matter containing a multitude of ordinary negative electrons, negative protons are expected to get annihilated by encountering positive protons in the atomic nuclei with which they collide. Since the energy involved in the process of proton anti-proton annihilation exceeds, by a factor of almost two thousand, the energy involved in an electron-anti-electron collision, the annihilation process proceeds much more violently, resulting in a "star" formed by many ejected particles.

The proof of the existence of negative protons represents an excellent example of an experimental verification of a theoretical prediction concerning properties of matter, even though at the time of its proposal the theory may have seemed quite unbelievable. It was followed in the fall of 1956 by the discovery of *anti-neutrons*, i.e., the particles that stand in the same relation to ordinary neutrons as negative protons do to positive ones. Since in this case the electric charge is absent, the difference between neutrons and anti-neutrons can be noticed only on the basis of their mutual annihilation ability.

PART THREE

MACROCOSM

OUR SOLID EARTH

The earth's solid surface, or lithosphere, which is the abode of our life, is often used as a symbol of permanence and invariability. The mountains and the plains, the shore lines and the canyons have been there as long as humanity can remember and do not seem to show any tendency to change radically. Sometimes a volcano may erupt, pouring streams of red-hot lava down its slopes, and sometimes an earthquake may shake a small part of the earth's surface, but on the whole, things seem to be tranquil and unchangeable. However, if we take a broader view and try to find what is happening deep under our feet all the way down to the center of the globe, we will encounter rather unusual and exciting phenomena. This chapter will be dedicated to the anatomy of our globe.

Fig. 15-1. Giant Geyser, Yellowstone National Park. *Haynes photo.*

The Deeper the Hotter

It is well known to mining engineers that as they dig deeper and deeper into the earth's crust they encounter a steady rise in temperature. Although in mines that are not very deep this rise of temperature is comparatively unimportant, the situation becomes rather drastic when they go much deeper. Thus, in the world's deepest gold mine, the "Robinson Deep" in South Africa, the walls are so hot that half a million dollars worth of air conditioning had to be installed to make the miner's life down there bearable. The most comprehensive information concerning the rise of temperature with increasing depth under the surface of the earth is obtained from deep-well boring, which has been carried on in several thousand localities all over the surface of the globe. Measurements made in these wells indicate that *the rate of temperature increase underground is practically independent of geographical location and amounts to 30°C for each kilometer of depth.*

Since the temperature of rocks immediately under the surface (such as in caves) is about 20°C (68°F), it follows that at a depth of only 2½ km the temperature of rocks reaches the boiling point of water. In certain localities, the conditions are such that the water penetrates through cracks into these hot regions and, being heated above the boiling point, is thrown up again in magnificent geysers, such as those in Yellowstone National Park (Fig. 15-1) and in Iceland. By extrapolating the observed temperature increase to still larger depths, we find that at a depth of about 50 km the temperature of rocks reaches 1,500°C, which is their melting point. However, due to the tremendously high pressure (about 20,000 atmospheres) that exists at this depth, the rocks apparently do not become really fluid, but acquire the property of *plasticity* and become similar to sealing wax (which breaks into fragments like a piece of glass if dropped on the floor but flows like honey—although much slower—if left alone for a sufficiently long period of time).

In the regions of the earth where the crust is weaker than in other places, occasional deep cracks are likely to be formed, and hot plastic material may be squeezed into these cracks and flow slowly upwards. Coming closer and closer to the surface, this material will enter the region of lower pressure, will become more and more fluid, and will finally erupt from volcanic craters in the form of red-hot lava (Fig. 15-2).

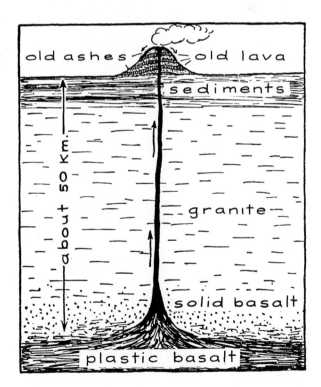

Fig. 15-2. A schematic diagram of a volcanic eruption.

Earthquakes

Besides outbursts of volcanic activity, which eject many thousands of tons of flaming lava and enough volcanic ash to bury entire cities (the Roman city of Pompeii being the outstanding example), these subterranean disturbances often take the form of vigorous tremors in the earth's crust that are felt to a larger or smaller degree all over the world.

In the year 1775, a violent earthquake all but annihilated the Portuguese capital, Lisbon, and killed 15,000 people; the Messina, Sicily, earthquake of 1908 cost 100,000 lives; and the San Francisco earthquake of 1906 claimed an estimated 452 lives. The Japanese, who live on what amounts to a powder keg, suffer the most from quakes. The 1923 earthquake alone took a toll in Japan of 99,331 killed, 103,733 injured, and 43,476 missing. On the other hand, British earthquake casualties have so far been limited to a single person, who was killed by a falling stone during the London earthquake of 1580.

Destructive as they are, earthquakes are of great help to scientists in their study of the interior of our globe, since earthquake waves originate in some point of the earth's crust and propagate to other points on the surface of the globe through its deep interior. As we have seen above (Chapter 3), there are two kinds of waves that propagate through a continuous medium:

1. *P-waves* (pressure or push waves) are longitudinal waves that can propagate equally well through a solid and through a fluid medium.

2. *S-waves* (shear or side waves) are transverse waves that can propagate through solids but not through liquids.

When an earthquake wave from a distant disturbance arrives at the surface of the earth, the motion of the ground in the case of P-waves will be in the direction of propagation, while in the case of S-waves this motion will be perpendicular to it. This permits us to distinguish between P- and S-waves by registering the movements of the ground by means of very sensitive instruments known as *seismographs*.

Seismographs are based on the law of inertia, according to which each body at rest tends to preserve its state of rest. A simple seismograph, known as the *horizontal pendulum*, is shown in Fig. 15-3 and consists essentially of a heavy weight, A, which can move with very little friction around the vertical pole, B. If the ground on which this instrument is installed is jerked by an earthquake wave in a direction perpendicular to the vertical plane passing through the pole and the weight, the weight remains immovable because of its large inertia, and the displacement of the stand relative to the resting weight is registered on the rotating drum,

C. Two such instruments installed at right angles to each other give us complete information about the horizontal displacements produced by the earthquake wave, and there are also seismographs that register the vertical displacements. The seismograms produced by these instruments

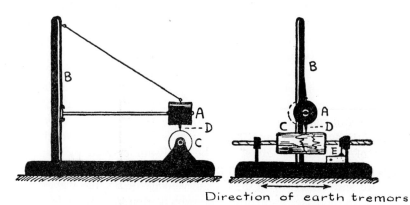

Direction of earth tremors

Fig. 15-3. A simple seismograph. A, a heavy weight suspended from a vertical support, B; C, a rotating cylinder driven by the clock mechanism, E; D, a writing pen. The arrow indicates the direction of earthquakes that can be registered by this apparatus.

permit us to carry out a complete analysis of the arriving disturbance.

Let us consider now what would be observed by seismic stations scattered all over the world when a sufficiently strong earthquake originates in some point of the earth's crust. Figure 15-4 shows the propagation lines of the disturbance originating in point *A* of the crust. At stations I, II, and III, located within 100 degrees from the center of the disturbance, both P- and S-waves are observed, which proves that the material of the earth possesses the property of an elastic solid (capable of experiencing a

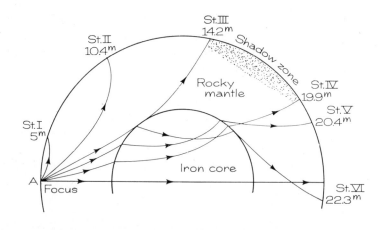

Fig. 15-4. The propagation lines of an elastic disturbance originating in the earth's crust.

shear) up to very great depths. This fact is the basis for the statement made above to the effect that, although the deep-lying rocks are heated well above their melting point, they retain the properties of an elastic solid in respect to rapid deformations such as those caused by a propagating S-wave.

The amazing point about earthquakes is that *beyond a distance of 100 degrees from the center of the disturbance, there always exists a ring-shaped "shadow zone" within which the earthquake waves are not felt at all.* Movements of the crust again become noticeable within 35 degrees of the antipode point (i.e., the point directly opposite the origin of the earthquake), but only those produced by the P-waves. To explain this unusual fact, seismologists, i.e., scientists who study earthquakes, had to assume that *the central part of the earth is occupied by a core that is in a liquid state and thus cannot carry S-waves.* With this assumption, the existence of the "shadow zone" can be easily understood by inspecting the rays of earthquake waves shown in Fig. 15-4. Due to a rapid increase of pressure and density with depth, the velocity of seismic waves (both P and S) also increases and causes the propagation lines to bend slightly towards the surface. Thus, the waves arriving at station III, after passing very close to the surface of the molten core, are the last ones that still propagate all the way through the plastic material of the rocky mantle. The rays that propagate deeper inward will hit the surface of the core, and while S-waves will not be able to propagate beyond this point at all, P-waves will be refracted as shown in Fig. 15-4. After the second refraction at the exit point from the liquid core, the P-waves will finally arrive at the surface much closer to the antipodal point and thus produce a ring-shaped shadow zone.

The knowledge of the propagation velocities of seismic waves at different depths under the surface enables us to get information concerning the material from which the interior of the earth is formed. It was found in this way that *our globe has an onion-like structure consisting of a large number of concentric shells.* Under a comparatively thin layer of granite rocks, which form the continental massifs, is located a layer of heavier basalt rocks. As it was indicated above, this basalt material below the depth of about 50 km is heated above its regular melting point but remains in a plastic state because of high pressure. The extensive studies of seismic waves propagating through the earth's interior led to the discovery of other layers with interfaces located at depths of 400 and 960 km. The most interesting discontinuity occurs, however, at the surface of the central core, 2,900 km under our feet, or at 60 per cent of the earth's radius from its center. At this interface, the density, which steadily increases (because of compression) from 3.0 at the surface to about 5.5 at this interface, jumps suddenly to 9.5, indicating that the core is composed of some considerably denser material. It is generally agreed that *the core of the earth lying within this interface is formed almost exclusively by molten iron with a small admixture of chromium, molybdenum, and nickel.* The temperature of the core is estimated to be at least 2,000°C, which is considerably higher than the melting point of iron (1,535°C).

Why Is the Earth Hot Inside?

Until a few decades ago, it was generally assumed that the earth, as well as all the other planets, was formed from the hot material of the sun and that its interior had just not had time to cool. We know now (see Chapter 18) that this is not so and that the planets of the solar system were formed by the aggregation of cool interstellar gas and dust particles during the formation of the sun itself. Thus, one possible way to explain the heating of the central part of the globe is to ascribe it to the compression of the material under the action of Newtonian gravitational forces. And, indeed, it can be calculated that the potential energy of gravity liberated in the process of the condensation of a body as large as the earth (from a thin dust cloud) would be enough to heat its material to a temperature of a few thousand degrees.

But there is another possibility that cannot be overlooked. It is that the heat now contained in the interior of the earth may not be left over from the original formation process of our planet, but, quite on the contrary, may be an accumulation that took place after its formation. In fact, we know that the rocks forming the crust of the earth contain a certain amount of natural radioactive elements which liberate nuclear energy at a slow but steady rate. It has been calculated that, if the concentration of these natural radioactive elements in the interior of the earth were about the same as we find on its surface, the amount of heat liberated since the formation of the earth would be large enough to turn it into a flaming red-hot sphere. Since this is not the case, we have to assume that *natural radioactive elements are considerably rarer in the earth's interior,* which is in good agreement with the observed fact that the deep lying basalt rocks are considerably less radioactive than the surface granite rocks. One ton of ordinary granite rock contains 9 gm of uranium and 20 gm of thorium, while for basalt rocks the figures are only 3.5 and 7.7. However, there is no way of setting a lower limit for the abundance of natural radioactive elements in the earth's interior, so the possibility is not excluded that the molten state of the earth's core is the direct result of this radioactive heating. Many scientists are even inclined to believe that, instead of cooling down, our planet is still being gradually heated up by radioactive decay.

We have just mentioned that natural radioactive elements are encountered almost exclusively in the thin outer crust of the earth. Why is this so? If the earth was formed by an aggregation of dust particles of interstellar material, its original composition should have been uniform from the center to the surface. The accumulation of radioactivity in the crust, therefore, must be a secondary effect. One possibility, the so-called "Alka Seltzer Theory," is that the parts of the earth's material which contained radioactive elements were heated above the temperature of their surroundings and floated up towards the surface. Another possible explanation of the high radioactivity of the surface crust is that the radioactive elements were acquired by the earth *after* its formation. In fact, it was recently demonstrated that the giant stellar explosions known as supernovae (see Chapter 20) produce large amounts of radioactive elements which are scattered through the space of the universe by the force of the blast. Thus, it may well be that during some phase of its early history our solar system passed through such a radioactive cloud and became contaminated by its material.

Upside-down Mountains

The plasticity of the earth's mantle is of paramount importance in determining the surface features of the earth with its extensive continental massifs, towering mountains, and deep ocean basins. If the earth's crust were smooth and uniform, like a layer of ice on a frozen lake, there would be no dry land, the entire surface of the globe would be covered by an ocean of uniform depth, and the higher forms of life on the earth would be confined to (maybe very intelligent) fish. That this is not so is due to the fact that the earth's crust does not have the same thickness and composition everywhere.

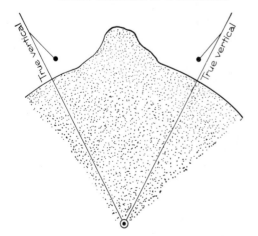

Fig. 15-5. The expected deflection of a pendulum by the Newtonian attraction of a mountain.

When we look at a high mountain range rising thousands of feet above the surrounding plain, we are inclined to consider it merely as a gigantic excrescence of rock piled on the surface of the earth, much as an artificial hill built up by engineers. Such a primitive view, which regards mountains as wholly a surface feature, was common in geology a century ago, and it was only comparatively recently that the students of the earth's surface features came to the conclusion that *the bulk of any mountain is situated under the surface of the earth.* The discovery of these "mountain roots" going very deep under the earth's surface resulted from the study of the gravitational action of a mountain upon two pendulums suspended on opposite sides of it. According to the law of Newtonian gravity, we would expect the great mass of a mountain to deflect the two pendulums from the "true vertical" as illustrated in Fig. 15-5. Of course, in this instance the term "true vertical" is defined not as a plumb line, but as the direction to the center of the earth given by the observation of stars in the two localities. To the great surprise of the scientists who carried out these experiments for the first time, the observed deviation of the plumb line from the true vertical in the vicinity of great mountains did not confirm the theoretical expectations. In the case of Mount Everest, for example, the observed deviations were about three times smaller than should be expected from its giant mass, while the Pyrenees even seemed to repel the pendulum instead of attracting it!

The absence of the expected additional gravitational attraction was originally interpreted as indicating that the mountains were hollow inside, something like giant blisters on the earth's crust. We know now that this interpretation was wrong and that the correct explanation of the observed facts can be traced back to the plasticity of semi-molten layers many hundreds of kilometers under the surface of the earth. According to the present view, the mountains on the surface of the earth represent formations similar to the ice hills produced on polar ice floes by the compression of ice. Every polar explorer knows that when crowded blocks of floating ice, broken by compression, are piled on top of one another, most of the ice sinks below the surface to keep the rest afloat. And when a polar bear sees a high hill rising above the surface of an ice floe, a seal swimming under it will notice an even larger bulge protruding down into the water. Similarly, *under each mountain rising above the surface of the earth there exists, so to speak, a "negative mountain" formed by rocky granite material protruding into the underlying plastic layers of more dense semi-molten basalt on which it "floats"* (Fig. 15-6).

According to Archimedes' law (Chapter 1), the weight of the floating body must be equal to the weight of the displaced material underneath, so that the presence of an elevation on a floating crust does not signify any actual increase in the weight or mass of material in this region. Accepting this point of view, known as the theory of *isostatic equilibrium,* we can dispose of the question: "Why does the mountain not affect the plumb line as much as would be expected from its apparent mass?" We should rather ask: "Why are there any deviations in the plumb line at all?" To answer this question we must bear in mind that the "weight" of the plumb bob is caused by the attraction between the bob and every separate piece of rock in the whole earth. Obviously, however, the cubic mile of rock directly underfoot will have much more influence than a cubic mile of rock in Australia.

If a mountain range rears up above the surrounding plains, it must be "floating" on an especially thick layer of light granite rock beneath it. This is the material that, being close, has a strong influence on how the plumb line behaves. Since this material is relatively light, its pull on the bob is weak, and the plumb line is deflected less toward the mountain than we would expect.

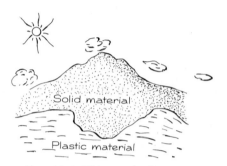

Fig. 15-6. The upside-down mountain. The weight of the rocky material protruding above the earth's surface is supported by an anti-mountain protruding down into the plastic interior of the earth.

Although beneath each mountain range there is a roughly corresponding "upside-down" range of light granite, the elasticity of the earth's crust prevents the "upside-down" mountains from looking *exactly* like their counterparts above the surface, and an imaginary "negative mountain" climber making his way through the masses of plastic basalt deep under the Rocky Mountains will look in vain for anything resembling an upside-down Pike's Peak. Neither should we expect such man-made mountains as the Egyptian Pyramids, New York's skyscrapers, or the Pentagon Building to have their counterparts in the upside-down mountain landscape hundreds of miles under our feet!

Floating Continents

The existence of five continents (North and South America, Eurasia, Africa, and Antarctica) separated by comparatively deep ocean basins also must be ascribed to isostatic equilibrium. As was mentioned above, the outermost layers of the earth's crust are formed by *granite* with a density of 2.65 with respect to water, while the deeper layers are formed by basalt with a density of 3.0. Although in the case of the continental massifs the thickness of the granite layer is quite considerable, this layer is much thinner or even absent at the bottom of the oceans. Thus, we may consider continental massifs as solid blocks of lighter material (granite) floating in heavier plastic material (basalt) in much the same way as icebergs float in water. Using Archimedes' law, we can calculate that in isostatic equilibrium only one-ninth of the granite blocks protrudes above the surface of the basalt. Since, however, the ocean basins are not empty, but are filled with water, which adds an extra weight, we would expect about one-seventh of the granite blocks to protrude above the ocean bottom. Since the mean depth of the ocean is about 4 km and the mean elevation of the continents above the ocean level is about 1 km, the granite blocks constituting the continents protrude about 5 km above the basalt surface. Thus, according to the above crude arguments, the thickness of the granite layer forming the continental massif must be about seven times that much or about 35 km.

This conclusion is in good agreement with the fact that the volcanic lavas apparently coming from a depth of about 50 km consist entirely of basalt material, whereas the volcanic eruptions of the past, which must have taken place at a time when the solid crust was somewhat thinner than it is now, were still ejecting large masses of molten granite. At the present stage of the cooling of our planet, the solidification of the crust under the continents has progressed beyond the demarcation line between the granite and basalt layers. We can, therefore, picture the solid crust of the earth as being composed of separate pieces of two rather different types of rocks (granite and basalt), strongly welded together and floating on the underlying layer of plastic basalt material (Fig. 15-7).

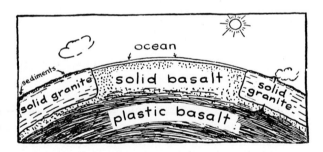

Fig. 15-7. The structure of the earth's crust.

The adjustment of the earth's crust under the shifts of mass on its surface has played a very important role in the evolution of the face of our planet. For example, considerable isostatic adjustment took place during the glacial periods when thick sheets of ice covered much of North America and Europe. The weight of the ice caused the northern regions of these continents to sink deeper into the plastic layer of basalt underneath. At the present time, when most of the ice is gone, the depressed parts of the continents are slowly rising towards their pre-Ice Age level, and we can notice a slow regression of the seas along many shore lines of the northern countries.

The Tides in Rocks

Everyone is familiar with the ocean tides caused by the gravitational attraction exerted by the moon and the sun on the ocean's water, and in Chapter 17 we will discuss the ocean tides in some more detail. But the effect of tidal forces is, of course, not confined to the periodic disturbances of the liquid envelope of our planet alone; the earth's rocky body itself is being periodically pushed and pulled by the changing gravitational forces on its opposite flanks. We have already seen that the matter of the earth's interior exhibits plastic properties in response to forces persistently acting in the same direction over very long periods of time. But, since the tidal forces change their direction every six hours, we may expect that in response to these forces the body of the earth behaves as an almost perfectly elastic sphere.

Since the solid body of the earth is less deformable than its liquid envelope, the "tides in the rocks" are smaller than the tides in the oceans, and the rise and fall of the water level that we observe at the seashore must result from the difference between the heights of the two tides. Although we can easily measure this difference, the determination of the separate heights of the two tides is very difficult. In fact, since the deformations of the earth's body result in the periodic rise and fall of the entire surface surrounding the observer, the tides in the rocks cannot be noticed by an observer on the ground, just as the ocean tides cannot be observed from a boat on the open ocean. One way to estimate the height of the rock tides is to calculate the expected height of oceanic tides on the basis of Newton's law and to compare this value with the observed relative elevations of the ocean and land levels. Unfortunately, the theoretical calculation of the ocean tides, which would be very simple if the earth were a smooth, regular sphere, becomes prohibitively difficult because we must take into account all the irregularities of the ocean shores and the varying depths of the ocean basins.

This difficulty was solved in a very ingenious way by the American physicist, Albert A. Michelson (1852-1931), who studied the "microtides" raised by solar and lunar attraction in comparatively small bodies of water. His apparatus consisted of a carefully leveled iron pipe, about 50 meters long, which was half filled with water (Fig. 15-8). Under the action of the gravitational forces of the sun and the moon, the water surface in this pipe behaved exactly like the water in the oceans, periodically changing its inclination to a fixed direction in space.

Since this "Michelson's ocean" has considerably smaller linear dimensions than, let us say, the Pacific Ocean (50 meters as against 16,000 kilometers), the same inclination of the surface will cause only very small vertical displacements of the water level at the opposite ends of the pipe, so small in fact that they cannot be noticed with the naked eye. Using a microscope, however, Michelson was able to observe these small variations of the water level, which amounted to only 0.0004 centimeter at

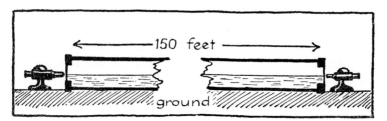

Fig. 15-8. Michelson's apparatus for the study of tides under laboratory conditions.

their maximum. In spite of the small size of these "microtides" he was able to observe all the phenomena familiar on a large scale in the ocean basins of our planet, such as the exceptionally high tides during new moon and full moon periods.*

By comparing the observed height of the tides in his "micro-ocean" with the theoretical values they should have, which can be easily calculated for this simple case, Michelson noticed that his "oceanic" tide amounted to only 69 per cent of the expected effect. The theoretical calculations predicted what the tides would have been if the earth were absolutely unyielding; what Michelson measured was, of course, the observed tide relative to the earth's surface. Since this relative motion was only 69 per cent of the theoretical total, the remaining 31 per cent must represent the actual tidal movement of the earth's solid surface.

The tides in open oceans measure about 75 cm (2½ feet).† As this is only 69 per cent of what they would be if the earth were absolutely unyielding, the theoretical total tide must be about 110 cm. The difference, or 35 cm, must represent the tidal movement of the solid earth itself. Thus, strange as it seems, *the ground under our feet is periodically moving up and down with all the cities, hills, and mountains on its surface.* It is pulled up every time the moon is high in the sky and sinks down again as soon as the moon approaches the horizon. The second upward motion occurs when the moon is directly under our feet and, so

---

* These high tides are due to the fact that during these periods the earth, moon, and sun are all in a line, so that the pulls of the sun and the moon on the earth's waters are combined.

† The values were observed from an isolated Pacific island that was too small to affect appreciably the motion of oceanic waters.

to speak, pulls the entire globe down from under us. It goes without saying that this up-and-down motion proceeds so smoothly that it cannot be directly detected by even the most sensitive physical apparatus. The observed fact that the tides in rocks are about three times smaller than the tides in water indicates that our globe is comparatively highly rigid, and, by using the theory of elasticity, we can calculate from these data the rigidity of the earth as a whole. By so doing, the famous English physicist, Lord Kelvin, was the first to arrive at the conclusion that *the rigidity of the earth's body is as high as if it were made of solid steel.* As was said above, this result does not contradict the fact that, in response to weak but persistent forces, our globe behaves like a soft plastic body.

The Rise of Mountains

In studying mountain ranges, geologists long ago noticed that most of them are made up of layers of rock that have been wrinkled up into great folds. Since these layers had originally been deposited in nearly flat sheets on the bottom of an ancient ocean, it was evident that some enormous force had slowly pushed them up into a series of giant wavy folds. If you push against the opposite edges of a pile of handkerchiefs, you will get a good idea of what must have taken place. This has happened in many places at many times in the earth's history, and it is difficult to escape the conclusion that the earth is shrinking and wrinkling up its crust in the same way that a smooth plum becomes a wrinkled prune as it dries out and becomes smaller.

In the days before the discovery of radioactivity, geologists tried to explain this shrinkage by saying that the earth was cooling. This, however, was not a very successful explanation. We know that since the temperature of the earth's crust rises about 30°C per kilometer of depth, there *is* a steady flow of heat from the interior out through the earth's surface into space. Physicists know the heat conductivity of basalt and granite, and from this and the known surface area of the earth it can be computed that the earth has lost something like 10^{30} calories in the past 4 billion years. Dividing this number of calories by the mass of the earth (6×10^{27} gm), we find that each gram of the earth on the average has lost about 165 calories. Since the heat capacity of the earth's material is about 0.2 cal/°C, this means that the earth must have cooled by about 800°C since the formation of its solid crust.

How much shrinkage would this amount of cooling cause? If we apply an average figure of $8 \times 10^{-6}/°C$ for the linear coefficient of the expansion of rocky material, we can, after a little arithmetical juggling, come to the conclusion that it would have shortened the earth's circumference by about 200 miles. This is only enough to wrinkle up one good-sized mountain range, and is obviously not nearly enough to explain the many ranges that have been forming and eroding away during the earth's long history.

Anyway, since the discovery of radioactivity and of the distribution of radioactive elements throughout at least the earth's outer layers, we may expect that the earth's interior is actually getting hotter rather than cooler. Is there any reasonable way in which we can picture the earth warming up on the inside and, at the same time, shrinking? There is, but to see it we must look, not at the surface, but in the deep interior at the boundary between the plastic mantle and the fluid core.

Imagine an earth made of a solid block of ice, with bits of radioactive materials scattered through it. As the radioactive heat collects, the center begins to melt, and the ice-earth has a core of water that continues to grow as more and more of the mantle melts away at its boundary. Since the density of ice is only about 90 per cent that of water, every cubic mile of ice that melts forms only 0.9 cubic mile of water, and the volume of the ice-earth is lessened by 0.1 cubic mile. (The great pressure will keep any cavity from forming, of course, and the whole mass of the mantle will slowly shrink inward.)

If this is what is happening to our own earth, we need only substitute for ice some unknown iron compound. The change in density from mantle to core is from 5.5 to 9.5, so that each cubic mile of mantle that changes to the fluid state of the core will shrink in volume by 0.42 cubic mile, with an equal reduction in volume for the whole earth.

This may be the answer. Our earth, heated inside by radioactive energy, may be growing smaller as its fluid core grows larger, causing its surface rocks to wrinkle into huge ranges of mountains as it shrinks.

SOME DETAILS OF MOUNTAIN FOLDING

In order to follow the processes of mountain folding in some detail, and, in particular, to understand the behavior of land and sea during the revolutionary epochs when the crust shook and crumpled all over the world, we must first bear in mind that the surface of our globe consists of two entirely different types of rocks: granite rocks forming the continents and basalt rocks forming the ocean beds.

Laboratory investigations show that basalt is considerably stronger than granite, from which it follows that most of the crumpling in the wrinkling process must be limited to the continental areas. This conclusion is in agreement with the observational evidence, which indicates that the mountain-folding activity is largely confined to the surfaces of the continents. Moreover, the weakest places of the earth's solid crust are evidently situated along the junction lines of its granite and basaltic regions, which accounts for the very pronounced volcanic and mountain-raising activity along the continental shore lines. In particular, the ring of mountains and active volcanoes surrounding the basin of the Pacific Ocean (the "ring of fire") is obviously attributable to the comparative weakness of the basalt-granite junction line.

In Fig. 15-9 we give a schematic view of what must happen to a granite continental block compressed on all sides by the layers of solid basalt forming the bottom of the surrounding oceans. The first effect of the compression is evidently a slow bending of the granite layer, resulting in a general uplifting of its surface above the level of the surrounding ocean. During this "bending-up" process, the central regions of the continent are obviously not in a state of isostatic equilibrium, and the weight of the elevated portion is largely supported by the rigidity of the continent's constituent rocks.

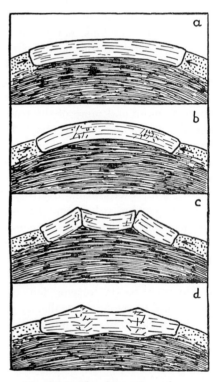

As the shrinking and compression continue, the bending of the continent progressively increases, and the internal stresses in the crust grow larger and larger until they finally reach the breaking point of granite. The rocks forming the crust are no longer able to resist the increasing pressure, the crust breaks and crumples,

Fig. 15-9. The formation of mountain folds as the result of the compression of the continental massifs.

and the "top of the dome" begins to sink in. This collapse of the continental dome occurs very slowly, of course, because it must be accompanied by the extrusion of the plastic material from below, and, as we have seen above, all movements in the viscous plastic layer of our globe are bound to be extremely slow. It may take millions of years before the central parts of the continent, uplifted by the previous contraction, return to their original level; when this state is finally reached, the surface will be covered by numerous high ranges of crumpled and folded rocks formed from the excess material.

The Rains Versus the Mountains

We have mentioned more than once that those parts of the continental massifs above sea level, especially the high mountains raised by the crumpling of the crust, are subject to the continuous destructive action of water, which pours down on them from the sky during rainy periods and carries large quantities of dissolved and mechanically eroded material into the surrounding seas. The amount of soluble salts carried to the ocean as the result of the past erosion of continental blocks totals about 20,000,000 cubic km. If we were able to extract all this salt from the sea and distribute it uniformly over the land surface of the earth, it would form a layer 135 meters (about 450 feet) thick. But salt represents only a very small portion of granite rocks (about 5 per cent), so that *in order to wash out the amount of salt now dissolved in the ocean, rain water has had to erode a granite layer more than 2 km thick!* The salt extracted from the rocks remains in solution, but the other products of erosion, such as sand and gravel, are deposited on the ocean bottom bordering the shore line or on the bottoms of intracontinental seas, forming a steadily growing layer of *sedimentary rocks.*

The idea that rain water can wash away thousands of feet of continental surface and level the highest mountain ranges will not seem so strange if we bear in mind the enormous periods of time during which this destructive process has been steadily going on. Direct measurements of the amount of mud carried away by rivers indicate that the surface of the United States alone loses about 800,000,000 tons of its rocky material annually, so that denudation by rain water reduces the average height of the continents by 0.22 mm per year.* Since Columbus first stepped on the shore of the New World, a layer of earth about 4 inches thick has been carried away into the oceans and seas!

Erosion by rain water is responsible for such peculiar features of the earth's surface as the Bad Lands of South Dakota (Fig. 15-10). Since the surface of the earth consists of various kinds of rocks with varying resistance to the destructive action of water, the landscape of denuded areas often assumes strange and fantastic shapes. One example is the impressive structure known as Devil's Tower (Fig. 15-11), familiar to travelers who

---

* The reader must remember that this rate of erosion, corresponding to the present epoch of high mountains, is several times larger than it was during the long submergence stages, when most of the mountains had already been washed away.

Fig. 15-10. The fantastically eroded escarpments of the Bad Lands of South Dakota. *Courtesy U. S. Geologic Survey.*

have driven through Wyoming along U. S. Highway 14. Once upon a time this spot was occupied by a magnificent volcano, which was an outlet for the masses of molten magma below. Later, the volcanic activity in this region ceased, and the solidified lava filling the volcanic crater formed a long vertical column of basalt. Rain water worked on the dead volcano for centuries upon centuries and after hundreds of thousands of years finally succeeded in washing away the outer part of the cone formed by the volcanic ashes of numerous eruptions. The remaining tower is merely the original column of solidified lava, and since basalt withstands erosion much better than the softer material of the cone, it will probably take many more hundreds of thousands of years for the rain to remove completely this last remainder of the ancient volcano.

Since the destruction of mountains by the rapid streams that rush down their steep slopes proceeds considerably faster than the erosion of flatlands, we must expect that the *general effect of the action of rain water will be to obliterate all the characteristic features produced by the crumpling of the crust and transform the continental surfaces into exten-*

Fig. 15-11. Devil's Tower, Wyoming, the solidified core of an old extinct volcano. Courtesy U. S. Geologic Survey.

sive low plains. It must be noted, however, that to wash away a mountain, rain water must do considerably more work than would seem necessary at first sight. As the material of the mountain is carried away by rushing streams, the mountain itself, of course, becomes lighter. As it does so, the process of isostatic adjustment described above operates so that new rock slowly rises up from below to restore the balance again. To remove the mountains completely and permanently from the surface of the earth, it would be necessary to erode away not only their visible protruding part, but also the "roots" (which penetrate deep into the crust) as they are slowly pushed up. If some ambitious railway company were constructing a new line through a mountainous region and should decide to remove a whole mountain instead of digging a tunnel through it, the advantage obtained by this gigantic construction job would be only temporary, since in a few hundred thousand years a new mountain, of only slightly smaller size, would again rise on the same spot!

Parallel with the upward movement of the mountain regions as they are eroded is the slow sinking of those parts of the earth's surface on which the streams and rivers deposit their loads of eroded material. Since the mountains are raised mainly along the continental shore lines, and since the rain water falling on a mountain runs down both its sides, these sinking regions of the crust form the ocean bottoms bordering the continents and the bottoms of the comparatively shallow seas that are often formed in the low central portions of the continental massifs. As we have said, the deformation of the earth's crust resulting from processes of this kind may cause some additional wrinkling of the surface and the formation of local mountain chains.

From the observed rate of denudation, it is estimated that the time necessary for rain water to obliterate the mountains raised during a revolutionary epoch of mountain formation is only a fraction of the length of the period between such revolutions. Hence we must conclude that *the surface of the earth has been quite featureless and flat during most of its history,* with many areas completely covered by shallow seas, and that it is our special privilege to live during one of the comparatively short epochs when the mountains raised by the last revolution are still standing proudly, providing us with beautiful scenery and splendid opportunities for climbing and skiing.

Terrestrial Magnetism

The knowledge that pieces of certain naturally occurring iron ores can indicate the direction of the north and south poles existed in China for countless centuries and was brought to Europe by Marco Polo, among many other oriental rarities. The extensive studies of the earth's magnetic field, which is of paramount importance for navigation, led to the construction of magnetic maps from which it became evident that the magnetic poles of the earth do not coincide with its geographic poles. The "north magnetic pole" (which is actually the south pole of the earth's magnet) is located in northern Canada, $11\frac{1}{2}$ degrees of latitude from the geographic pole, and the "south magnetic pole" lies at the same distance from the geographic south pole in Antarctica. The famous German mathematician, Karl Friedrich Gauss (1777-1855), showed that the magnetic field of the earth can be described, in a very good approximation, as being produced by a single magnet located in its interior and slightly inclined with respect to the rotation axis (Fig. 15-12).

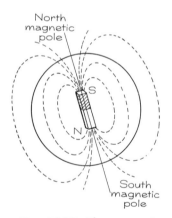

Fig. 15-12. The magnetic field observed on the surface of the earth can be explained (in its main features) as being due to a magnet placed in the center of the globe.

However, on this primary geomagnetic field is overlapped a second weaker field of magnetic forces that shows a rather irregular pattern. If we subtract from the actually observed field, the field that would corre-

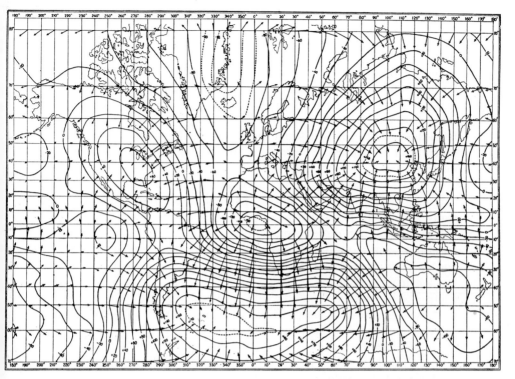

Fig. 15-13. Deviations of the earth's magnetic field from the field that would be produced by a single magnet in the center of the earth in the year 1945. From E. C. Bullard, C. Freedman, H. Gellman, and J. Nixon, Phil. Trans. R. Soc. 243 A. 1950.

spond to a single magnet in the center of the earth, we obtain the distribution shown in Fig. 15-13, which has no apparent correlation with the rotation of the earth around its axis. The characteristic features of this secondary field are that it is slowly changing and that its entire pattern is drifting westward at a rate of 0.18 degrees per year. This movement causes secular (i.e., slowly varying) changes in the direction assumed by magnetic needles in fixed localities on the earth's surface and necessitates the redrawing of navigational maps from year to year. In addition, there is also a magnetic component produced by electric currents in the uppermost layer of the terrestrial atmosphere known as the *ionosphere* (Chapter 17).

For a long time the origin of geomagnetic fields was surrounded by the fog of mystery, but recent developments have been made, mostly due to the work of Sir E. Bullard in England and W. M. Elsasser in the United States, that strongly suggest that these fields are caused by the nonuniform rotation of different layers in the molten iron core, which occupies about 60 per cent of the radius of our globe. In fact, it is natural to assume that the heat conduction in the molten iron core of the earth is mostly due to convective currents between the hot center and the cooler outer regions of the core. Because of the earth's rotation around its axis, the rising convective currents will be deflected *westwards* in the same way the air masses are that move along the surface of the earth from the poles to the equatorial regions. Thus, we would expect that the outer layers of the molten iron core would be rotating *slower* than its inner layers.

How can such a differential rotation of the electrically conductive iron core give rise to a magnetic field? A possible way is represented schematically in Fig. 15-14, which is a so-called "self-exciting disc dynamo." It consists of a rotating metal disc, A, and a ring-shaped conductor, B (which may have many windings), connected by brushes, C and C', with the disc and the axle, respectively. Imagine that a weak magnetic field is applied, let us say upwards, parallel to the axle. According to the law applicable to a conductor moving through a magnetic field (Chapter 5), an electric current (the so-called "Foucault current") will be induced in the disc and will flow radially from the periphery to the axle. Flowing through the ring-shaped conductor, this current will increase the strength of the magnetic field, which will, in turn, increase the strength of the

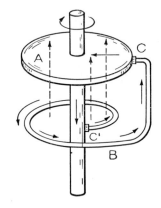

—————— Direction of electric current

◄— — — Direction of magnetic field

Fig. 15-14. A self-exciting disc dynamo.

current, etc. Thus, a very weak magnetic field applied to this system will rapidly grow to an upper limit determined by the electric resistivity of the metallic parts. These dynamos are impractical for technical applications because of their small electromotive power, but it is very likely that they represent a good model of what happens inside the earth where the inner part of the conductive iron core rotates with respect to its outer part. The calculations carried out in this direction indicate that such a process may lead to magnetic fields strong enough to account for the main magnetic field surrounding the earth.

The Wandering Poles

The most exciting recent development in the field of terrestrial magnetism is the discovery that in the distant geological past the magnetic poles of the earth were in entirely different locations from where they are now. This discovery came from the study of the natural magnetization of rocks that contain iron or iron compounds and that were magnetized in the direction of the geomagnetic field which existed in their locality at the time of their formation. These rocks may be igneous rocks containing iron that solidified after being erupted to the surface of the earth, or perhaps deposits on the bottoms of prehistoric lakes that contain tiny iron grains that originated from meteorites which fell on the earth millions of years ago. Imbedded in solid rocks, these tiny magnetic needles faithfully hold for us the record of the geomagnetic field in the distant past. These studies are made difficult by the fact that, since their formation, most geological layers have been folded and tilted by various tectonic processes so that the prehistoric compass needles imbedded in them were turned from their original direction. This difficulty can be overcome, however, by introducing the required correction, and the original direction of the magnetic field can be found rather exactly.

Fig. 15-15. The changing locations of the magnetic north pole.

In doing so, geologists have discovered that in past geological eras compass needles pointed in directions different from the present one. In Pre-Cambrian times (500,000,000 years ago), the north pole was located not far from Hawaii; in the Silurian period (300,000,000 years ago) it moved to Japan; and in the Eocene period (25,000 years ago) it was in northern Siberia not very far from its present location (Fig. 15-15). Since, because of the law of inertia, we cannot believe that the entire body of the earth was changing its axis of rotation, a plausible explanation is that the crust was slowly slipping over the surface of the plastic mantle. This slippage could be caused, for example, by the forces resulting from the uneven distribution of mass on the rotating crust. If, because of some mighty tectonic processes, a large mass of mountains (such as the Himalayas, or larger) were formed somewhere on the surface of the crust, the centrifugal force of the earth's rotation acting on it would tend to turn the entire rigid-crust shell in such a way as to bring that large mass to the equatorial region.

Another intriguing discovery pertains to what can be called the "pole exchange phenomenon." It seems that the north and south poles of our globe have a tendency to exchange places or "flop over" by 180° almost instantaneously from the geological point of view. And there are indications that there have been several hundred such "flop overs" during geological history! But the question of *why* the "flop over" takes place and *why* it happened so often in geological history is still a mystery.

SIXTEEN

THE "BOOK

OF SEDIMENTS"

Mechanics of Sedimentation

The continuous erosion of the continents and the deposition of the eroded materials at the bottoms of the seas
and the oceans give geologists an invaluable source of
information concerning the past history of the surface of
the earth. The reason for this is that the nature of these
deposits depends, to a large extent, on the characteristics
of the eroded surface. During the eras, such as the one in

which we are living, that follow revolutionary mountain-forming periods, high mountains exist on the surface of the continents and rapid streams rush down them and break off comparatively large pieces of rocks by purely mechanical action. Thus, the deposits formed during these periods contain much rather rough material, such as gravel and coarse sand. During the long inter-revolutionary periods, on the other hand, when most of the mountains have already been washed away and the surface of the continents is level and dull, the process of erosion is slower and proceeds in a gentler manner. There are no rushing mountain streams, no noisy waterfalls, and the rain water falling on the flat surface of the continents is drained into the oceans and seas by broad, slow-moving rivers.

Minor scenes of history can be read in the rocks that have been exposed by, for example, a new roadway cut through a section of old sedimentary deposits. The layers of these deposits, which were originally laid down flat, may be tilted nearly up on edge, the result of some great upheaval in the past. And these layers may contain imbedded in them first-sized or even head-sized rocks that were long ago carried down by a swift torrent and deposited in a shallow sea. Since these large rocks would sink at once, we know that the ground on which we stand was at one time at the mouth of a steep, rushing stream. If another one of these layers is made of shale, which is a soft, crumbly rock that is formed into many sheet-like layers from fine clay particles, we know the land must have sunk, so that the gravel and sand had already settled out, leaving the fine particles of clay to sink slowly to the bottom here, far out from the shore. A layer of limestone tells us that this spot was once at the bottom of a calm, quiet sea where shellfish flourished and buried the bottom deep with fragments of their shells, which were later formed into limestone by the pressure of succeeding deposits.

These regular deposits have often been intruded by igneous rocks that have erupted from the interior of the earth through the volcanoes of the past. Geologists can set up the time scale of the various sedimentary layers by measuring the ratio of uranium to lead in these intruded materials (see Chapter 14). Sedimentary layers may also contain the fossilized remains of the plants and animals that lived and died during the period when the deposits were made—a shell of a prehistoric clam, a leaf from a tree growing at the time when the world deposits of coal were formed, or the complete skeleton of a mighty dinosaur. By studying this nature-written "Book of Sediments" left to us by the world of the past page by page, we can reconstruct in detail the past geological history of our planet as well as the evolutionary history of the life that flourished on it many millions of centuries ago.

Since the surface of the continents has been moving up and down irregularly throughout the earth's history and since the interior seas have always been changing their sites, the records contained in the sediments left at any one place are necessarily incomplete. In Fig. 16-1 is a schematic picture of what we can expect to find at a spot that has been subjected to three submergences but is now on dry land. Let us suppose that during the first submergence period the deposits carried down by the rivers formed six successive layers, which we distinguish by the numbers 1 to 6. And suppose that after these layers, which represent a continuous record of the corresponding interval of the earth's history, were formed, movements of the crust elevated this particular locality above sea level, so that the newly formed layers were exposed to the destructive action of rain water. During the period of elevation, part of the sedimentary layers would be carried away by erosion, and this material, mixed with material taken from other places, would be deposited elsewhere. While new sedimentary layers (let us say 7, 8, 9, and 10) were being formed on the bottom of the ocean, where deposits accumulate continuously, our locality would lose the three upper layers (6, 5, and 4). Thus, when the new submergence occurred, layer 11 would begin to be deposited directly on top of the old layer 3.

If we inspect Fig. 16-1 further, we will find that the only sedimentary layers left in this hypothetical locality to present themselves to the hammer of the geologist are those numbered 1, 2, 3, 11, 12, 13, 19, 20, 21, 22, 23, 24. All the others were never formed, or else were eroded away by rain water.

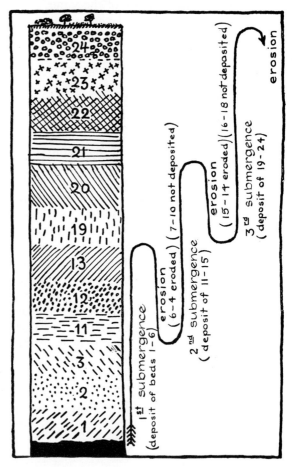

Fig. 16-1. A diagram showing how the periodic elevations of the ground spoil the continuity of geologic records.

Although the layers deposited in any given locality represent only occasional pages of the "Book of Sediments," we can try to reconstruct the complete copy of the book by comparing the findings in a number of places that were submerged at different times. This task is, of course, a very difficult one, and work in this field represents the main subject of historical geology. The principal method used in the reconstruction of the complete "geological column" from the disunited fragments is based on the "principle of overlapping" explained schematically in Fig. 16-2. By comparing two separate fragments of the sedimentation process in different localities, we may notice that the upper layers of one fragment are of the same nature as the lower layers of another. If such is the case, the conclusion is inevitable that the layers at the top of the first fragment were being formed simultaneously with the bottom layers of the second, and if we put the two fragments together so that the layers formed at the same time overlap, we get a continuous record covering the larger time interval.

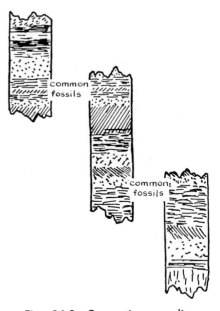

Fig. 16-2. Connecting up disconnected fragments of the "Book of Sediments."

A similar method of overlapping is very successfully used in studying prehistoric Indian villages in different parts of North America. Since most such villages were situated on a lake shore, at the bottoms of these lakes can be found a large number of petrified logs that once formed the village buildings. The pattern of concentric annual-growth rings in the cross-section of a tree trunk is just as characteristic of the time interval during which the tree was growing as a fingerprint is characteristic of a man, and the growth of the rings depends upon the climatic conditions during the life span of the tree. During warm summers with plenty of rain, the annual rings will grow thicker, whereas very thin rings will grow in dry summers, so that the pattern formed by the sequence of wide and thin rings forms a record of the weather during the time the tree was growing. Thus, if two logs can be found in which the patterns of annual rings partly overlap, we can be sure that the two trees were growing at the same time. By putting together a large number of logs, selected in such a way that the outer rings of each (i.e., the rings formed shortly before the tree was cut down) coincide with the more central rings on the next log, it is possible to build a continuous "tree column" covering an interval of many centuries. From this column, we can get exact information as to the dates when different logs were cut down for construction purposes, and, what is more interesting, we can also get a rough meteorological record of the climatic changes in this particular locality over a period of time during which the word "meteorology" itself was unknown.

It must be borne in mind, however, that since the differences between the physical and chemical characteristics of various rock deposits may not be very large, and since the same kinds of deposits are repeated periodically in time, the method of overlapping described above might not yield much in the way of results if the sedimentary layer did not contain the fossilized remains of different plants and animals living during the various epochs (Fig. 16-3). In fact, the development of historical geology is inseparably connected with the development of paleontology (i.e., the science of ancient life); in addition to the complete geological column representing the history of land and sea, we also get the complete record of the evolution of life.

The work of collecting the fragmentary pages of the earth's history here and there and binding them together into one consistent volume becomes increasingly difficult, of course, as we go back into more and more remote epochs. The later parts of the "Book of Sediments" are fairly complete by now, but the records of earlier periods are still in a very imperfect state. The classification of these early pages of the book is particularly difficult because at the time they were "written" life on the earth either did not exist at all or was limited to the simplest organisms, which left no trace in the sediments of that time.

Even a completed "Book of Sediments" would possess one essential defect: It would lack any chronology, and though we could say that one layer was formed after or before another, we would have no idea of the period of time separating them. In order to get the "timing" of geological events, very elaborate but uncertain speculations about the deposition rates of different types of materials have always been necessary, and it is therefore very fortunate that the discovery of radioactivity has given us a much simpler and much more exact method of establishing a geological time scale.

In Chapter 14 we described in some detail how radioactivity gives us a fairly good idea of the time when different igneous rocks solidified. By studying the relative amounts of the disintegration products of uranium and thorium contained in eruptions in the past that are found now

Fig. 16-3 (left). A fossilized fish from Eocene deposits near Green River, Wyo. *Courtesy Nancy Atkins, Boulder, Colo.*

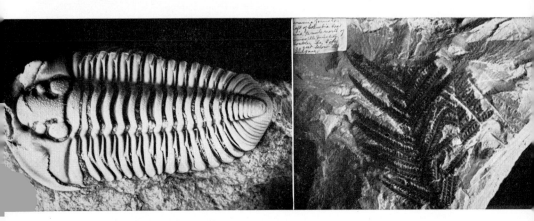

Fig. 16-3. (Left above) A fossil of a trilobite from Ordovician deposits in Quebec excavated by Dr. F. Rasetti. These animals dominated the earth about 400 million years ago. (Right above) The fossil of a plant that grew on the earth's surface during the late Mesozoic era. *Courtesy Museum of the Univ. of Colo.* (Below) The giant dinosaur *Tyrannosaurus rex* that roamed North America in the Cretaceous period. *Courtesy American Museum of Natural History.*

and then in different sedimentary layers, we can add the last touch to the "Book of Sediments" by marking on each page the approximate date on which that page was "written."

Chapters and Paragraphs
of the "Book of Sediments"

The "Book of Sediments," as reconstructed by the work of generations of geologists, represents a most extensive historic document, alongside which all the thick volumes of the history of the human race are no more than an insignificant booklet. The layer eroded from continental surfaces by rain water is, on the average, some 2 kilometers thick. Since these disintegration products are mostly deposited in comparatively small areas along the shores, however, the actual thickness of the geologic column is considerably greater. By putting together all the fragmented pieces that have been found so far, geologists have calculated that the resulting column has a total thickness of about 100 kilometers, with each year corresponding to a layer of about 0.1 millimeter thick. *If we consider a year's deposit as one "page" of the "Book of Sediments," such a page will be comparable in thickness with a page in any ordinary book. The reconstructed part of the "book" will have about one billion pages, covering the same number of years in the earth's history.* This thickness, however, is only that of the later part of the evolution of the surface of our planet, and there probably are several billions of earlier fragmented pages that are still largely hidden under the surface. Pursuing our analogy with an ordinary book, we must bear in mind, of course, that one page of the "earth book" does not record much of its history and that in order to notice any changes one must thumb through at least several hundred thousand pages. This fact is also true of the book of human history; although the year-to-year changes may have been of special interest to the persons living during those epochs, considerably longer periods of time are needed to manifest any interesting changes in the evolution of humanity.

The first important feature of the "Book of Sediments" is that, like any other book, it is divided into a number of separate chapters, which correspond to the mountain-building epochs and to the intermediate long periods of submergence discussed above. It is very hard to say how many chapters there are in the "book," since its earliest parts are still in a very fragmentary and incomplete state; only the last three chapters covering the last 500,000,000 years tell a more or less complete and consistent story. These last three chapters represent about one-tenth of the total life span of our planet and are of particular interest, since, as we indicated

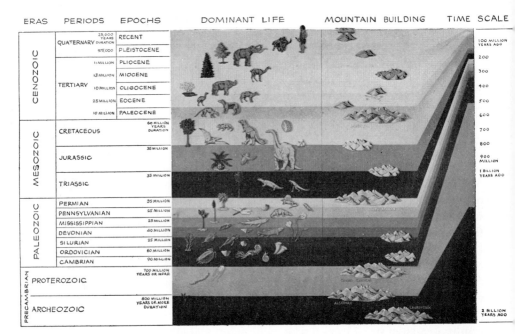

ERAS	PERIODS		EPOCHS	DOMINANT LIFE — MOUNTAIN BUILDING	TIME SCALE
CENOZOIC	QUATERNARY	25,000 YEARS DURATION	RECENT		100 MILLION YEARS AGO
		975,000	PLEISTOCENE		200
	TERTIARY	11 MILLION	PLIOCENE		300
		13 MILLION	MIOCENE		400
		10 MILLION	OLIGOCENE		500
		25 MILLION	EOCENE		600
		10 MILLION	PALEOCENE		
MESOZOIC	CRETACEOUS	60 MILLION YEARS DURATION			700
	JURASSIC	35 MILLION			800
	TRIASSIC	35 MILLION			900 MILLION
PALEOZOIC	PERMIAN	35 MILLION			1 BILLION YEARS AGO
	PENNSYLVANIAN	25 MILLION			
	MISSISSIPPIAN	25 MILLION			
	DEVONIAN	40 MILLION			
	SILURIAN	25 MILLION			
	ORDOVICIAN	60 MILLION			
	CAMBRIAN	90 MILLION			
PRECAMBRIAN	PROTEROZOIC	700 MILLION YEARS OR MORE			
	ARCHEOZOIC	800 MILLION YEARS OR MORE DURATION			2 BILLION YEARS AGO

Fig. 16-4. A chart showing the geological history of the earth divided into eras, periods, and epochs. Adding up the durations of the various periods as shown on the chart, we find that the *Cenozoic* era lasted for 70 million years, the *Mesozoic* era for 130 millions years, and the *Paleozoic* era for 300 million years. The *Proterozoic* and *Archeozoic* eras may have lasted together more than 1,500 million years. Note that the accepted division of the geological history of the earth is similar to the division of human history, where modern history covers a considerably shorter period of time than medieval history, which in turn covers a shorter period than the ancient history and the prehistory of the human race. *Courtesy the Museum of the University of Colorado.*

above, they cover practically the entire period during which life has left its record in the fossils. The three periods of time described in these last three chapters are known as the *Early Paleozoic, Late Paleozoic,* and *Mesozoic eras* of the earth's history. Finally, at the very end of the "book" we find the beginning of the new Cenozoic chapter, which commenced just recently. In geological language, the expression "just recently" means "about seventy million years ago" and is completely justified by the fact that this period of time is short indeed compared with the average length of each chapter, which covers between one and two hundred million years.

Besides the natural division of the earth's history into chapters, each starting with a revolutionary epoch of mountain formation, geologists divide the separate chapters into a number of smaller paragraphs. Thus the Paleozoic chapter is divided into the *Cambrian, Ordovician, Silurian, Devonian, Carboniferous,* and *Permian periods,* and the subdivisions of the Mesozoic chapter are known as the *Triassic, Jurassic,* and *Cretaceous periods.* These subdivisions are entirely arbitrary and are based on the fact that different parts of the geological column were originally studied in different localities. For example, the name "Cambrian" indicates simply that the deposits of that period were first discovered and studied in Wales, which was called "Cambria" by the Romans. The name "Jurassic" refers to deposits first found in the Jura Mountains between France and Switzerland. Since there are no natural grounds for any more logical way of subdividing geological time, this terminology can be retained simply for the sake of convenience.

The division of geological time discussed above is shown in Fig. 16-4; in the following sections we will give a short account of the major happenings during these different periods of the earth's history.

THE EARLIEST FRAGMENTED PAGES

The very first pages of the "Book of Sediments" must, of course, date back to the day when the first drop of rain fell from the sky onto the slowly cooling surface of our planet and the first mountain stream started its destructive work on the primeval granite crust. Most of the deposits of this early epoch are hidden deep under the earth and come to the surface in a very few places. They consist chiefly of thick sheets of *mica schists* and *dolomitic marbles,* which under careful microscopic and chemical analysis prove to be ordinary shales and limestones greatly compressed and "metamorphosed" by exceedingly high pressures and temperatures at the great depths to which they were thrust by the weight of the later sediments formed above them. These primeval sedimentary layers are sometimes well over 100,000 feet thick, indicating that their formation must have taken place in the course of several hundred million years—quite a large fraction of the earth's total life span. It is of interest to note that, unlike later deposits, these early sediments contain but little salt, indicating that sea water must have been quite fresh at that time. Since the salinity of sea and ocean water has been steadily increasing ever since the oceans first appeared, we must conclude that the formation of these deposits coincided approximately with the time when the ocean basins first filled up, and that they really represent the very first deposits of eroded material ever formed on the surface of the earth.

This first extensive period of sedimentation was evidently followed by the revolutionary crumpling of the earth's crust known as the *Laurentian revolution,* during which large masses of molten granite poured over these layers while the layers themselves were uplifted and folded into giant mountains. It is useless, of course, to look for these mountains on present-day maps, for they were completely obliterated by the action of rain water many hundreds of millions of years ago. Since the deposits of that distant past can now be found in but few places on the surface of the earth (for example, in eastern Canada), it is altogether impossible to form any idea of the geographical distribution of these early mountains from their remaining roots. The study of the radioactivity in the granite layers formed during this first recorded revolution indicates that their age is only somewhat less than one billion years.

After the erosion of the first recorded mountain chains, large areas of the continents were again covered by water, and thick layers of new deposits were formed on top of the previous ones. Then another revolution, the *Algoman,* ensued, accompanied by new mountain formation processes and new intrusions of granite lavas, again followed by a long quiet sedimentation period. Then again a revolution and still another sedimentation period. . . .

But the reader is probably growing tired of this constant repetition of the words "revolution" and "sedimentation"; to cheer him up we can tell him that there will be some more color to the picture after one more repetition. In fact, beginning with the fifth recorded revolution, known as the *Charnian,* we leave the dark prehistoric periods of the earth's life and enter the epoch comparable to that of ancient Egypt in the history of humanity. The sedimentary layers formed during the epochs following the Charnian revolution have been studied in many places on the earth; they give us a rather complete picture of the evolution of its surface. Besides, they begin to contain the fossils of different primitive animals in steadily increasing numbers, which is of great help in establishing the "page sequence" in the book of the earth's history. The deposits formed after the Charnian revolution represent three complete chapters of the "Book of Sediments," and on top of them we find the comparatively thin layers constituting the beginning of the latest chapter, in the "writing" of which we have the pleasure of participating ourselves.

THREE COMPLETE CHAPTERS OF THE "BOOK OF SEDIMENTS"

As a result of the Charnian revolution, which opens the historical era of the earth's history, all the continents were lifted high above sea level, and they were probably considerably larger in extent than they are today. In North America, for example, this general uplift caused the Atlantic and the Pacific to recede so that dry land extended many hundreds of miles into the regions now covered by the oceans. The present basins of the Gulf of Mexico and the Caribbean Sea were also occupied by land, while both the Americas, now united only by a narrow isthmus, formed one enormous continuous continent. On the other side of the Atlantic the continents also protruded much farther west than they do now; in particular a long string of land known as "Atlantida" * reached out from the British Isles toward Greenland.

Following the same cycle that occurred after all the previous revolutions, the uplifted continents slowly began to sink back into the plastic mass below, and the incessant pounding of the rain washed away the rocky material of the mountains and high plateaus. Ocean water crept inland, covered the lower parts of the continents, and formed numerous inland seas. On the continent of Eurasia, the waters of the ocean penetrated deep into the interior and formed an extensive inland basin covering all the area now occupied by Germany, southern Russian, the southern part of Siberia, and most of China. This large inland sea was surrounded by a ring of highlands passing through the present positions of Scotland, Scandinavia, northern Siberia, the Himalayas, the Caucasus, the Balkans, and the Alps. The continent of Africa, however, seems to have been completely out of the water during all that time, and it was connected with Europe by dry land extending over the present Mediterranean basin. The northern part of Australia was submerged by the waters of the Indian Ocean, and its southern part extended much farther south toward the Antarctic. On this side of the Atlantic, the advance of the ocean in the equatorial region almost split the American continent in two (North and South America), and much of what is now Mexico and Texas was also inundated. The waters of the North Pacific Ocean covered most of the central area of North America, including the entire Mississippi Valley, the region of the Great Lakes, and part of southern Canada. South of the equator, the advancing Atlantic waters formed an extensive shallow sea covering most of what is now Brazil.

Although this extensive inundation was the most characteristic feature of the Early Paleozoic chapter of the earth's history and lasted for about 160 million years, one must not think that this epoch was completely devoid of movements of the crust. There are, in fact, some traces of minor mountain formation activity during this era, and the slow elevations and sinkings that took place in the continental areas caused the inland seas to change the shape of their shore lines continuously. But all these changes were on a minor scale, and the stresses in the crust resulting from the shrinking of the earth were only slowly gathering their forces for the major outbreak that finally took place in the year 280,000,000 B.C.

The great disturbances of the earth's crust that opened the next, the Late Paleozoic, chapter of the "Book of Sediments" are known as the *Caledonian revolution,* the name being derived from the mountains of

---

* This land, of course, has nothing to do with the mythical "Atlantis" of the ancients, since it existed hundreds of millions of years before man appeared on the surface of the earth.

the same name in Scotland and northern Ireland, where the results of the revolution were particularly pronounced. As the result of this revolution, a large mountain chain was elevated along a line running through Scotland, the North Sea, and the Scandinavian peninsula up to Spitsbergen.

An extension of this chain ran across northern Siberia and formed the elevated northern border of the Asiatic continent. Another mountain chain extended from Scotland through the North Atlantic all the way to Greenland, completely separating the Arctic Ocean from the waters of the North Atlantic. In North America, where the revolutionary activity began somewhat later than in Eurasia, high mountain ranges were raised along a line running from the eastern extremity of Canada through Nova Scotia and continuing farther south along the Atlantic coast. There was also very pronounced activity at many points in South America, South Africa, and Australia (Fig. 16-5).

In spite of all this large-scale mountain-folding activity, the Caledonian

Fig. 16-5. The three great mountain-folding revolutions in the earth's history during the last 300,000,000 years.

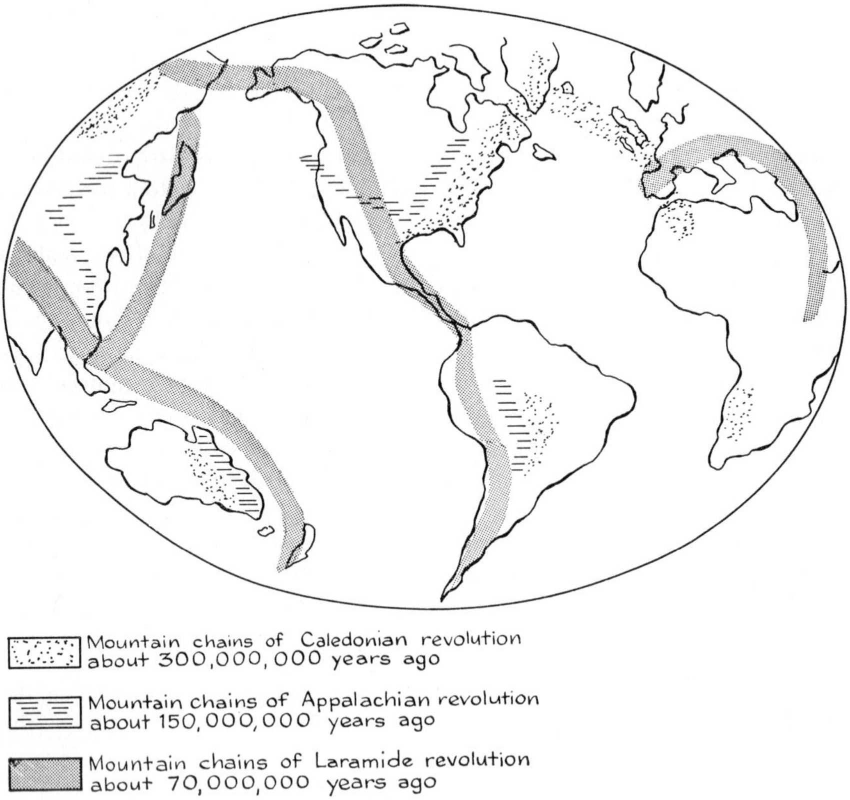

Mountain chains of Caledonian revolution about 300,000,000 years ago

Mountain chains of Appalachian revolution about 150,000,000 years ago

Mountain chains of Laramide revolution about 70,000,000 years ago revolution apparently was far from being as intensive as the previous one, and the general upheaval of land was considerably less pronounced. The waters were completely forced away from the continental surfaces during the Charnian revolution, but the Caledonian uplift left the sea in central North America almost untouched, together with the large water basin of central and eastern Europe. Another indication of the comparative mildness of the Caledonian revolution is the fact that it evidently did not relieve the stress in the earth's crust completely, since we find rather pronounced activity of the crust through the entire Late Paleozoic chapter. There were countless small elevations and sinkings of land, and various small mountain chains were formed throughout the 150 million years that separated the Caledonian from the subsequent *Appalachian revolution.* This revolution, which opens the Mesozoic chapter, culminated the crust movements that had been continuing on a minor scale all through the previous period of submergence and raised a number of high mountain chains all over the world.

In North America, the folding of the crust formed a V-shaped mountain system with its apex in Texas. One branch of this system extended along the Gulf Coast and all along the present site of the Appalachian Mountains, while another branch ran northwest, forming the ancestral Rockies and extending all the way to Puget Sound. In Europe, the compression of the crust formed a long chain beginning somewhere in Ireland (or farther out in the Atlantic), running through central France and southern Germany, and probably joining the Asiatic mountain chain north of the present site of the Himalayas. Like all the other mountains of the past, these once magnificent chains were long ago obliterated by rain, and the fact that some of them are at present slightly elevated above the continental plains is due to much later upheavals. The present Appalachians, from which the name of the revolution itself is derived, and the Vosges and Sudeten Mountains represent but poor reminders of the glory of the year 150,000,000 B.C.

The Mesozoic submergence period, lasting down to the most recent revolution that took place only 70 million years ago, was in many respects analogous to the previous periods of submergence. Countless lowlands, marshes, and shallow seas provided vast playgrounds for the giant lizards that dominated the animal world of that time. But the stresses in the crust were gathering new strength, and the earth was preparing for its latest revolution, which gave its surface its present aspect.

THE BEGINNING OF THE MOST RECENT CHAPTER

As we have said, the latest mountain-forming period, known as the *Laramide revolution,* began about 70 million years ago and, according to all indications, is still going on at the present time. The fact that we live in a revolutionary period should not lead us to expect new mountains to rise from the earth every day like mushrooms! As we have seen above, all the processes in the earth's crust take place extremely slowly, and it is quite possible that all the earthquakes and volcanic activity occurring throughout the recorded history of the human race represent preparations for the next major catastrophe, which will result in the formation of new chains in some unexpected place. The evidence forcing us to assume that the activities of the Laramide revolution are still far from concluded is based on the fact that everything accomplished by this latest revolution up to now (i.e., the Rockies, the Alps, the Andes, the Himalayas, etc.) is still considerably short of the achievements of any of the previous ones. Though "our" revolution may simply not be so worldshaking as past revolutions were, it seems more reasonable to assume that it has not reached its peak as yet and that we are now living during one of the relative lulls in activity.

Nearly all the mountains now existing on the surface of the earth were raised up by this last revolution, and if our conclusion that this revolution is not yet completed is true, more mountain chains are bound to be formed in the "immediate future" (in the geological sense of the word, of course). The last 70 million years, representing the beginning of the Cenozoic chapter, are arbitrarily divided into six consecutive paragraphs known as: *Paleocene, Eocene, Oligocene, Miocene, Pliocene,* and *Pleistocene periods.** The latest of these periods began in the great epoch of glaciation that we shall discuss in the next section, and it continues down to the present time.

One of the first great achievements of the Laramide revolution was the giant crumpling of the crust in the southern part of Asia, which raised the brand new mountains of the Himalayas high above the surrounding plains (Fig. 16-5). The crumpling was accompanied by terrific volcanic activity, and unprecedented quantities of basaltic lava were spread over the surrounding regions. The Deccan plateau, for example, which includes a large part of the Indian peninsula, rests upon basaltic rocks 10,000 feet thick formed from the cooled-down lava that poured over the surface of the earth during this period of upheaval. Another giant eruption of subterranean material also occurred in Japan at about the same time.

On this side of the Atlantic, the compression of the crust during the early part of the Laramide revolution (in the Paleocene period) raised a giant mountain chain running almost from pole to pole and now known

---

* The first five periods are often united under the general name of *Tertiary* and the latest one is then called the *Quaternary period.* In some classifications, the Paleocene epoch is included in the Mesozoic era.

as the Rockies in North America and the Andes south of the equator. The folding of the major American mountain system was also accompanied by volcanic activity second only to that on the Indian peninsula mentioned above; the layers of erupted lava, in some places several thousand feet deep, formed the extensive Columbia plateau in the states of Washington and Oregon.

These great events of the "first days" of the revolution evidently re-lieved the stress in the crust somewhat, and the Eocene and Oligocene periods were characterized by comparative quiescence and the lowering of the land elevated previously. But during the following Miocene period, only about 20 million years after the first outbreak, the revolutionary activity was resumed. The land was again elevated considerably, the ocean waters that had managed to creep up on it during the period of quiescence were pushed back, and new mountain folds, including the Alps in Europe and the Cascade Range in North America, were formed on the surface of our planet. This second outburst of the revolution continued on a somewhat smaller scale during the subsequent Pliocene period and is still continuing at the present time. Whether the Miocene outburst was really the final one of this revolution we do not know, but, as we have indicated above, it is likely that our present comparatively quiet epoch is merely a short breathing spell before the next outburst of revolutionary activity.

The Ice Ages

The study of the "Book of Sediments" also supplies us with important information concerning the climatic conditions that existed on the earth during the past geological eras. Large areas of Europe and North America are covered by deposits known as "drift," which are formed by a mixture of large rocks, gravel, sand, and clay. Such material could not possibly be formed by the regular sedimentation process, and its origin was explained in 1840 by a Swiss geologist, Louis Agassiz. He said these deposits of drift were produced by moving sheets of ice grinding, mixing, and carrying along rock and soil as they moved southward. This debris, mixed in with the ice, was deposited in irregular layers on the ground as the glaciers later melted away. To the surprise of contemporary geologists, Agassiz was able to prove that in the not so far distant past not only were the flourishing valleys of his native Switzerland completely hidden under the glaciers descending from the Alpine heights, but that another giant sheet of ice, coming from the Scandinavian highlands, covered much of northern Europe, including northern Germany, France, and the entire area of Great Britain (Fig. 16-6). Further studies have shown that on this side of the Atlantic thick sheets of ice descending from the Canadian highlands covered about half the present area of North America, reaching as far south as the present location of the state of Kentucky. Only northern Siberia escaped this glaciation, apparently because of the absence of the high mountains that are necessary for the formation of glaciers. During the Permian period at the end of the

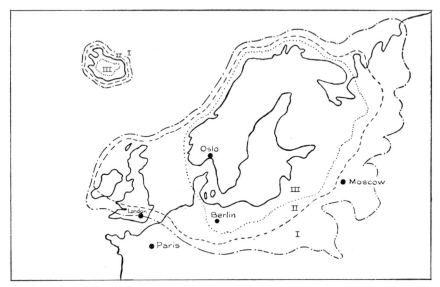

Fig. 16-6. The maximum areas covered by the last three glaciers in Europe. From G. Gamow, *Biography of the Earth.* Courtesy The Viking Press.

Paleozoic era over 200,000,000 years ago, southern Africa, South America, and Australia were similarly covered with deep ice sheets. There is good evidence that the Northern Hemisphere was also glaciated at least once before, more than a half-billion years ago.

It has been estimated that the total volume of ice piled upon the continents amounted to many million cubic kilometers. Since this frozen water was taken from the oceans, the sea level at that time must have been about 100 meters lower than it is now, and dry land must have extended far beyond the present shore lines. Under the enormous weight of this ice, the crust of the earth in the northern parts of the continents was pressed down into the plastic mass underneath by as much as several hundred meters, and, as soon as the ice melted, these depressions were filled up by water, forming large shallow inland lakes. Later on, the depressed part of the crust was pushed up again, carrying with it the deposits made while it was covered with water. This accounts for the discovery of marine shells and even skeletons of whales in many regions that are now far away from the coastline.

Careful studies of glacial deposits indicate that there were at least four (and probably more) consecutive advances and retreats of ice separated by long interglacial stages of much warmer climates, during which the present climatic zones were shifted by as much as 20 or 30 degrees of latitude towards the poles. The Eocene deposits in the northern states of the United States and in the British Isles that were formed only about 40 million years ago contain numerous fossils of palms, magnolias, and other subtropical plants. It seems that we are now living during the receding stage of the last glaciation period, and the climate of the earth is becoming warmer and warmer as geological time goes by. It is interesting to notice that the ice sheets still remaining on the surface of the earth (notably in Greenland and Antarctica) cover an area that is only three times as small as the area covered during the maximum phase of glaciation.

WHAT CAUSES PERIODIC ADVANCES OF ICE?

The periodic advances and retreats of ice must have resulted from a variation in the amount of heat received by the earth's surface from the sun. In fact, we can show that comparatively small variations in this amount could have caused either a very extensive spread of or the complete extinction of the ice sheets. The distribution of glacial deposits clearly indicates that the ice came from high mountains where it was formed mostly during the winter periods. The spread of glaciers descending along mountain valleys is, however, checked by their melting at the lower end during the summer months. The two processes—freezing and melting—are very delicately balanced, and a slight increase or decrease in one of them can result either in a steady advance of the ice sheets or in their progressive retreat. Variations in the amount of solar energy falling on the surface of the earth can hardly affect the amount of ice formed on the mountain tops during winter, since (provided winter temperatures are below the freezing point of water) nearly *all* humidity brought in by air currents into these regions will fall out in the form of snow. On the other hand, the rate of melting of glaciers at their lower end is directly affected by the amount of solar radiation, and a variation in that amount can turn the tables one way or the other. Colder summers may cause glaciers to advance and to spread over extensive areas of the earth's surface, while warmed summers can make them gradually retreat to the mountain tops.

But what could have caused these periodic variations in the amount of solar energy falling on the surface of the earth? This is a question about which geologists and paleoclimatologists still cannot agree. One of the proposed theories attempts to tie the glaciations to changes in the carbon dioxide content of the atmosphere. Since carbon dioxide absorbs long wave length infrared, it acts as an insulator to prevent the earth from radiating its heat away into space at night. Hence any decrease in the carbon dioxide of the atmosphere will tend to make the climate cooler, thus cooling the oceans, which will then dissolve more of the carbon dioxide from the air, and so on. Therefore, even a small change in this vital part of our atmosphere may have far-reaching effects. Since some volcanoes erupt large amounts of carbon dioxide into the air, a period when there was very little volcanic activity of this type may have allowed the carbon dioxide content of the atmosphere to become smaller and set off such a cooling cycle. It is known, too, that the fine volcanic dust (which reflects the radiations of the sun) thrown out into the air by the eruption of Krakatoa in the year 1883 lowered the mean temperature of the earth by about 5° Centigrade for a period of several years (until the dust settled down to the ground). The effect of volcanoes on our climate, however, cannot be checked observationally, at least at present, since geological data do not provide any information concerning the periodicity of volcanic activity in the past.

Another point of view maintains that the change in the amount of heat received by the earth was caused by periodic variations in the brightness of the sun itself. Here again, we have no way of checking this hypothesis because we have no records of the sun's brightness during past geological eras. As we will see in Chapter 19, there are slight variations of solar activity with a period of $11\frac{1}{2}$ years which result in certain periodic changes on the earth. But from what we know now about the internal structure of the sun and the nature of its energy sources, there seem to be no reasons to expect variations of the sun's brightness to extend over periods of many millions of years.

Still another hypothesis, proposed by the Yugoslavian climatologist, A. Milankovitch, blames the ice ages on the periodic deformations of the earth's orbit caused by the perturbations of other planets. If the earth were the only planet, it would move around the sun along a fixed elliptical orbit, but the gravitational attraction of the other planets (notably Jupiter and Saturn) causes the earth's orbit to become periodically more or less elongated and to tilt slightly one way or the other with respect to an invariant plane in space. Both of these motions affect the amount of solar radiation that falls on a given area of the earth's surface, and, according to Milankovitch's calculations, they may have produced an increase or decrease of the mean annual temperature of the earth by as much as

10°C. Since these changes in the earth's orbit are extremely slow and extend over periods of hundreds of thousands of years, the effect of the changed climate on the summer melting of glaciers could easily have led to their extensive advances or complete retreats.

In contrast to the other two theories, Milankovitch's point of view can be directly tested because the deformations of the earth's orbit in the past have been calculated by exact astronomical methods. The science of celestial mechanics has supplied us with exact data concerning the shape and the tilt of the earth's orbit during the last million years, and these data are guaranteed to be correct within at least 10 per cent. Using these data, Milankovitch constructed the curve shown in the upper part of Fig. 16-7 which gives the variations of the mean summer tem-

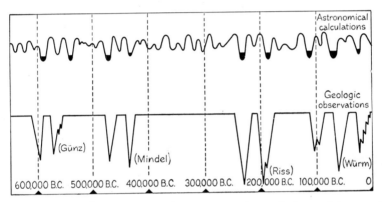

Fig. 16-7. The upper graph represents the variations of temperature during summers at 65° north latitude (after Milankovitch). The lower graph gives the different glaciation periods as deduced from geological data. From G. Gamow, *Biography of the Earth.* Courtesy The Viking Press.

peratures at 65 degrees northern latitude during the last 600,000 years. The particularly high maxima and the particularly low minima of temperature came in the geological epochs when the two above mentioned factors (eccentricity and tilt of the earth's orbit) acted in the same direction. Below this curve we give the dates of various glaciations as estimated by recent geological methods. The agreement between the two sets of data is rather satisfactory and this speaks in favor of Milankovitch's theory. However, the subject is still being disputed by paleoclimatologists who believe that a variation in temperature of only 10° may not be enough to cause such drastic changes in the expansion of ice sheets.

SEVENTEEN

OCEAN OF WATER
AND OCEAN OF AIR

The Hydrosphere

More than three-quarters of the earth's surface is covered by oceans and seas containing an estimated one and one-half billion cubic kilometers of water. The mean depth of the ocean is 4 km, though in some places depths of more than 10 km have been recorded. Ocean water, as we all know, tastes salty and bitterish in comparison to the fresh water of lakes and rivers. This is because ocean water contains about 3 per cent of dissolved salts of many kinds, mostly sodium and magnesium chloride. We can begin our discussion by asking how these salts got into the ocean water. Surprisingly enough, the answer is that the salt was brought into the oceans by rivers that carry admittedly fresh water. The point is, however, that river and spring waters do contain small amounts of dissolved salts, which give them their pleasant taste; if you have ever tried to drink distilled water, which is really quite pure, you can substantiate this. Hydrologists have estimated that the rivers of the world carry yearly 4×10^8 tons of salts into the ocean. Since the total amount of salts now dissolved in the ocean waters is about 4×10^{16} tons, we can conclude that the rivers, if they operated at the same rate as they do today, must have worked for about 10^8 years to build up the present concentration of oceanic salts. Actually, the necessary time period was considerably longer, since, as we have seen in Chapter 15, the rate of erosion of continents in the present geological era is much more rapid than it has been on the average over past eras.

The deposition of salts in the ocean must have occurred mostly during the "mountainous periods" in the earth's surface history, and these periods form only a small percentage of total geological time. Thus, we must conclude that *the actual age of the oceans is not 10^8 years, but several billions of years,* which is in good accord with the estimated age of the continental massifs obtained from the uranium-lead ratio (Chapter 14). Although the figure for the age of the oceans is only an approximation, we can tell with certainty that oceans could not possibly have existed for hundreds of billions of years, since, in that case, they would now be saturated with salt like the Great Salt Lake in Utah. Incidentally, the high salinity of the Great Salt Lake, as well as that of the Caspian Sea in Russia and the Dead Sea in Palestine, is due to the fact that these bodies of water were once gulfs directly connected with the ocean, but were later separated by geological movements of the earth's crust and are now partially dried out.

OCEAN TIDES

Since in this book we have discussed the solid crust of the earth before investigating its liquid envelope, we have spoken about "tides in rocks" (a novelty for most readers) before taking up the well-known phenomenon of the tides in the ocean. Everyone knows that the periodic rise and fall of ocean waters is due primarily to the gravitational attraction of the moon and, to a lesser degree, to that of the sun. But many people would not be able to answer the question of why there are *two high tides daily,* one when the moon is high in the sky and the other when the moon is under our feet shining on our antipodes. At first glance, it would seem that the ocean water, being attracted by the moon, should rise on the moonlit side of our globe and fall on the opposite side. The explanation of the 12-hour period of ocean tides lies in the fact that tides are *dynamic* and not *static* phenomenon. If the earth and the moon were rigidly fixed in space, the ocean *would* bulge in the direction of the moon, and flatten down on the opposite side (Fig. 17-1a). However, our earth moves freely through space, and the solid body of the earth, as well as its liquid envelope, is attracted by the moon. Since the force of gravity rapidly decreases with distance, the force acting on the ocean water at the hemisphere turned toward the moon is larger than the force acting on the body of the earth itself, and this force in turn is larger than the force acting on the ocean water in the opposite hemisphere. Thus, in respect to the earth's center the ocean waters look as if they are "repelled" from it in the direction of the moon as well as in the opposite direction (Fig. 17-1b).

Solar tides are similar to lunar tides but they are much smaller since the sun, though it is much more massive than the moon, is a great deal farther away. During the full and new moon phases, when the sun, the moon, and the earth are on the same straight line, the sun and the moon work together in pulling the ocean waters, and the tides are especially high. During the moon's first and last quarters, the solar low tide coincides with the lunar high tide (and vice versa) so that they partially cancel one another, and the tides are at their minimum.

As the earth rotates around its axis, tidal bulges travel around its surface from east to west. These bulges experience friction at the ocean

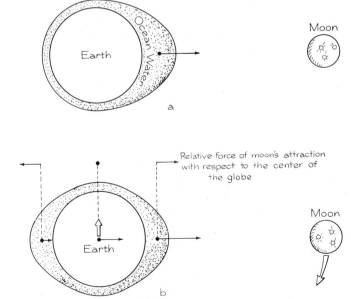

Fig. 17-1. The explanation of ocean tides: (a) if the earth and the moon were rigidly fixed in space, the surface of the ocean would bulge only on the hemisphere facing the moon; (b) since the earth and the moon revolve around a common center of gravity, the surface of the ocean will bulge in both hemispheres.

bottom (especially in shallow places like the Bering Sea) and encounter the resistance of the continents that stand in their way. Our globe, in effect, rotates between two brakeshoes fixed in space with respect to the moon. This braking action gradually slows down the rotation of the earth, and it has been calculated that tidal friction lengthens the period of the earth's rotation, i.e., the length of a day, by 0.0007 seconds every century. The cumulative effect of such lengthening in the course of a century (36,500 days) amounts to about 14 seconds and should show itself in astronomical observations. Astronomers have found, in fact, in their studies of the timetables of such unrelated periodic phenomena as the eclipses of Jupiter's satellites and the motion of Mercury, Venus, and our moon that, as the years go by, they all seem to occur more and more ahead of schedule (Fig. 17-2). Since there is no apparent reason why

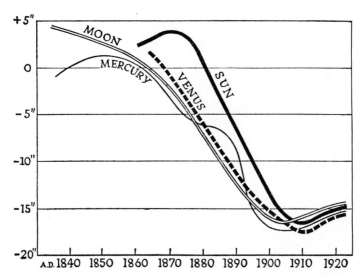

Fig. 17-2. The discrepancy between the calculated and observed positions of the sun, moon, Mercury, and Venus in the course of a century. The fact that all curves run essentially parallel proves that the discrepancy is not due to some irregularities in the motion of these celestial bodies, but to the gradual slowing of the earth's rotation around its axis.

such unrelated phenomena should run in advance of schedule all by the same amount, it is much more reasonable to assume that *the effect is actually due to the slowing down of the astronomical clock, i.e., the rotation of the earth.* This observed slowing down of the earth's rotation amounts to 0.0007 seconds per century, which stands in perfect agree-

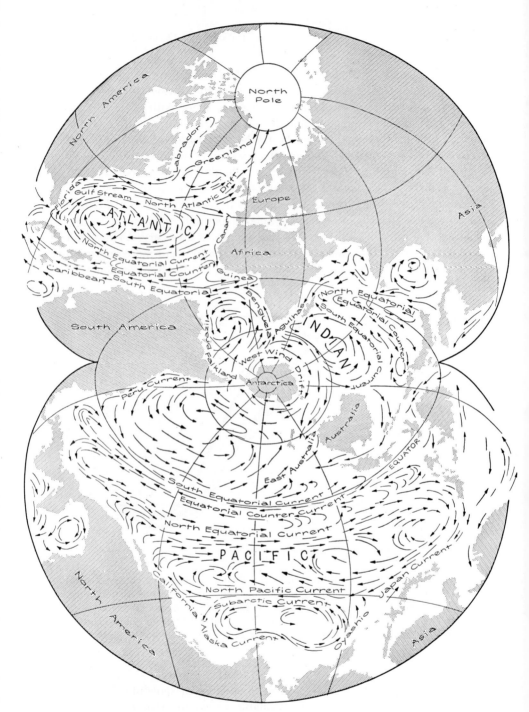

Fig. 17-3. A map showing the currents of the world's oceans. From an article by W. Munk in *Scientific American*, September, 1955.

ment with the above quoted theoretical value expected on the basis of tidal friction.

The slowing down of the earth's rotation results in a gradual increase of 10 cm per month in the distance from the earth to the moon, and this fact has certain important cosmogonical consequences which we will discuss in more detail later in the book.

OCEAN CURRENTS

The waters of the world's oceans do not remain stagnant, being carried around by an intricate system of ocean currents. These currents are of great importance to the navigators who steer their ships to faraway shores, and they also play a very important role in regulating the climates of different parts of the earth. The Gulf Stream, for example, carries warm waters from the Gulf of Mexico to the Northern shores of Europe and is responsible for the pleasant, mild climate of that subcontinent, while the cold waters of "Kurosiva" (North Pacific Current) act as an air conditioner for the west coast of North America.

The principal features of the world's ocean currents are shown on the map in Fig. 17-3, which is drawn in a rather unusual projection in order to show all the important oceans in one piece. From a casual look at the map it might seem that the current system is so complicated that there is no way of explaining its origin in a simple way. However, this is not so, and modern oceanography explains that *the system of currents is driven by the prevailing winds and that the presence of continents breaks up the liquid envelope of the earth into a number of individual basins.* Figure 17-4 is the simplified situation that would exist if the Atlantic and Pacific Oceans were not what they are but were limited by two meridians in the east and west and by a parallel in the north. We have not drawn any limiting line in the south because, in contrast to the northern oceans, southern oceans are directly connected with each other so that one continuous current can flow freely around the Antarctic. The prevailing winds, the origin of which will be discussed later in this chapter, are shown schematically on both sides of the diagram. The wind system of the world consists essentially of *easterly winds* near the north and south polar regions and on both sides of the equator (the former are known as "trade winds") and *westerly winds* in the moderate latitudes. Since the north polar ocean is permanently covered with ice, there are no well defined currents in it except the rather irregular drifts of the ice fields. The waters around the Antarctic, on the other hand, form a regular whirlpool driven by Antarctic winds.

From what we know of the prevailing winds around our globe, we would expect that the waters between the north polar region and the

equator would form two large whirlpools: (1) a counterclockwise whirlpool between the arctic easterly wind region and the mid-latitude belt of
westerly winds, and (2) a clockwise whirlpool between the westerly
winds belt and the easterly trade winds of the subtropical region. In

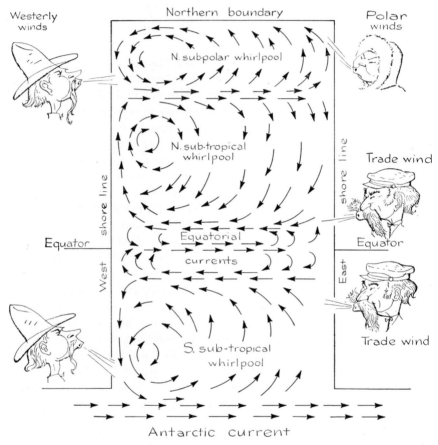

Fig. 17-4. A simplified model of either the Atlantic or the Pacific Ocean
(according to W. Munk).

the southern hemisphere, we would expect the situation to be reversed.
Just along the equator there should also be a reversed current separating
the trade winds of the northern and southern hemispheres. One important feature of the expected distribution of the ocean currents shown in
Fig. 17-4 is that the centers of the whirlpools are displaced toward the
western shores of the ocean basins. This effect is due to the rotation of

the earth, which deflects westward the masses of water flowing from polar regions toward the equator.

If we now compare the highly schematized picture of expected ocean currents with the observed current map (Fig. 17-3), we find that there is a definite similarity between them, which supports the point of view that ocean currents are produced by winds. The complex structure of the ocean currents as they actually exist is due to the irregular shape of the ocean basins and also partially to the deviations of atmospheric circulation from the simple picture assumed in the construction of the diagram in Fig. 17-4.

Fig. 17-5. Torricelli's experiment.

The Atmosphere

The gaseous envelope, or atmosphere, that surrounds our globe is essentially a mixture of *nitrogen* (77.3 per cent) and *oxygen* (20.5 per cent) plus small amounts of *carbon dioxide, argon,* and some other gases. At lower altitudes, it also contains variable amounts of water vapor, which can be more conveniently considered as an admixture rather than as a permanent ingredient of the atmospheric air. The total weight of the terrestrial atmosphere is 5×10^{15} tons (0.3 per cent of the total weight of the hydrosphere), which amounts to about one kilogram for every cm^2 of the earth's surface. The weight of the air above our heads was first measured by an Italian physicist, E. Torricelli (1608-1647), in an arrangement shown schematically in Fig. 17-5. He took a long vertical glass tube that was closed on the top, completely filled it with water, and placed it in a water-filled dish. When he opened the faucet at the bottom of the tube, the water level in the tube fell to a height of only about 10 meters above the water level in the dish, leaving "Torricelli's emptiness," or vacuum as we call it now, at the upper part of the tube. The weight of air above our heads, or *barometric pressure,* can be more conveniently measured by a *mercury barometer* in which the difference in levels is only 760 mm,* or by an *aneroid barometer* which records varying atmospheric pressures by the deformations of a thin-walled metal box. The microbarograph in Fig. 17-6 is an aneroid barometer that records the pressure on a revolving graph.

Fig. 17-6. An aneroid microbarograph, which records, by means of the pen, pressure changes on the graduated chart that revolves on a drum. From George F. Taylor, *Elementary Meteorology* (Englewood Cliffs, N. J.: Prentice-Hall, Inc., 1954). *Courtesy Bendix-Friez.*

As we rise above the earth's surface (or rather, above sea level) by climbing high mountains or in a balloon or airplane, less and less air is left above our heads, and the atmospheric pressure decreases corre-

---

* Because mercury is 13.6 times heavier than water.

spondingly; the amount of air over the top of Mt. Everest is only one-third of that above sea level, and climbers on it are forced to carry oxygen tanks with them in order to breathe. The temperature of air also decreases with increasing altitude at a rate of about 6°C per kilometer. This decrease is due to the fact that *atmospheric air is not heated directly by the sun's rays, but gets its heat through the convective currents that rise from the warmed surface of the earth.* As the air that is heated by a direct·contact with the ground rises, it expands because the pressure at high altitudes is less than that at low altitudes. We know (Chapter 4) that such an expansion inevitably causes a decrease in temperature. In fact, the observed temperature gradient of 6°C per kilometer is in perfect agreement with the cooling that we would expect to result from the expansion of the ascending air masses. The vertical convective currents in the terrestrial atmosphere assure a thorough mixture of air up to certain altitudes and a particularly thorough mixture of its water vapor content.

Up to the beginning of the present century, it was believed that the decrease of air temperature with altitude continues all the way up to the upper fringes of the atmosphere, the temperature of which approaches the nearly absolute zero temperature of interplanetary space. Subsequent studies, carried out by means of balloons and more recently by rockets, indicate, however, that this is not true. It has been found that the decrease of air temperature continues only up to an altitude of about 20 km, where it reaches a minimum of about 210°K (−60°C or −76°F). At still higher altitudes, the temperature begins to rise again, reaching a value close to the freezing point of water, but it then drops down to about 180°K (−90°C or −130°F) at an altitude of 80 km (Fig. 17-7). The vertical convective currents stop short of the altitude of 20 km, and from 20 to 80 km there is practically no mixing at all between the layers (strata) of air lying above each other. The lower, convective layer of the atmosphere is called the *troposphere.* The moistureless and cloudless air layer above 20 km is known as the *stratosphere.*

Above 80 km, the temperature changes are reversed again, and the temperature begins to increase with increasing altitudes, reaching "room temperature" at about 130 km, the temperature of boiling water at 160 km, and the temperature of molten lead at 250 km! (See Fig. 17-7.) You should not think, however, that this means that if you ascended to these altitudes you would be roasted alive. Although the air molecules there have the velocity they would have at these high temperatures on the earth's surface, the density of the air becomes extremely low (one hundred-billionth of its standard density) and its ability to conduct heat to or from material bodies becomes negligibly small. In a warm or a cold room on the ground, each cm^2 of the surface of our body receives

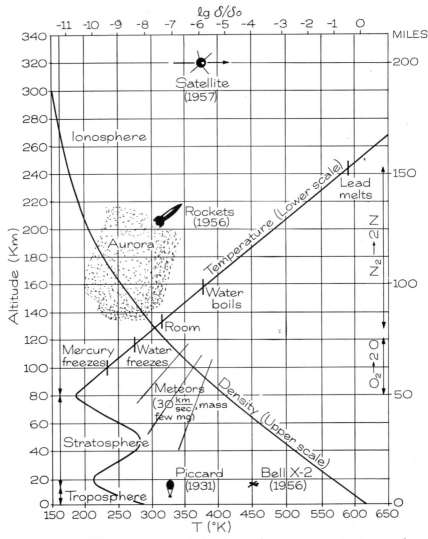

Fig. 17-7. Distribution of density and temperature in terrestrial atmosphere.

some 10^{25} molecular impacts every second, and this enormous number of impacts heats or cools our body very rapidly. At an altitude of 250 km, however, the number of molecular impacts is reduced by a factor of many billions, and the amount of heat the molecules can communicate or take away from the body becomes correspondingly lower. The temperature of any material object, such as an ascending rocket or an artificial satellite, at these altitudes is completely determined by the absorption of the sun's rays and by the re-emission of the absorbed energy in the form of heat radiation.

The increase of the temperature of the air in the upper atmosphere is due to the strong absorption of the ultraviolet radiation of the sun. When the energy-loaded ultraviolet light quanta from the sun enter the upper fringes of the atmosphere, they kick off the electrons from the outer shells of the nitrogen and oxygen atoms, communicate to them high velocities, and thus maintain a high degree of thermal agitation. Because of the extremely low densities and the correspondingly low collision probabilities at these altitudes, the positive ions and the electrons travel for a long time before they have a chance to recombine into neutral atoms. As a result, *the air in this region is continuously maintained at a high degree of ionization.* This region of the terrestrial atmosphere, known as the *ionosphere,* possesses a high degree of electrical conductivity (because of the free electrons and positive ions) and is a good reflector for radio waves, which can propagate all the way around the globe by bouncing between the earth's surface and the reflecting layers of the ionosphere (Fig. 17-8). Another consequence of the high elec-

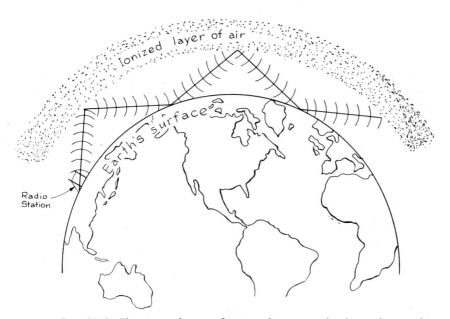

Fig. 17-8. The ionosphere reflects radio waves back to the earth's surface.

trical conductivity of the ionosphere is the presence in it of electric currents that flow through it in a more or less regular fashion. The variable magnetic fields produced by these ionospheric currents overlap on the permanent magnetic field of the earth, which is caused by the currents in its fluid iron core (see Chapter 15).

In addition to the ultraviolet radiation from the sun, which is almost completely absorbed in the ionosphere and gives it its very high temperature, this space frontier of our atmosphere is subject to continuous bombardment by other high energy radiations. It is penetrated by streams of comparatively slow moving electrically charged particles that come

Fig. 17-9. Aurora draperies over Oslo, Norway, October 13, 1916. From George F. Taylor, *Elementary Meteorology* (Englewood Cliffs, N. J.: Prentice-Hall, Inc., 1954). Courtesy U. S. Weather Bureau and Carl Stormer.

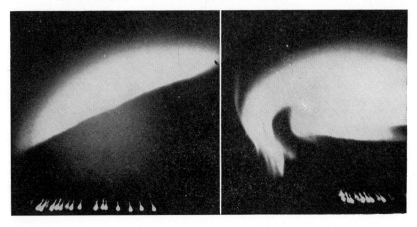

from the sun and that are being deflected by the magnetic field of the earth to the poles where they produce the magnificent phenomenon of the aurora (Fig. 17-9). It is pierced by multi-billion-volt cosmic ray particles that produce all kinds of secondary radiations in it. It is visited by meteors that shoot in at high speed from interplanetary space. It is now the abode of man-made artificial satellites from the earth, and it may house the "space platform" that may serve in the future as a space terminal for interplanetary travel.

HUMIDITY OF THE AIR

"It is not the heat, it is the humidity," is the standard expression of inhabitants of localities where the air customarily contains unduly high amounts of water vapor. Meteorologists speak about two kinds of humidity: absolute and relative. *Absolute humidity is defined as the total*

Fig. 17-10. Cumulus clouds over Yosemite National Park. From George F. Taylor, *Elementary Meteorology* (Englewood Cliffs, N. J.: Prentice-Hall, Inc., 1954).

amount of water vapor (*in grams*) *per cubic meter of air*, and *relative humidity is the ratio of the amount of water vapor present to the maximum amount of water vapor which can be contained in the air at a given temperature.* Since this maximum amount decreases with decreasing temperature, the same absolute humidity corresponds to a higher and higher relative humidity as the temperature of air drops. If warm air containing a certain amount of moisture cools by rising to higher altitudes (either in a vertical convective current or moving up the slope of a mountain), its relative humidity increases, and, at a certain point, it will not be able to contain all the water vapor it initially had. As a result, the water vapor will condense into a multitude of tiny water droplets and form what is known as a cloud.

Cloud formations are good indicators of all kinds of atmospheric circulation, for, although their presence or absence does not influence the motion of air masses very much, they make these motions directly accessible to visual observation. Probably the most important, and certainly the most beautiful kind of clouds are the so-called *cumulus clouds* (Fig. 17-10), which are particularly conspicuous during hot summer months over dry lands as well as over the ocean. They are formed by ascending currents of moist air, the water vapor of which condenses out into a cloud of microscopic droplets when the currents enter the higher,

Fig. 17-11. The formation of rain in a cumulonimbus cloud.

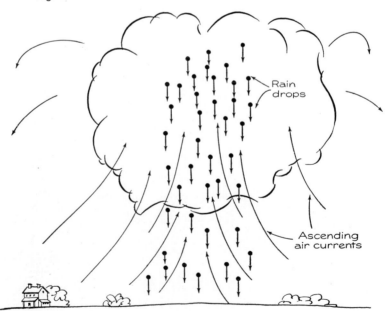

cooler regions of the atmosphere. If the current is a strong one and contains large amounts of moisture, the concentration of the tiny water droplets that form the cloud may become sufficient to cause their fusion into larger droplets that cannot be supported by the ascending air currents. These droplets then fall to the ground in the form of rain. The formation of rain droplets in these so-called *cumulonimbus clouds* is shown schematically in Fig. 17-11. If the temperature of the air is below the freezing point of water, snowflakes or hailstones will be formed.

Since the concentration of water vapor usually takes place much easier on positively and negatively charged particles, or ions, the movement of these charged particles in the cloud often produces very high electric potential differences that result in the violent electric discharges known as lightning. The thunder that accompanies the lightning is, of course, of the same origin as the crack of electric sparks in a laboratory experiment. It is a shock wave (see Chapter 3) that is sent into the surrounding air by the rapid expansion of the column of air heated to a high temperature by the passing electric discharge.

THE CAUSE OF WINDS

The horizontal motion of air masses over the surface of the earth (known as wind) is due to the uneven heating of the various parts of the earth's surface. The simplest example is presented by the so-called

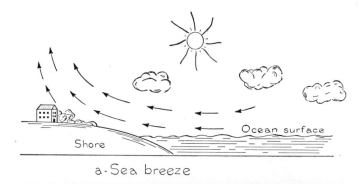

a-Sea breeze

Fig. 17-12. The cycle of winds at the shore line: (a) a sea breeze, and (b) a land breeze.

b-Land breeze

"sea and land breezes" familiar to any inhabitant of a coastal line. Since solid ground possesses considerably lower heat capacity than bodies of water, it heats quickly during the day under the action of the sun's rays and cools rapidly during the night. Thus, in the daytime the air heated by contact with the hot ground rises and is replaced by cooler air flowing in from the water surface (Fig. 17-12a), while during the night, when the ground cools faster, the reverse situation takes place (Fig. 17-12b).

In speaking about the motion of atmospheric air, we can describe it in terms of atmospheric pressure as well as in terms of velocity of motion. *The flow of air along the surface of the earth always takes place from regions of higher pressure to regions of lower pressure.* The lines of equal atmospheric pressure, as measured on the surface of the earth, are known as *isobars,* and in Fig. 17-13 we present a typical correlation between the pattern of isobars and the direction of winds.

GENERAL CIRCULATION OF THE ATMOSPHERE

While the liquid envelope of the earth is badly cut into separate pieces by continental massifs, the circulation of the terrestrial atmosphere is affected only slightly by the surface features of our globe. The two main factors that account for the motion of air masses over the surface of the earth are:

1. *The uneven heating of the polar and equatorial regions of the globe,* which creates the driving force for atmospheric circulation.

2. *The rotation of the earth around its axis,* which causes the deflection of air streams moving from the poles to the equator and from the equator to the poles.

If the earth were not rotating, atmospheric circulation would be quite

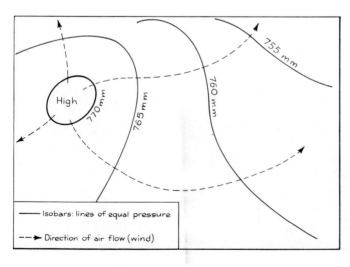

Fig. 17-13. The correlation between the pattern of isobars and the direction of winds.

simple. The cold air from the polar regions would flow along the earth's meridians toward the equator, becoming gradually warmer as it went. The warmed air would then rise and flow back to the poles at high altitudes. Except for local irregularities, there would be nothing but steady polar winds (north winds in our hemisphere). However, due to the rotation of the earth, the air masses traveling from the poles to the equator are deflected westward. This results from the fact that the speed with which the points on the earth's surface are carried around by its rotation increases from the poles to the equator. At Hudson Bay this velocity is quite small, at the latitude of New York it is about 800 miles per hour, and at the equator it exceeds 1,000 miles per hour. Since the air masses traveling from northern latitudes southward tend to retain their initial low velocity (Newton's law of inertia), the ground will, so to speak, "run away from under them" and, as observed from the ground, they will be deflected westward. Similarly, the air traveling from equatorial regions toward the poles will be deflected eastward since it goes from faster moving regions to slower moving regions. Consequently, the air will "run ahead" of the surface of the earth.

These deflections from the strictly meridional motion of air masses cause the single convection current that would have existed in each

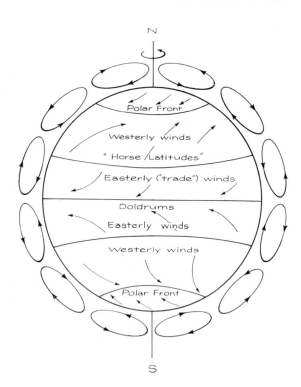

Fig. 17-14. The general circulation of the atmosphere. (The thickness of the atmosphere is strongly exaggerated in relation to the earth's diameter.)

hemisphere on a non-rotating earth to break up into the three separate currents shown in Fig. 17-14.

Thus, each hemisphere can be divided into three zones in respect to the prevailing ground winds:

1. The polar zone with cold *easterly winds* that extend from the poles to about 60° latitude.

2. The temperate zone between the 60th and 30th latitudes with prevailing *westerlies.*

3. The subtropical zone between the 30th latitude and the equator with prevailing *easterly winds* also known as "trade winds" (in the Northern Hemisphere).

At the boundaries between these zones lie the regions of ascending and decending air currents (vertical winds), and the horizontal motions of air masses (ordinary winds) in these regions are variable and slight. The equatorial calm zone is known as the *doldrums,* and the zone between the trade winds and the prevailing westerlies (near the North 30th latitude) carries the peculiar name of *horse latitudes.* This name is said to have arisen in the days when horses were transported to the New World in sailing ships. It was the custom to throw the horses overboard when the ship was unduly delayed by the calms often encountered at these latitudes, since there was no food left for them.

The boundary between the cold polar winds and the prevailing westerlies is known as the *polar front* and is of paramount importance for the weather in the temperate zone. It is the region where the warm air masses advancing from the south collide with the cold air descending from the north. Being lighter than the cold air, the warm air flows up the frontal slope of the cold air as if it were a mountain slope, and the cold air forms a wedge near the ground (Fig. 17-15). Depending on the relative strength of the polar winds and the westerlies, the polar front swings northward and southward in a rather unpredictable way. In general, the polar front moves toward the equator during the winter and

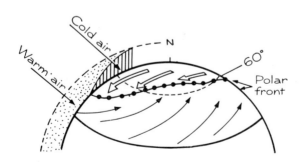

Fig. 17-15. The polar front is formed between the arctic and mid-latitude currents of air.

recedes back to the poles during the summer. Figure 17-16 shows the average summer and winter positions of the north polar front over the North American continent. We notice from this picture that the seasonal displacement of the polar front is much more pronounced over dry land than over ocean areas, which is due to the heat stabilizing properties of large bodies of water. The irregular movements of the polar front relative to its mean seasonal position usually amount to a few hundred miles per day, but if there are especially strong conflicts between the opposing air masses, the front can be displaced by as much as 1,000 miles in a single day. When the cold air is pushing the warm air away, we speak of an advancing *cold front.* The opposite is true in the case of an advancing *warm front.* If no motion of the air masses takes place, we call it a *stationary front.*

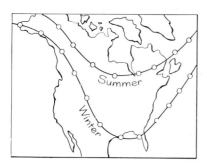

Fig. 17-16. The average location of the polar front on the North American continent during the summer and winter months.

In both an advancing warm and an advancing cold front, the warm moist air from the south is forced up over the masses of heavier cold air. Being cooled by expansion, the warm air loses its moisture and forms the heavy clouds that are always connected with advancing fronts. The rain, snow, and strong winds that prevail in the vicinity of the moving air masses make the weather unpleasant and perilous for sea and air travel.

WINDS IN THE HIGH ATMOSPHERE

The atmospheric circulation discussed on the previous pages pertains exclusively to the lower layer of the troposphere and to the winds that are measurable on the surface of the earth. Modern meteorological research has penetrated into the higher levels of the troposphere by the use of balloons and others means, and today we are able to investigate such atmospheric conditions as pressure, temperature, and winds in a vertical direction as well as in the directions of latitude and longitude. In Fig. 17-17a and b, we give diagrams of wind velocities at different heights up to 20 km and along the meridional line extending from the equator up to a high northern latitude. The most characteristic feature of this diagram is the extremely strong, sharply localized westerly wind that exists at a height of about 13 km and at a latitude that varies from

45°N in winter to 55°N in summer. The cross-sections shown in Fig. 17-17a and b pertain to the meridian passing through the North American continent, but similar maps have been obtained for other meridians. They indicate that a vigorous air current or "air jet" circles the north pole at the upper limit of the troposphere. (The boundary between the troposphere and the stratosphere, at which the temperature inversion takes place, is shown by a heavy line in Fig. 17-17a and b.) Comparing this situation with the wind diagram given in Fig. 17-14, we notice that this circular stream is an extension of the familiar westerlies of the temperate zone. On the ground, the westerlies usually travel about 10

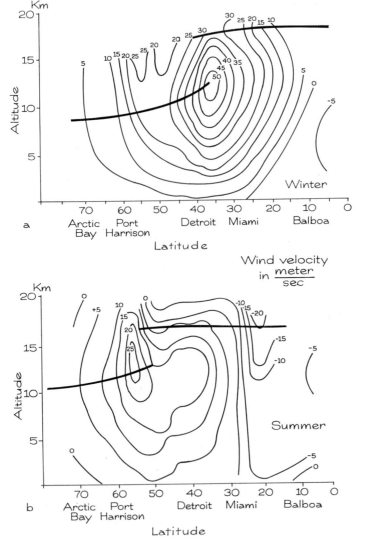

Fig. 17-17. Wind velocities at different heights and latitudes. After G. P. Kuiper, ed., *Atmospheres of Planets* (Chicago: Chicago University Press).

or 20 miles per hour, but the speed at the center of the powerful air jet is over 100 miles per hour! A similar air jet also exists, of course, in the Southern Hemisphere.

ATMOSPHERIC WHIRLPOOLS

The constant battle between the onrushing cold and warm air masses at the polar front causes its line to bend and twist, and sometimes the situation becomes unstable, or "fluid," to use a military term. A typical example of such an unstable front is illustrated in Fig. 17-18a, b, and c, which shows what happens if a particularly strong southwesterly wind makes a "bulge" (a) in the polar front line. The masses of cold air coming from the northeast are first deflected northward, and then they turn southward to begin an "envelopment movement" around the intruding warm air. Meanwhile, the warm air penetrates farther north and is gradually deflected westward (b, c). This situation results in the formation of an atmospheric whirlpool rotating in a counterclockwise direction. (It would be a clockwise direction in the Southern Hemisphere.) Such whirlpools, which are known as *cyclones,* often separate from the polar front line and travel as self-sustaining units. A typical distribution of the winds in a cyclone is shown in Fig. 17-19. The rising air currents within a cyclone cause the formation of clouds and precipitation, just as they do in the case of moving cold and warm fronts. The prevailing westerly winds in the temperate zone

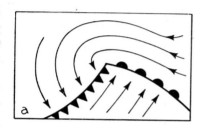

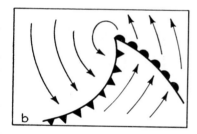

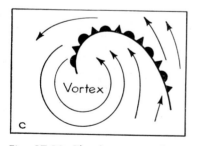

Fig. 17-18. The formation of a cyclone.

move cyclones from west to east, and a cyclone usually covers about 500 miles every day in its translatory motion. Thus, a cyclone first recorded on the west coast will arrive on the east coast about a week later. In Figs.

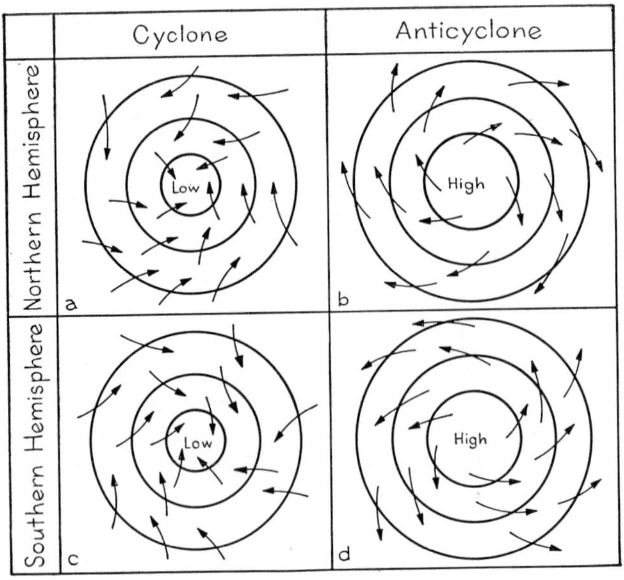

	Cyclone	Anticyclone
Northern Hemisphere	Low (a)	High (b)
Southern Hemisphere	Low (c)	High (d)

Fig. 17-19. The direction of the winds in cyclones and anticyclones.

17-20 and 17-21 we give two weather maps showing the motion of a cyclone over the North American continent in the course of one day.

Closely related to cyclones are their more aggressive brothers, *tropical hurricanes*. (Perhaps they should be called "sisters," since they are assigned girls' names alphabetically as they appear.) Hurricanes usually

Fig. 17-20. Surface weather chart, January 1, 1948. From George F. Taylor, *Elementary Meteorology* (Englewood Cliffs, N. J.: Prentice-Hall, Inc., 1954).

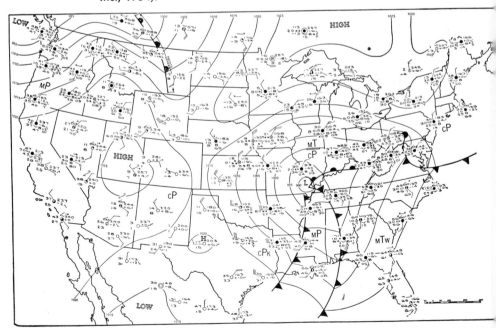

originate over the ocean within the tropical air circulation zone, but the way in which they are formed is not yet well understood. Like cyclones, they are associated with a vertical stream of rising air masses and strong winds blowing toward the center ("the eye of the hurricane"). In Fig. 17-22 we show the tracks of the 1938 and 1944 hurricanes across the North Atlantic Ocean. In Fig. 17-23 we give a radar picture of a hurricane showing its "eye" (i.e., the region of rising air masses) and the distribution of the clouds around it.

While cyclones are associated with rising air currents and converging winds rotating in a counterclockwise direction in the Northern Hemisphere, *anticyclones* have directly opposite properties. They are caused by descending air currents (which are, of course, necessary to compensate for the ascending air currents in cyclones) and possess a diverging wind system that is turned into a clockwise rotating whirlpool by the rotation of the earth (Fig. 17-19b). Since the vertical air motion in anticyclones is downwards, the air masses are warmed up by compression, no condensation of water vapor takes place, and the weather is clear and pleasant.

Since cyclones are prevalent only in the middle latitudes, they are driven by the westerly winds in both hemispheres, and their general pattern of motion is from west to east. This pattern of motion has been

Fig. 17-21. Surface weather chart, January 2, 1948. From George F. Taylor, *Elementary Meteorology* (Englewood Cliffs, N. J.: Prentice-Hall, Inc., 1954).

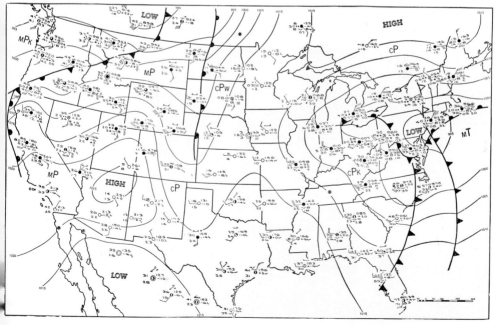

used as a prototype for explaining the westward drift (opposite direction!) of the terrestrial magnetic field that supposedly results from similar motions on the boundary between the plastic mantle of our earth and its molten iron core (see Chapter 15).

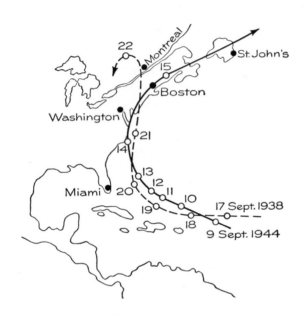

Fig. 17-22. The tracks of the destructive September hurricanes of 1938 and 1944.

WEATHER FORECASTING

There is a story about a man browsing through a pawn shop who found an object labeled "Barometer . . . To be used to tell the weather.

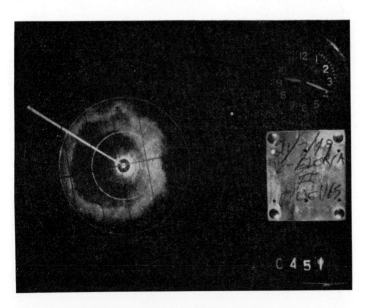

Fig. 17-23. Radar photograph of the eye of a typhoon. From George F. Taylor, *Elementary Meteorology* (Englewood Cliffs, N. J.: Prentice-Hall, Inc., 1954). *Courtesy Lt. Hughes and U. S. Air Force Air Weather Service.*

Price 25¢." After buying the instrument the man asked the shopkeeper: "How does one use it to tell the weather?" "Very simple," answered the shopkeeper. "Put it out of the window and keep it there for a while. Then bring it back in and look at it. If it is dry, the day is probably not bad. If it is wet, it must certainly be raining." "Oh, gosh!" exclaimed the customer, "Why did I spend my quarter? I could tell the weather without it." "Quite correct," agreed the shopkeeper, "It can be done without it. But doing it with an instrument makes it more scientific."

But apart from jokes, the prediction of weather, which only a few decades ago was about on a level with the understanding manifested in the story quoted above, is making rapid advances, largely because of the widespread system of stations that continuously record barometric pressures, temperatures, wind velocities, and other data that characterize the motion of air masses. To predict what the weather will be tomorrow, the weatherman must extrapolate from the data found in the weather maps for several previous days and construct the map for that day. At present, the construction of such maps is more an art than a science, and success depends to a considerable extent on the experience and skill of the individual forecaster.

The present development of *synoptical meteorology* (prediction meteorology), however, is progressing in two directions: the gathering by balloons and airplanes of much more information about conditions at high altitudes, to supplement the information from the many weather stations on the earth's surface; and the devising of methods by which weather prediction can be put into the hands, or rather the tubes, of large electronic computers. These computers, when supplied with information about the atmosphere at all altitudes, will be able to solve the complex hydrodynamic problems of the motions of air masses with great precision and in practically no time. When and if this is achieved, the name "meteorology" should be changed to "meteoronomy," in the same way that "astrology" became "astronomy" several centuries ago.

EIGHTEEN

THE PLANETARY

SYSTEM

Planets mean "wanderers" in Greek, and they were called so because, in contrast to the "fixed stars" that maintain their relative positions in various constellations, the planets travel across the sky from constellation to constellation closely following the path of the sun, which is known as the *ecliptic*. The band of the sky extending 8° north and south of the ecliptic within which the wandering planets, with the exception of Pluto, always remain, is known as the *Zodiac* and the twelve constellations that are located in this region are known as the *signs of the Zodiac*. The signs of the Zodiac through which the sun passes in consecutive months beginning in January and ending in December are *Capricorn* (unicorn), *Cancer* (crab), *Aquarius* (water carrier), *Pisces* (fishes), *Aries* (ram), *Taurus* (bull), *Gemini* (twins), *Leo* (lion), *Virgo* (virgin), *Libra* (scales), *Scorpio* (scorpion), and *Sagittarius* (archer).*

The signs of the Zodiac were ascribed a mystic meaning by ancient and medieval astrologers, and the fate of any person was supposed to depend on the signs of the Zodiac in which the sun, moon, and planets were on the day he was born. Unfortunately, this practice is continuing at present, along with other superstitions, and the number of astrological magazines exceeds the number of scientific astronomical publications. In scientific astronomy the signs of the Zodiac, along with all the other constellations, represent only convenient traditional landmarks for talk-

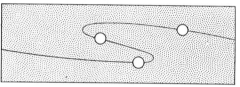

Fig. 18-1. The motion of Jupiter as observed from the earth.

ing about the positions of planets in the sky. While the sun moves along its celestial track in a more or less uniform way, the motion of planets is more complicated: instead of proceeding steadily forward, they often reverse their motion and form loops, as shown in Fig. 18-1.

Old and New Systems of the World

To explain the observed motion of the sun, the moon, the planets, and the stars over their heads, ancient astronomers assumed that the "fixed" stars were rigidly attached to a large dark sphere rotating around the earth once each day, while other celestial bodies had crystal spheres of their own that rotated with various different periods. And to explain the occasional retrograde motion of the planets, Fig. 18-1, it was further assumed that planets also had a secondary motion revolving along circular orbits (*epicycles*) attached to the corresponding crystal spheres. In the case of what we now call the "inner planets" (i.e., Mercury and Venus),

---

* Of course, the correlation between the months and the signs of the Zodiac is only approximate, and the sun does not pass from one to another at the first of each month.

which always appear close to the sun, it also had to be assumed that their crystal spheres revolved around the earth with the same period as

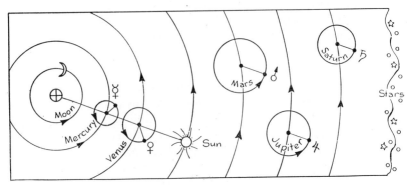

Fig. 18-2. The Ptolemaic system of the universe.

that of the sun. This complicated picture, which was championed by the Alexandrian astronomer, Ptolemy, in the second century A.D. (Fig. 18-2), was in accord with the hidden human desire to be in the center of all things, and, being supported by the church, it persisted as the generally accepted view for the next fourteen centuries.

Although some of the ancient Greek philosophers had expressed the idea that it is not the sun which revolves around the earth, but rather the earth which rotates around the sun, the first clear-cut scientific proof of that statement was given only in the middle of the sixteenth century by a Polish astronomer, Nicholas Copernicus (1473-1543), in his book *De revolutionibus orbium celestium* (*On the Revolution of Celestial Bodies*), which appeared only at the year of his death. In this book Copernicus gives a picture of the planetary system which is today familiar to every school boy or girl:

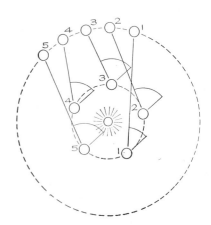

Fig. 18-3. The explanation of the motion of Jupiter (shown in Fig. 18-1) from the point of view of the Copernican system.

1. The sun and not the earth is in the center of our system.

2. While the moon *does* revolve around the earth, all the other planets, along with the earth itself, are revolving around the sun.

3. The earth, and not the sphere of the fixed stars, rotates around its axis every 24 hours.

The complicated loops described by the outer planets in their motion across the sky were explained by Copernicus as being due to the *combined motion* of the earth and the planets along their orbits, as is shown in Fig. 18-3, while Mercury and Venus remain always near the sun because their orbits lie *within* the orbit of the earth. Thus emerged the *Copernican system of the world* (Frontispiece) which rapidly, in the medieval time scale of course, gained universal recognition in spite of many vicious attacks by powerful proponents of the "old faith."

THE SHAPE OF PLANETARY ORBITS

The original Copernican system of the world maintained that the orbits of planets, including that of the earth, are circles, in accordance with the old Greek philosophical tradition that considered a circle and a sphere to be "perfect figures." However, more detailed studies of planetary motion, notably by a Danish astronomer, Tycho Brahe (1546-1601), who built himself an observatory ("Uranienburg") on a little island 20 miles north of Copenhagen, showed that the motion of planets does not quite fit into the picture of concentric circles. Since Tycho was occupied mostly by direct observations and measurements, he did not make any attempt to analyze theoretically his results, and this task fell into the hands of Johannes Kepler (1571-1630), a German who was Tycho's assistant during the last years of his life. Although at the time of Kepler the knowledge of absolute distances in the planetary system was still lacking (he was using Hipparchus' value for the distance of the sun, which was 20 times smaller than the correct value), the exact angular measurements by Tycho permitted him to establish the *relative scale of planetary distances* with great precision. For example, the fact that Venus never gets farther from the sun than an angle of about 45° leads to the conclusion that its

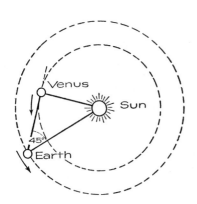

Fig. 18-4. Estimating the relative distances from the sun to Venus and the earth.

distance from the sun is equal to 0.7233 of the earth's distance (Fig. 18-4). Similarly, though in a somewhat more complicated way, one could establish the relative values of the radii for all other planets. The modernized version of Copernicus' map of the solar system is shown in Fig. 18-5.

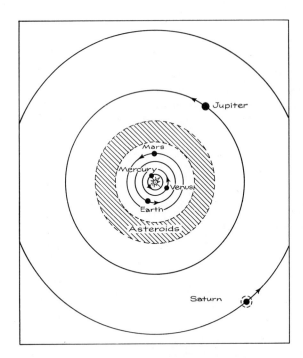

Fig. 18-5. The solar system, showing the relative distances of the planets from the sun. Uranus, Neptune, and Pluto are beyond the limits of the figure. The shaded area shows the location of the asteroids.

Kepler, driven by the Pythagorean idea that "numbers govern the world," was trying to express the observed motion of planets by means of some simple mathematical relations. After years of work he came to his first important discovery; he found that, while in their motion around the sun the planets do not follow exactly circular orbits, they describe another class of curves just as famous as circles in the frame of old Euclidean geometry. This class of curves is known as *conical sections* and can be defined as the intersections of a circular cone—i.e., a cone, the cross-section of which (perpendicular to its central axis) is a circle —with differently oriented planes. If the plane is strictly perpendicular to the axis of the cone, the cross-section is (by definition) a circle (Fig. 18-6a). If the plane is somewhat tilted in respect to the axis, the intersection is called an *ellipse* (Fig. 18-6b), and it is more and more elongated with the increase in the tilt of the plane. When the plane becomes parallel to the side of the cone, one extremity of the ellipse disappears into infinity, and we have an open curve known as a *parabola* (Fig. 18-6c). At still larger tilts the original parabola becomes "more open," and a curve of this kind is known as a *hyperbola* (Fig. 18-6d). It should

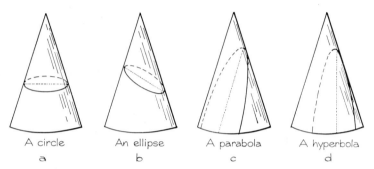

| A circle | An ellipse | A parabola | A hyperbola |
| a | b | c | d |

Fig. 18-6. The conical sections formed by the intersection of a cone with a plane that is tilted at different angles. A *parabola* is obtained if the plane is parallel to the side of the cone, and if the angle is larger than this, a *hyperbola* is obtained.

be noticed that, in the case of a hyperbola, we have actually two dis-connected branches, the second branch being provided by the inter-section of the plane with the second (upside-down) part of the cone.

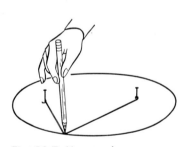

Fig. 18-7. How to draw an ellipse.

According to a well-known theorem of geometry, an ellipse can be defined also as a set of points, all of which have a common property, namely, that the sum of their distances from two fixed points (known as *foci*) is always the same. (Similarly, a hyperbola is a set of points for which the difference of the distances from the two foci is constant.) We can use this property to draw an ellipse by attaching a string to two pins driven into a cardboard and moving the pencil in the way indicated in Fig. 18-7.

His discovery that **all planets move along elliptical orbits with the sun located in one of the foci** gave Kepler great satisfaction since, after all, the ellipse is just a generalization of the circle and becomes a circle when its two foci coincide with one another. Considering the motion of planets along their elliptical orbits, Kepler found a second mathematical relation which states that **an imaginary line connecting the sun and a planet sweeps over equal areas of the planetary orbit in equal inter-**

vals of time. Thus, when the planet is closest to the sun (in its *peri-helion*), its linear velocity is higher than at the opposite point (*aphelion*) of its trajectory (Fig. 18-8). These two basic laws of planetary motion

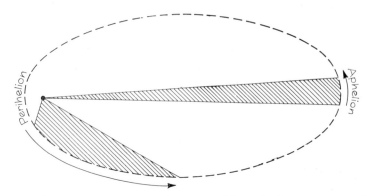

Fig. 18-8. According to Kepler's second law, the line connecting the sun and a planet sweeps over equal areas in equal intervals of time. (In this drawing, the eccentricity of the planetary orbit is highly exaggerated.)

were announced by Kepler in 1609 and are known as *the first and second Kepler's laws*.

Having found the laws of motion of individual planets, Kepler began to look for the correlation between the motion of different planets, but it took him another 9 years to find it. He was trying all kinds of possibilities, such as, for example, the correlation between the planetary orbits and the regular polyhedra of solid geometry, but nothing seemed to fit. Finally, Kepler made a brilliant discovery that is known today as his *third law*. It states that **the squares of the periods of revolution of different planets around the sun stand in the same ratio as the cubes of their mean distances from the sun.** For example, the distances of Mercury, Venus, Mars, and Jupiter expressed in terms of the distance of the earth from the sun (the so-called "astronomical unit") are: 0.387, 0.723, 1.524, and 5.203, while their rotation periods are: 0.2409, 0.6152, 1.881 and 11.860 years. Taking the cubes of the first sequence of numbers (distances) and the square of the second sequence (periods), we obtain identical numerical results, namely: 0.0580, 0.3785, 3.5396, 140.85. In this case the proportionality turns out to be an equality (1:1) only because our reference planet, the earth, has a distance of 1 A.U. and a period of 1 year. If the distances had been given in miles and the periods in days, the proportionality constant would have been quite different.

SIR ISAAC NEWTON, THE APPLE, AND THE MOON

For ancient astronomers, as well as for Copernicus and Kepler, a circular (or nearly circular) motion of celestial bodies was a "natural motion," just as the "natural motion" of any unsupported material object was considered to be a downward motion. They were interested in the question *how* the objects move, but the question *why* was never asked. The idea that *the only "natural motion" of material objects is the uniform motion along a straight line* ("inertial motion") and that any deviation from that motion must be ascribed to some *physical forces* acting on that object was first conceived by Sir Isaac Newton in his famous *Principia* (see Chapter 2). For Newton, the fact that the moon revolves around the earth and that the planets revolve around the sun meant that there must be some force that causes these celestial bodies to deviate from their "natural" rectilinear trajectories and to move in circles. The force that can do it must apparently be *an attraction to the center around which the circular motion takes place.* Thus, the moon must be revolving around the earth because it is attracted to it. But the material bodies on the earth's surface fall down also because they are attracted to the earth. Could it not be the same force? Indeed, as Newton was able to prove, the forces causing ripe apples to fall down from the tree are the same forces that are responsible for the motion of the moon around the earth.

To understand Newton's argument let us consider a bullet shot horizontally with a certain velocity at a certain height above the ground (Fig. 18-9). If there were no gravity, the bullet would continue to move horizontally and cover the stretches between equidistant points *A, B, C, D,*

Fig. 18-9. The motion of a horizontally-fired projectile.

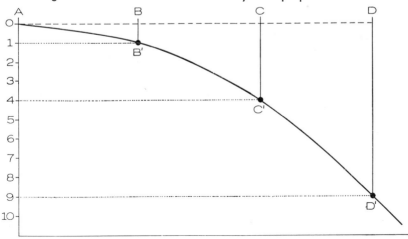

etc. at equal intervals of time. If, on the other hand, the bullet is released without initial velocity it would fall down in a uniformly accelerated fashion and in equal time intervals would pass through points B', C', D', the distances of which from point A increase as the *squares of integral numbers* (see prior discussion in Chapter 2). In an actual case both motions will be combined into one, and the bullet will fly along the parabolic trajectory as shown in Fig. 18-9. (Of course, in all these considerations we neglect the friction of the air.) If the earth were flat, a bullet shot horizontally from a certain height would always hit the ground even though it may be very far away from the starting point. But, since the surface of the earth continuously curves as the bullet proceeds on its way, the falling of the bullet due to gravity will be compensated for by the "curving of the ground," and the bullet may circle the earth at a constant altitude and finally return to the original point. Of course, these are now very familiar arguments and are the ones that underlie the idea of an artificial satellite, but at the time of Newton arguments of this type were quite novel.

Considering the motion of the moon around the earth as a "continuous fall" under the action of a certain attractive force, Newton was able to compare that ("astronomical") force with the ("terrestrial") forces which cause all material objects to fall down. His argument, in a somewhat modified form, is represented in Fig. 18-10, which shows the moon (M) revolving around the earth (E) along a (nearly) circular orbit. At position M the moon possesses a certain velocity which is perpendicular to the radius of the circle. If there were no forces, the moon would proceed along a straight line

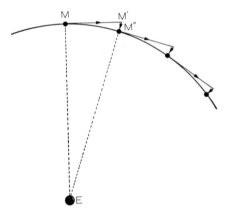

Fig. 18-10. Newton considered the motion of the moon around the earth as a *continuous fall* caused by the force of universal gravity.

and, a unit of time later, would move to position M'. Since, however, it arrives at position M'', the stretch $M'M''$ should be considered as the distance covered by the moon during a unit time, in its *free fall* toward the earth. According to the Pythagorean theorem:

$$M'M'' = \sqrt{(EM)^2 + (MM')^2} - EM \text{ (since } EM'' = EM)$$

which can be algebraically shown to be closely equal (for $MM' \ll EM$) to:

$$\frac{(MM')^2}{2EM} \quad \text{or} \quad \frac{1}{2}\left(\frac{MM'}{EM}\right)^2 \times EM$$

where MM'/EM is apparently the *angular velocity* of the moon in its motion around the earth[*] (i.e., 2π divided by the length of a month expressed in seconds $= 2.66 \times 10^{-6}$). But, in the discussion of accelerated motion we have already seen that the distance covered during the first second is equal to one-half of the quantity known as "acceleration," so that we conclude that the acceleration due to the force holding the moon on its circular orbit is $(MM'/EM)^2 \times EM$. Using the above given value for angular velocity and substituting for the distance to the moon the values of 384,400 km or 3.844×10^{10} cm, Newton obtained, for the acceleration due to gravity at the distance of the moon, the value: 0.27 cm/sec², which is much smaller than the acceleration of gravity on the surface of the earth (981 cm/sec²). There exists, however, a very simple correlation between these two quantities on one hand and the distances of the moon and of a falling apple from the center of the earth on the other. Indeed, the ratio of 981 to 0.27 is 3,640, which is exactly equal to the square of the number representing the ratio of the radius of the moon's orbit to the radius of the earth. Thus, Newton arrived at the result that *the forces of terrestrial gravity decrease as the inverse square of the distance from the center of the earth.*

UNIVERSAL GRAVITY

It was, of course, natural for Newton to generalize these findings concerning the moon for the case of the planets revolving around the sun, and the satellites revolving around these planets. To do this, he had to make an additional assumption concerning the dependence of gravitational force on the masses of the two material bodies between which it is acting. From the fact that all material objects fall with the same acceleration (Chapter 2), he concluded that the force of gravity is proportional to the mass of the object on which it acts. It was therefore natural to assume that this force is also proportional to the mass of the body which causes the gravitational pull (the earth), and, in its complete form, Newton's law of gravity states that **any two material bodies in the universe are attracted to each other with a force directly proportional to the product of their masses, and inversely proportional to the square of the distance between them.** Accepting this law as holding for all

---

[*] This relation becomes more and more exact the smaller MM' is in respect to EM.

bodies of the solar system, and using a new mathematical method (now known as "calculus") which he specially developed for attacking this class of problems, Newton was able to derive all three of Kepler's laws of planetary motion, thus giving additional support to his theory of universal gravity. However, although the development of *celestial mechanics* in the centuries following Newton's work has permitted the description, in great detail, of the motion of all the members of the solar system, the nature of gravitational force, itself, remained a complete mystery until Einstein's formulation of the general theory of relativity, which will be discussed in the last chapter of this book.

THE DISTANCE SCALE OF THE PLANETARY SYSTEM

The attempts to estimate the distances to celestial bodies range back to the time of ancient Greece when Hipparchus (160-125 B.C.) carried out a very successful measurement of the distance to the moon. The principle used by Hipparchus for that purpose is illustrated in Fig. 18-11, which shows the geometrical relations (strongly exaggerated) pertaining to a lunar eclipse. The dark converging cone, *CDN*, is the shadow (or *umbra*) thrown by the earth into space. When the moon is within this cone, it is completely obscured, and an observer on the

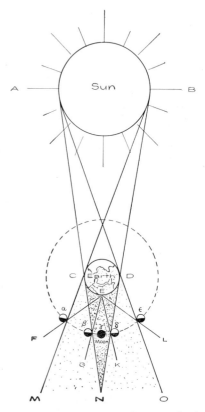

Fig. 18-11. Hipparchus' method of measuring the distance to the moon and to the sun. It gave the correct value for the moon's distance, but failed to give the distance to the sun.

moon would see a total eclipse of the sun by the earth. The lighter diverging cone, *MCDO*, is a semi-shadow (or *penumbra*) corresponding to a partial obscuration of the moon (a partial solar eclipse as seen from the moon). Hipparchus knew that in the case of central lunar eclipses (i.e., when the moon passes right through the middle of the shadow), about ten hours elapse between the moment when the moon first enters the semi-shadow (at *F*) and the moment when its surface is again brightly illuminated by the sun's rays, at *L*. Since the moon is moving through the sky at a rate of one diameter (or about one-half of a degree) per hour, the angle (*FEL*) is equal to five degrees. On the other hand, complete obscuration of the moon (*G* to *K*) lasts for only five and one-third hours, indicating that angle *GEK* is only $2\frac{2}{3}$ degrees. Angles *ACB* and *ADB* are also known since they represent the angular diameter of the sun as seen from the earth; they are about one-half degree each. Knowing these angles, and also the distance *CD* (diameter of the earth) one can, by simple geometrical construction, find the distance to the moon as well as the distance to the sun.

The procedure is as follows: Assume *some* value for the distance of the moon and draw its circular orbit. From the intersections, α, β, γ, and δ with the lines *EF*, *EG*, *EK*, *EL*, drawn according to numerical values of angles as given above, draw tangents *MC*, *NC*, *ND*, and *OD* to the surface of the earth. Their intersections at *A* and *B* will determine the position (and the size) of the sun. However, for an arbitrarily assumed value of the moon's distance, angles *ACB* and *ADB* will not be necessarily equal to 0.5 degree each as they should. Thus, we will have to change the assumed distance to the moon until an agreement is reached. Using this method, Hipparchus found that *the distance to the moon is about sixty times the radius of the earth*. This is very close, indeed, to the modern value of 60.267 times the earth's equatorial radius.

However, Hipparchus was considerably less successful in his estimate of the distance to the sun. Indeed, because the sun is very far away, lines *MC* and *ND*, as well as lines *NC* and *OD*, in Fig. 18-11 run almost parallel, making the positions of intersection points *A* and *B* quite indefinite. Thus, the only conclusion Hipparchus could reach on the basis of his data was that the sun is at least 20 times farther away than the moon, and that the sun's diameter was at least 7 times greater than that of the earth. Hipparchus' figure for the distance to the sun remained essentially unchallenged for seventeen centuries, and the correct value was obtained only after the invention of the telescope and the development of precise astronomical instruments.

The measurement of the distances from the earth to the sun, and to more distant objects, can be carried out with certainty only by the observation of the so-called *parallactic displacements* of the objects. This method can be easily understood if you stretch forward your hand and look at your thumb first with the left eye (closing the right one) and then with the right eye. You will see that the thumb is projected in these two cases on different parts of the background (Fig. 18-12), and, knowing the length of the *base* (in this case the distance between the two eyes) and the angle of displacement, we can easily calculate the distance to the object (in this case, the length of the outstretched arm). This method is widely employed by geodesists, who observe a distant marker (a tree or a vertical stick on a mountain top) through two theodolites placed a known distance from one another.

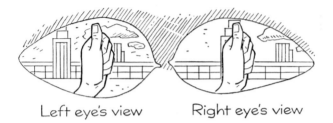

Left eye's view   Right eye's view

Fig. 18-12. A down-to-earth view of parallactic displacement.

The distance of the moon can be easily estimated this way by taking two simultaneous photographs of the moon and the surrounding stars from two observatories located a few hundred miles apart. From these observed results, astronomers can compute the displacement which would have been observed if the two pictures had been taken from two points located at a distance apart equal to the earth's radius. For the moon, the mean value of this so-called *equatorial parallax* has been found to be 57′ 2″.7, which leads to the mean distance to the moon of 384,403 km (238,857 miles).

In the case of the sun, the direct measurement of the parallax is considerably more difficult, partially because the expected angular displacement is much smaller, but mostly because the nearby stars which should serve as a distant background are lost in the brilliance of the sun's rays. Thus, astronomers prefer to use here an indirect method based on the observation of the "transit of Venus" when this planet is projected, as a small black point, on the disc of the sun. If observed simultaneously from two observatories on the surface of the earth, Venus shows an easily measurable parallactic displacement with respect to the sun's rim. Of course, the sun cannot be considered as an infinitely distant background with respect to Venus, but, since their relative distances are known, it is very easy to introduce the necessary correction. The situation is illustrated in Fig. 18-13, where all distances and angles are, of course, strongly exaggerated. (The actual displacement of Venus, as observed from diametrally opposite points on the earth, is only about one per cent of the solar diameter, or about 20″.) Knowing from observation the angle, $B'AA'$, and noticing that the ratio of the sides, $B'V$ and AB', in the triangle $AB'V$ is equal to the distance of Venus from the sun relative to that of the earth, i.e., 0.7233, we can easily calculate the parallax of the sun (referred to the terrestrial base AB).

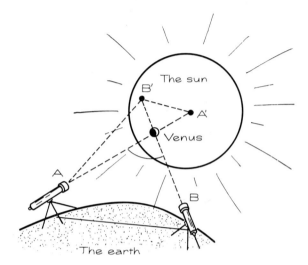

Fig. 18-13. The parallactic displacement of Venus with respect to the sun's disc. (The angles are strongly exaggerated.)

Using this method during the transit of Venus in the year 1752, the French astronomer, Lacaille, obtained the first exact value for the distance to the sun, the value exceeding by a factor of twenty the old Hipparchus figure. Since this time, much more exact values have been ob-

TABLE 18-1

Planet	Distance from the sun km	Astr. units	Eccentricity of the orbit	Equatorial diameter (km)	Mass earth = 1	Number of satellites	Temp (°C)
Mercury	57.94 × 10⁶	0.3871	0.206	5,000	0.04	0	191
Venus	108.27 × 10⁶	0.7233	0.007	12,400	0.81	0	69
Earth	149.68 × 10⁶	1.0000	0.017	12,742	1.00	1	17
Mars	228.06 × 10⁶	1.5237	0.093	6,780	0.11	2	−37
Asteroid ring (Ceres)*	414.19 × 10⁶	2.7673	0.077	770	Very small		
Jupiter	778.73 × 10⁶	5.2028	0.048	139,760	316.94	12	−146
Saturn	1427.7 × 10⁶	9.5388	0.056	115,100	94.9	9	−179
Uranus	2872.4 × 10⁶	19.1910	0.047	51,000	14.7	5	−207
Neptune	4500.8 × 10⁶	30.0707	0.009	50,000	17.2	2	−220
Pluto	5914.8 × 10⁶	39.4574	0.249	uncertain	Small	0	−226

* These data are given for the asteroid, Ceres, which is typical of the other asteroids forming the ring.

tained by using as an "intermediary" body the planet Mars and, in particular, the asteroid Eros, which sometimes comes as close to the earth as one-sixth of the solar distance. The correct value of the mean solar parallax is now known to be 8″.80, which corresponds to a mean distance of 149,450,000 ± 17,000 kilometers (or 92,870,000 ± 11,000 miles). Using this distance, we can obtain the exact values of the orbital radii of the different planets, as well as their diameters. These data are tabulated in Table 18-1. The table also gives the eccentricity of the orbit (the ratio of the distance between two foci of the ellipse to its major axis), which is very small except for Mercury and Pluto. The last column gives the *mean temperature* of the planet's surface as caused by the sun's rays, which (if expressed in the absolute scale) can be shown to be inversely proportional to the square root of the distance from the sun. The variations of that temperature between day and night are largely dependent on the properties of the planetary atmospheres.

The Earth as an Astronomical Body

Astronomically speaking, the earth is the largest of the four inner planets, rotating around its axis once a day (by definition) and revolving around the sun in one (sidereal) year, i.e., 365.256 days. Its axis of rotation is inclined to the plane of its orbit (ecliptic) by an angle of $66\frac{1}{2}°$ so that, in the course of its orbital motion, the earth periodically turns toward the sun either its northern or its southern hemisphere. This accounts in a well-known way for the seasonal changes on the earth.

If the earth were perfectly spherical, its rotation axis would maintain a constant direction in space, i.e., in respect to the fixed stars. However, as the result of its

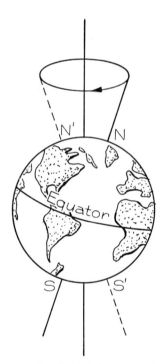

Fig. 18-14. The earth's rotation axis describes the surface of a cone.

axial rotation, the earth has the shape of an ellipsoid, with its equatorial radius being 21 km (13 miles) longer than its polar radius, and the uneven action of solar gravity on the forward and backward parts of this equatorial bulge causes the earth's rotation axis to describe the surface of a cone, with respect to the line perpendicular to its orbit (Fig. 18-14). This so-called *precession* of the earth's rotation axis is very slow, and a complete turn is accomplished only every 26,000 years. This phenomenon causes slow changes in the position of the *equinoxes,* i.e., the intersection points between the *celestial equator* (defined as the intersection of the plane of the terrestrial equator with the celestial sphere) and the *ecliptic* (defined as the intersection of the plane of the earth's orbit with the same sphere). Moving along the ecliptic, the sun passes through the equinox points and enters either into the Northern Hemisphere, which signifies the beginning of spring (*spring equinox*), or into the Southern Hemisphere, which signifies the beginning of autumn (*fall equinox*). Because of the slow change in the direction of the earth's rotation axis, the points of equinox move westward along the ecliptic at the rate of about 50 angular seconds a year. Thus, whereas at the time of Ptolemy, who was the first to discover the precession of the equinoxes (eighteen centuries ago), the spring equinox was in the constellation of *Aries,* it has now shifted to the constellation of *Pisces.*

Eclipses

If the plane of the moon's orbit around the earth coincided with the plane of the earth's orbit around the sun, the moon would eclipse the sun every month and would be itself obscured by the earth every month. However, the two planes do not coincide, but are tilted by 5° 8′ with respect to one another. As the earth moves around the sun, the plane of the moon's orbit remains parallel to itself in space so that twice a year the line of intersection between the two planes points toward the sun.

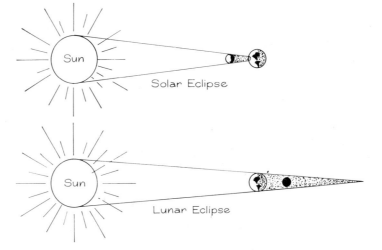

Fig. 18-15. Solar and lunar eclipses.

Only at these times is it possible for all three bodies to be located along a straight line. If this happens, an *eclipse* will take place; it will be a *solar eclipse* if the moon gets between the sun and the earth and a *lunar eclipse* in the opposite case (Fig. 18-15).

Since the eclipses of either the sun or the moon require a double coincidence in the position of the earth and of the moon in their orbits, they happen comparatively rarely. It has been estimated that the maximum number of eclipses per year is 7 (5 solar and 2 lunar, or 4 solar and 3 lunar), and that the minimum possible number is 2 (both solar). This does not mean, however, that a person living in a certain locality on the earth will observe solar eclipses more often than lunar ones. In fact, when the moon is obscured by the shadow of the earth, the eclipse can be seen by everybody located on the night side of the globe. On the other hand, the moon's shadow on the surface of the earth covers an area of only 65 miles in diameter, so that we must be lucky enough to be located within a narrow band formed by that shadow when it runs across the earth's surface to observe a total solar eclipse (Fig. 18-16).

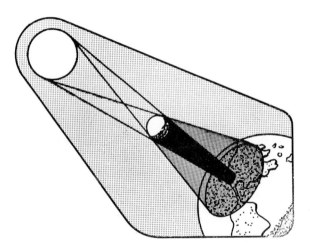

Fig. 18-16. The shadow and semi-shadow on the surface of the earth during a solar eclipse.

In any given location on the earth, a total solar eclipse happens only once in 350 years.

Since, owing to a cosmic coincidence that dates back to the epoch when the solar system was formed, the moon and the sun as seen from the earth have about the same apparent diameter, the disc of the moon is just about large enough to cover the disc of the sun. However, because of slight variations in the earth-sun and moon-earth distances caused by the ellipticity of their orbits, the moon sometimes appears slightly larger than the sun, and sometimes slightly smaller. In the first case we observe *total solar eclipses*, which are of particular interest for astronomers, while in the second case we have *annular eclipses* in which the bright ring of the solar surface is seen around the dark disc of the moon.

Turning to lunar eclipses, we must distinguish between two cases. Since the cross-section of the earth's shadow (umbra) at the distance of the moon is more than twice the moon's diameter, the moon can be completely hidden for as long as an hour and a half. On the other hand, the region of semi-shadow (penumbra) is much wider, so that the partial eclipse of the moon can last considerably longer. At the time of total lunar eclipses, an observer on the moon would see a total solar eclipse by the earth, while in the second case a part of the solar disc would always protrude beyond the earth's rim. The satellites of other planets are also subject to periodic obscurations. The observation of the eclipses of Jupiter's satellites, predicted in advance by astronomical calculations, served navigators as a substitute for chronometers before the invention of radio.

The Moon vs. Other Satellites

Our moon occupies an exceptional place among the satellites of all the planets. In fact, the only other inner planet that has satellites is Mars, but both of its satellites, known as "Phobos" and "Deimos," are a few hundred times smaller (in diameter) than our moon. True enough, some of the satellites of Jupiter and Saturn are up to 50 per cent larger than our moon, but then we must remember that the diameters of these two planets themselves exceed the diameter of the earth by more than a factor of ten! As we have seen in the previous chapter, the moon exercises a gravitational pull on the earth, raising periodic ocean tides and slowing the daily period of rotation of the earth by about 0.001 sec every century. According to basic laws of mechanics, the slowing of the earth's axial rotation must result in a corresponding acceleration of the orbital motion of the moon, so that our satellite is expected to move slowly away from us along an unwinding spiral orbit. It is calculated that the distance to the moon increases at present by 10 cm per month; thus, each time we see a new moon it is that much farther away from us. Of course, 10 cm per month is not a very large quantity, but the point is that, according to present views, the planetary system was formed about 5 billion years, or 60 billion months, ago. During that period of time the moon must have receded from the earth by several hundred thousand km, which is of the same general order of magnitude as the 384,400 km that is the present distance of the moon.* Thus, we come to the conclusion that *when the earth and the moon were first formed, they must have been very close to one another.*

The British astronomer, George Darwin (the son of the famous author of the *Origin of Species*), who was the first to discover this fact, proposed a theory stating that the material of the earth and the moon originally formed one single body ("Earthoon" or "Moorth"), which then broke up into two parts as the result of a fission process caused by the tidal forces of the sun. According to this theory, the Pacific Basin represents the scar in the earth's crust marking the spot from which the material of the moon was extracted. However, mathematical studies of this hypothesis, largely by another British astronomer, Harold Jeffreys, failed to find any possible way in which such a separation of the moon from the earth could have taken place, and many investigators in this field are now inclined to believe that, although the earth and the moon must have been formed very close together, they were never a single body. Now, fifty years after Darwin's proposal, the discussion still rages, and, whereas a smaller fraction of scientists (to which the author belongs) still prefer to believe in the validity of Darwin's views, another fraction maintains that he was definitely wrong. The problem will probably be solved one way or the other only after the complicated theory of a fission process under the action of tidal forces is put on an adequately powerful electronic computing machine.

NO AIR, NO WATER, NO LIFE ON THE MOON

Looking at the moon even through a small telescope, we are surprised by the sharpness of its surface features, which are formed by a combination of brightly illuminated areas and completely black shadows. There are no half shades on the moon, no dusks or dawns as we have on the earth, and the sunrise and sunset lines form a perfectly sharp division between the brightness of the day and the profound darkness of the night. And, of course, we never observe on the moon anything like the clouds that are so characteristic of our terrestrial atmosphere. All this spells one thing: *the moon has no atmosphere, and its surface is directly exposed to the almost complete vacuum of interplanetary space.*

It is not difficult to understand the absence of air on the moon. It is well known to geophysicists that the terrestrial atmosphere slowly loses its molecules, which escape against the force of gravity into the surrounding space. The escape velocity from the earth is 11.3 km/sec as

---

* The discrepancy between the two figures can be easily ascribed to the fact that the surface features of the earth were different during past geological eras, thus affecting the tidal friction and the rate of the moon's recession.

compared with the mean molecular velocity of less than 1 km/sec, which corresponds to the temperature of the upper layers of the terrestrial atmosphere. The escape velocity from the moon is only about 2.4 km/sec, and if any air were present at its surface, it would be very rapidly dissipated into the surrounding vacuum.*) For the same reason, no water can be present on the surface of the moon in any reasonable amounts. When the first space ship lands on its rugged surface, the travelers will have to wear the same space suits they did on the intermediate space platform, and, of course, they will not find any traces of life on the surface of our satellite. It is barren and dead as dead can be!

SURFACE FEATURES OF THE MOON

Looking at the moon's surface through a good-sized telescope (the picture in Fig. 18-17 was taken by the 36-inch refractor of the Lick Observatory), we notice large darkish areas known as *maria* or seas, so named because they were mistakenly taken by Galileo for large bodies of water. They carry such romantic names as *Mare Tranquillitatis* (Sea of Serenity), *Mare Imbrium* (Sea of Showers), and *Oceanus Procellarum* (Ocean of Storms). Numerous small dark areas are called gulfs, lakes, and even marshes: *Sinus Iridum* (Gulf of Rainbows), *Lacus Mortis* (Lake of Death), and *Palus Somnii* (Sleepy Marsh).

---

* Because of the Maxwellian distribution of thermal velocities (see Chapter 8).

Fig. 18-17. A composite picture of the moon made by blending two photographs taken during the first and last quarters that show the surface features with more contrast. In front is Prof. Harold Urey of the Univ. of Chicago who has made major contributions to the theory of the origin of lunar surface features.

Fig. 18-18. The northeastern corner of Mare Imbrium showing the craters, Archimedes (lower center), and Aristillus (upper right). Courtesy Lick Observatory.

Mountain ridges on the moon were given the names of various terrestrial mountains, so that we have lunar *Alps, Apennines,* and *Pyrenees,* and *Caucasian,* and *Carpathian* mountains. Since the surface of the moon was telescopically explored and named before the American continent was settled, no familiar American mountains appear on the lunar map. But, when the map of the opposite side of the moon is drawn in the future, on the basis of photographs taken from the first round-the-moon rocket, we certainly will have lunar *Appalachians, Rockies, Sierra Madres,* etc.

The most characteristic features of the lunar landscape are the circular *craters,* which are usually called by the names of the great philosophers and astronomers of the past. We have craters of *Aristarchus, Archimedes, Plato, Copernicus, Tycho, Kepler,* etc. The photograph in Fig. 18-18 shows the northeastern corner of Mare Imbrium with the two large craters Archimedes, 40 miles in diameter, and Aristillus, about half that size. A large number of smaller craters are scattered all around, and the smallest of them measures less than a mile across. The Pentagon Building constructed on the moon would look, under this magnification, as a tiny dot, a fraction of the size of the smallest of the craters.

In the upper part of the picture, we see the mighty mountain range of the lunar Apennines rising some 18,000 feet above the level of the plain. Astronomers find it easy to measure the height of the mountains on the moon by observing the length of the shadows cast by them on the plains near the time of sunset or sunrise. Paralleling the edge of the Apennines runs a long crooked furrow or *rill*. This and similar formations seen in other regions of the moon are most probably cracks on its surface that originated sometime long ago in its past.

The surface of the "sea" itself looks rugged and desert-like, and, if Galileo had been able to see it as clearly as we do now, he would certainly not have given it the romantic name, Sea of Showers! Astronomers feel quite sure now that the so-called lunar "seas" actually are thick layers of some kind of loose material, such as small rocks, gravel, and dust. No telescope, of course, can show gravel and small rocks directly, and these conclusions are based on the observed temperature changes on the lunar surface. Using specially built "bolometers," i.e., instruments sensitive to heat rays, astronomers can measure temperature variations of the lunar surface directly. They have found that during long lunar nights the surface temperature of the maria drops to $-153°C$ ($-243°F$), while in the middle of the lunar day it rises to $101°C$ ($214°F$). These temperature changes take place quite slowly since a lunar day and a lunar night last a terrestrial fortnight each. But, during the eclipses of the moon, when the shadow of the earth moves rapidly across the lunar surface, temperature changes take place much faster and have been observed to drop from $71°C$ to $-79°C$ (from $160°F$ to $-110°F$) in the course of one hour. If the surface of the moon were formed by solid rocks, the surface temperature certainly would not follow the changes of solar radiation that quickly. Indeed, a rather thick layer of rock would be heated during the long lunar day, and as the sun is suddenly obscured by the earth, the heat from this vast reservoir would be able to maintain its high surface temperature for a considerable period of time. The fact that this does not happen proves that the surface of the moon is covered by some heat insulating material so that the temperature changes are limited to comparatively thin upper layers. Small loose stones, gravel, sand, and dust seem to be the most logical kind of insulating material to be found on the surface of the moon.

THE ORIGIN OF LUNAR CRATERS

For a long time there existed two rival hypotheses concerning the origin of lunar craters. According to one of them, these craters were of tectonic origin, similar to the volcanic craters on the surface of the earth, while according to the other, lunar craters were produced by the impact of meteorites, similar to the famous "Meteor Crater" in the state of Arizona. At the present time there is hardly any doubt that lunar craters are of purely meteoric origin and that the fact that the face of the moon is covered with scars of old meteorite impacts is due to the absence of air and water on the surface of the moon. Big meteorites must have been striking the surface of the earth just about as often as they have been striking the surface of the moon (per unit area), but the craters formed in these collisions were rapidly (in a geological sense, of course) leveled off by weathering and rain. The dozen or so meteoric craters existing presently on the surface of the earth represent comparatively recent formations resulting from meteoric impacts within the last 10 to 100 thousand years, while the face of the moon keeps the record of all the punishment it got over a period of almost five billion years.

It has been estimated that the meteorite which formed the crater in Arizona about eight thousand years ago must have been a ball of nickel-iron over one hundred feet in diameter that weighed about 200,-000 tons. To produce the crater of Archimedes on the moon, the meteorite must have weighed about 25 billion tons and been comparable in size to a fairly large mountain. The total mass of meteorites that must have fallen on the moon to account for its very badly scarred face must be many million billion tons, which, however, represents only a negligibly small fraction of the total mass of our satellite. When the sun stands high over the lunar surface (full moon), we observe long rays spreading radially from the craters over the surface of surrounding seas. These are probably formed by the sprays of fine dust thrown sideways during the meteoric impacts.

Mercury and Venus

Mercury and Venus are as different from each other as the moon and the earth, and, indeed, they resemble their familiar counterparts very closely. Mercury is only about 50 per cent larger than the moon in its diameter, and, due to its small mass, cannot retain an atmosphere any better than the moon does. Its surface probably resembles very closely that of the moon and must be covered with numerous craters of meteoric origin. Because of the great distance, we cannot see the details of this surface, but the rapid increase of surface brightness with increasing distance from the line—called the *terminator*—separating the light half from the dark half indicates that its surface is as rugged as that of the moon. The observation of some faint markings on Mercury indicates that its period of axial rotation is equal to its revolution period. Thus, just as the moon always faces the earth with one side of its body, Mercury exposes only one side of its body to the shining sun. On the sunlit side the temperature of rocks must be high enough to melt lead, while the temperature of the opposite hemisphere is probably close to absolute zero.

Venus, on the other hand, is rather similar to our earth. Its mass, 80 per cent of the terrestrial mass, is large enough to prevent atmospheric molecules from escaping into space, and, indeed, the high surface brightness of that planet indicates that the sun's rays are reflected by a tenuous cloud-filled atmosphere. The greenhouse effect of that cloudy atmosphere and the proximity to the sun may lead to temperatures well above the boiling point on the hidden surface of the planet, and it is hard to imagine how any form of life could have been developed under these conditions. This conclusion is strongly supported by spectroscopic observations which indicate that the atmosphere of Venus contains practically no oxygen, but shows, instead, a tremendously high concentration of carbon dioxide. We know that the presence of oxygen and the low concentration of carbon dioxide in our atmosphere is due to the work of plants which absorb carbon dioxide for building their growing bodies and release free oxygen into the atmosphere. In fact, if the plant life on the earth were suddenly extinguished, our atmosphere would undergo drastic changes in a comparatively short (geologically speaking) time. Its oxygen would disappear, being used for various inorganic oxidation processes, while its content of carbon dioxide would be increased by volcanic activity, which ejects large amounts of carbon dioxide into the atmosphere. The observed fact that such is the situation on Venus definitely proves that there is no plant life on it, and consequently no animal life either.

The Arid Face of Mars

Although Venus comes closer to the earth than any other planet when it passes between us and the sun, its dark side is turned toward us when it is closest, which is not good for any observation of its surface. On the other hand, the distance to Mars is at a minimum when it is on the opposite side of the earth from the sun (in "opposition"), which is most favorable for observations. Owing to the eccentricity of the orbits of both planets, the distance between us and Mars at opposition varies quite considerably, and, in favorable cases, may be as small as 56 million km (35 million miles). The two latest favorable oppositions took place in 1939 and 1956, giving astronomers a much better chance to study the surface of that planet.

While the climate of Venus may be compared with that of the hot and humid tropical regions (much too hot, however, to sustain any life), the climatic conditions on Mars are more similar to those of arid, high mountain plateaus. Its surface temperature rises to about 27°C (80°F) at noon in equatorial regions and sharply drops at night. Mars's atmosphere, though existent, is very rarefied, and the air density corresponds to that of our own atmosphere at an altitude of 17 km. Spectroscopic studies show no noticeable amounts of either oxygen or water vapor in the Martian atmosphere.

The surface features of Mars have been more extensively studied than those of any other planet, and there exists an extensive "Marsographical" nomenclature referring to various seas, gulfs, etc., although there aren't any. In Fig. 18-19 appears a photograph of Mars taken under very

Fig. 18-19. A photograph of Mars taken by the 36-inch refractor of the Lick Observatory. Courtesy Lick Observatory.

favorable conditions. It must be noticed here that, because we look at Mars through our turbulent terrestrial atmosphere, visual observations may show more details, since the eye grasps the picture almost instantaneously, while the photographic plate averages the changing features (because of atmospheric interference) over a comparatively long exposure time. Visual observations of Mars's surface carried out by various astronomers (notably by the American astronomer, Percival Lowell, at his Arizona observatory) seemed to show long thin lines which were often interpreted as *canals* constructed by Martian inhabitants. At present no astronomer believes, however, in this fantastic possibility.

It is definitely established by observation that the reddish areas which occupy most of Mars's surface and which are responsible for its color are extensive sand deserts, and we even sometimes observe large sand storms moving across the face of the planet. The greenish areas, which were originally taken to be the Martian seas, are probably the lower lying plains which, though not filled with water, may possess some degree of humidity. The studies of the Dutch-American astronomer, G. P. Kuiper, carried on during the recent opposition of Mars, make it very plausible that the greenish color of these regions is due to some kind of primitive vegetation. In fact, his spectroscopic studies of light reflected by these greenish spots indicate that they may be formed by thin layers of mosses or lichens, similar to those covering terrestrial rocks. But it is very doubtful that any higher forms of life exist on the surface of that planet.

In the photograph in Fig. 18-19, notice the white spot near the north pole of the planet which resembles very much the polar caps of the earth. It is very likely that the analogy is correct and that we really see here a layer of frozen water. However, since water is very scarce on Mars, the future travelers to that planet may find that its polar caps resemble the frost on the ground more than the massive ice sheets of our arctic regions. Mars has two satellites, *Phobos* and *Deimos* (fear and horror), the diameters of which are about 10 and 5 miles, respectively. Larger than the inhabitable artificial satellite ("Space Platform") planned by the Earthlings, they are still much much smaller than our moon!

The Ring of Asteroids

Near the end of the eighteenth century a German astronomer, Bode, (not to be confused with Baade, shown in Fig. 20-11) noticed a very remarkable regularity in the distances of the planets from the sun. If we write a line of numbers: 0, 3, 6, 12, 24, 48, etc., doubling the figures each time (except in the first step!), add 4, and divide the results by 10, we obtain the distances of planets in astronomical units with a fair degree of approximation. The correlation between "Bode's numbers" and the actually observed distances is quite good, as is shown in Table 18-2, but, in order to achieve the agreement, we have to omit the number 2.8 in Bode's series.

Could it not be, thought Bode, that there is another planet between Mars and Jupiter which has not yet been discovered? He invited con-

TABLE 18-2   BODE'S LAW OF PLANETARY DISTANCES*

Bode's numbers	Planetary distance in astr. units	Name of planet
0.4	0.387	Mercury
0.7	0.723	Venus
1.0	1.000	Earth
1.6	1.524	Mars
2.8	—	(Missing!)
5.2	5.203	Jupiter
10.0	9.539	Saturn
19.6	19.191	Uranus
(38.8)	30.071	Neptune
(77.2)	39.457	Pluto

* Bode's numbers for Neptune and Pluto are in parentheses since these planets were not yet discovered in Bode's time.

temporary astronomers to search for this hypothetical planet, and on the 1st of January, 1801, the "missing planet" was actually discovered, quite by accident, by a Sicilian astronomer, Piazzi, who called it *Ceres,* at a distance of 2.8 astronomical units from the sun. But it was not much of a "planet"—it is only 480 miles across—and so it was given the name, *asteroid.* Within the next few years three more asteroids were picked up and named *Pallas, Juno,* and *Vesta,* and from there on the discovery of new asteroids went at a crescendo rate. At present more than fifteen hundred asteroids have had their orbits determined, and no Greek mythology can supply names for all of them. The first one discovered,

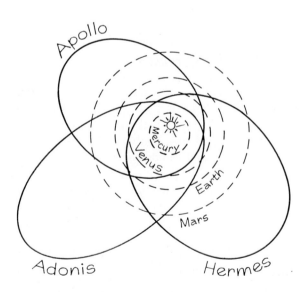

Fig. 18-20. The orbits of three asteroids that come close to the earth.

Ceres, remains the largest of them; about a dozen have diameters exceeding 100 miles, but the diameters of most of them are much smaller, coming all the way down to yards, feet, and inches. Although most asteroids move within a ring located between the orbits of Mars and Jupiter, many of them have elongated orbits extending as far out as Saturn, or as close as Mercury. In Fig. 18-20 we show the orbits of three of these far-traveling asteroids.

Thus, instead of the planet suggested by Bode's law, we find a bunch of rocks of various sizes traveling in the general region where the hypothetical planet should have been. Is it possible that *there was a planet once upon a time*, but that it was later shattered by some unknown force and broken up into thousands of small pieces? This assumption is not so fantastic and is even supported by some observational evidence. It seems likely, in fact, that the *meteorites* that often fall to the surface of the earth (Fig. 18-21) are small fragments of the same original celestial body of which the asteroids are the larger chunks. Studying the meteorites, astronomers find that some of them ("stony meteorites") have a constitution rather similar to the rocks of the earth's crust, while others ("iron meteorites") correspond to the inner iron core of our planet. Thus it may well be that we deal here with the fragments of a planet which was once moving along its orbit between Mars and Jupiter. If so, what could have caused this missing planet to break up into millions, nay, billions of pieces? Of course, we could speculate that this planet was once populated by intelligent beings who, long before earth men learned to shape flints into arrowheads, conquered (*but not quite*) atomic energy. Such a hypothesis is, however, not very likely, since the meteorites which

Fig. 18-21. A meteorite that fell in Cañon Diablo, Arizona.

fall on the surface of the earth do not carry many traces of radioactive fission fragments. It is more likely that this "missing" planet, if it ever existed, was broken up either in a collision with another celestial body or crushed by the combination of the gravitational forces exerted by other planets.

Outer Planets

The planets located beyond the ring of asteroids are in notable contrast to the four inner planets. Their diameters and their masses are considerably larger than those of the inner planets, but, what is more surprising, their mean densities are amazingly low. Whereas the mean densities of Mercury, Venus, earth and Mars are 3.8, 4.86, 5.52, and 3.33, respectively, as is to be expected for rock bodies, the mean densities of Jupiter, Saturn, Uranus, and Neptune are only 1.34, 0.71, 1.27, and 1.58, respectively. This can be explained only by the assumption that the observed discs of these planets do not correspond to the actual size of their solid bodies, but are only the outer boundaries of their very extensive atmospheres. In fact, detailed studies have proved that in the case of Jupiter, for example, the solid kernel of the planet is only 113 times more massive than the earth and measures only 4.7 earth diameters across. The rest of the planet is formed by a gaseous envelope of a hydrogen and helium mixture forming a layer which exceeds the radius of the solid

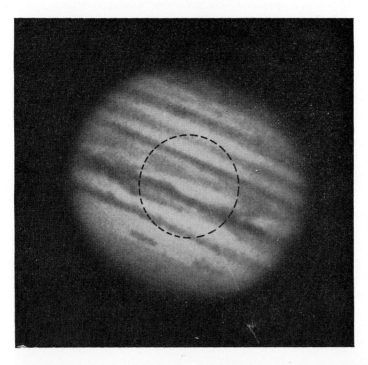

Fig. 18-22. A photograph of Jupiter taken by the 36-inch refractor of the Lick Observatory. The dashed line indicates the size of the planet's solid sphere. *Courtesy Lick Observatory.*

kernel (Fig. 18-22). At the base of this thick and heavy outer envelope, the gases are subjected to terrific pressure and must be compressed to almost the density of water. The rocky core of the planet is probably covered by a thick layer of frozen water, ammonia, and methane, although it is quite probable that deep in its interior the core may be hot and molten like the inner core of the earth. The markings we observe on the surface of Jupiter are exclusively exterior features of its atmosphere, though they may be connected with some phenomena taking place on the surface of the deeply-hidden solid core.

Similar situations exist in the cases of Saturn, Uranus, and Neptune. Very little information is available concerning the recently discovered ninth planet named *Pluto*. According to some theories, Pluto is not a planet in the same sense as the other eight, but is a former satellite of Neptune which has escaped the attraction of that planet, and which is now moving along its own orbit around the sun. This assumption is supported by the fact that Pluto does not seem to be much larger than our moon.

Saturn's Ring

The ring of Saturn (Fig. 18-23), first seen by Galileo through his primitive telescope, is one of the most remarkable structures in the family of planets. When the ring is tilted so that we can see its surface, we can observe that it consists of several concentric parts with circular slits be-

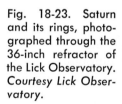

Fig. 18-23. Saturn and its rings, photographed through the 36-inch refractor of the Lick Observatory. Courtesy Lick Observatory.

tween them. Although, at first glance, the rings look like thin, solid plates, they are actually formed by billions of small bodies, much like small asteroids or meteorites, and each one revolves around the planet along its own circular orbit. In fact, by observing the Doppler effect (Chapter 6) in the sunlight reflected by the rings, we find that their outer fringes

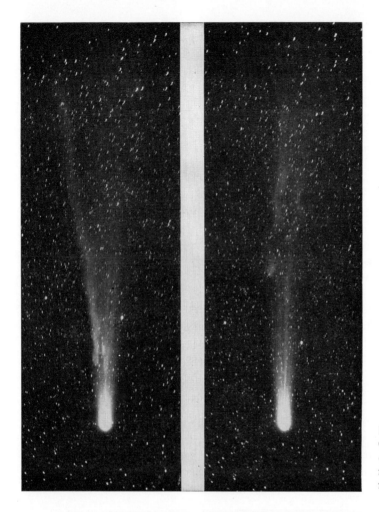

have smaller angular velocities than their inner fringes, as is to be expected from the third law of Kepler concerning objects moving independently around a common center of attraction. In a way, Saturn's rings resemble the belt of asteroids circling the sun between the orbits of Mars and Jupiter, except that in the rings the traffic is considerably more congested. The crushed material forming the rings could have originated from the break-up of one or more of the previously existing satellites of Saturn, or, more likely, it may be material that failed to condense into more satellites.

Comets and Meteor Showers

The most spectacular, although rather rare, astronomical phenomena are the appearances of great comets which spread their magnificent tails across the starry sky (Fig. 18-24). In olden times the appearances of comets were interpreted as signs of coming wars or pestilences, and, more recently, there was a fear that our earth would be destroyed in a collision with the head of a comet or even by passing through its tail. We know now that such fears were completely groundless since, in spite of their impressive appearance, comets can be best characterized by Professor Russell's expression: "airy nothings." The "head" of a comet is formed by a very loose swarm of small particles, and if our earth should pass through such a swarm, as it undoubtedly must have done many times in its history, the only result would be a brilliant display of *meteors*, or "shooting stars," caused by the burning of those particles that enter the terrestrial atmosphere at high speed. While such swarms of particles are traveling far away from the sun, they remain competely inaccessible to any observation, but on approaching the sun the particles begin to evaporate under the influence of solar radiation pressure. These gases become luminescent under the action of the sun's ultraviolet rays and produce bright comet tails that always point in the direction opposite to the sun. Spectral analysis of the light emitted by comets' tails shows the presence of compounds of hydrogen, oxygen, carbon, and nitrogen, indicating that their material is composed, to a large extent, of light chemical elements.

Comets move along highly elongated elliptical orbits oriented at odd angles in respect to the plane of the ecliptic, and they often go so far outside the limits of the planetary system that, after being seen once, they do not return again within the period of human history. There are, however, a number of comets that have a shorter revolution period

Fig. 18-25. The orbit of Halley's Comet.

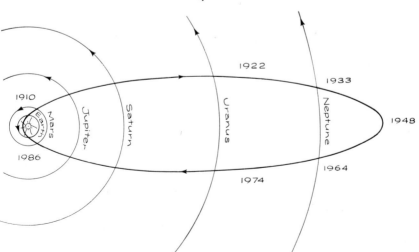

and that appear in the sky at well-appointed intervals. The most famous of such periodic comets (Fig. 18-24) is the one named after the English astronomer, Edmund Halley, a contemporary of Isaac Newton. Halley observed the comet in 1682, calculated its orbit, and suggested that it must be the same comet that had appeared in 1607 and 1531, i.e., 75 and 150 years earlier. He predicted that the comet would return again "about the year 1758," and, indeed, the comet was sighted on Christmas night of that year. It returned again in 1835 and in 1910, and is expected next in 1985. In Fig. 18-25 we give the orbit of *Halley's Comet,* which extends somewhat beyond the orbit of Neptune. Other comets have considerably shorter periods; one of these, *Encke's Comet,* returns every 3.3 years, but it does not come close enough to the sun to develop a bright tail, and is not visible to the naked eye.

In their periodic passage close to the sun, comets are treated rather roughly by the sun's radiation, and consequently they have only a limited life span. For example, *Biela's Comet* was for a long time observed circling the sun every $6\frac{1}{2}$ years, but at its return in 1846 it split into two independent parts that traveled side by side, and at the next return the separation between the two components had increased to about 2 million kilometers. After this the comet was never seen again, but on the dates it was due (late November of the years 1872, 1885, and 1898), the earth experienced brilliant showers of meteors, known as "Andromedes." *) Presumably these meteor showers were formed by the debris of the broken-up Biela Comet. As the years passed, the showers became fainter, and not much has been seen of them recently. It is very likely that other meteor showers, such as "Lyrids" (each April 21st), "Leonides" (each November 15th), etc., result from the encounter of the earth with the debris of old comets that are now spread over long sections of their original orbits. As the old comets are gradually broken up and turned into swarms of meteor showers, new comets are probably continuously being formed from the dispersed material on the outskirts of our planetary system.

The Origin of the Planetary System

How did the system of planets circling the sun come into being, and what are the chances that other stars in the Milky Way have similar planetary systems? One of the early theories of the origin of planets was proposed independently by the two greatest brains of the eighteenth century, the German philosopher, Immanuel Kant (1724-1804), and the

---

* So named because they appear (each November 20th) in the constellation of Andromeda.

French mathematician, Pierre Simon de Laplace (1749-1827). According to their views, the formation of planets was a part of the process in which the sun itself was formed. They maintained that the sun was formed once upon a time by the condensation of an originally highly rarefied, cool, and slowly rotating cloud of interstellar material, and this point of view is also fully accepted in modern cosmogony. This original gaseous cloud, or "primary" nebula, must have been in a state of rather irregular internal motion, and its various parts must have had different angular velocities with respect to its center. In modern language we say that it was a large "turbulent eddy" of interstellar gas. While the cloud was slowly contracting under the action of Newtonian gravity, its axial rotation was becoming faster and faster. Under such circumstances, we would expect that the parts of the cloud which happened to have small angular velocities would fall towards the center and form what is now the body of the sun, while the faster rotating parts would be flattened into a disc surrounding the central condensation. As the result of gravitational pull between different parts of the rotating gas disc, its material could be expected to break up into separate condensations which then contracted further into individual planets.

This familiar picture dominated cosmogonical thought until the end of the last century, when very serious objections against it were brought up by the famous British physicist, Clerk Maxwell, who has been mentioned several times earlier in this book. Maxwell's objections arose from his earlier work on the theory of Saturn's rings in which he showed that gravitational forces between the particles forming the ring are not strong enough to cause the condensation of the ring's material into one or more extra satellites. Applying the same argument to the hypothetical nebulous disc which must have been surrounding the sun according to the Kant-Laplace cosmogonical hypothesis, Maxwell came to the conclusion that in this case, too, the material should have remained forever in the form of a ring and could not possibly have condensed into the individual planets.

Maxwell's criticism led to the rejection of the original Kant-Laplace hypothesis, which was superseded by the so-called *collision hypothesis,* according to which the system of planets was formed in a collision, or rather a close passage, between our sun and some other star the sun encountered on its way in some distant past. The collision hypothesis turned out, however, to be completely unsatisfactory and, in particular, failed to explain the fact that planetary orbits are so nearly circular.

At the close of World War II, cosmogonists returned to the original Kant-Laplace view in a modified form formulated by a German physicist, Carl von Weizsacker. Weizsacker showed, indeed, that *Maxwell's objections became invalid in the light of our new knowledge concerning the*

Fig. 18-26. The origin and evolution of the solar system.

(1) About 5 billion years ago the material now forming the solar system was spread thinly in space as a gas and dust cloud.

(2) A few hundred million years later a major part of that material condensed in the center and formed the sun, while the rest condensed into the original protoplanets (the protoplanets of Mercury, Venus, and the earth are shown here).

(3) The ultraviolet radiation of the sun blew away the gaseous envelopes of the inner protoplanets and the solar system assumed the familiar look of today.

(4) About 5 billion years from now the sun will begin to expand and become brighter and hotter. The oceans on the earth will begin to boil.

(5) After another few hundred million years, the expanding sun will engulf Mercury and Venus, but its maximum expansion will probably never reach the orbit of the earth.

Courtesy The Grolier Society, Inc.

chemical constitution of matter in the universe. It was always supposed until only a few decades ago that the constitution of the earth is representative of all other planets of the solar system, the sun itself, and the universe in general. This would make *oxygen, silicon, iron,* and other "terrestrial elements" the most abundant universal elements. It has been found, however, that this is not true. In fact, the sun and other stars contain 99 per cent hydrogen and helium with only one per cent of all other elements. We have also seen earlier in this chapter that the outer planets, such as Jupiter and Saturn, have a large preponderance of hydrogen and helium gases. Thus, it is natural to suppose that the original material that formed a flat disc around the sun in its early days was also almost exclusively a hydrogen-helium mixture that contained only one per cent of heavier elements in the form of thin dust. It follows that the total mass of the original disc must have been much larger than was assumed by Maxwell, and we can show that, under such circumstances, the forces of gravity between different parts of this disc were strong enough to cause its break-up into the individual condensations.

These condensations, known as *protoplanets,* went through a process of subsequent evolution. The dust particles that were originally mixed uniformly with the gas gradually settled down towards the center and finally formed solid planetary cores surrounded by an extended gaseous atmosphere. One interesting point, proposed by the Dutch-American astronomer, G. P. Kuiper, who was mainly responsible for the further development of Weizsacker's original ideas, is that the formation of protoplanets took place while the sun was still in the process of early condensation and was nothing but a giant sphere of gas that was gradually warming up. When the sun finally came to the stage at which we know it now and began to pour into the surrounding space large amounts of radiant energy, radiation pressure acting on the outer envelopes of the protoplanets began to blow away their gaseous material. For a while, the solar system looked like a company of giant comets with their luminous tails stretching far outward into space, and this stage must have lasted until most of the hydrogen and helium gases were blown away. In the case of the planets closest to the sun (Mercury to Mars), solar radiations pressure made a clean job, exposing the rocky kernels of the original protoplanets. In the case of the outer planets, considerable amounts of the original gaseous material were left over, which accounts for their present state described earlier in this chapter. This currently accepted theory of the origin and evolution of the solar system is illustrated in Fig. 18-26. A mathematical treatment of the above described picture enables us to understand all the general features of our planetary system and, in particular, the above mentioned Bode's law governing the distances of the planets from the sun.

The return to the Kant-Laplace view has an important consequence for the exciting problem of the plurality of inhabitable worlds. If our planetary system were formed as a result of a close passage of the sun and some other star, we could hardly expect more than just a few such systems in the entire Milky Way, since stellar traffic is very uncongested and even the close passage of two stars is an extremely rare event. Since, as we know now, planets can be produced by a star without any help from another star, a large number of stars can have planetary systems of their own. It has been estimated theoretically that *one out of a hundred stars is able to form a planetary system of its own.* Since the Milky Way contains altogether about a hundred billion stars, *about a billion of these stars must have planetary systems, among which we should certainly find millions of planets with conditions close to those existing on our earth.* And there is no reason why life, maybe rather similar to ours, would not flourish in these distant worlds.

NINETEEN

OUR SUN

As seen from the earth, the sun appears as a shining disc a little over half a degree in diameter (more exactly, 31′ 59.3″). Knowing that it is 149,500,000 km away from us, we can easily calculate that the diameter of the sun is 1.39×10^{11} cm, i.e., about a hundred times the diameter of the earth. Remembering that the mass of the sun is 2×10^{33} gm (Chapter 18), we find that the *mean density* of the material from which it is made is 1.6 of the density of water. As we shall see later, however, the density inside the sun varies widely with the depth under its surface, and, while a thin outer layer of gas ("solar atmosphere") in which the Fraunhofer absorption lines are formed is much rarer than atmospheric air, the material near the solar

center is compressed to a density exceeding that of water by a factor of one hundred. At the surface of the sun the variation of density is extremely rapid, and it was found that with each 70 km of depth (i.e., only 0.01 per cent of the solar radius) the density increases by a factor of two. Thus, the depth is rapidly reached at which the gaseous material of the sun is so dense that it begins to emit a continuous spectrum. This visible surface of the sun is known as the *photosphere,* i.e., the sphere of light.

The Surface Temperature of the Sun

The temperature of the sun's photosphere can be estimated by a study of the energy distribution in the continuous spectrum of the sun. In fact, we have seen in Chapter 6 that the wave length corresponding to the maximum intensity in the spectrum decreases in inverse proportion to the absolute temperature (Wien's law). In the observed solar spectrum the maximum intensity falls on the wave length, 4,700Å, from which we deduct that the surface temperature of the sun is about 6,000°K. An alternative method is based on the Stefan-Boltzmann relation between the temperature of the surface and the amount of radiation it emits, and it leads to about the same numerical value. But the most exact method of estimating the surface temperature of the sun, as well as of all other stars, is based on the study of the relative intensities of Fraunhofer lines formed in the thin solar atmosphere. In fact, it turns out that the intensities of these absorption lines for different elements depend on the temperature in different ways, so that the general appearance of the line absorption spectrum represents a very sensitive natural thermometer.

The surface temperature of the sun estimated by this method comes out to be 5,800°K.

The Turbulent Solar Surface

Although when we look at the sun through an ordinary smoked glass we see nothing but a uniformly illuminated disc, telescopic observations show that the surface of the sun is very far from being smooth and undisturbed. On the contrary, it swirls and spurts and boils as lava does in the crater of an active volcano. In Fig. 19-1 we see the general pattern of the solar surface, which is formed by a rapidly changing network of lighter and darker areas known as *granulation.* This rapid fluctuation of light and shadow shows that the hot gases forming the solar photosphere are in a state of rather violent turbulent motion that causes slight variations in local temperatures all over the disc. Apart from these *granulae,* which are just barely visible in the telescope, we observe from time to time larger increases of local surface brightness that are known as *faculae* and *flocculi,* if the increase of brightness is moderate, and as *flares* in the cases of exceptionally bright ones. There is no doubt that these larger local increases of surface brightness are also due to the turbulent motion of photospheric gases, and are probably associated with large-sized turbulent eddies.

One of the reasons why astronomers wait impatiently for total solar

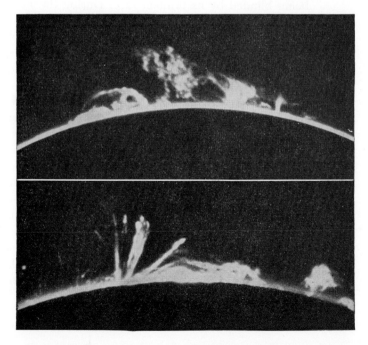

Fig. 19-2. Solar prominences, the giant streamers of hot gas that rise over the surface of the sun.

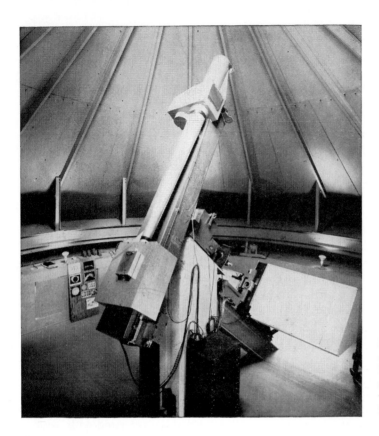

Fig. 19-3. The new coronagraph of the High Altitude Observatory of the University of Colorado in Climax, Colorado.

eclipses and travel to the far corners of the earth to observe them is that during a total eclipse of the sun they can see its delicate profile without being blinded by its brilliant face. During the short period of time that the disc of the moon completely obscures the brilliant photosphere of the sun, we can see bright tongues of flame shoot many thousands of miles out from the sun's surface (Fig. 19-2). These luminous formations, known as *prominences* are also part of the general turbulent state of the solar photosphere and are associated with faculae, flocculi, and flares. Our knowledge of prominences has been considerably advanced during recent decades by the invention of the so-called *coronagraph* (Fig. 19-3), an instrument in which the bright disc of the sun is artificially obscured by means of an ingenious optical arrangement. With this instrument, astronomers no longer have to wait for the rare occasion of a total eclipse in order to take photographs of the solar prominences, and they can, in fact, take continuous movies of them every sunny day of the year. In particular, the two pictures of prominences shown in Fig. 19-2a and b were not taken during an eclipse but are just two frames from the many films taken by the High Altitude Observatory of the University of Colorado at Climax, Colorado, which has carried on continuous observations of the sun since the foundation of the Observatory

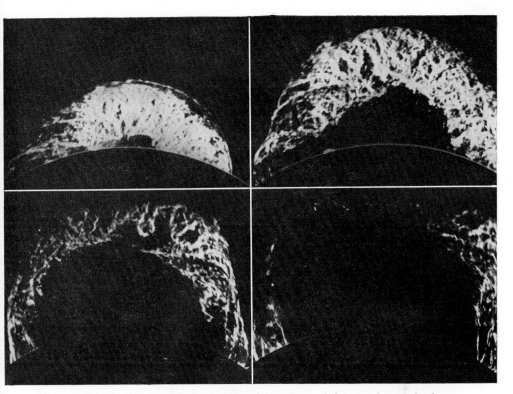

Fig. 19-4. The giant eruption on the surface of the sun that took place June 4, 1946. (Top left) at 16.03 hours, Greenwich time; (top right) at 16.36 hours; (bottom left) at 16.51 hours; and (bottom right) at 17.03 hours. *Courtesy High Altitude Observatory, University of Colorado.*

in 1941. When one observes something uninterruptedly over a long period of time, one is bound to stumble onto some rare events, and such an event really happened on the surface of the sun on June 4, 1946. Four frames from the movie film on which this event was recorded are shown in Fig. 19-4, and these photographs speak for themselves. These were the largest prominences ever seen on the surface of the sun, and nothing even approaching them has been seen since.

SUNSPOTS

Apart from the general turbulent motion that characterizes the surface of the sun, we can often observe large darkish areas known as *sunspots* (Fig. 19-5) which appear usually in groups in medium latitudes on both sides of the solar equator. Large spots can be seen with the naked eye (through a smoked glass, of course) and were indeed recorded by Chinese astronomers a thousand years ago. However, detailed studies of sunspots were made possible only after the invention of the telescope, and Galileo was the first man who recognized them as an integral part of the solar surface, and not something that passes between us and the sun. Although, because of the contrast with the rest of the solar surface, sunspots appear to the observer as dark regions, they are actually quite luminous and their temperature is only about 2,000 degrees lower than

Fig. 19-5. A day-by-day record of the great sunspot group of 1947 which demonstrates the rotation of the sun. *Courtesy Mount Wilson and Palomar Observatories.*

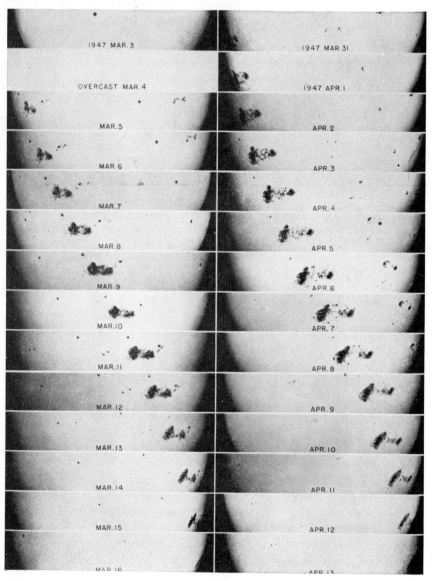

that of the rest of the solar surface. In fact, if we could obscure the entire surface of the sun, leaving only a good-sized group of sunspots, they would illuminate the earth as a hundred moons, and it would be painful to the unprotected eye to look at them.

The observation of sunspots has revealed that the sun is revolving around its own axis in the same direction that our earth is. Whenever a group of spots appears on the surface of the sun, they always move from the eastern to the western rim of the disc (Fig. 19-5) indicating that the sun's rotation period is about 25 days. The fact that the observed motion of the spots reflects the motion of the entire solar body, and is not just a drift of spots across the surface of the sun, can be established by the direct measurements of solar rotation based on the observation of the Fraunhofer lines. Indeed, if the sun rotates around its axis, spectral lines in the light coming from the eastern rim of the sun (which is moving toward us) must be shifted to the violet end of the spectrum because of the Doppler effect, discussed in Chapter 6. Similarly, the light from the receding western rim of the sun's disc must show a shift toward the red. These expected shifts of the spectral lines have actually been observed, with the interesting result that the angular velocity of the rotation of the solar surface has been found to vary from the equatorial to the polar regions of the sun. The observed rotation periods at different solar latitudes are shown in Table 19-1, from which we can see that the material at the solar equator moves faster than that near the poles. The situation is somewhat similar to that in the case of a river where the flow is faster in the

TABLE **19-1**

Solar latitude	Rotation period (days)
0°	24.65
20°	25.19
30°	25.85
40°	27.48
60°	30.93
75°	33.15
Near pole	About 34

middle of the stream and slower near the shores, and suggests that sunspots may be something like giant whirlpools formed because of this difference in relative velocities at different latitudes.

THE SUN'S MAGNETIC FIELD

Astronomers have been interested for a long time in knowing whether the sun possesses a magnetic field similar to that of the earth. Since, of course, no one can get to the sun with a magnetic needle, the presence of that magnetic field could be revealed only through its influence on the light emitted by the sun. Laboratory experiments show that the line spectra of elements are influenced by magnetic fields. If, for example, we place a Bunsen burner flame containing some table salt between the poles of a strong electromagnet, the yellow lines of the sodium spectrum will split into several components, and the separation of these components will increase in proportion to the magnetic field. This so-called *Zeeman effect* is caused by the action of the magnetic field on the orbital motion of atomic electrons, and can be used for a direct measurement of the intensity of that field. The application of this method to the study of magnetic fields on the surface of the sun was initiated in 1908 by an American astronomer, G. E. Hale, and it led to many important discoveries. While it seems that the sun does not possess a regular magnetic field similar to that of the earth, very strong magnetic activity is associated with sunspots, flares, prominences, and other irregular features characteristic of the solar surface. We know that the regular magnetic field of the earth is occasionally disturbed by what we call "magnetic storms"; there seem to be nothing but violent magnetic storms on the surface of the sun!

Sunspots, in particular, seem to be governed equally by the laws of gas dynamics and the laws of magnetism. In fact, the light emitted by sunspots shows Zeeman's splitting of spectral lines corresponding to magnetic fields thousands of times larger than the magnetic field of the earth. One of the most intriguing features of sunspots is that they almost always appear *in pairs*, the two components of the pair showing the opposite magnetic polarity. It looks almost as if in each case there were a magnet located not too deep under the surface of the photosphere, which, by its field, influences the disturbances that erupt on the solar surface. We have seen in Chapter 15 that the permanent magnetic field of the earth is most probably caused by slow convection currents in its molten iron core. Magnetic phenomena on the sun must be of a similar nature, with the difference that the gaseous material of the solar body is

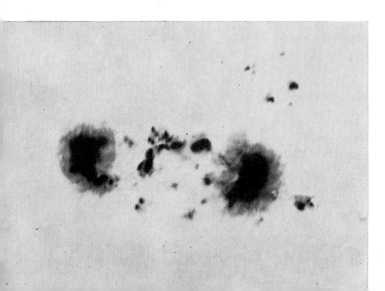

Fig. 19-6. A pair of sunspots. *Courtesy Meudon Observatory.*

Fig. 19-7. Solar co-
rona photographed
during the total
eclipse, September
22, 1922. *Courtesy
Lick Observatory.*

much more fluid than molten iron, and that the convection currents in that case are much closer to the surface. Thus, according to current views, the photosphere of the sun represents the upper boundary of a violently convective region extending about 10^5 km under the solar surface. The ascending and descending currents of gas in this region, being deflected by solar rotation and local magnetic fields, are, no doubt, responsible for all the complexity of the phenomena taking place on the surface of the sun. In particular, the peculiar shapes of the prominences must also be influenced to a great extent by the combination of gas dynamic and magnetic laws. The study of these phenomena belongs to a very young branch of science known as *magnetohydrodynamics,* which is just as complicated as its name implies.

SOLAR CORONA

The most impressive feature of total solar eclipses is a luminous aureole, or halo, surrounding the obscured disc of the sun, and known as a *corona* (Fig. 19-7). In olden times observations of the corona were limited to the rare occasions of total eclipses of the sun, which provided a few minutes of observation time, and that only if the weather during the eclipse were good. With the invention of the "coronagraph," which has already been mentioned in connection with the observation of solar prominences, the study of the corona became more or less routine work, and, although the coronagraph does not give such beautiful pictures as can be obtained during eclipses, it has the definite advantage of being always on the job.

The spectrum of light emitted by the corona consists of a faint continuous background similar to that of the sun, and a number of sharp bright

lines which *do not seem to coincide with the emission spectrum of any
known chemical element.* In an attempt to explain the origin of these
mysterious lines, astronomers went so far as to suggest the presence on
the sun of a new hypothetical element, "coronium," unknown on the
earth. But in 1940 the mystery of these coronal lines was explained in a
much simpler way by the Swedish physicist, B. Edlen, who proved that
these lines are emitted by ordinary atoms, mostly those of iron and
calcium, but under rather unusual circumstances. As we have stated
above, the characteristic line spectra of different elements are due to
the motion of the electrons forming their outer shells, which electrons
are also responsible for the formation of chemical bonds between the
atoms (valence electrons). According to Edlen, however, *the atoms of
various common elements present in the corona in the form of very
rarefied gases are completely stripped of their outer electron shells so
that the inner shells must take on the responsibility of emitting light.*

In the case of iron atoms, which normally contain 26 electrons, only 13
electrons are left. In the normal state, an atom of iron has two complete
shells (K and L), one partially completed shell (M), and two extra
electrons forming the beginning of the N-shell. It is these two outer electrons that are responsible for the chemical properties and the ordinary
optical spectrum of iron. With thirteen electrons removed, the structure
of an iron atom becomes similar to that of aluminum, with completed
K- and L-shells and three outer electrons beginning the formation of the
M-shell (Fig. 19-8). Thus, while in the first case the emission of spectral

Fig. 19-8. A neutral iron atom (left) and an iron atom that has lost 13
electrons (right). The electron shells are shown by circles (solid lines
for completed shells and a broken line for an incompleted shell).

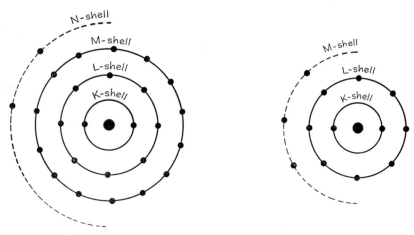

lines is due to electron transitions from higher levels (*O, P, Q,* etc.) to the energy level corresponding to the N-shell, in the second case we deal with the transition to the energy level corresponding to the M-shell. The difference is similar to that between the Lyman, Balmer, and Paschen series in the hydrogen atom, and results in an entirely different emission spectrum. On the basis of this kind of consideration, Edlen was able to prove beyond doubt that all the principal lines previously ascribed to "coronium" can be explained as being produced by iron, nickel, and calcium atoms stripped of a considerable number of their outer electrons. This stripping of outer electron shells must be due to the violent collisions between the atoms which can be caused only by a very high temperature. In order to explain the fact that the atoms of iron, nickel, etc., are stripped of about half of their electrons, it is necessary to assume that *the temperature of the gases forming the solar corona is about one million degrees.* A similar value for the coronal temperature is obtained from the study of its continuous spectrum, which is due to the scattering of solar light by a multitude of free electrons stripped loose from their parental atoms.

What can be the reason for such unbelievably high temperatures of the corona gases? Clearly they cannot be heated to such an extent by the underlying layer of the photosphere which is only about 6,000°K! The problem remained a mystery for a number of years until it was finally explained by a German-born American astronomer, M. Schwarzschild. According to Schwarzschild, *the gases of the corona are heated by the "noise" produced by the turbulent motion of the solar photosphere.* Just as a choppy sea, even away from the shore line, produces a characteristic noise which can be heard from a balloon floating above the waves, so the choppy surface of the sun emits a mixture of intense sound waves into the surrounding layers of solar atmosphere and into the coronal gases. Propagating into the more and more rarefied layers of the gas, these sound waves are gradually transformed into shock waves that cause strong local compression and intensive heating of the rarefied gases through which they pass. Under our terrestrial conditions, the idea that a symphonic orchestra playing a Beethoven concerto in the open, or the noise of a crowd at a county fair, might cause intense heating of the upper stratosphere sounds completely ridiculous, but in the case of the solar atmosphere it is just about what happens. And, indeed, Schwarzschild was able to prove, by direct mathematical calculations, that the sound emitted by the turbulent solar surface can maintain the rarefied gases of the corona at a temperature of one million degrees. It makes truth of the old Goethe verse: "Die Sonne tönt nach alter Weise in Bruder-Spheren Wettgesang" (The sun is chanting his ancient song in contest with the brotherly spheres).

SOLAR RADIO NOISE

The discovery of radio waves from the sun occurred in a rather dramatic way. Late one afternoon during World War II, the radars of the "early warning" system along the coast line of the battered British Isles went berserk: strong high-frequency radio waves were blanketing regular radio reception. It was assumed at first that this must be some new enemy trick, and that hordes of German bombers were flying under the cover of the radio noise that was jamming British radars. It was soon found, however, that it was not the Nazis but the sun that was causing all of this commotion, for all radars were pointing at the sun, which was slowly sinking toward the horizon. Later it turned out that on this particular day several exceptionally bright flares appeared at the solar surface, and it became clear that involved here was a natural radio emission caused by some electromagnetic disturbances on the solar surface. It appears that our sun is, in fact, a source of constant, though comparatively weak, radio waves which may, however, increase a thousandfold during certain periods of exceptionally violent solar activity. Considering what was said above about strong variable magnetic fields existing in the vicinity of sunspots and in the flares and prominences erupting from the solar surface, we can consider the radio signals coming from the sun as being caused by the acceleration and deceleration of electronic beams by these variable fields.

SOLAR ACTIVITY AND ITS EFFECT ON THE EARTH

As was discussed in Chapter 17 the phenomena in the upper atmosphere of the earth are strongly dependent on various kinds of radiation coming from the sun. We have seen, in fact, that the aurora borealis is caused by fast particles that are ejected from the sun by forces of light pressure, and that the high ionization of the upper atmosphere, which plays such an important role in radio communication, is caused by the sun's ultraviolet radiation. Also, a part of the earth's magnetic field is due to the electric current flowing through the ionosphere. Whenever a burst of activity occurs on the surface of the sun, it results in violent magnetic storms on the earth, the disruption of radio communications, and an increase in the number and the brilliance of auroral displays.

One mysterious thing about solar activity in general, and sunspots in particular, is that it shows a well-defined periodicity in time, with a period of about $11\frac{1}{2}$ years. In Fig. 19-9 we show an over two-centuries-long record of the observed number of sunspots, with the years of maxima printed in heavy type. We do not know the explanation of this periodicity though it is undoubtedly connected with some kind of magnetohydrodynamic phenomena in the convective layers hidden under the surface of the photosphere. An interesting point about this periodic behavior of sunspots is that during the years of maxima the spots appear closer to the solar equator and more away from it during the minima. Another interesting point, which may help in the future understanding of the mystery of sunspots, is that they change their magnetic polarity after each period, as if the hypothetical magnet hidden under the solar surface were tipped over every $11\frac{1}{2}$ years.

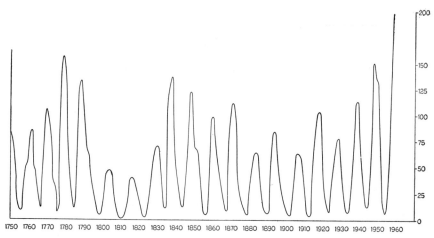

Fig. 19-9. A record of the number of sunspots for the past two hundred years, compiled by the Zurich Observatory. Notice the substantial increases in activity around 1780, 1840, and at the present time.

The periodic behavior of sunspots is closely correlated with the connected phenomena on the earth, and the curves that describe the variation of the aurora and the quality of radio reception run closely parallel to sunspot curves. An interesting correlation exists between the sunspot number and the Hudson's Bay Company's record of the number of lynx and fox skins bought during different years: the more sun spots, the larger the trade. This unexpected correlation is probably explained by the fact that the polar hunters and trappers have a better chance of success during the polar nights that are illuminated by bright auroras. Many attempts have been made to correlate sunspot numbers with the fluctuations of the world trade market, with various political events, etc. For example, on the list of maxima shown in Fig. 19-9 we find the years of the American and French Revolutions (1775 and 1789), and the years of both Russian revolutions (1905 and 1917). If it is not sheer coincidence, as it well may be, it may indicate that increased solar activity has a trigger effect on human passions.

The Properties of Matter inside the Sun

Direct observations of the sun are limited to the surface of the photosphere, and no human eye can penetrate into its deep interior. Yet, we know more about the central regions of the sun than about the core of the earth, in spite of the fact that the earth is right under our feet while the sun is a hundred million miles away! The reason for this strange fact is that in both cases we have to make conclusions on the basis of theoretical considerations which require knowledge of the properties of matter under the physical conditions existing in the deep interior of these two celestial bodies. In the case of the earth, we have to deal with the physical properties of a molten substance subjected to extremely high pressures inaccessible in our laboratories. Being unable to study these properties experimentally, we also lack any reliable theoretical predictions concerning them, since, as was mentioned earlier in the book, the theory of the liquid state of matter is extremely difficult. It would seem that in the case of the sun's interior, where the temperatures and pressure exceed, by a large margin, those encountered in the interior of the earth, the situation would be even worse. But this is not so. It turns out, in fact, that just because of these tremendously high temperatures which exist in the solar interior, the properties of matter become very simple and easily predictable on the basis of our present knowledge concerning atomic structure. The reason for this is that, *under the conditions existing in the solar interior, all molecules and atoms which form ordinary matter are almost completely broken up into their constituent parts.* Consider a glass of water that is brought gradually to a higher and higher temperature. At room temperature, we have a complicated structure in which water molecules composed of hydrogen and oxygen atoms are held together by intermolecular cohesive forces. With the increase of the temperature, the molecules will be torn apart and we obtain water vapor, in which individual molecules fly freely through space and very rarely collide with one another. The physical properties of water vapor, being subject to classical gas laws, are much simpler than those of liquid water. However, the properties of individual molecules (such as an absorption spectrum) are still almost as complicated as those in the liquid state. When the temperature rises to still higher values, violent thermal collisions between the water vapor molecules will break them up (*thermal dissociation*) into individual atoms of hydrogen and oxygen. In this state the optical properties of the gas become more predictable since they pertain now to individual atoms of hydrogen and oxygen, which are simpler than the composite molecules of water. Now, if the temperature goes still higher, the increasing violence of thermal collisions will begin to strip the individual atoms of their electronic shells (*thermal ionization*). At the temperature of 6,000°K that prevails on the surface of the sun, all hydrogen atoms are broken up into protons and electrons, while the atoms of oxygen are stripped of two or three electrons from their outer shells. At the still higher temperatures that are encountered in the solar interior, oxygen atoms, as well as the atoms of all other heavier elements, will be almost completely stripped of all their electron shells, and there will be a *mixture of bare nuclei and free electrons involved in a violent thermal motion.*

This situation simplifies the picture quite a bit. First of all, we can expect that no matter how high the density, solar matter can be considered as an *ideal gas*. Indeed, as we have seen in Chapter 8, an ideal gas is characterized by the smallness of the individual particles as compared with their relative distances. As long as the material consists of atoms and molecules which are about 10^{-8} cm in diameter, the particles are packed tightly together at a density comparable to that of water. But, once the atoms are broken into nuclei and free electrons, which have diameters of only 10^{-12} to 10^{-13} cm, the situation becomes entirely different, and the properties of gas will be retained up to much higher densities. In fact, in order to make completely ionized matter deviate from the laws of ideal gas, we have to compress it to densities at which the electrons and the nuclei are squeezed together as are sardines in a can. This density exceeds that of water by a factor of $(10^{-8}/10^{-12})^3 = 10^{12}$ gm/cm^3, and is far beyond the densities that are encountered inside any star. Thus, even though the material in the center of the sun is at 100 times the density of water, it can still be considered as a perfect gas, obeying the simple laws formulated in Chapter 1.

This almost complete thermal ionization of matter caused by very high temperatures in the solar interior also simplifies considerably the analysis of the optical properties of matter. *There are no complex molecules left to interact with the light waves.* We have nothing but free electrons, bare light nuclei (H, He, etc.), and the atoms of heavy elements, which are stripped of their electron shells to the extent that *only one K-electron is left over* and are therefore very similar to the simple atoms of hydrogen. In short, the entire situation becomes so simple that all optical properties of the material can be calculated theoretically with the greatest of ease.

TEMPERATURE AND DENSITY DISTRIBUTION INSIDE THE SUN

Knowing the physical conditions (temperature, density, etc.) on the surface of the sun and the laws governing the gaseous material in its interior, we can calculate, step by step, the change of these conditions as we proceed below the solar surface and toward its center. Such calculations were first carried out by the famous British astronomer, Arthur Eddington, and gave us the first insight into the inside of our sun as well as of the other stars. Figure 19-10 shows the variation of the tem-

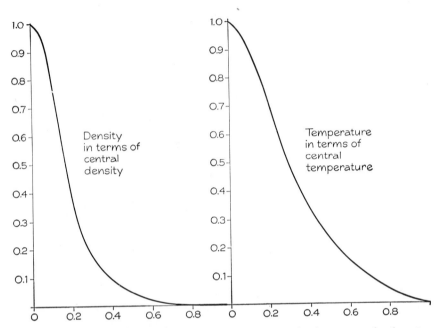

Fig. 19-10. The density and temperature inside the sun as the function of the distance from its center (in terms of the sun's radius).

perature and density inside of the sun's body as derived by the most recent calculations. Similar curves can be obtained for other stars located hundreds and thousands of light-years away from us.

Energy Production in the Sun

The amount of solar energy that falls per second on a unit area (cm^2) located outside the terrestrial atmosphere is 0.032 calories or 1.33×10^6 erg. Considering that the sun is 1.49×10^8 km away, we can easily compute that the total radiation of the sun is 4×10^{33} erg/sec. Since, on the other hand, the mass of the sun is 2×10^{33} gm, we find that the mean rate of solar energy production is about:

$$2 \frac{\text{erg}}{\text{gm} \times \text{sec}} \quad \text{or} \quad 5 \times 10^{-8} \frac{\text{cal}}{\text{gm} \times \text{sec}}$$

This is a very low rate of heat production, indeed, being only a small fraction of one per cent of the rate at which heat is produced in our body by metabolic processes. If the heating unit in a coffee pot would produce heat at the same rate as it is produced in the sun, it would take many months before the coffee started boiling, provided no heat were lost. As was explained in Chapter 4, the fact that, in spite of such a low "metabolic rate," the sun is so hot and luminous is due to its very large size, which makes its volume very large compared to its surface. However, in spite of the slowness of the thermonuclear reactions in the sun, they have been operating for billions of years, which makes the *total* energy production per gram of solar matter very large indeed. It should be mentioned here that, as we shall see later, the energy is not produced uniformly through the entire body of the sun, and that its main energy sources are located in its hot central regions. The rate of energy production in these regions is estimated to be about

$$100 \, \frac{\text{erg}}{\text{gm} \times \text{sec}}$$

BURNING AND CONTRACTION HYPOTHESES

A primitive man, as well as a modern man with little education in the field of science, would consider the sun as "burning" in very much the same way as logs burn in a fireplace or as kerosene burns in a lamp. However, it is easy to show that, even if it were made of the best rocket fuel mixture, the burning sun would not last for more than just a few thousand years.

In the middle of the last century, shortly after the discovery of the law of equivalence of mechanical energy and heat (see Chapter 4), a new theory of solar energy production was proposed simultaneously by H. von Helmholtz in Germany (1821-1894) and Lord Kelvin in England (1824-1907). They indicated that, being a giant sphere of hot gas which loses its energy through radiation from the surface, the sun is bound to contract, though very slowly. During this contraction, the Newtonian forces of gravity acting between different parts of the solar body do certain mechanical work that is then turned into heat, according to the equivalence principle of mechanical and thermal energy. It has been calculated that, being much more powerful than chemical reactions (such as burning), this process could maintain the sun at its present luminosity for a couple of hundred million years. At the time of Kelvin and Helmholtz, a few hundred million years seemed to be a sufficiently long period to explain the events of historical geology, and so their point of view was accepted without objection. We know now, however, that life on the earth must have existed for at least half a billion years, while the solid crust and the oceans must be much older still. Thus, the contraction of the sun certainly could not provide enough energy to maintain the surface of the earth and its oceans comfortably warm for the origin and evolution of living organisms.

THERMONUCLEAR REACTIONS

The discovery of radioactivity and the recognition of the fact that the energy stored within atomic nuclei exceeds, by a factor of a million, the energy liberated in ordinary chemical transformations, threw an entirely new light on the problem of solar energy sources. If the sun could have existed for several thousands of years fed by an ordinary chemical reaction (burning), nuclear energy sources are surely rich enough to supply an equal amount of energy for billions of years. The trouble is, however, that in natural radioactive decay the liberation of nuclear energy is extremely slow. In order to explain the observed mean rate of energy production in the sun (2 erg/gm-sec), we would have to assume that the sun is composed almost entirely of uranium, thorium, and their decay products. Thus, we are forced to the conclusion that the liberation of nuclear energy inside the sun is not an ordinary radioactive decay, but rather some kind of induced nuclear transformation caused by the specific physical conditions in the solar interior. It is natural to expect that the factor responsible for the induced nuclear transformations is the tremendously high temperature existing in the solar interior. Indeed, at a temperature of 2×10^{7}°K, the kinetic energy of thermal motion is 4.2×10^{-9} erg per particle, which, expressed in electric units, amounts to 3 Kev. This is considerably smaller than the energies ordinarily used in the experiments on nuclear bombardment (1 Mev and up), but we must take into account that, whereas artificially accelerated nuclear projectiles rapidly lose their initial energy and have only a small chance to hit the target nucleus before coming out of the game, thermal motion continues indefinitely and the particles involved in it collide with each other for hours, centuries, and billions of years. And, indeed, the calculations carried out in this direction in 1929 by the Austrian physicist, F. G. Houtermans, and the British astronomer, R. Atkinson, led to the conclusion that at the temperatures existing in the solar interior, thermonuclear reactions between hydrogen nuclei (protons) and the nuclei of other light elements can be expected to liberate sufficient amounts of nuclear energy to explain the observed radiation of the sun.

CARBON CYCLE AND H-H REACTION

Although the work of Houtermans and Atkinson proved, beyond any doubt, that the energy production inside the sun is due to thermonuclear reactions between hydrogen and some light elements, the exact nature of these reactions remained obscure for another decade because of the lack of experimental knowledge concerning the result of nuclear bombardment by fast protons. However, with the pioneering work of Cockcroft and Walton on artificially accelerated proton beams and subsequent work in this direction, enough material has been collected in this field to permit the solution of the solar energy problem. One possible solution was proposed in 1937 by H. Bethe in the United States and C. von Weizsacker in Germany (independently of one another) and is known as the *carbon cycle*, while the other possibility was conceived by an American physicist, Charles Critchfield, and is known as the *H-H reaction*. The net total result of both reactions is the transformation of hydrogen into helium, but it is achieved in a different manner in each reaction.

In carbon cycles, the atom of carbon can be considered as a "nuclear catalyst" that helps unite four independent protons into a single α-particle by capturing them one by one and holding them together until the union is achieved. After 4 protons are caught and the newly formed α-particle is released, we get back the original carbon atom which can go again through the next cycle. The series of reactions constituting the carbon cycle is shown in Fig. 19-11. The total period of the cycle is 6×10^6 years while the total energy liberated by the cycle is 4×10^{-5} erg, which

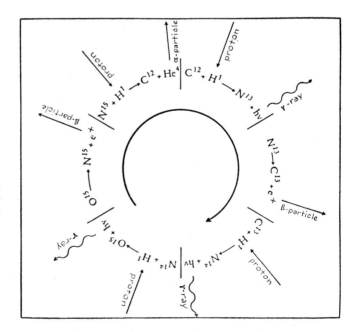

Fig. 19-11. The carbon cycle responsible for the energy production in bright stars.

yields for the rate of energy liberation per cabon atom the value of 2×10^{-19} erg/sec. Since, according to present data concerning the chemical composition of the sun, each gram of solar material contains 10^{-4} gm of carbon (5×10^{18} carbon atoms), this leads to the total rate of energy liberation of 1 erg/gm $\times$ sec, which is only one per cent of the observed energy production in the sun.

In the H-H reaction, the first step is the formation of a deuterium nucleus in the process of thermal collision between two protons:

$$_1H^1 + _1H^1 \longrightarrow _1D^2 + e^+ + \text{neutrino}$$

This is followed by a series of thermonuclear reactions which build up the so-formed deuteron into an α-particle:

$$_1D^2 + _1H^1 \longrightarrow _2He^3 + \gamma\text{-ray}$$
$$_2He^3 + _2He^3 \longrightarrow _2He^4 + 2_1H^1$$

This series of reactions takes 3×10^9 years and liberates 4×10^{-5} erg, leading to an energy production rate of 5×10^{-22} erg/sec per proton. Since hydrogen constitutes about 50 per cent of the solar material (2×10^{23} protons per gram), the total rate of energy liberation comes out to be 100 erg/gm $\times$ sec, in good agreement with the observed value.

The predominance of the H-H reaction over the carbon cycle in the sun, however, is not the general rule, and is reversed in many other stars. The point is that these two sets of thermonuclear reactions possess different sensitivities to temperature. While the rate of the H-H reaction increases comparatively slowly with increasing temperature, the rate of the carbon cycle goes up very rapidly. We shall see in the next chapter that the brightness of various stars depends essentially on their mass, which determines the temperatures in their deep interior: the more massive the star, the hotter it is inside and the more violent are the energy-producing thermonuclear reactions. Thus, if we take Sirius, for example, we find that its central temperature is $2.3 \times 10^7 °K$ (compared with only $2.0 \times 10^7 °K$ in the center of the sun). At this higher temperature the rate of energy production by the carbon cycle becomes considerably larger than that of the H-H reaction, so that it plays here the principal role. On the other hand, in all stars less massive than the sun (and 95 per cent of all stars belong to this group), the carbon cycle becomes quite unimportant, and these stars draw their energy entirely from the H-H reaction.

The Future of Our Sun

Since the energy radiated by the sun is due to the continuous transformation of hydrogen into helium in its interior, the sun evidently cannot shine for an eternity and is bound to run out of fuel sometime in the future. It is estimated that during the 5 billion years of its existence our sun has used about one-half of its original supply of hydrogen, so that it still has enough nuclear fuel for another 5 billion years. What will happen 5 billion years from now when our sun comes close to the end of its resources? To answer this question we have to remember that thermonuclear reactions proceed almost exclusively near the center of the sun, where the temperature is the highest. Thus, the shortage of nuclear fuel will be felt first in the central regions of the sun, where all the originally available hydrogen will have been transformed into (unburnable) helium. We can easily visualize that this will result in a rearrangement of things in the solar interior in such a way that the high-temperature region will move to the interface between the "burned-out core" and the outer layers that still contain enough hydrogen to maintain a nuclear fire. The internal structure of the sun, therefore, will be transformed from a so-called *point source model* (energy source in the center) to a *shell source model* in which the energy is liberated in a thin spherical shell that separates the burned-out core from the rest of the solar body (Fig. 19-12). As more and more hydrogen is consumed, the "shell" will move outwards

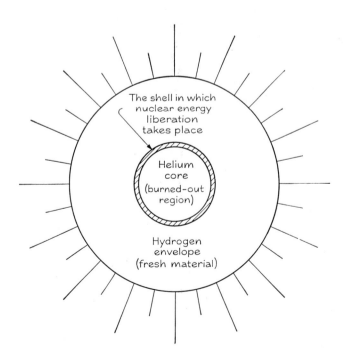

Fig. 19-12. A shell source model of red giant stars.

The shell in which nuclear energy liberation takes place

Helium core (burned-out region)

Hydrogen envelope (fresh material)

from the center, as a ring of fire does that has been started by a carelessly dropped match in a dry grass field.

It was suggested by Charles Critchfield and the author, and later confirmed by the more detailed calculations of M. Schwarzschild and his associates, that the formation of such a shell source inside the sun (or any other star) must result in a steady growth of the star's body and in a gradual increase of its luminosity. In fact, within a few hundred million years after the shell source is formed the diameter of the sun is expected to become as large as the orbit of Venus, and its luminosity will increase by a factor of between 10 and 20, making the oceans on the earth boil violently. After this last effort, the sun will begin to shrink and fade out again, until it becomes quite faint and insignificant. But there is no reason for immediate panic—we still have five billion years to go.

Man-made Thermonuclear Reactions

Considerably closer to us than the future progress of thermonuclear processes in the interior of the sun is the development of thermonuclear power by man on the earth, and its use for peaceful, as well as for military (alas!) purposes. We have already learned how to make giant thermonuclear explosions and are on the way to developing methods for carrying out controlled thermonuclear reactions. As we have seen above, thermonuclear reactions involving ordinary hydrogen are too slow for practical purposes and are of importance in the sun and stars only because of their very large size. For man-made thermonuclear reactions, we should use the "faster burning" heavier isotopes of hydrogen: *deuterium* (D^2), which occurs in nature, and *tritium* (T^3), which must be produced in an artificial way.

All the possible reactions between these two isotopes are summarized below:

$$_1D^2 + _1D^2 \longrightarrow _2He^3 + n + 3.25 \text{ Mev}$$

$$_1D^2 + _1D^2 \longrightarrow _1T^3 + _1H^1 + 4 \text{ Mev}$$

$$_1D^2 + _1T^3 \longrightarrow _2He^4 + n + 17.6 \text{ Mev}$$

Since these reactions do not involve either the slow processes of β-decay essential for the H-H reaction, or penetration into heavier nuclei as in the case of the carbon cycle, they go very fast even at "moderately high" temperatures. In Fig. 19-13 we give the calculated rate of energy production for the D-D reaction. A similar curve can be constructed for the D-T reaction and runs somewhat above the D-D curve. We see that, while at $10^5°$K this energy production is negligibly small, at a temperature of only $10^6°$K it rises to 10^7 erg/gm-sec, which corresponds to 100 horse-power per each kilogram of material. At the temperature of 2×10^7, and the density of about 100, corresponding to the interior of the sun, the reaction rate is 10^{24} erg/gm-sec and the entire material will be consumed in 0.03 sec. This almost instantaneous release of nuclear energy leads to an explosion and is used in the construction of the so-called H-bomb. However, to start the explosion, one has first to heat the material to the required high temperature, which can be done by using ordinary fission bombs. The details of how it is done are beyond the scope of this book. It may be noticed here, however, that the efficiency of such a thermonuclear bomb can be considerably increased simply by surrounding it with a layer of ordinary (cheap) uranium. In fact, although no fission chain reaction can be maintained in ordinary uranium, the numerous neutrons released by a thermonuclear reaction will cause individual fissions of uranium nuclei and add to the total energy release. Of course, such a design will result in the production of very large amounts of fission products, which will contaminate a wide area around the explosion and will be distributed by winds all over the globe.

If, instead of having a violent explosion, we prefer to run a controlled thermonuclear reaction at a steady low rate, the physical conditions under which such a reaction can take place should be drastically changed. First of all, the reaction should be run at *extremely low gas densities,* since otherwise the pressure of the gas at the required temperatures of a few hundred thousand degrees will rise to millions of atmospheres and no walls will be able to contain it. Secondly, this rarefied gas *should somehow be kept away from the walls of the vessel,* since otherwise the process of heat conduction into the walls will rapidly reduce the temperature of the gas below the minimum value required for ther-

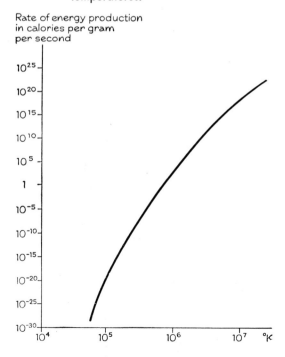

Fig. 19-13. The calculated rate of thermonuclear energy production in deuterium (at liquid density) for different temperatures.

monuclear reactions. This can be achieved in several different ways, all of which are based essentially on the use of strong magnetic fields. At the very high temperatures required in this case, the deuterium gas in the tube will be completely ionized and will consist entirely of negatively charged electrons and positively charged deuterons. (This state of matter is described nowadays by the term "plasma.") We know that when an electrically charged particle moves through a magnetic field, it experiences a force perpendicular to the direction of its motion and to that of the field (Chapter 5). This force compels the particles to spiral along the direction of the magnetic lines, as is shown in Fig. 19-14. Thus, by

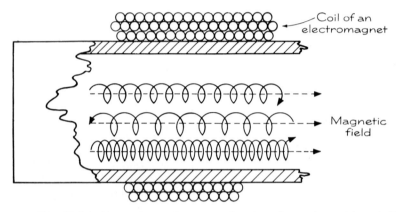

Fig. 19-14. Magnetic confinement, showing charged particles circling along the magnetic lines in a tube. The direction of motion and the "step" of spirals are determined by the horizontal component of the particles' velocity and are not influenced by the field.

forming a strong axial magnetic field in a tube, we can effectively prevent free deuterons and tritons from coming close to the walls. If this can be achieved, the collisions between the particles spiraling along the tube are expected to result in D-D or D-T reactions with the release of nuclear energy and of large amounts of neutrons. Of course, in order to start such a process the gas in the tube must first be heated to a very high temperature by some outside agent.

The second possibility consists in using magnetic forces caused by short but strong electric discharges through the tube. As we have seen in Chapter 5, two parallel electric currents flowing in the same direction are magnetically attracted towards each other so that, in the case of a sufficiently strong current, the gas (or rather the plasma) inside the tube will have a tendency to detach itself from the walls and to be squeezed into a narrow jet along the axis. How this so-called *pinch effect* operates can be understood by inspecting Fig. 19-15a and b. In contrast to the previously described method, the pinch-effect device operates in jerks, as an automobile engine does, but it has the advantage that the gas in the tube is automatically heated by the electric discharge, and no outside

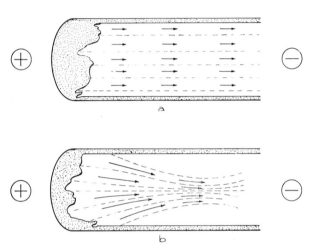

Fig. 19-15. The "pinch effect." (a) An electric current through the tube can be considered as a bunch of parallel "elementary" currents; (b) when the strength of the current is suddenly increased, the magnetic attraction between the "elementary" currents causes the "pinch effect."

heating is needed. It has been estimated that a current of several hundred thousand amperes lasting for a few microseconds would produce a "pinch" strong enough to cause a thermonuclear reaction in deuterium. The work in the above described directions is being carried out now in many laboratories of the world, and it is entirely possible that the problem of controlled thermonuclear reactions will be solved before this book comes off press.

TWENTY

STARS

AND STELLAR SYSTEMS

When one looks at the starry sky on a clear moonless night, one easily gets the impression that stars are practically innumerable. This impression is, however, far from being correct, for the number of stars visible to the naked eye in both celestial hemispheres is only about 6,000, while the number of stars that can be seen at any one time is less than half that because of the poor visibility near the horizon. But, of course, even the use of ordinary binoculars increases the number of visible stars to about 100,000,

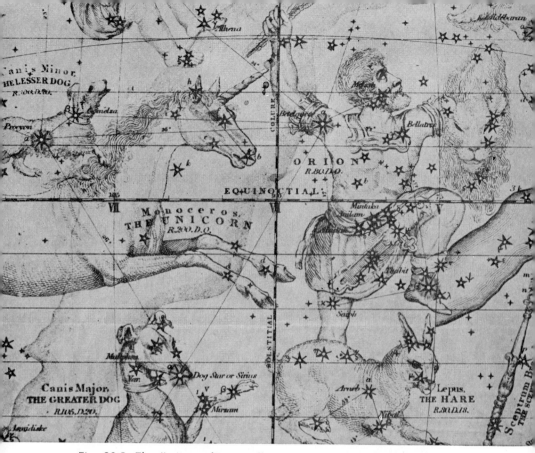

Fig. 20-1. The "animated" constellations as seen by ancient astronomers. From *Geography of the Heavens* by F. Huntington, published in 1835.

while the number of stars that can be photographed by the 200-inch telescope of the Palomar Mountain Observatory exceeds a billion. The brightest stars in the sky have their own personal names, mostly of Arabic and, in a few cases, of Greek or Latin origin. Thus, Aldebaran means "the flower" in Arabic; Antares stands for the "rival of Mars," which was so named because of its reddish color, while the names of Castor and Pollux date back to the ancient Greek legend about the two brothers.

Only a score of stars possess personal names; the others are designated according to the constellations to which they belong. As with the names of stars, the names of most of the constellations are of ancient origin, being associated with various animals, such as the *Great Bear*, or mythological heroes, such as *Orion*. The book *Almagest*, written by Ptolemy about 150 A.D., contains the description of 48 original constellations and designates the bright stars in each constellation as various parts of mythological or zoological figures. The ancient Greeks never went to the Southern Hemisphere so the regions of the sky there are deprived of any mythological interpretation. This gap was filled later, mostly by the early navigators, who used more prosaic names such as *Southern Cross* and *Triangulum*. At present we recognize 88 constellations which cover the entire celestial sphere. And, instead of the vague boundaries of the various constellations that were introduced in conjunction with the shape of the imaginary figures they were supposed to represent, such as those shown in Fig. 20-1, modern astronomy draws the boundaries of the constellations in a less romantic, but more definite way. Within each constellation the stars are designated by the letters of the Greek alphabet, generally in the order of their decreasing brightness. Thus, Aldebaran, being the brightest star in the constellation of Taurus (the bull), is also known as α Tauri (possessive form of Taurus), while the fourth brightest star in the constellation of Cepheus is called δ Cephei. (The Greek alphabet runs α, alpha; β, beta; γ, gamma; δ, delta, etc.) When the astronomers ran out of Greek letters to designate stars in a given constellation, numbers were used; thus 61 Cygni means the 61st star in the constellation of the Swan. Most faint stars are called simply by the catalogue number in which their exact position, brightness, etc. are listed. For example, Ross 248 pertains to the number in Ross's Stellar Catalogue.

Ancient astronomers beginning with Ptolemy described the brightness of stars by dividing them into six classes, or *magnitudes*, the first magnitude being ascribed to the brightest ones, and the sixth magnitude to

TABLE 20-1   THE BRIGHTEST STARS

	Personal name	Constellation affiliation	Stellar magnitude	Color
1	Sirius	α Canis Majoris	−1.58	Blue
2	Canopus*	α Carinae	−0.86	Yellowish
3	*	α Centauri	0.06	Yellow
4	Vega	α Lyrae	0.14	Blue
5	Capella	α Aurigae	0.21	Yellow
6	Arcturus	α Boötis	0.24	Orange
7	Rigel	β Orionis	0.34	Blue
8	Procyon	α Canis Minoris	0.48	Yellowish
9	Achernar*	α Eridani	0.60	Blue
10	*	β Centauri	0.86	Blue
11	Altair	α Aquilae	0.89	Blue
12	Betelgeuse	α Orionis	0.92	Red
13	*	α Crucis	1.05	Blue
14	Aldebaran	α Tauri	1.06	Reddish
15	Spica	α Virginis	1.21	Blue
16	Pollux	β Geminorum	1.21	Orange
17	Antares	α Scorpii	1.22	Red
18	Fomalhaut	α Piscis Austrini	1.29	Blue
19	Deneb	α Cygni	1.33	Blue
20	Regulus	α Leonis	1.34	Blue

* Not visible as far north as latitude 40°N.

those that were barely visible to the naked eye. The exact measurements of relative stellar brightness showed later that a difference of one magnitude between two stars in Ptolemy's terminology corresponds to an intensity ratio of about two and a half, and it was decided to make the old notion more precise by *defining* the difference of one stellar magnitude as *corresponding exactly to the ratio 2.512 in intensity*. This introduced the modern scale of stellar magnitudes which extends from negative values for very bright stars (−1.6 magnitude for Sirius) down to the 23rd magnitude, which represents the observation limit of the 200-inch Palomar reflector. In Table 20-1 we list the 20 brightest stars with their personal names and their relation to various constellations. The third column gives the stellar magnitude, while the last one describes the color of the star, which is determined by its surface temperature.

Constellation Guide

Since most of us live in the medium northern latitudes (from approximately 32°N for New Orleans and Los Angeles to approximately 45°N for Boston and Seattle), we can observe considerably more than half the entire celestial sphere. The stars that are located within about 45° from the north celestial pole never sink below the horizon and can be seen every clear night of the year. The stars located in a belt 45° north and 45° south of the celestial equator, i.e., in the vicinity of the ecliptic can be seen only during the seasons of the year when the sun in its annual trip around the celestial sphere is on the opposite side of the belt. The stars located within 45° of the south celestial pole cannot be seen at all from our geographical location.

The stellar maps in Fig. 20-2a, b, c, and d show the main constellations and the most prominent stars that can be seen from the medium northern latitude at about nine o'clock in the evening during the four seasons of the year. Each of these maps represents the picture seen by a person lying flat on his back on the ground (grass or snow), with his feet pointing southwards, and watching the starry sky above him (Fig. 20-2e). In the northerly direction the picture is always about the same except that the constellations located in this part of the sky revolve around the Pole Star (or Polaris), which is located at the end of the handle of the Little Dipper (part of the constellation *Ursa Minor*, i.e., the small bear). Probably the most familiar stellar configuration, commonly known as the Big Dipper (part of the constellation *Ursa Major*, i.e., the great bear) is located between the Little Dipper and the zenith during the spring months, and between it and the horizon in the fall. Thus, it looks as if somebody is pouring soup from the big dipper into the small one in April, and

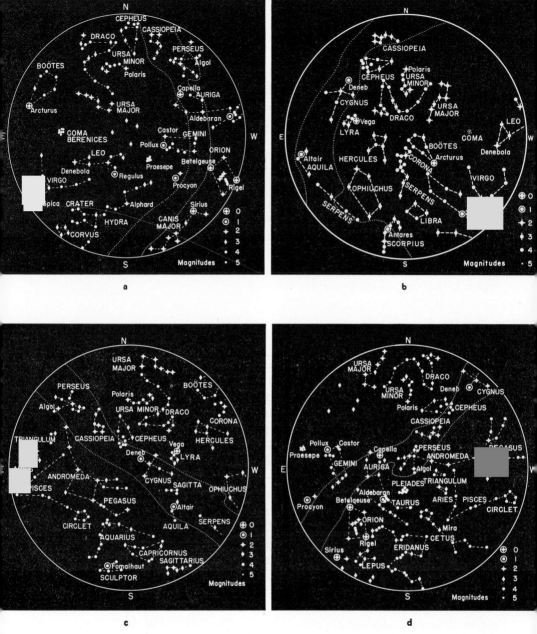

Fig. 20-2. Major stars and constellations as seen in the evening sky (9 p.m.) in the four seasons from a medium northern latitude (45°). The dotted lines represent the boundaries of the Milky Way. (a) April 1; (b) July 1; (c) October 1; (d) January 1. *Prepared by Dr. G. Athay, High Altitude Observatory, Boulder, Colorado.*

502

vice versa in October. Just across the Pole Star from the Big Dipper is the constellation *Cassiopeia*, which looks like the letter *W* in the spring and like the letter *M* in the fall. Two other prominent constellations in this region of the sky are *Cepheus*, which looks like a kite, and *Draco*, which resembles a long serpent stretching over 135 degrees of celestial longitude between *Cepheus* and *Ursa Major*.

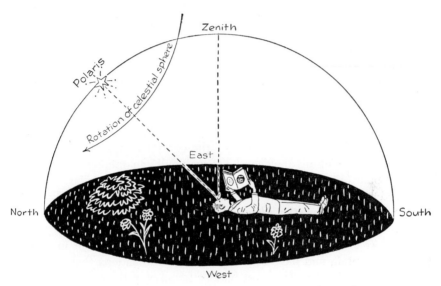

Fig. 20-2e. The correct position for comparing the stellar maps with what you see in the sky.

In the southern direction, the sky looks rather different during the different seasons of the year since, as we stated above, the stars located in these regions can be seen only when the sun moves to the opposite point on the celestial sphere. During spring evenings (Fig. 20-2a), high above the horizon we see the constellation *Leo* (lion) with its brightest star, Regulus (or α Leonis), already mentioned above, and the constellation, *Virgo* (maiden), with its brightest star, Spica. Still closer to the horizon we can see the constellations, *Hydra* and *Canis Major* (Great Dog), with Sirius as its brightest star.

The midsummer picture of the sky (Fig. 20-2b) looks rather different from that presented in the spring. The center of the "southern exposure" is now occupied by the constellations *Ophiuchus* (serpent holder), *Hercules*, *Libra* (scales), and *Boötes* (herdman), with Arcturus as its brightest star. Close to the zenith is located the constellation *Corona Borealis*, a diadem of five bright stars. In the constellation *Hercules* is located one of the most beautiful of the globular clusters of stars, a photograph of which appears in Fig. 20-13.

When the autumn leaves begin to fall and the evenings become noticeably cooler (Fig. 20-2c), the dominant features of the starry sky are the constellations *Andromeda, Pegasus, Pisces* (fishes), *Cygnus* (swan), and *Aquila* (water carrier). In the constellation *Andromeda*, not far from its second brightest star (β Andromedae), is located a very interesting celestial object known as the Great Andromda Nebula, which can be seen by the naked eye as a faint elongated nebulosity. Photographs taken by means of a large telescope show a very complicated structure consisting of a central elliptical body and two spiral arms wound around it (Fig. 20-11.) This is the nearest large neighbor in space to our stellar system of the Milky Way and is another giant swarm of stars about one hundred billion strong.

During the snowy winter months around Christmas and New Year's day, the evening sky is dominated by the constellation *Orion*, with three bright stars forming his "belt" and *Taurus* (bull) containing the so-called Crab Nebula (Fig. 20-8), which resulted from a violent stellar explosion observed by Chinese astronomers about nine centuries ago. The well-known stellar cluster, the *Pleiades,* appears almost straight above our heads.

Travelers to the Southern Hemisphere can borrow a stellar map from the ship's captain and have fun identifying constellations that are never seen from our country. The most famous features of the southern sky are the Southern Cross (*Crux*) and two shapeless luminous patches, first described by Magellan and known as the Large and Small Magellanic Clouds (Fig. 20-4). These two faint nebulosities are known now to be formed by billions of individual stars, and they, along with the Great Andromeda Nebula, are our nearest neighbors in the countless society of stellar systems populating the infinite space of the universe.

How Far Away Are the Stars?

There does not seem to be any definite record of what ancient Greek astronomers thought about the nature and distances of stars, and the statement that stars are actually giant suns comparable to our own, but located much farther away, was first made by Copernicus in his epoch-making book on the solar system. For the observation of stellar parallaxes, the base line supplied by the diameter of the earth is hopelessly short, but fortunately we can use a much longer base line provided by the revolution of the earth around the sun. At one time we are on one side of the sun and six months later we are on the opposite side, 300,000,000 km from the former position (Fig. 20-3.) Thus, a star which is located comparatively close to us must show a parallactic displacement with respect to the background of more distant stars if observed half a year apart. The famous Danish astronomer, Tycho Brahe (1546-1601), was probably the first to attempt the observation of the yearly parallactic displacement of stars, but he came out with a nega-

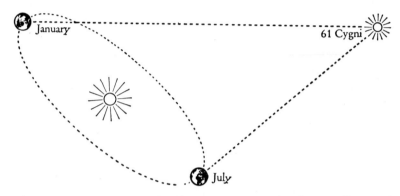

Fig. 20-3. Measuring the distance to a star by the parallax method, using the diameter of the earth's orbit as a base.

tive result and interpreted his failure as proof that the earth is really at rest. We know now that this failure was due partially to the imperfection of contemporary astronomical instruments, but mostly to the fact that Tycho Brahe did not happen to pick up stars that are really close to us. The first reliable measurement of stellar parallax came much later, in the year 1838, when the German astronomer, F. W. Bessel, found that the star known as 61 Cygni shifts by about two-thirds of an angular second in six months' time.

As in the case of parallactic measurements that are referred to in terms of the earth's semi-diameter, stellar parallaxes are always referred to in terms of the mean semi-diameter of the earth's orbit, and thus represent the angle which this semi-diameter would subtend if seen by an observer located on the star in question. The exact value of the parallax of 61 Cygni is 0".300 ± 0.003 and corresponds to a distance of 108,000,000,000,000 kilometers, 690,000 astronomical units, or 11 light-years. It may be noticed here that stellar distances often are expressed in units that are directly derived from the measurement of the parallax. The unit is known as a *parsec,* and represents the distance from which the radius of the earth's orbit would subtend an angle of one second.

Thus, if the parallax of a given star is 4″, its distance is one quarter of a parsec and, inversely, a star with a parallax 0″.25 is 4 parsecs away. One parsec equals 206,265 astronomical units, or 3.256 light-years. In measuring very large distances, such as the diameter of our stellar system of the Milky Way, or the distances to other galaxies scattered through space, we often use the term, *kiloparsec*, which is defined as one thousand parsecs. We may mention here still another unit that was once introduced, in a none-too-serious manner, at the Pulkovo Observatory (Russia). The unit was known as a *Marsec*, and was defined as the distance from which the tallest Russian astronomer, Dr. Markov, would appear to subtend an angle of one second. Since Dr. Markov must have been at least 6′6″ tall, one marsec is about 260 miles. With today's precise instruments, we can measure stellar parallaxes that are as small as 0″.005 and correspond to a distance of 200 parsecs or 650 light-years. To appreciate the smallness of this angle, we should remember that it is the angle under which a tall man, like Dr. Markov, would be seen at a distance of 200 marsecs, i.e., 52,000 miles, or about one-fifth the distance to the moon!

Measurements of parallax have been carried out for well over two thousand stars, and Table 20-2 gives the data for 20 of the nearest stars. The names of the stars given in this table demonstrate the rather cumbersome astronomical nomenclature.

TABLE **20-2**   THE TWENTY NEAREST STARS

Name	Distance in light-years	Luminosity (in terms of the sun)
α Centauri A		1.3
α Centauri B	4.28	0.36
α Centauri C		0.00007
Barnard's Star	5.05	0.00044
Wolf 359	8.0	0.000023
Lalande 21185	8.4	0.0058
Sirius A	8.6	30.0
Sirius B		0.01
Ross 154	9.1	0.0003
L789-6	9.8	0.0001
Ross 248	10.8	0.00016
ε Eridani	10.8	0.33
τ Ceti	10.9	0.4
Procyon A	11.1	6.9
Procyon B		0.00052
61 Cygni A	11.1	0.069
61 Cygni B		0.036
Ross 128	11.2	0.00044
Groomb 34A	11.7	0.0076
Groomb 34B		0.00058

Fig. 20-4. The Large Magellanic Cloud, our neighbor in space. S. Doradus, a star 500,000 times brighter than our sun, is in the center of the cluster indicated by the arrow. Courtesy Mount Wilson Observatory.

In addition to their distances, the table also gives the brightness of the various stars in terms of the brightness of the sun, which can easily be calculated from their apparent brightness and their distance from us. An inspection of this table is very useful for acquiring a general idea about the world of stars. We notice that only three of them (Sirius A, Procyon A, and α Centauri A) are brighter than the sun. Three stars are between 1 and 0.1 of the sun's brightness, three between 0.1 and 0.01, while the remaining eleven are well below one per cent of the luminosity of the sun. Thus we conclude that, as stars go, our sun must be considered as a rather bright object, with most of the stars being considerably fainter.

The brightest star in the table (Sirius A) is only 30 times brighter than the sun, but if we go farther into space we will pick up stars compared with which our sun looks very insignificant indeed. Rigel (β Orionis), located 540 light-years away, is 21,000 times brighter than the sun and is still one of the brightest stars in the sky in spite of its great distance from us. But the real Goliath in stellar society is a variable supergiant known as S. Doradus (Fig. 20-4), which, at its maximum, exceeds the brightness of the sun by a factor of 500,000. It seems to consist of two components, each equal to 250,000 suns, which alternately eclipse one another every 40 years. But S. Doradus is very far away from us, being located within the larger Magellanic Cloud that floats in space some 150,000 light-years away from our system of the Milky Way, and, in spite of its terrific brightness, it is invisible to the naked eye.

Inspecting Table 20-2, we also notice another important characteristic of stellar society, *the tendency of stars to gather into groups of two or more*. Stars belonging to such systems are given one name and are distinguished by the letters, A, B, C, etc. placed after the name. We see, indeed, that 11 out of 20 stars included in the table belong to such multiple systems, forming 4 doublets and one triplet.

Stellar Eclipses

When the plane of the orbit of a double star is oriented so that we see it exactly on edge, each star periodically hides behind the other as they revolve around each other, so that the brightness of the couple as seen by us is then reduced. One of the most famous of such *eclipsing variables* is Algol, which in Arabic means "the demon." It is also known as β Persei, and, in the old picture book of Heaven, represents the winking eye in the head of Medusa, which Perseus holds in his extended hand. The "luminosity curve" of that star, representing the variation of brightness with time, is shown in Fig. 20-5, and we notice that halfway between

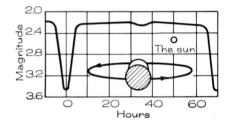

Fig. 20-5. The light curve of the eclipsing variable, Algol, and a diagram showing the relative motion of its two components. The size of the sun is given for comparison.

the sharp minima, which repeat every 68 days, there are other very weak minima. To interpret this curve we assume that the two stars forming the Algol system have rather different luminosities and that in one case the bright star hides behind the faint one and that in the other the faint one is hidden. Analyzing the observed curve and using Kepler's laws concerning motion under the action of Newtonian gravity, we can reconstruct a complete picture of the orbital motion of the two stars, and also find their diameters and masses. The model of the Algol system obtained in this way is also shown in Fig. 20-5, with the size of the sun given for comparison.

Since, as we have seen above, multiple stellar systems represent the rule, rather than the exception, in the stellar world, eclipsing variables are rather numerous and are very helpful to astronomers in the study of the properties of individual stars. The period of light variation of eclipsing variables varies from a few hours, when the two components are almost in contact, to several months. An extreme case is represented by the system of ε Aurigae, in which the eclipses occur at intervals of

27 years and last for about 2 years. As this book goes to press, ε Aurigae is passing through one of its dark periods.

Normal Stars, Stellar Giants, and Dwarfs

As we have mentioned before, different stars have different colors, ranging from a brilliant bluish hue to a dull red. This is, of course, due to the difference in their surface temperatures, and it makes it possible for us to learn about the physical conditions on their surfaces. More exactly, the surface temperatures of stars can be estimated by the study of the absorption lines in their spectra, in the same manner as it is done in the case of our sun (Chapter 19). We find that, while the surface temperature of Capella is 6,500°K, i.e., about the same as that of our sun, the temperature of Rigel tops the 11,000°K mark. The reddish star, Antares, on the other hand, has a temperature of only about 3,000°K.

Knowing the surface temperature and the absolute brightness of a star, we can find its linear diameter, even though through the largest telescope the star appears no larger than a point. According to the Stefan-Boltzmann law (Chapter 6), the temperature determines the amount of light emitted by a unit area of stellar surface. Thus, dividing the total light emission of a star by the emissivity per unit area, we can calculate the total surface, and, hence the diameter of the star. In this way we find that, whereas Sirius A is only 1.8 times larger than the sun, Capella and Antares are larger than the sun by factors of 12 and 450, respectively. On the other hand, Sirius B is much smaller than the sun, being, in fact, only slightly larger than the earth.

Plotting the magnitudes of a large number of stars against their surface temperatures (both in logarithmic scale) we obtain the very interesting diagram (Fig. 20-6) associated with the name of a famous

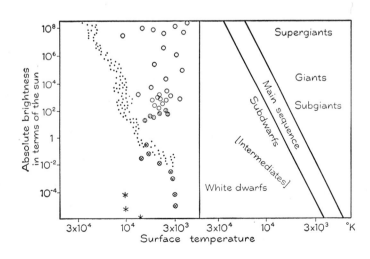

Fig. 20-6. The Russell diagram for the stars near the sun that form the spiral arms of our galaxy (see p. 516). Adapted from Fig. 11.6, Payne-Gaposchkin, *Introduction to Astronomy* (Englewood Cliffs, N. J.: Prentice-Hall, Inc., 1954).

American astronomer, H. N. Russell. We find that most of the stars in this diagram fall within a narrow band known as the *main sequence*. Our sun, Sirius, Rigel, and many other stars belong to this sequence. As we go along this sequence towards brighter and brighter stars, the radius increases, but only moderately. If we check on the masses of the stars belonging to the main sequence (these masses can be estimated if the stars in question belong to a double system), we find that they also increase along the sequence. Thus, we conclude that the increase of radius is simply due to the increase of stellar mass and that the mean density of stars belonging to the main sequence varies but little.

An entirely different picture emerges if we take stars such as Antares, or ε Aurigae. The points representing these stars in the Russell diagram fall far to the right of the regular main sequence, indicating that these stars must have entirely different internal structures. This class of stars is known under the general name, *Red Giants*—red because they all have a low surface temperature and thus a red color, and giants because of their abnormally large geometrical dimensions and their very high luminosity. Taking into account the measured masses of these stars (30 sun masses for Antares, and 15 for ε Aurigae), we find that their material is extremely rarefied. While the mean density of our sun is 1.6 with respect to water, the mean densities of Antares, and ε Aurigae are only 0.02, and 0.000003, respectively, as compared to atmospheric air.

In contrast to the Red Giants are the so-called *White Dwarfs*, which are located in the lower left corner of the Russell diagram. A typical representative of this class is the companion of Sirius (Sirius B) which, having a mass almost equal to that of the sun, is only slightly larger than the earth. Thus, its mean density must be 500,000 times greater than that of water!

Pulsating and Exploding Stars

While most of the stars are seen as luminous points, shining quietly with a constant light, there are many wide deviations from this general rule. To this class of unusual stars belong the stars known as *Cepheid variables*, or simply *Cepheids*, which are subject to periodic pulsations because of some as yet unknown reason. The giant bodies of these stars expand a contract with a rhythmic regularity, and this periodic change of dimensions is accompanied by corresponding periodic changes of color and luminosity. The luminosity curve of δ Cephei, after which all this class of stars is named, is shown in Fig. 20-7 and is distinctly different from the luminosity curve of an eclipsing variable. The interesting point about the Cepheids is that their pulsation period, which varies for different stars from a fraction of a day to several months, is directly correlated with their intrinsic brightness: *the brighter the star, the longer is its pulsation period*. This gives astronomers an invaluable method for the measurement of distances that are too large to be tackled by the

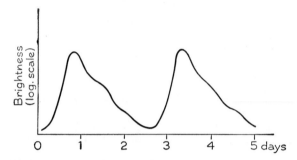

Fig. 20-7. Luminosity changes of δ Cephei.

parallax method. Indeed, by observing the changes of luminosity of a distant Cepheid variable, we obtain directly its pulsation period from which we can determine its absolute brightness. Comparing this brightness with the observed one, and using the inverse square law, we obtain a very exact measurement of the distance of that star from us.

Somewhat similar behavior is observed in the case of the so-called *U Geminorum* stars, named after a star in the constellation of Twins that was the first star of this type to be studied. Instead of going through smooth continuous changes of luminosity as Cepheids do, these stars remain completely tranquil for a longer or shorter period of time, and then burst in the process of a minor explosion. Some of these stars blow up every week and some others only every few months. It is interesting to note that the intensity of these periodic explosions increases in direct proportion to the interval between them.

The extreme case of the periodic explosions of the U Geminorum-type stars is probably represented by the so-called *novae*, stellar explosions in which a star's brightness may increase overnight by a factor of many thousands, as compared with a factor of only 30 or 40 for typical U Geminorum stars. These violent stars were given the name, *novae*, i.e., "new ones," because it was originally believed that they were not in the sky before they were first seen. However, later observation proved that these "new stars" were actually not new at all, but rather old stars which, because of some catastrophic process, suddenly increased their luminosity. It is very likely, indeed, that the novae are rather similar to the U Geminorum-type stars except that they explode only once in a few

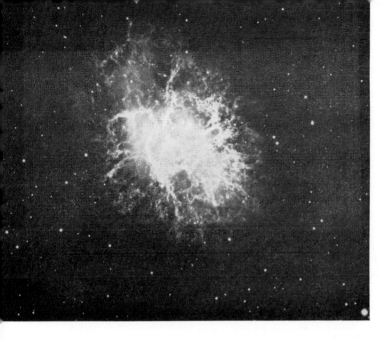

Fig. 20-8. The Crab Nebula in the constellation of Taurus, photographed here by a 200-inch telescope in red light, is the result of the supernova explosion observed by Chinese astronomers in A.D. 1054. *Courtesy Mount Wilson and Palomar Observatories.*

thousand years and with correspondingly higher intensity. About a hundred novae appear in our stellar system of the Milky Way each year, but very few of them are close enough to us to be seen by the naked eye.

But the real standouts among exploding stars are the so-called *supernovae,* which stand in about the same relation to ordinary novae as the H-bomb does to a small A-bomb. When a star becomes a supernova its luminosity increases by a factor of a few hundred million and at its maximum the exploding star may become as bright as the rest of the galaxy to which it belongs. The first historically recorded explosion of this type took place in the constellation of Taurus on July 4, 1054, and is described in detail in the chronicles of the Peiping Observatory. We read:

In the first year of the period Chihha, the fifth moon, the day Chi-chou [i.e. July 4, 1054], a great star appeared approximately several inches southeast of T'ien-Kuan [i.e. ζ Tauri]. After more than a year, it gradually became invisible.

If we look now at the point in the sky where the Chinese astronomers observed a new star nine centuries ago, we see a very interesting object known as the *Crab Nebula* (Fig. 20-8). It does look like an expanding smoke cloud caused by some vigorous explosion, and, indeed, comparing the older photographs of the Crab Nebula with more recent ones, we find that this nebulosity *is* expanding at the rate of 0.18 angular seconds per year. Since the present angular radius of the Crab Nebula is about 160″, we conclude that the expansion must have started about 900 years ago, which is in perfect agreement with the date of the new star in Taurus as given in Chinese chronicles.

Careful observations reveal that in the center of the Crab Nebula is a faint, but very hot, star, apparently all that is left of the star that must have blown up nine centuries ago. The mass of that star is estimated to be about 25 per cent larger than that of the sun, while the mass of the expanding nebulosity is about 10 per cent of solar mass. It may be added that the Crab Nebula is 5,000 light-years away from us, which means that, whereas the explosion was observed on the earth only nine centuries ago, it actually took place during the beginning of human civilization.

Since the time of the Chinese supernova, only two explosions of comparable violence have taken place among the stars of our Milky Way system. One of them occurred in the constellation of Cassiopeia in 1572 and was described by Tycho Brahe in his book, *De Stella Nuova*; one of the illustrations from this book is shown in Fig. 20-9. Another similar explosion took place soon thereafter in the year 1604 and was observed by Tycho's assistant, Johannes Kepler. Since that time no new supernovae have appeared in our galaxy, and, considering that statistical data indicate that the average interval between the supernovae in a given galaxy is about 300 years, we may expect to see one in the sky pretty soon (i.e., within a month or within a century).

However, our stellar system of the Milky Way is only one of the billions of other similar stellar systems, known as *galaxies*, that float in space within the range of modern telescopes, and we have a much better chance to observe supernovae in these far-away stellar systems. As a matter of fact, a bright supernova appeared in 1885 in our nearest cosmic neighbor, the Great Nebula in Andromeda. By constantly observ-

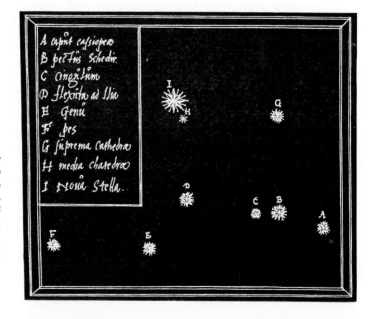

Fig. 20-9. An illustration from Tycho Brahe's book, *De Stella Nuova*, indicating the position of a new star (marked by *I*) in the constellation of Cassiopeia.

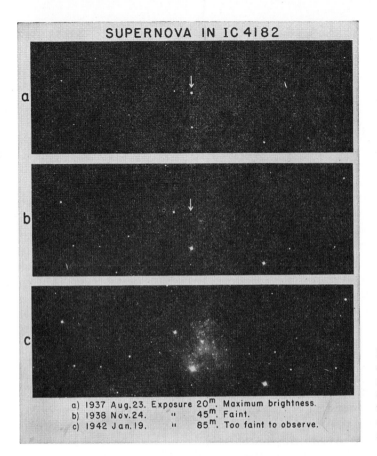

SUPERNOVA IN IC 4182

a) 1937 Aug.23. Exposure 20ᵐ. Maximum brightness.
b) 1938 Nov.24. " 45ᵐ. Faint.
c) 1942 Jan.19. " 85ᵐ. Too faint to observe.

Fig. 20-10. The evolution of a supernova over a period of five years. *Courtesy Mount Wilson and Palomar Observatories.*

ing a few hundred of our neighboring galaxies, the Mount Wilson astronomers, W. Baade and F. Zwicky, were able to observe and to study the luminosities of a dozen supernovae going off in them. The photographs representing the appearance and subsequent fading of one of these distant super-explosions are shown in Fig. 20-10.

The Evolution of Stars

Since the stars forming our system of the Milky Way are similar to our sun, differing from it essentially only in their mass, their evolutionary history must be similar to that of the sun, described in the previous chapter. Like the sun, the stars must have condensed once upon a time from a dilute mixture of gas and dust, and have finally reached the steady (main-sequence) state in which they consume their original hydrogen supply by means of carbon cycles or H-H reactions.

However, stars of different masses go through their evolutionary cycles at different rates. According to observationally established, and theoretically confirmed, *mass-luminosity relations,* the brightness of the stars, and hence their rate of hydrogen consumption, increases as the cube of their mass. Since the original supply of hydrogen in a star is apparently proportional to its mass, we must conclude that *the total life spans of different stars must be inversely proportional to the squares of their masses*. Thus, we speak about the "calendar age" of a star, which simply refers to the number of years it has existed, and of its "genetic age," which represents its age as the fraction of its total life span. Stars of the same calendar age may have entirely different genetic ages. Imagine a human being, a dog, and a mouse—all three having been born five years ago. The human being is still a baby; the dog is already a mature dog; and the mouse is a *dead* mouse since mice do not live that long. A similar situation exists in the world of stars, and, by observing the stars that are seen in the sky now, we may expect to find among them representative examples of all different stages of stellar evolution. Thus, our theoretical considerations concerning our sun's past and future can be directly compared with the observed properties of stars that are at the present time passing through these evolutionary stages.

A very important fact about the stellar population of our system that was emphasized by the Mount Wilson astronomer, W. Baade (Fig. 20-11), a number of years ago is that there exist two different types of stellar population. In the neighborhood of the sun, which Baade calls the "local swimming hole," the space between the stars is filled by a very diluted mixture of gas and dust that forms giant interstellar nebulae

Fig. 20-11. Dr. W. Baade of Mount Wilson and Palomar Observatories inspects the center of the Great Nebula of Andromeda.

Fig. 20-12. The "Horsehead" Nebula in Orion, composed of gas and dust clouds floating in interstellar space that obscure the stars behind them. This is the material from which new stars are formed. *Courtesy Mount Wilson and Palomar Observatories.*

obscuring the stars located behind them (Fig. 20-12). The density of this interstellar material is about 10^{-24} gm/cm³, which means that a cube of space 1,000 km on a side contains only one gram of matter. This material, the total mass of which is comparable to the total mass of the stars themselves, serves as the source for the formation of new stars by a slow condensation process. The continuous formation process of stars from the dilute interstellar material accounts for the fact that this type of stellar population contains very bright stars like Rigel, which, because of their very short life span, must be considered to have been born considerably later than our sun and its planetary system. It is interesting to notice that stars are apparently born in large groups that originate from large contracting nebulosities and then disperse in different directions as the children of one large family. This fact was recently emphasized by a Russian astronomer, V. A. Ambarzumian, in his studies of the so-called *stellar associations* formed by dispersing groups of stars, all of the same comparatively small age.

In contrast to the above described stellar communities, known as *Population I,* there exists also stellar communities known as *Population*

Fig. 20-13. A globular cluster of stars in the constellation of Hercules. *Courtesy Mount Wilson and Palomar Observatories.*

II that are characterized by the complete absence of any interstellar material. A typical example of such a stellar community is represented by the *globular clusters* (Fig. 20-13) that float in space far away from us near the center of our stellar system. Apparently in this case the formation of the stars took place all at once in some distant past, with all the available material being completely utilized. All stars of Population II are of the same calendar age, and no new stars can be formed any more. Thus, while stellar Population I can be compared with the population of a city containing the members of all ages, from newborn babies to grayhaired veterans, stellar Population II resembles more the alumni of the class of 1912 (or any other year) of some large university. No new members are admitted, and the membership is gradually extinguished by the dying-out process.

Stellar Population II presents particular interest for the study of stellar evolution, since, being of the same calendar age, the stars of different masses belonging to it show a clear picture of their genetic age differences. In Fig. 20-14 we give the Russell diagram of the Population II stars forming a typical globular cluster like the one shown in Fig. 20-13. Comparing it with the corresponding diagram of the Population I stars (Fig. 20-6), we notice that the main sequence is sharply limited from above and that the stars that are more than 3.5 times more luminous (and more than 50 per cent more massive) than our sun are completely absent. These are the "dead mice" stars which, because of their fast fuel consumption, were completely extinguished a long time ago. The demarcation line between the existing and non-existing stars of the main sequence of Population II corresponds to stars with the

517

calculated life span of about 5 billion years, a figure that must represent the age of our stellar system. This figure closely agrees with the estimated age of various other characteristic features of our universe, be it the oceans, the earth's crust, or the moon. It underlines once more the general belief of scientists today that *the universe as we know it now was formed about five billion years ago.*

LATER STAGES OF STELLAR EVOLUTION

What happens to a star when all the hydrogen in its central regions is turned into helium? We have already mentioned in the previous chapter in relation to the future of our sun that such exhaustion of hydrogen is expected to result in the formation of an *energy-producing shell* at the base of the outer hydrogen-rich envelope, and that the growth of that shell should lead to a gradual increase of stellar radius and luminosity. The stars that come to that stage of their evolution are bound to take off from the main sequence of the Russell diagram and to travel toward its upper right corner. And, in fact, that is exactly what one observes in the case of globular star clusters. In Fig 20-14 we notice a narrow band that starts from the cut-off point of the main sequence and extends in the predicted direction; this band represents those stars that apparently have exhausted their central hydrogen supply and are in various stages of their shell-source development.

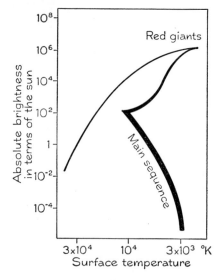

Fig. 20-14. The Russell diagram of stars that form the central body of the Milky Way system and of globular clusters.

Theoretical studies of this phase of stellar evolution indicate that a new kind of thermonuclear reaction begins to be of importance in addition to regular $H \rightarrow He$ transformations. In fact, the rapidly increasing central densities in shell-model stars begin to favor triple-collision processes in which the helium forming the isothermal core is transformed directly into carbon:

$$_2\text{He}^4 + _2\text{He}^4 + _2\text{He}^4 = _6\text{C}^{12} + \text{radiation}$$

This important reaction, first proposed by the American physicist E. E. Salpeter, is followed by other reactions, such as:

$$_6\text{C}^{12} + _2\text{He}^4 = _8\text{O}^{16} + \text{radiation}$$
$$_8\text{O}^{16} + _2\text{He}^4 = _{10}\text{Ne}^{20} + \text{radiation}$$
$$\text{etc.}$$

which gradually build up the original hydrogen of the stellar interior into more and more complex nuclei. This continuous build-up process is presumably terminated when nuclei of iron atoms are formed, since iron nuclei are the most stable nuclei among all chemical elements.

In order to maintain the high central temperature and density needed for the maintenance of the above described reactions, the star must begin to contract, and its luminosity gradually fades; this is responsible for the band in the Russell diagram for Population II that runs downward and to the left from the highest luminosity point reached by the evolving stars. During this descent into oblivion, stars pass through various unstable states and are subject to the pulsations and periodic minor explosions described earlier in this chapter.

Arriving at the end of their evolutionary track at the lower left corner of the Russell diagram, stars become internally unstable and blow up in the brilliant display of supernovae explosions. The explanation for these explosions is not yet definitely established, but it is very likely that they are associated, as was proposed some time ago by the author and his Brazilian colleague, M. Schoenberg, with the production in their interior of large amounts of neutrinos (Chapter 14), which makes it impossible for the central core to balance the increasing pressure of the outer layers.

WHITE DWARFS—DEAD STARS?

In describing the Crab Nebula we mentioned that in the very center of this expanding nebulosity there is a very faint star, apparently the remnant of the one whose explosion was observed by the Chinese in 1054. Detailed study of that star indicates that its surface temperature is extremely high—about 500,000°K—and a star of normal size possessing such a high surface temperature would be many thousands of times brighter than it actually is. Thus, we must conclude that the star in the center of the Crab Nebula must have shrunk way below its normal size and that its material must have a density exceeding that of water by a very large factor. Such a highly collapsed state is just what one would expect in the case of a massive stellar body which has lost all of its nuclear energy sources.

While the collapsed central star of the Crab Nebula is of comparatively recent formation and is still surrounded by the "smoke of the explosion," there are many similar stars in the sky whose origins date much further back in time. Their original gaseous nebulosities must have dispersed into surrounding space many millions of years ago, and their surface temperatures have dropped to only 10 or 20 thousand degrees, which is still high enough to emit brilliant white light. These stars are generally known as *White Dwarfs,* described earlier in this chapter, which are the collapsed stellar bodies with mean densities exceeding that of water by a factor of 500,000. As we have already mentioned in connection with the interior of our sun, such very high densities can be easily achieved by a material, the atoms of which are completely broken into free electrons and bare atomic nuclei.

About 5 per cent of all stars in the sky are in the collapsed white-dwarf state, but, because of their extremely low luminosities, only about a dozen of them, which are located comparatively close to us, have been observed. They represent the dead, but "still warm," bodies of the brilliant stars of the past and now are gradually cooling down to become in the future cold, dark memories of the stellar world.

The Structure of the Milky Way

On clear moonless nights, we can see a faintly luminous band stretching across the sky from horizon to horizon, and travelers to the Southern Hemisphere tell us that it forms a complete circle across the sky (Fig. 20-15). Ancient Greek poets called it the *Milky Way* and ascribed it to the milk spilled by Hera, the goddess of family happiness, when she tried to feed the hungry baby, Hercules.

The famous British astronomer, William Hershel (1738-1822), gave to it, however, a more prosaic explanation, interpreting this faint luminosity as due to a multitude of distant stars occupying a lenticular volume in space. Today we know that the system of the Milky Way contains about 100 billion stars and has the form of a disc 100,000 light-years in diameter and 10,000 light-years thick. This picture of the stellar system of the Milky Way, or our "galaxy," is strengthened by the fact that other stellar systems floating in space show similar flattened disc shapes (Figs. 20-16a, b, and c). These other galaxies have a characteristic spiral structure, which also exists in the case of our galaxy, but cannot be observed very readily because we are located inside of it and because our vision is, to a large extent, obscured by dust

Fig. 20-15. A section of the southern Milky Way, centered on the Southern Cross, just below which appears the dark nebula called the Coal Sack—a huge cloud of gas and dust between us and the Milky Way stars that obscures their light. *Courtesy Harvard Observatory.*

clouds floating around us in interstellar space. These photographs clearly show that galaxies are formed by a large elliptical central body and spiral arms that wind around them. The central bodies and their aurora of globular clusters are formed by stellar Population II, being deprived of interstellar material, while the spiral arms contain vast quantities of gas and dust.

The flattened shape of the galaxies and the pattern of their spiral arms suggest that these giant stellar systems are in a state of rapid rotation, and indeed the rotation of our own galaxy can be proved by

521

observations of the individual motions of its stars. This proof is credited to the Dutch astronomer, J. H. Oort, and is, in a way, similar to Copernicus' explanation of the retrograde motion of the outer planets. In Fig. 20-17 we give a schematic presentation of the sun and 8 other stars revolving around the center of our galaxy. According to the second of Kepler's laws, generalized for galactic rotation, the stars on the outer orbit have a longer revolution period than the sun, while the stars on the inner orbit have a shorter revolution period. Thus, as it can be easily seen from the figure, the distance to the stars C and F will decrease with time while the distance to the stars A and H will increase. On the other hand, the stars B, E, G, and D will have no radial velocity component with respect to our sun. Oort measured, by means of the Doppler effect, the radial velocities of a large number of stars located along the belt of the Milky Way, and, plotting them against the galactic latitude, i.e., the angular distance along the plane of the Milky Way, he was able to show that such periodic changes in radial velocities do exist. This curve distinctly shows the double periodicity expected on the basis of previous theoretical considerations, thus proving beyond any doubt that our sun, as well as the other stars, are revolving around the center of

Fig. 20-16a. A spiral galaxy in Virgo seen edge-on. It is formed by many billions of stars. The dark rim is caused by an accumulation of dust particles. *Courtesy Mount Wilson and Palomar Observatories.*

Fig. 20-16b. A spiral galaxy in Canes Venatici, seen looking into its flat side. Its companion galaxy at the left is psyhically connected with the main galaxy. *Courtesy Mount Wilson and Palomar Observatories.*

the galaxy along more or less circular orbits. On the basis of this data, the period of the sun's revolution around the center of our galaxy, which is located in the direction of the constellation of Sagittarius, is estimated to be 230 million years. Thus, during the 5 billion years of its existence, our sun must have made about 22 revolutions around the galactic center!

The first direct estimate of the dimensions of our stellar system and the position of the sun in it was made by an American astronomer, Harlow Shapley (Fig. 20-18), who used as a distance yardstick the above described properties of the pulsating stars (Cepheids). As we saw there, the directly observable pulsation period of Cepheids permits us to find out their absolute brightness, which, being combined with their visual brightness, gives us the exact value of their distances. Using this method, Shapley undertook the measurement of the distances to the globular clusters (Fig. 20-13), a large number of which are located in the region of the constellation of Sagittarius, i.e., in the direction of the apparent center of the Milky Way system, and contain a number of pulsating variables of comparatively short periods (also known as

Fig. 20-16c. A "barred" spiral in Eridanus. Courtesy Mount Wilson and Palomar Observatories.

"cluster variables"). Combining the measured distances with the angular coordinates of the globular clusters on the celestial sphere, Shapley was able to find their actual location in space, as shown in Fig. 20-19.

The exciting result of this work was the finding that the majority of globular clusters are located within a sphere, the center of which lies in the direction of Sagittarius, 26,000 light-years away from us. They form, so to speak, an aureole around the central body of our galaxy

Fig. 20-17. The relative motions of our sun and eight neighboring stars in their movements around the center of our galaxy.

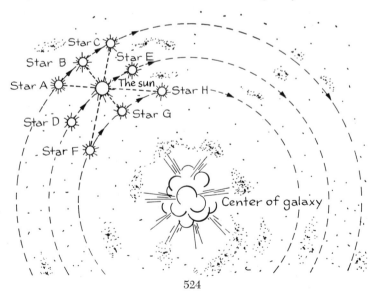

Fig. 20-18. Dr. Shapley (with Mrs. Shapley) discussing cosmogonical problems in the Vatican with Pope Pius XII, who is very interested in astronomy, and agrees with the theory that the universe was created 5 billion years ago.

which is obscured for us by the dense interstellar dust clouds floating within the spiral arms in our line of vision. Shapley's measurement of the distance of our sun from the center of the stellar system of the

Fig. 20-19. The stellar system of the Milky Way seen on edge. Our sun is located about 30,000 light-years from the center. The globular clusters show an almost spherical distribution around the center.

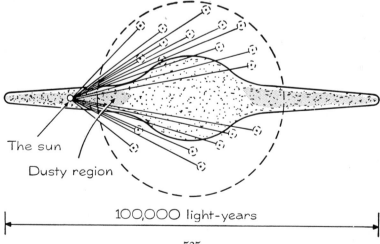

The sun

Dusty region

100,000 light-years

Milky Way introduced the first correct scale of galactic distances and led to the above quoted figures for the general dimensions of our stellar system. It was also the first direct proof that our solar system is not located anywhere near the center of the Milky Way, but rather far out on its outskirts.

RADIO STUDIES OF SPIRAL ARMS

Much of the progress in our knowledge of our galaxy made during the last decade is due to the study of radio signals coming to us from interstellar space. We mentioned in the previous chapter that our sun emits noticeable radio noise, which increases quite considerably during the periods of increased solar activity. It was found later that very strong radio signals also come from other locations within our galaxy, especially from celestial objects that exibit violent turbulent gas motion. Thus, the Crab Nebula as well as the remnants of the two later supernovae observed by Tycho Brahe in 1572 and by Johannes Kepler in 1604 represent strong sources of radio noise. But, apart from these so-called "radio stars," we also observe radio waves coming more or less uniformly from certain regions of the sky, especially those along the belt of the Milky Way.

These "background" radio waves are emitted by atoms of interstellar hydrogen, which is present in an extremely rarefied form (about one atom per cubic centimeter of space). We have seen in Chapter 13 that the hydrogen atom consists of a proton with a single electron rotating around it. We have also mentioned the fact that electrons as well as protons can be considered as tiny spinning tops possessing certain magnetic properties. Thus, two different states of the hydrogen atom can exist with the electron moving in both cases along the first quantum orbit: one in which the electron's and the proton's magnet are pointing in the same direction, and one in which these directions are opposite. Because of the very small numerical value of the proton's magnetism, the energy difference between these two states is very small, and the transitions from one of them into another leads to the emission of energy quanta corresponding, not to optical, but rather to radio frequencies. The wave length expected to be emitted in these transitions is 21 cm, and this is exactly the wave length of the radio signals coming to us from the Milky Way region.

The use of short radio waves for the study of the structure of our galaxy has a tremendous advantage over the optical method because these waves penetrate, without difficulty, through the thick interstellar clouds of dust that often obscure optical vision. It is the same kind of advantage that ordinary radar has in sea or air navigation in fog and bad weather.

While the original work in radio astronomy was carried out by means of rudimentary wartime "radar-dishes," we now have powerful giant *radio telescopes* (Fig. 20-20). Radio telescopes must be made very

Fig. 20-20. Radio telescope at Ohio State University. *Courtesy Dr. John D. Kraus.*

large in order to have a reasonably good resolving power, because of the great length of radio waves compared to waves of light. In Fig. 20-21 we give a detailed map of radio signal intensities coming to us from a part of the sky in the vicinity of the galactic center.

The Origin of Cosmic Rays

Cosmic rays, which were discovered in 1913 by an Austrian physicist, V. F. Hess, have been of tremendous service to physicists in their study of high-energy phenomena and various types of elementary particles. Positive electrons, as well as all kinds of mesons, have been discovered and studied in the cosmic ray phenomena. Nowadays, when we have learned how to build giant accelerators that artificially produce particle

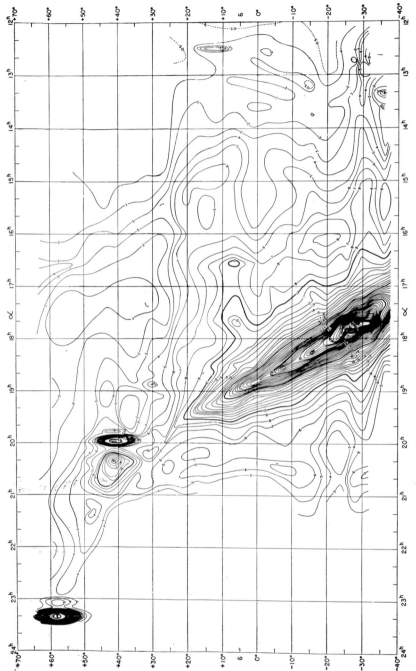

Fig. 20-21. A radio map of a part of the Milky Way. The concentration of lines at the bottom is the galactic center, that at upper center the collision between the two galaxies shown in Fig. 20-26, and that at upper left the remnant of an old supernova. Courtesy Dr. John D. Kraus, Ohio State University.

528

beams with energies of many billions of electron volts, the importance of cosmic ray studies for the purposes of pure physics has been considerably reduced, and, for example, negative protons have been discovered in the "Bevatron" beam and not in cosmic radiation.

However, the cosmic rays coming to us from interstellar space carry a hidden message concerning the processes taking place in the universe, and the understanding of their origin is of very great importance from a purely astronomical point of view. It has been established that primary cosmic radiation, which produces showers of electrons and mesons upon entering the terrestrial atmosphere, consists mostly of very fast-moving protons with a small admixture of α-particles and other heavier nuclei. The primary cosmic ray particles move with energies ranging from the comparatively "low value" of a few billion electron-volts to the tremendously high value of 10^{18} electron-volts or 10^6 erg per particle. This means that a single cosmic ray proton carries the same kinetic energy as 0.2 kg of mass moving at a speed of one meter per second!

What cosmic forces can accelerate the ionized hydrogen atoms to such extremely high energies? The present theory holds that the production of cosmic rays is the joint work of exploding stars and of interstellar gas clouds like those shown in Fig. 20-12. Recent observations have revealed that the intensity of cosmic rays as observed on the earth increases sometimes several times when a bright flare appears on the surface of the sun. This indicates beyond any doubt that a part of these fast-moving particles is due to solar activity, probably being produced by the fast-changing magnetic fields in the vicinity of sunspots. But even if we assume that all other stars forming our system of the Milky Way participate in the production of cosmic rays equally with our sun, the result will be far too small to explain the observed intensity of cosmic radiation coming to us from all directions of the celestial sphere. Apparently we have to assume the existence of some much more powerful sources, and it has been recently suggested that *the bulk of cosmic ray particles have their origin in the powerful supernovae explosions* which flare up in our galaxy every few hundred years. The tremendously high magnetic fields that can be expected to exist in the hot turbulent gases ejected into space by the force of these explosions can easily accelerate the ionized hydrogen atoms to very high velocities. Traveling through interstellar space, these fast-moving protons have a good chance to be further accelerated by the magnetic fields of interstellar gas clouds they encounter on their way, which is apt to bring their kinetic energy up to the tremendously high values observed in the cosmic ray radiation. The picture is still dim, but there is hardly any doubt that it accounts for the main features of the high-energy radiation falling on our earth from interstellar space.

The Realm of Galaxies

So far we have been concerned mainly with our own galaxy of stars and have mentioned other galaxies only as examples of other stellar systems similar to ours. In fact, our stellar system of the Milky Way belongs to a group of galaxies containing somewhat more than a dozen galaxies, which include the *Great Andromeda Nebula* (Fig. 20-11) and both *Magellanic Clouds*. The Milky Way and the Andromeda systems are by far the largest members of this so-called "local group," the geometry of which is shown in Fig. 20-22. However, in the universe at

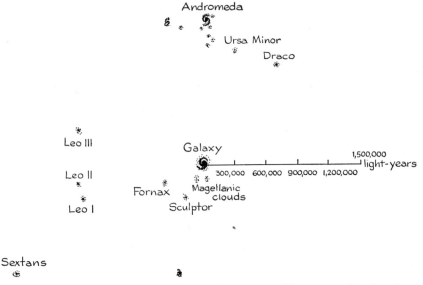

Fig. 20-22. The local group of galaxies is roughly projected in the plane of the page. Our galaxy is in the center. The form of the galaxies is schematically shown, but their size is exaggerated. From an article by J. Neyman and Elisabeth L. Scott, *Scientific American*, Sept., 1956.

large, our stellar system of the Milky Way plays just as unimportant a role as the role played by our sun among the hundreds of billions of other stars of the Milky Way. Within the range of the 200-inch telescope, there are several billions of individual galaxies, a fact that is dramatically represented by the map (Fig. 20-23) showing the galaxies observed in a small area of the sky covering only 6 angular minutes on

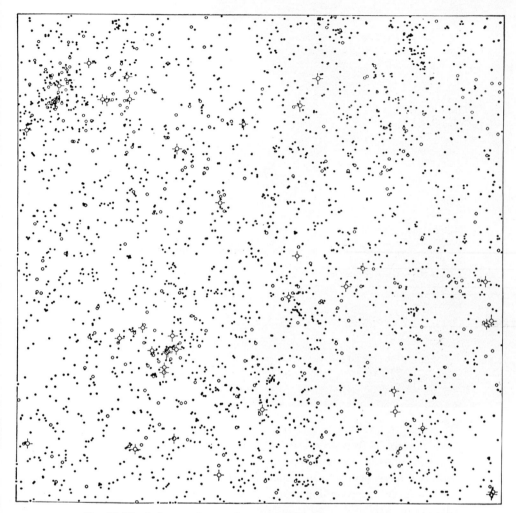

Fig. 20-23. Galaxies observed in a small area of the sky (6 × 6 angular minutes) by C. D. Shane of Yerkes Observatory. The sizes of the various symbols indicate roughly the relative brightness of the galaxies they represent. *Courtesy C. D. Shane.*

each side. It looks, in a way, like a stellar map, except that each point on it is not a star, but a giant group of a few billion stars each! The spiral galaxies like ours, or that of Andromeda, are comparatively rare members of galactic society. Most of the galaxies populating the universe are smaller in size and do not have spiral arms; they are known as *elliptical galaxies* (Fig. 20-24). Some of the galaxies do not have any well-defined shape; they are *irregular galaxies* such as the Large and the Small Magellanic Clouds.

It appears that the different observed shapes of the galaxies represent different stages of their evolution, which, just as in the case of indi-

531

Fig. 20-24. An elliptical galaxy in Andromeda (not related to the Great Andromeda galaxy) showing a resolution into stars. The bright stars in the foreground belong, of course, to the Milky Way. *Courtesy Mount Wilson and Palomar Observatories.*

vidual stars, may proceed at a different rate, depending on the original galactic masses. The fundamental questions concerning the evolution of galaxies have been barely touched upon by today's astronomy, and we are certainly approaching many interesting and exciting findings in this direction.

One characteristic feature of the distribution of galaxies in space is that they very often cluster into groups that are presumably held together by the forces of gravity. We have already mentioned that our own galaxy belongs to a small local group containing slightly over a dozen members. But there are also clusters of galaxies containing a hundred or more individual members, as for example the cluster in *Coma Berenices* (Fig. 20-25), which is located 85 million light-years away from us.

COLLISIONS BETWEEN THE GALAXIES

We have mentioned before that some "radio stars" have been identified with the turbulent expanding gas clouds resulting from old supernova explosions within our galaxy. But some of the "radio stars" do not seem to correspond to any known object on existing celestial maps. To these belongs one of the most intensive radio sources, located in the constellation of the Swan (Cygnus) close to the projection of the spiral arm and known as Cygnus A. When radio astronomers succeeded in pinpointing the location of this mysterious radio source, W. Baade took a photograph of that spot in the sky through the 200-inch telescope and obtained the dramatic picture shown in Fig. 20-26. The source of the radio waves from distant space turned out to be nothing less than two galaxies which had run into one another! Do not think that in the case of galactic collisions anything happens to the individual stars of which the galaxies are composed. The distances between the stars in galaxies are so great as compared with stellar diameters that the two colliding galaxies would pass through each other without any noticeable effect. What really collides is the interstellar gas and dust that fill the galactic volume. And when the gaseous contents of both galaxies run into one another at high speed, they are heated to temperatures of up to 100 million degrees and become the source of an intense blue light that can easily be detected by spectroscopic observations. When the two galaxies are finally separated, they are mutually filtered free of their interstellar material, which is left in the space between them.

From the Doppler shift of hydrogen lines it has been estimated that the two colliding galaxies of Cygnus A are 270 million light-years away from us. Since the intensity of the radio signal from Cygnus A is 3,000 times stronger than the minimum intensity that can be noticed by present methods, it follows that, being placed at the maximum range of the 200-inch telescope (i.e., about 2×10^9 light-years), Cygnus A would still be 50 times stronger than the weakest observed signal. Thus, it is quite possible that about 2,000 weak radio stars observed by radio

Fig. 20-25. A group of galaxies in Coma Berenices located 85 million light-years away. *Courtesy Mount Wilson and Palomar Observatories.*

Fig. 20-26. A collision between two galaxies in Cygnus, 270 million light-years away. This collision gives rise to the second strongest radio signal in the sky (Cygnus A). Courtesy Mount Wilson and Palomar Observatories.

astronomers today may be galactic collisions far beyond the limit of observation of the biggest optical telescopes. If galaxies were distributed uniformly through space, the chances of collisions would be comparatively small. However, the clustering of galaxies increases the hazard of their travel through space, and within large clusters of galaxies collisions seem to be rather common events.

GENERAL RELATIVITY

AND COSMOLOGY

Einstein's Box

In his special theory of relativity, discussed in Chapter 7, Einstein showed that it is senseless to speak of absolute motion, and that only the relative motion of one system with respect to another can be considered a physical reality. He showed, in fact, that an observer, enclosed in a windowless vehicle moving with a constant speed, has no way of finding out whether he is in a state of motion or

535

at rest, no matter what kind of physical experiments (mechanical, optical, electric, or magnetic) he performs inside his enclosure in an attempt to answer that question. We gave an example of a passenger, occupying an inside cabin on the "Queen Mary" sailing across the smooth waters of the Atlantic, who has no possible way of determining whether the ship is speeding through the ocean or lying quietly at the dock. But what about accelerated motion? If the train or the automobile in which we are riding is sharply jerked forward (accelerated) or suddenly stopped (decelerated), we would certainly notice it beyond any doubt. Does this mean that while the notion of velocity is relative, the notion of acceleration is absolute?

Einstein's answer to this question was in the negative. He showed that the effects observed in an accelerated or decelerated vehicle could be ascribed, not to the sudden change of velocity, but to the appearance of an additional gravitational field. In order to prove this point, he introduced the notion of an observer (a trained physicist) sitting with all kinds of experimental gadgets inside a windowless box freely floating somewhere in interstellar space. In the absence of a gravitational field, the conditions in the box will be similar to those described by the famous French scientific fiction writer, Jules Verne, in his novel A *Trip around the Moon.* The observer, and all objects inside the box, will be freely floating in the air, since they are subject to no gravitational attraction at all in any direction.

"Suppose now," said Einstein in 1914, "that some fantastic creature were to grab a rope attached to the roof of that box and pull it with a certain force upwards." (In modern language we would say: "Suppose now that the rocket motors attached to the bottom of the box were set into action.") The box is now moving with a certain constant acceleration.

Fig. 21-1. Einstein's chamber: A, an accelerated observer; B, a nonaccelerated observer; C, a massive sphere; D, a light sphere.

What will the physicist enclosed in the box feel and see? First of all, he will find himself being pressed to the bottom of the box, and, after rising to his feet, he will stand firmly on the floor. Even though there is no gravity, the soles of his shoes will experience a pressure from the floor that is necessary to accelerate his body in the direction of the motion of the speeding-up box.

Suppose now that our physicist holds an apple in his hand (Fig. 21-1). He will feel a pressure on his hand since his palm on which the apple rests has to accelerate the apple in the same way as he, himself, is being accelerated by the pressure of the floor on his feet. If he now releases the apple, the apple will continue to move according to Newton's first law of mechanics with the same velocity it had at the moment of release. On the other hand, since the box is accelerated, it will move faster and faster, so that its advancing floor will overtake the apple and then remain in permanent contact with it. For the observer in the box, the above described phenomena will look quite trivial: he released the apple, the apple fell to the floor, and stayed there. In fact, there will be no way to tell whether the observed behavior of the apple was due to gravitational attraction by a large mass located under the floor of the box or to the steady acceleration of the box!

Suppose now that our physicist has an apple in one hand and a much heavier cast-iron ball in the other. If the apple and the ball are released simultaneously, they will continue to move *side by side* with the velocity which the box had at the moment of release. Thus, the floor of the box will overtake them simultaneously (neglecting the friction of air), a fact that will remind our physicist of the famous experiments of Galileo in which he dropped a light and a heavy object from the top of the Leaning Tower of Pisa! (Fig. 2-4). But, whereas Galileo's finding that *all material bodies fall in a vacuum with exactly the same acceleration* presented a mystery in pre-Einsteinian physics, the physical meaning of the experiment performed inside an accelerated box is quite clear, almost commonplace.

By this example of an accelerated box, Einstein established the fundamental principle of the *equivalence of gravity and acceleration*. According to this principle, a person thrown from his seat in a Pullman car does not necessarily have to conclude that the engineer sharply put on his brakes or that his train collided head-on with another. It is physically possible for the train to have been stationary with its brakes locked, and that the force which threw him from his seat could have been caused by the attraction of a huge gravitating mass which suddenly appeared in front of the standing train.

Geometrization of Gravity

If the forces of Newtonian gravity can be replaced by the effect of the acceleration of a moving mechanical system, then they cannot be "real forces" such as the pull of a stretched string. They must rather represent some geometrical property of a space-time continuum in which the motion of material bodies is taking place. The four-dimensional space-time continuum used by Einstein in his special theory of relativity was completely homogeneous, having exactly the same geometrical properties in all its parts. In order to explain the gravitational field which may be very strong in one place (near the sun) and practically absent in another (between the stars), it was necessary to introduce some geometric property which can vary from place to place. This brought Einstein to the idea of *curved space* of variable curvature, which was developed by mathematicians a long time before he was born.

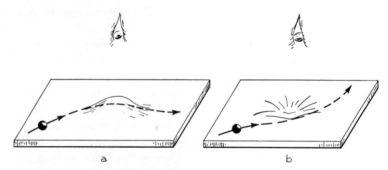

Fig. 21-2. The deviation of a rolling ball caused by (a) a bulge and (b) a depression on a horizontal surface.

In Fig. 21-2a, and b, we illustrate how a varying curvature may be mistaken for the presence of a real physical force. In case (a) we have the flat surface of a table with a slight bulge in the middle; in case (b) instead of a bulge there is a depression. If we roll a ball across the table the presence of the bulge will deflect the ball away from the center, while the depression will deflect it in the opposite direction. If we look at the table from above we will not notice the deviation from perfect flatness, and we may be inclined to interpret the motion of the ball as being due to the action of a repulsive (case a) or attractive (case b) force. Similarly, argued Einstein, the motion of material bodies conventionally interpreted as being caused by the forces of Newtonian gravity might simply be due to the curvature of the four-dimensional space-time continuum in the vicinity of massive bodies such as our sun.

NON-EUCLIDEAN GEOMETRIES

The fact that classical Euclidean geometry is not a unique, logically unavoidable system, but one of many different possible geometries, was realized in the middle of the last century by two inquisitive mathematical minds: a Russian named Nikolai Lobatchevsky and a Hungarian named Janos Bolyai. This discovery resulted from an attempt to prove that the Euclidean postulate which states that *through each point in space one can draw one and only one straight line parallel to a given straight line not passing through that point* must follow from other postulates of Euclidean geometry. If this were true, a system of geometry in which the postulate of the unique parallel is abolished (or violated) should lead to a logical contradiction, thus proving the point. However, this was not the case, and the new geometry, though differing from Euclidean geometry in many respects, turned out to be perfectly logical and self-consistent.

It is easier to visualize the situation by considering the two-dimensional case of Euclidean and non-Euclidean geometries. Two-dimensional Euclidean geometry, also known as "plane geometry," because all geometrical figures are drawn on a plane surface, is a subject that all of us have learned in school. Suppose, now, we want to construct a system of

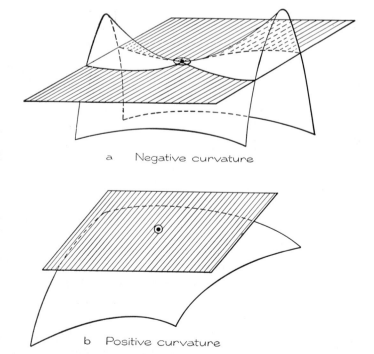

Fig. 21-3. Surfaces of (a) negative curvature and (b) positive curvature. Note that in the case of positive curvature the entire curved surface lies on one side of the tangential plane, whereas in the case of negative curvature the tangential plane and the curved surface intersect one another.

a   Negative curvature

b   Positive curvature

two-dimensional geometry, not on a plane surface, but on a curved surface resembling that of a western saddle, extended beyond any limits in all directions (Fig. 21-3a). When constructing geometrical figures on the curved surface, we must first decide what is, in this case, equivalent to the straight lines of plane geometry. The most reasonable definition of a straight line in Euclidean geometry is that of the shortest distance between two given points, and we may extend this to the case of curved surfaces. However, to avoid a mix-up in terminology, we will refer to these lines as *geodesic lines* or simply *geodesics*.

It can be shown in the geometry of curved surfaces that one can draw through a given point on a saddle surface *a large number* of geodesic lines, none of which intersects a given geodesic, *AB*, no matter how far extended in either direction (Fig. 21-4a). All of these lines "parallel" to

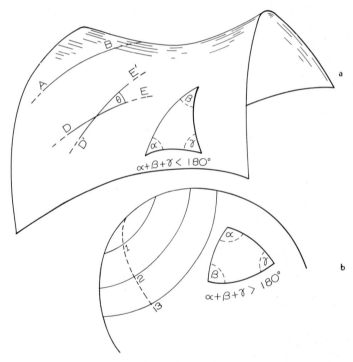

Fig. 21-4. Geometry on the surfaces of negative and positive curvature.

AB lie between two limiting lines, *DE*, and *D'E'*, forming an angle, θ, between themselves. The flatter the saddle surface, the smaller is angle θ. In the limiting case when the surface becomes practically flat and indistinguishable from a plane, angle θ becomes equal to zero and it is possible to draw only one line parallel to AB. Because of the absence of the notion of a single parallel line in saddle-surface geometry, many theorems of plane geometry do not hold for this case. For example, the Euclidean theorem, "the sum of three angles of a triangle is equal to two right angles," is not true on the saddle surface. In fact, when we connect three points on that surface by three geodesics, we find that *the sum of the three angles of the triangle formed by them is always smaller than two right angles*, the difference depending on the size of the triangle.

Another difference lies in the property of a saddle-surface circle, which is defined as a set of points on that surface equi-distant from a given point. Whereas in plane geometry the circumference of a circle is proportional to its diameter, and its area is proportional to the square of its diameter, both the circumference and the area of a saddle-surface circle *increase faster* than that. This is due to the fact that there is more surface area around a point on a saddle surface than around a point on a plane. Indeed, if we cut out a circular piece of leather from the surface of a western saddle and try to flatten it out on the table, we will find that the leather along the rim has a number of folds and has to be shrunk in order to fit the plane surface. Surfaces having the properties of a saddle surface are known as surfaces of *negative curvature*.

The case opposite to that of the saddle surface is presented by the geometry on the surface of a sphere. In this case (Fig. 21-4b), geodesic lines are simply the arcs of great circles, and, since any two great circles always intersect in two points, *there are no parallel lines at all*. In this geometry, which was developed by the German mathematician, Bernhard Riemann, *the sum of the three angles of a triangle is always larger than the sum of two right angles*, and the circumference, as well as the area, of a circle increases more slowly than the first and second power of its diameter. This fact can be visualized easily by considering geographical "parallels" on a globe that represent concentric circles on the sphere with the pole as the center. We find that in this case the length of the "parallels" and the area enclosed by them increase more slowly than on a plane surface, and, in fact, the circumference of these circles begins to *decrease* with increasing diameter when the latter exceeds half of the earth's circumference. Geometries similar to that on the surface of a sphere are said to correspond to *positive curvature* (Fig. 21-3b).

The above examples of positive and negative curvatures are comparatively easy to visualize, since, being three-dimensional creatures, we can look on the two-dimensional surfaces "from the outside." However, *the nature of the deviations from Euclidean plane geometry on spherical and saddle surfaces do not depend on the fact that mathematicians are three-dimensional creatures*. If we imagine two-dimensional intelligent beings, who would be something like flat cartoons drawn on a surface, they would be able to tell which kind of surface they are living on by studying the properties of triangles and circles drawn on that surface. Similarly, the three-dimensional mathematicians living in three-dimensional space should be able, by studying the geometrical properties of that space, to give the answer to the question whether their space is flat (Euclid), curved negatively (Lobatchevsky and Bolyai), or positively (Riemann). The mathematical procedure for describing curved three-dimensional spaces, as well as curved spaces of higher dimensions, was developed by Reimann and was ready for use by Einstein when the latter conceived the idea of a curved space-time continuum.

CURVED SPACE-TIME CONTINUUM

In his special theory of relativity, Einstein showed that time can be considered as the "fourth coordinate," supplementing the three spatial coordinates and thus forming a four-dimensional space-time continuum. However, in order to become formally equivalent to the three space coordinates, time must be multiplied by an "imaginery unit" ($i = \sqrt{-1}$), which emphasizes the fact that space and time are physically rather different entities.

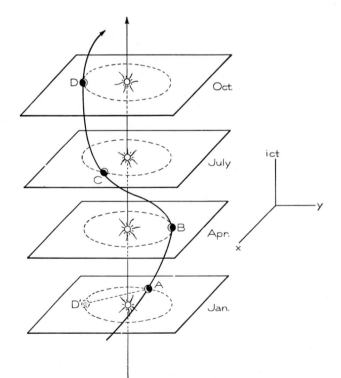

Fig. 21-5. The world line of the orbital motion of the earth.

By selecting *ict* for the unit of time (the velocity of light, *c*, is introduced to satisfy the requirements of physical dimensions), we can represent the motion of an object by a line in the four-dimensional space-time continuum known as the "world line" of this object. In Fig. 21-5 we show the world line of the earth around the sun; only two space coordinates, *x* and *y*, which lie in the plane of the orbit, are shown in the diagram, while the third space coordinate, *z*, is pointing into the fourth dimension, perpendicular to *x*, *y*, and *ict*. Since the motion of the earth around the sun lies in a plane (plane of the orbit), the omission of the *z*-axis (which would be impossible for a three-dimensional artist to draw) does not imperil the generality of the picture.

In the special theory of relativity, in which the phenomena of universal gravity are neglected, the geometry of the four-dimensional time-space continuum is strictly Euclidean. The great idea of Einstein concerning the nature of gravity was that the gravitational fields produced by masses distributed in space and moving in time are equivalent to the curvature of that four-dimensional space-time continuum. Instead of the classical Newtonian statement that "the sun produces a field of force which impels the earth to deviate from a straight-line motion and to move in a circle around the sun," Einstein substituted a statement to the effect that "the presence of the sun causes a curvature of the space-time continuum in its neighborhood, and the world line of the earth is the helical geodesic in this curved four-dimensional space." Thus, the line *ABCD* in Fig. 21-5 corresponds to the *shortest four-dimensional distance* between the position of the earth at *A*, in January, and its position at *D*, in October. It goes without saying that the distance from *A* to *D'*, which is a projection of the October position on the January time plane, *is not* the shortest three-dimensional distance between these two geometrical points.

Three Proofs of General Relativity

When Einstein obtained the law of gravity from his consideration of the curved space-time continuum, he did not get it in exactly the same form as Newton had it originally; there were some slight deviations, which, however, could be verified or disproved on the basis of exact astronomical observations.

In the first place, whereas according to Newtonian mechanics a planet moving around the sun under the action of gravity was expected to describe an ellipse, the position of which was fixed in space, Einstein's theory predicted that the long axis of that ellipse should slowly turn around in a direction opposite to the revolution of the planet (Fig. 21-6). This so-called relativistic *precession of the perihelion,* which is very small for the planets revolving at a large distance from the sun, was proved by Einstein to become noticeable for Mercury, the planet closest to the sun. He calculated, indeed, that the major axis of Mercury's orbit must turn around by 42.9 angular seconds each century. No special astronomical observations were necessary to prove this conclusion of Einstein's theory, since, indeed, astronomers had been breaking their heads for many decades in the vain attempt to understand the observed rotation of Mercury's orbit, which was 43 angular seconds per century greater than could possibly be explained by the perturbation of Mercury's motion by other planets of the solar system.

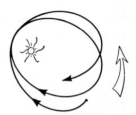

Fig. 21-6. The rotation of the axis of an elliptical orbit, according to Einstein.

The second important consequence of Einstein's new theory of gravitation pertained to the light rays from distant stars that passed close to the surface of the sun. If the space near the sun is curved, the light rays following geodesic paths should be curved inwards as if attracted to the sun. This conclusion could be checked by observing the stars located near the sun during a total solar eclipse when they are not lost in the brilliance of the sun's rays.

Consider two stars, S_1 and S_2, with an angular distance slightly larger than the angular diameter of the sun (Fig. 21-7). In the absence of the sun in this part of the sky, the observer at A will receive the rays from these two stars and will measure the angular distance between the

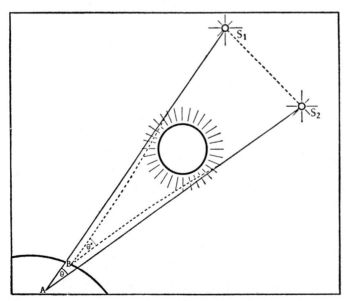

Fig. 21-7. The light from stars is bent when it passes close to the sun.

two stars as being equal to θ degrees. However, if these rays are bent toward the sun (dotted lines), they will then intersect before reaching the observer, and they will as a consequence form between themselves a larger angle θ'. The situation should look as if the two stars had been moved somewhat farther apart from one another by the eclipsing sun between them. A special British expedition was sent to observe the total solar eclipse in Africa in 1916 (German astronomers could not go because of war blockades), and photographs of neighboring stars during the eclipse fully confirmed the expected change of the angle. When Einstein was told about that result and asked what he would say if his prediction had not been confirmed, he answered simply, "I would have been very much surprised."

The third consequence of the theory states that in places of higher gravitational potential all processes (physical, chemical, biological, etc.) must go at a slightly lower rate, or that, in other words, time must flow slower at such places. For example, on the surface of the sun atomic vibrations should be slowed by 2.12×10^{-4} per cent with respect to the earth, while on the surface of the moon they should be speeded up by 10^{-6} per cent. The expected change of the frequencies of spectral lines in the light coming from the sun is so small it is difficult to measure, and different observers disagree about its reality. However, in the case of the white dwarf stars, the shift is much larger, due to their great mass and small radius. A study of the spectral lines of Sirius B (Chapter 20) definitely shows agreement with Einstein's predictions.

Static Cosmological Models

Following the successful application of his idea that the forces of gravity are simply manifestations of the curvature of the space-time continuum, as seen in the motion of planets around the sun and the deflection of light in the sun's gravitational field, Einstein attempted a generalization for the entire universe. Whereas in the case of the sun we have a concentrated "point mass" surrounded by a spherically symmetrical gravitational field, which rapidly decreases with distance, the universe as a whole should be considered as being uniformly filled with gravitating material. Astronomical observations indicate that the galaxies scattered through the space of the universe are distributed rather uniformly as far as the largest telescopes can see, and one is tempted to make an heuristic assumption that the same is true also beyond the present limits of observation. Since the distances between neighboring galaxies are very small as compared with the known extension of the universe, we can rightfully apply a "smoothing-out procedure" and consider space to be filled with a homogeneous material with a mean density of about one hydrogen atom per cubic meter. The basic correlation between the mass density and the curvature of space brings one to the conclusion that the space of the universe has a *constant* curvature, like the surface of a tennis ball, not the surface of an egg. But, if the space of the universe is curved, what is the sign of this curvature? Is it a positive curvature, similar to our two-dimensional example of a spherical surface, or is the curvature of space negative, being more similar to the two-dimensional example of a saddle surface? And, since we must not speak about the curvature of space alone, but also about the curvature of the four-dimensional space-time continuum, how is this space curvature correlated with time?

Analyzing the basic mathematical equations representing the relation between space curvature and the distribution of masses, Einstein came to the conclusion that the curvature of space must be independent of time, i.e., that the universe at large must necessarily be in a static state. (We shall see later that this conclusion turned out to be wrong.) However, looking for the static solutions of these equations, i.e., the curved geometry of space with the curvature independent of time, Einstein found to his surprise that no such static solution exists at all. Something must have been wrong! To repair the situation, Einstein was forced to introduce an additional hypothesis which amounted to the assumption that a new kind of force was acting between the galaxies. In contrast to Newtonian forces, which are proportional to the mass of material objects and rapidly decrease with distance, the new hypothetical forces had to be taken as *independent of the mass* (being the same for an apple, the moon, and the sun!) *and as increasing with the distance between the interacting objects* (as no other forces ever do in physics!). They were called the forces of "cosmic repulsion," and their introduction permitted two stable mathematical solutions of the cosmological problem.

One solution was discovered by Einstein himself, and is known as *Einstein's spherical universe.* According to this mathematical model, the space curvature of the universe is *positive,* i.e., its geometrical properties are similar to those of the surface of a sphere. In particular, just as the surface of a sphere has a finite area that is closed on itself, the space of the universe must have a finite volume, and a rocket ship which started from a certain point and moved at all times along a straight (geodesic) line would be expected to return to the same point from the diametrically opposite direction. Although the space coordinates in Einstein's spherical universe were curved in the same way as the latitude and longitude coordinates on the surface of the earth, the time axis ran quite straight as in the good old Euclidean world, and events were not expected ever to recur. The two-dimensional analogy of Einstein's space-time continuum is a cylindrical surface with the time axis running parallel to the axis of the cylinder, and with the space axis perpendicular to it (Fig. 21-8a).

Another, and the only other possible, solution for a static universe involving the mysterious cosmological repulsion forces was discovered by the Dutch mathematician, de Sitter. In his model of the universe both

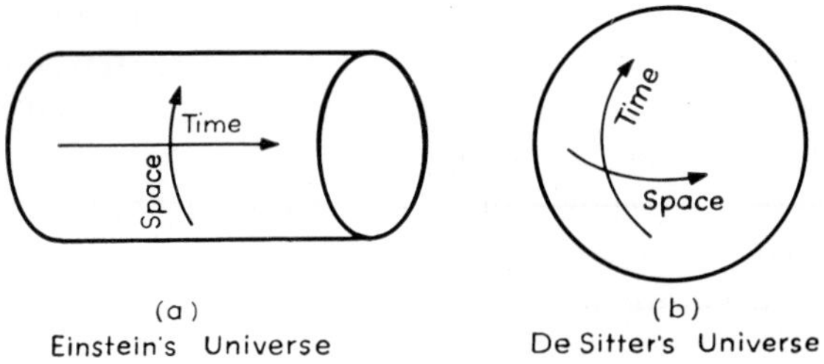

Fig. 21-8. Two-dimensional analogies of the two static cosmological models.

(a)
Einstein's Universe

(b)
De Sitter's Universe

space and time were curved, and the situation was similar to the geometry of a globe, with the longitude serving as the space coordinate and the latitude as time (Fig. 21-8b). However, neither Einstein's nor de Sitter's static models of the universe were in agreement with astronomical observations, and they had to be abandoned in favor of the newly proposed expanding model of the universe.

The Expanding Universe

In the year 1920, a Russian mathematician, Alexander Friedmann, from whom the author of this book learned his relativity, discovered an error in Einstein's proof of the static nature of the solutions of the basic cosmological equation. In carrying out his proof, Einstein divided both sides of an equation by a quantity which, under certain circumstances, may become zero. Since division by zero is not permitted in algebraic computations, Einstein's proof of the static nature of the solution was not valid in this case, and one obtains in fact *two new possible models,* both depending on time. One of Friedmann's non-static universes is expanding with time, the other is contracting. Einstein, himself, rapidly recognized the importance of this discovery, and in conversation with the author many years ago remarked that the introduction of cosmic repulsion was the biggest blunder he made in his entire life. However, even today some cosmologists stubbornly hang on to the idea of universal repulsion.

The mathematical discovery by Friedmann coincided with an observational discovery made by the Mt. Wilson astronomer, Edwin P. Hubble (Fig. 21-9). He found that the light coming to us from distant galaxies exhibits a shift of spectral lines towards the red end of the spectrum, and that this shift increases in direct proportion to the distance of the galaxies from us. Interpreting this observed red shift as being due to the recession velocities of the light sources (and there is at present no other reasonable explanation of it), one arrives at the conclusion that *our universe is in a state of uniform expansion*, with the mutual recession velocities between any two galaxies in space being proportional to the distance between them. The work of Friedmann, Hubble, and his collaborator, Milton L. Humason laid the foundation for the "Theory of the Expanding Universe," which was further developed by a Belgian theoretical astronomer, Georges Lemaitre.

According to Lemaitre's idea, our universe started its evolutionary history from a highly compressed, extremely hot, and completely homogeneous state which he called the *primeval atom*. (Modern physicists would prefer the term *primeval nucleus*.) As the result of progressive expansion, the masses of the universe have been gradually thinning out, cooling down, and differentiating, giving rise to the highly complex structure of the universe as we know it today.

Fig. 21-9. Dr. Edwin P. Hubble, the great explorer of the realm of nebulae (galaxies), on a fishing trip in Colorado. Courtesy Mrs. Hubble.

From the time of its formulation, and until only a few years ago, the Theory of the Expanding Universe faced a very serious contradiction that was threatening its very existence. From the recession velocities of various galaxies as measured by Hubble and Humason, and the distance of these galaxies from us, one could find by simple division how long ago the recession must have started and thus estimate the age of our universe. The age obtained in this way turned out to be *1.8 billion years*, a figure considerably smaller than the age of certain ancient rocks, whose ages were estimated by comparing their uranium and lead content. In fact, some of these rocks were found to be at least *3 billion years* old, and more recent estimates based on the rubidium-strontium ratio raise the age of the earth's crust to almost *5 billion years*. Clearly, a universe that is less than two billion years old cannot contain five-billion-year-old rocks! However, this contradiction in common sense was removed by the recent studies of W. Baade, who has shown that the distances between galaxies are actually 2.5 times larger than they were previously assumed to be. This change in distances raised the age of the universe, as estimated from its expansion rate, from 1.8 to 5 billion years and brought this figure into complete agreement with the age estimated by geological methods. We may remember that the study of stellar evolution also leads to the same figure of 5 billion years for the age of the stars forming our system of the Milky Way.

WILL THE EXPANSION EVER STOP?

Friedmann's solution of Einstein's cosmological equation permits two types of time behavior of the universe: a *periodic* type and an *aperiodic* one. In the case of the periodic, or pulsating, universe, the distances between neighboring galaxies are expected to reach certain maximum values, after which they will begin to decrease. The universe will contract until a certain maximum density of matter in space, possibly the density of "nuclear fluid" (which is 10^{14} times denser than water), is reached. This highly compressed state is followed, again, by an expansion ("on the rebound"), a maximum extension, and then again by a contraction. This kind of behavior is shown graphically in Fig. 21-10a). The aperiodic or hyperbolic solution makes the universe contract from an infinitely thin state, which existed an eternity ago, until it reaches a maximum density at a certain point of time, when it bounces again into a state of unlimited expansion (Fig. 21-10b). Which of the two solutions correctly represents our universe can be decided only on the basis of astronomical observations concerning the rate of present expansion. The situation here is rather similar to the problem of a rocket shot upwards from the surface of the earth. If the velocity of the rocket is smaller than the escape velocity from the earth (11.2 km/sec), it will climb to a certain height, stop, and fall back to the earth. If the rocket were as elastic as a tennis ball, it would bounce up again, etc., etc. On the other hand, a rocket shot with a velocity higher than that of the escape velocity, will defy gravity and will disap-

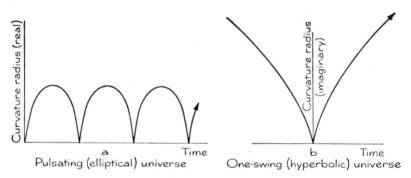

Fig. 21-10. Pulsating and "one-swing" universes, represented by curves.

pear into the infinity of space. The case of the receding system of galaxies is very similar to that of an escape rocket, except that instead of just two gravitationally interacting bodies (the rocket and the earth) we have an unlimited number of them escaping from one another. Comparing the kinetic energies of galactic recessions with the forces of gravity acting between them, we find that *the velocities with which galaxies fly away from each other are seven times larger than the velocity necessary for mutual escape.* Thus, we conclude that our universe corresponds to a "hyperbolic" solution of the cosmological equation and that its present expansion will never stop.

There is one possibility, though, which can change this conclusion. The above given estimate is made on the assumption that there are no masses in the universe except those concentrated in galaxies. If there is some material scattered through intergalactic space with a total mass exceeding that of all galaxies by a factor larger than seven, the conclusion will have to be reversed, and our universe will have to be considered as pulsating. It is quite certain that such a large amount of extra material cannot exist in intergalactic space in the form of gas and dust, since this would produce an observable reddening of distant galaxies and would also result in strong absorption lines in the galactic spectra. But if that material is present in the form of stones and rocks, as small as seashore pebbles, or as large as the moon, its presence will not show in the observation of distant galaxies. It seems very unlikely, however, that such stones and rocks would exist in the absence of dust particles and gas.

IS THE SPACE OF THE UNIVERSE FINITE OR INFINITE?

As we have seen, surfaces of positive curvature, like that of a sphere, are closed on themselves and possess a finite area, whereas negative curvature, as in the case of a saddle surface, leads to infinite extension. The same is true for three-dimensional space, and we can ask ourselves to which of the two classes belongs the space of the universe in which we live. This question can be answered by studying the properties of various geometrical figures in space, but, since the radius of curvature of the universe is admittedly very large, we must carry out these studies on a very large scale. The most convenient geometrical relation from the point of view of astronomical observations is the relation between the volume of a sphere and its radius. Just as in the case of the relation between the area and the radius of a circle, the observed deviations from the theorems of Euclidean space geometry would indicate here the curvature of our three-dimensional space.

Following this idea, Edwin Hubble undertook the study of the increase of the number of galaxies located within a certain distance from us with the increase of that distance. A faster increase than the cube of distance would indicate a negatively curved infinite space, whereas the opposite case would show that the space of our universe is positively curved and finite. The distance of the remote galaxies was estimated by Hubble by applying the inverse square law to the visual magnitudes of the observed galaxies. It is known that the intrinsic brightness of galaxies varies in rather wide limits around a certain mean value, but in handling the observational material pertaining to the very large number of galaxies forming the clusters, these deviations from the average were expected to cancel out. Hubble's studies led to the result that the space of the universe has a positive curvature, with a surprisingly small radius of only a few billion light years.

This result is, however, far from being conclusive, since the estimate of large galactic distances involves the assumption that the intrinsic luminosity of individual galaxies does not change with time. In fact, observing galaxies located 500, 1,000, 1,500, and 2,000 million light-years away, we observe the light emitted by them 500, 1,000, 1,500, 2,000, etc., million years ago. Since the galaxies are composed of individual stars which go through a process of definite evolution, we may expect that their stellar content and over-all luminosity depend on their age. In particular, the burning out of especially luminous stars (like blue giants), which may not be compensated for by the formation of new stars, would lead to the decrease of galactic luminosities with their age. Introducing a correction for this luminosity change, we would have to place distant galaxies at relatively larger distances than assumed in Hubble's analysis, which would swing the conclusion concerning the sign of space curvature the other way. In fact, the assumption of only a few per cent of luminosity decrease per billion years would permit the interpretation of Hubble's galactic counts in terms of negative curvature and an infiniteness of space. Unfortunately, our present knowledge of galactic evolution does not permit us to make any definite conclusions in this direction.

Another way of attacking the problem of the curvature of space is presented by the relation of that curvature to the temporal behavior of the universe. Mathematical solutions of fundamental cosmological equations suggest, indeed, that a pulsating universe, being periodic in time, should also be periodic, i.e., closed, in space, while an aperiodic, ever-expanding universe should be infinite and open. Since, as we have seen above, our universe seems to belong to the second class, we may conclude that it is open and infinite in space.

A COMMON MISCONCEPTION

When a person who has never heard about it before is told that "our universe is expanding from an originally highly compressed state," the usual question is: "How large was the universe at the beginning of this expansion?" If our universe were finite, being let us say 10 times larger in linear dimensions than the presently observed region, such a question would make definite physical sense. Since the present mean density of the universe is 10^{-30} gm/cm^3, and since the density of nuclear fluid which probably corresponded to maximum contraction is 10^{14} gm/cm^3, the universe must be at present diluted by a factor of 10^{44} with respect to its original state. This corresponds to a factor of $\sqrt[3]{10^{44}}$ or about 5×10^{14} in linear dimensions, so that the observed region, which is now about five billion light-years in diameter, must have been squeezed within a sphere of only 0.00001 light-years or 10^8 km across. Thus, the diameter of the universe at the time of the maximum contraction would have been 10^9 km or smaller than the size of Jupiter's orbit around the sun.

However, as we have said before, it is more likely that our universe is infinite in dimension, with a hyperbolic geometry. In this case the space of the universe must have remained infinite no matter how much it was squeezed. The situation can best be illustrated by an example given by a famous German mathematician, David Hilbert, in his lectures on the properties of infinity.

"Imagine," said Hilbert, "an hotel with a finite number of rooms, all of them being occupied. If a new customer arrives, the room clerk will have to send him away. But," continued Hilbert, "let us imagine an hotel with an infinite number of rooms. Even if all the rooms are occupied, the room clerk can accommodate the new customer by shifting the occupant of No. 1 to No. 2, the occupant of No. 2 to No. 3, the occupant of No. 3 to No. 4, and so on, and give to the new customer room No. 1. Even if an infinity of new customers demands rooms, the problem can still be solved. All one has to do is to move the occupants of rooms No. 1, No. 2, No. 3, and so on into the even-numbered rooms No. 2, No. 4, No. 6, and so on, and let the new customers occupy the odd-numbered rooms (1, 3, 5, and so on), which become free as the result of this procedure."

Thus, *the infinite remains infinite no matter how much it is contracted or expanded,* and *an infinite expanding universe must have been infinite all the time.* The only thing that happens in this case is that if we divide the infinite space at its present state into a system of cubic meters, we will find that in the past each cubic meter was a cubic millimeter or less, and that in the future it will become a cubic kilometer or more. This also makes it clear that it is nonsensical to talk about "the center of expansion." Indeed, we can take any of the cubes as such a center, and consider the universe as expanding "from it." Living in the stellar system of the Milky Way, we can perfectly well consider the universe as expanding from our location in space, but the inhabitants of other galaxies will have an equal right to consider themselves as being in the "expansion center."

EARLY STAGES OF EXPANSION

It was indicated some time ago by the author that, whereas at the present stage of evolution the behavior of our universe is essentially determined by the material objects (galaxies of stars) populating it, the early stages of expansion were dependent exclusively on radiant energy. In the process of expansion, the density of radiant energy decreases as the fourth power of linear dimensions, while the density of ordinary matter decreases as the inverse third power (i.e., volume). Thus, although at the present time the mass density of radiation (i.e., energy density divided by the square of the speed of light) is negligibly small as compared with the mean density of ordinary matter concentrated in galaxies, there must have been an era in the past when the two densities were equal. *Prior to this era, radiation must have played the main role in all gravitational interactions, since there were pounds and pounds of radiant energy per single ounce of ordinary matter.*

For the case of an expanding universe filled entirely by radiation, a cosmological equation permits a very simple solution which indicates that all distances were increasing as the square root of time, while the temperature, being uniform through the entire universe, was dropping inversely proportional to the square root of time. One can show that the temperature of the universe was equal to 250 million degrees when it was only one hour old, 6,000 degrees (surface temperature of the sun) when it was 200,000 years old, and about 100 degrees below the freezing point of water when the universe reached its 250,000,000th birthday. This particular birthday was characterized by the fact that the mass density of radiant energy, decreasing faster than the density of ordinary matter, became smaller than the latter, so that matter assumed the leading role in the dynamics of the later expansion stages. In Fig. 21-11 we give a graphical presentation of the changes in the density of radiant energy and of ordinary matter with time, as derived from these theoretical considerations.

THE ORIGIN OF GALAXIES

The transition from the reign of radiation to the reign of matter in the history of the expanding universe was commemorated by a very important event. While the mass-density of radiation was greater than that of matter, material particles (atoms, electrons, etc.) were completely subjugated to the will of light quanta and must have been distributed uniformly throughout space in the form of thin gas and dust. However, as soon as matter became gravitationally more important than radiant energy, the situation radically changed. Sir James Jeans showed a half century ago, in his classical studies of the formation of stars from interstellar material, that a gravitating gas filling a very large volume is intrinsically unstable and is bound to break up into individual "gas balls" the size of which is determined by the density and the temperature of the gas.

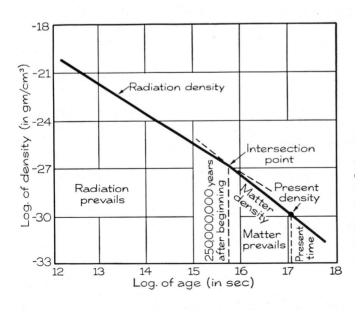

Fig. 21-11. The theoretical dependence of radiation and matter densities on the age of the expanding universe. The intersection point corresponds to the transfer of the "radiation regime" to a "matter regime."

Similar *gravitational instability* must have also existed in the case of the primordial gas in the expanding universe during the era when matter got rid of the dictatorship of radiant energy, and in the year 250,-000,000 A.B.E. (after the beginning of expansion) the matter of the universe must have been broken up into individual giant gas spheres that slowly drifted apart in the process of general expansion. Applying Jeans's formula to the case of the gas filling the universe at that time, we can show that the size and the mass of these primordial gas spheres equal the mean mass and size of the stellar galaxies of today. But, at the epoch of their formation these *protogalaxies* did not display the brilliance of today's stellar galaxies. They were cold and dark, and only through the subsequent condensation of the protogalactic gas into individual stars did our universe assume its present appearance.

THE ORIGIN OF CHEMICAL ELEMENTS

During the early stages of expansion, characterized by extremely high temperatures, various thermonuclear reactions must have been taking place in the matter constituting the universe, and it is inviting to believe that the present relative abundance of different chemical elements was determined, at least partially, by the physical conditions existing at that time. Assuming the above mentioned dependence of the temperature of the universe on time, we come to the conclusion that during the first 5 minutes of expansion matter must have been completely dissociated into a mixture of protons, neutrons, and electrons, a mixture which can be characterized by the name *Ylem* that was coined by Aristotelian philosophy. After 5 minutes of its existence, the universe must have cooled enough to permit the aggregation of protons and neutrons into complex nuclei such as deutrons (H^2), tritons (H^3), tralphas (He^3), alphas (He^4), etc., etc. This process must have lasted for only about 30 minutes, since at that time the temperature of the expanding universe must have dropped below the threshold of thermonuclear reactions in light elements, and the free neutrons, which were very abundant at the origin, must have practically disappeared, being used up in the formation of elements or having decayed into protons. Thus, from this point of view, the processes that took place during the first half hour of the existence of our universe were primarily responsible for its present chemical constitution!

To many a reader, a statement about something that happened five billion years ago and lasted only half an hour will sound entirely nonsensical. In fact, the ratio of half an hour (about 10^3 seconds) to five billion years (about 10^{17} seconds) is ridiculously small (only about 10^{-14}). But imagine a U.S. Senator who visits the Atomic Proving

Ground somewhere in Nevada and is shown the site at which a bomb was detonated three years (10^8 seconds) ago. The place is still "hot" due to the long-living radioactive fission products formed during the explosion. The nuclear reaction that resulted in the formation of these fission products lasted only one microsecond (10^{-6} second), and the ratio of one microsecond to three years (10^{-14}) is the same as the ratio of half an hour to five billion years. Why should one be surprised at the statement that natural radioactive elements were formed in such a comparatively short period of time, if one accepts the statement that the same is true for artificial fission products?

The detailed study of the thermonuclear reactions that must have taken place during the first half hour of expansion were undertaken by the Italian- and Russian-born American physicists, E. Fermi and A. Turkevich, and their results are shown graphically in Fig. 21-12. This

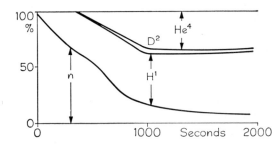

Fig. 21-12. The concentrations of neutrons, protons, deuterons, and helium nuclei during the first half hour of the expanding universe (according to calculations by E. Fermi and A. Turkevitch).

diagram shows that the reactions must have resulted in the formation of about equal amounts of hydrogen and helium, with about one per cent of deuterium from which heavier elements could have been formed. This result is in good agreement with empirical findings that heavier elements constitute about 1 per cent of the matter of the universe, and that the remaining 99 per cent is about equally distributed between hydrogen and helium. If the temperatures and matter densities during the early expansion stages had been different from those assumed on p. 553, the results of the early thermonuclear reactions would also have been entirely different.

The process of the building up of heavier elements, which must have been mostly due to neutron capture, was investigated theoretically by R. Alpher, H. Bethe, and the author. They were able to show (in the so-called "alphabetic theory") that, assuming the empirical neutron-capture probabilities in different elements, one can give a satisfactory explanation of a rapid decrease of abundances through the first part of the periodic system of elements, and the constancy of these abundances through the second part. However, the absence of any stable nucleus with atomic weight 5 makes the abundances of heavier elements, calculated on the basis of this theory, much lower than actually observed. This fact speaks in favor of the possibility that the main bulk of heavy elements was formed later in the history of the universe.

Since temperatures of the order of ten million degrees, which exist inside the sun and other normal stars, are not nearly high enough to account for the formation of heavy elements, the only possible cosmic furnaces where the cooking of heavy elements could take place are the interior regions of exploding supernovae. And indeed, as it was first suggested by F. Hoyle, the British theoretical astronomer, the studies of supernovae exploding in other galaxies seem to confirm this conclusion. In Fig. 21-13 we show the luminosity curve of a typical supernova

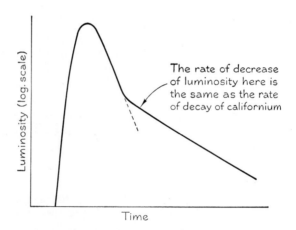

Fig. 21-13. The luminosity curve of a supernova.

as observed by W. Baade. After a rapid rise and the initial rapid decline, the luminosity curve becomes considerably less steep and, in a logarithmic plot, becomes a straight line. This means that we deal here with a purely exponential decay, which suggests that in this stage the luminosity of the expanding gas cloud is supported by some strongly radioactive element formed in the explosion. It was recently noticed by Hoyle and the American nuclear physicist, W. Fowler, that the observed decay period of supernova luminosity of 55 days coincides with the natural decay period of the spontaneous fission of californium. Thus they concluded that large amounts of californium (atomic number 98) are formed in the process of a supernova explosion. If this conclusion turns out to be true, we would have to accept the fact that in the process of supernovae explosions all other heavy elements must be formed in large amounts. Being dispersed by the force of the explosion and mixed with the already existing interstellar material (mostly hydrogen and helium), these newly formed elements could become incorporated into stars either through the formation of new stellar bodies or by the contamination of the surfaces of the old, already existing stars.

Steady-State Cosmology

In the year 1951, H. Bondi, T. Gold, and F. Hoyle of Cambridge University proposed an entirely new cosmology, according to which *the universe has neither a beginning nor an end,* and is as invariant in time as it is invariant in space. This assumption necessitates a special postulate involving *the continuous creation of matter* in space at a rate that exactly compensates for the decrease of the mean density in space caused by the recession of galaxies. The newly created matter is assumed to condense into new galaxies and the show goes on without a beginning or an end. Whereas, according to conventional cosmology, all the galaxies observed in the sky have about the same age (about 5 billion years) the steady-state cosmology leads to the conclusion that the galactic population of space represents a mixture of galaxies of all possible ages, ranging from mere youngsters not yet a billion years old to veterans of five, ten, twenty, and more billions of years. Furthermore, the steady-state cosmology leads to the conclusion that *our system of the Milky Way must be about three times older than an average galaxy in the space of the universe,* being, in this sense, just as much of an exception as a Civil War veteran sitting on a bench in a high school. This conclusion seems to contradict the observational data concerning the neighboring galaxies, which are apparently in the same stage of evolution (judged by their stellar content) as our system of the Milky Way. However, in order to pass a definite judgment on the validity of this theory, more detailed observational data concerning the neighboring and more distant galaxies are required.

SCIENCE TODAY
AND TOMORROW

Looking back on the major developments of the physical sciences from the days of the ancient Greek philosophers to modern times, and on the increase of human knowledge concerning the forces of nature and the utilization of this knowledge for the benefit of humanity, one cannot help but notice the tremendous acceleration in learning and discoveries. It was many thousands of years between the time primitive man learned how to make fire for cooking his food and the time when the burning of wood, coal, oil, and what have you was first used for the propulsion of boats, cars, planes, and space vehicles. It took centuries for electromagnetic phenomena, which were studied as mere curiosities by Dr. Gilbert in the days of Queen Elizabeth I, to become of primary importance in the lighting of homes, in telephone conversations, and in TV programs. But, only fifty years elapsed between the discovery of radioactivity and the development of nuclear power reactors. The great discoveries of the past, such as the Copernican system of the world, Newton's law of gravity, and Dalton's atomic theory of chemical reactions, were like brilliant comets that appear maybe only once in a generation. The discoveries of electromagnetic waves, X-rays, electrons, radioactivity, and the theories of relativity and quanta, on the other hand, crowded the lives of a single generation of physicists. During the last fifty years, tremendous advances have also been made in the understanding of the interior of the earth, the outer fringes of terrestrial atmosphere, the energy sources of the sun and stars, and the structure of the universe as a whole. Although the biological sciences are outside the scope of this book, we may nevertheless mention here that tremendous advances have been made in them too since the beginning of the present century, and that we are at present on the verge of understanding the mystery of life itself.

Where does it all lead to, and what lies ahead for future generations of scientists? Will the progress of science be accelerated to such an extent that in order to keep up with it we will daily have to read the morning and afternoon editions of *Physical Review* and other scientific periodicals? Or, on the contrary, will the speeded-up developments exhaust the treasury of nature, solve all the riddles and subdue all the forces so that science will finally come to an end? Well, probably none of these will happen. The author's opinion, which is strongly disputed by many of his scientific colleagues, is that the development of science in general can be compared with the development of geography during the millennia of the human exploration of the surface of the earth.

The famous French mathematician, Laplace, said once in reference to the development of human knowledge: "The larger is the explored area, the larger are the boundaries of the unknown." * Impressive as this sentence is, it certainly does not apply to certain categories of human knowledge, such as, for example, the exploration of the surface of the earth. It is true enough that at the time when knowledge of geography was limited essentially to the Mediterranean basin, the travels of Marco Polo and of Columbus resulted in a broadening of the frontiers of explored areas. But the earth happens to be round, and the era of great discoveries soon came to an end. In fact, at the present time we can hardly hope to learn more about the surface of our globe than what can

---

* In mathematical terms: "When πR^2 increases, $2\pi R$ increases too."

be found in the pages of the *National Geographic* magazine or in the pamphlets of Cook's Travel Agency. It seems to the author (with due allowance to the opinion of those of his colleagues who disagree with him) that we are approaching now a similar situation in the exploration of the universe around us. In the study of the structure of matter, we have dug all the way down to what are now known as elementary particles, which may well be the ultimate constituent units of matter in the sense in which Democritus used the word "atom" (indivisible). In the study of the universe, we have expanded our knowledge to a limit beyond which nothing basically new has been found. Even the 200-inch telescope of the Palomar Mountain Observatory permits us to see only more of the same galaxies that were seen through the 100-inch telescope on Mount Wilson, and a 300-inch, 400-inch, etc. telescope will most probably see just more of the same. Thus, it seems that we now have a rather complete general picture of the universe around us—both of the vast expanses of the macrocosm and of the vanishingly small structures of the microcosm. Using our analogy with geography, we could say that America has been discovered, Magellans have sailed around the world, and the contours of the land and oceans have been roughly plotted on maps.

But, even though the rapid progress of science permits us to paint a much clearer picture of the physical world than was possible less than a century ago, there is still a tremendous amount of work to be done fitting important details into the existing general scheme. We still know very little about the nature of various elementary particles and it is a challenge to future generations of physicists to understand them as thoroughly as the present generation understands atoms and their nuclei. We still are in the dark about the origin of many important features of stellar galaxies, even though in the last few decades we have cleared up to a large extent the problems concerning the evolution of individual stars. In the field of fundamental biology, which is now rapidly evolving into one of the fields of the physical sciences, we have even more unsolved riddles than in the study of inorganic matter. In particular, in spite of the often-used analogy between the brain and an electronic computer, we are still quite far from a physical explanation of mental processes.

To sum up, we can say that the state of the physical sciences today can be compared with the state of geography a few centuries ago: there are no Americas to be discovered any more, but there is enough interesting and exciting work to keep busy the generations upon generations of scientists to come.

QUESTIONS

1. Is the center of gravity of a table fork located closer or farther away from its middle than that of a table knife?

2. Does the center of gravity of an empty glass differ from the center of gravity of the same glass filled with water?

3. Archimedes measured the density of a golden crown by submerging it in water on a string. Using the same method, how would you estimate the density of a piece of balsa wood?

4. What do you think a goldfish in an aquarium does in order to rise towards the surface, or to descend to the bottom?

5. A block of wood (density 0.60) weighing 1 kg floats on the surface of water. What is the weight of the piece of iron (density 7.7) that must be attached to it in order to make it sink?

6. Suppose that a blimp with a volume of 3,000 cubic meters is filled with helium, which is about 8 times lighter than air. Assuming that air weighs 1 kg per cubic meter, estimate the maximum weight of covering material and cabin that the blimp could still lift.

7. If a small boat loaded with rocks floats in the middle of a swimming pool and a man in the boat throws all the rocks overboard, what happens to the water level in the pool?

8. If two glass tubes with diameters of 0.5 mm and 1 mm are placed vertically into a dish of water, what will be the relative height of the capillary columns?

9. In the experiment with three matches in a bottle (Fig. 1-13), the matches sink to the bottom when one applies pressure to the water surface at the top of the bottle. After a while the matches will get soaked in water and will sink to the bottom. What should one do to make them float up?

10. If a garage attendant finds the pressure in an automobile tire to be only 1 atmosphere and inflates the tire until the pressure gauge shows 2 atmospheres, how much more air (in percentage) did he pump into the tire?

Chapter 2. THE LAWS OF MECHANICS

1. If a man hits the anvil of a "strength meter" (a device often encountered in amusement parks) with a sledge hammer and sends the weight up 10 feet, how high will the weight go if the hammer were twice as heavy and if the man struck the anvil with twice as much speed?

2. The hydroelectric power station at Niagara Falls uses 500 tons of water per second and the difference of water levels is 50 meters. At the Boulder Dam power station, the difference of water levels is 200 meters and the consumption of water 400 tons per second. What is the relative power of the two installations?

3. If a bullet weighing 50 gm is shot from a rifle weighing 5 kg with a velocity of 100 meters per second, what is the recoil velocity of the rifle?

4. Suppose an (inexperienced) hunter aims his gun directly at a monkey hanging on a branch of a tree and pulls the trigger, and the monkey, seeing the flash of the gun, releases his grip on the branch and begins to fall to the ground. Will it be hurt by the bullet?

5. How long will it take a weight dropped from the top of the Empire State Building (1,472 feet or about 500 meters) to hit the ground? (Neglect air friction.)

6. If a pump operated by a motor that develops 10 horsepower (1 horsepower = 745 watts or 745×10^7 ergs per second) pumps water from a lake into a reservoir located 50 meters above the level of the lake, how many tons of water will be pumped up in the course of one hour?

7. In CGS units, normal atmospheric pressure is about 10^6 dynes/cm^2. What will this pressure be in MKS units?

8. Which of the quantities given below have the same physical dimensions?

a) force $\times$ length	f) work
b) pressure	g) velocity/time
c) acceleration	h) area $\times$ height
d) power $\times$ time	i) energy
e) volume	k) force/area

9. What is the density of water in MKS units?

10. If a pendulum and a weight suspended on a spring have equal periods on the surface of the earth, how would their periods be changed if they were taken to the surface of the moon? (Acceleration of gravity on the moon is 5.9 times smaller than on the earth.)

Chapter 3. ELASTIC VIBRATIONS AND WAVES

1. What is Hooke's law?

2. Suppose we have two rubber bands made of the same amount of rubber and one band is twice as long as the other and correspondingly thinner. What will be the relative vibration periods of two equal weights suspended on these two bands?

3. Give a few examples of resonance from everyday life.

4. Will a submarine sailing 100 feet below the surface experience any effects of the surface waves?

5. The sound of thunder came 12 seconds after the flash of lightning. How far away is the thunderstorm?

6. During the atomic bomb test at Bikini Atoll, the television audience in New York heard the noise of the explosion several seconds earlier than the bomb-test personnel, who observed the explosion from their ships a few miles away from the lagoon. Can you explain why?

7. If a siren with 100 holes makes 30 rotations per second, what is the wave length of the sound it produces?

8. How would you use sound waves for measuring the depth of the ocean?

9. What is the difference between *ultrasonics* and *supersonics*?

10. Is it true that one is hit by a supersonic missile before one hears its approach?

Chapter 4. HEAT AND TEMPERATURE

1. Why is a gas thermometer preferable to thermometers based on the thermal expansion of liquids or solids in establishing a temperature scale?

2. If 300 grams of alcohol at room temperature (assume it to be 20°C) are poured into a liter of boiling water, what will be the temperature of the mixture?

3. If 50 grams of ice are thrown into a half liter of boiling water, what will be the temperature of the water when the ice melts?

4. Suppose a mass of 1 kg falls to the ground from a height of 500 meters, and the liberated energy is applied in the form of heat to 10 gm of ice cubes at 0°C. What will be the result?

5. If one end of a thermally insulated copper rod 1 m long and 2 cm in diameter is placed in boiling water and the other end in ice water, what is the flux of heat flowing along the rod?

6. What is the difference between heat *conduction* and heat *convection*?

7. What is the principle of cryogenic equipment?

8. What is the principal difference between turning "motion into heat" and "heat into motion"?

9. Define the absolute zero of temperature.

10. What is entropy and what is its principal property?

Chapter 5. ELECTROMAGNETISM

1. Two spheres are located 3 cm apart. One of them has a mass of 10 grams and carries a positive charge of 6 esu. Another has a mass of 20 grams and carries a negative charge of 3 esu. What will be the accelerations of these two spheres under the action of electric forces?

2. What is the orientation of a magnetic needle placed in the neighborhood of a straight wire carrying an electric current?

3. If a movable and a fixed wire are placed parallel to one another, what happens when an electric current is sent through the fixed wire?

4. Formulate Ohm's law.

5. What is the mechanism of an electric current in metallic conductors?

6. What were Faraday's and Maxwell's views concerning the nature of electromagnetic fields?

7. Describe the process of electromagnetic oscillations in a discharge between two conductors.

8. What is the difference in the functioning of a *diode* and a *triode* tube?

9. How can one use a triode tube to maintain continuous oscillations in an electric circuit?

10. Write the following arithmetical operations in the two-digital system:

$$154 + 60 = 214$$

$$42 \times 5 = 210$$

Chapter 6. LIGHT, VISIBLE AND INVISIBLE

1. In the famous painting by Diego Velásquez entitled "Venus and Cupid" (National Gallery, London), which is probably familiar to many readers, we see

"The Bar of the Folies Bergères," by Manet. *Courtesy Courtauld Collection, London.*

Venus lying on a sofa with her back to the audience. A cupid holds in front of her a mirror in which her face is reflected. Although this painting is one of the finest products of seventeenth century art, it violates the laws of geometrical optics. If Venus were looking at herself in the mirror, as she presumably is, we would not see the reflection of her face in it. Because of the "reciprocity of the optical path" and with the position of the mirror as drawn by Velásquez, Venus would see the face of the painter instead of her face in the mirror, thus using it as a kind of periscope.

Another violation of the laws of geometrical optics can be found in the famous painting, "The Bar of the Folies Bergères," by Manet, reproduced here. Can you find what is wrong with it?

2. When you look into two mirrors M_1 and M_2 put together at right angles (try it), you will see the image of your face with the line between the two mirrors passing right through the tip of your nose and dividing your face into two equal halves. No matter how you move your head the situation will not change. Can you explain why?

3. What is meant by the *focal point* of a parabolic mirror?

4. Formulate the law of refraction.

5. How should the velocity of light change after it enters a glass plate according to Newton's and Huygens' views on the nature of light? Who was right?

6. What physical phenomenon is used in electron microscopes instead of the refraction of light used in ordinary microscopes?

7. The temperature of a heating unit in a kitchen range is about 750°C, while the surface temperature of the sun is about 6,000°K. What is the ratio of the energy emission per unit surface of the sun and the kitchen range?

8. Why does the spectrum of gases consist of sharp lines while the spectrum of solids form a continuum?

9. What is the difference between color reception by the eye and tone reception by the ear?

10. If in the spectrum of a certain star, the blue hydrogen line is observed to have a wave length of 4,340.90 Å instead of the value of 4,340.47 Å observed in terrestrial spectra, which way is this star moving, and how fast?

Chapter 7. MODERN VIEWS ON SPACE, TIME, AND MOTION

1. What is the delay in the eclipse of Jupiter's moons when the earth moves from a position between the sun and Jupiter into the opposite position? (The radii of the earth's and Jupiter's orbits are 149 and 778 million kilometers respectively.)

2. Why was "world ether" considered to be a solid?

3. What did Michelson expect to observe in his apparatus on the basis of classical ideas?

4. What is the Fitzgerald contraction?

5. What did Einstein substitute for "world ether" as the carrier of electromagnetic interaction and light waves?

6. A kilogram of TNT liberates in an explosion 1.2×10^6 calories (or 5×10^{13} ergs). What is the mass of energy liberated in the explosion of a 20-kiloton atomic bomb?

7. What is the increase of mass when 1 liter of water is heated from 0°C to 100°C?

8. What is the proof of the fact that the velocity of light does not depend on the speed with which the source is moving?

9. What is the (relativistic) sum and the difference of two velocities equal to 0.7 c and 0.5 c?

10. What is the geometrical interpretation of the shortening of a moving yardstick, and the slowing down of a moving clock?

Chapter 8. RESTLESS MOLECULES

1. What is Brownian motion?

2. State the equipartition theorem.

3. In a mixture of hydrogen and oxygen gases at a certain temperature, the average velocity of the hydrogen molecules is 1 km/sec. What is the average velocity of the oxygen molecules?

4. What method was used by O. Stern to measure molecular velocities directly?

5. At what temperature is the velocity of air molecules twice their velocity at 0°C?

6. Discuss in terms of the kinetic theory of gases the dependence of gas pressure on density and absolute temperature.

7. What property of molecules is responsible for the wetting of a vessel's wall by the liquid contained in it?

8. How much oil would be needed to cover Lake Michigan (38,500 square miles or about 100,000 square kilometers) with a monomolecular oil layer?

9. Suppose a gas molecule has a thermal velocity of 100 meters per second and diffuses through the air changing its direction at random in collisions with air molecules every 10^{-5} cm. How long will it take for the molecule to cover a distance of 10 meters?

10. Why is a diamond so hard and graphite so soft?

11. What is the molecular interpretation of entropy?

12. What do the sun's rays contribute to a growing plant?

Chapter 9. THE BASIC LAWS OF CHEMISTRY

1. What is the molecular weight of $CuSO_4$? (The atomic weights of Cu, S, and O are 63.54, 32.07, and 16.00, respectively.)

2. Can you correct the following formula for TNT? (Remember that the valences of H, C, O, and N are 1, 4, 2, and 5.)

3. Which of the following formulas are correct, and which are wrong? H_2, He_2, CH_2, Na_2O, $NaOH_2$, CH_5, CO, CO_3.

4. Which pairs of the following elements have similar chemical properties? H, He, Na, Cl, O, F, A, Si.

5. How did Mendeleev arrange the elements in his original periodic table?

Chapter 10. INORGANIC FAMILY ALBUM

1. What is the difference between water molecules (H_2O) and similar molecules such as H_2S, H_2Se, and H_2Te?

2. Write the formula for *hydrogen fluoride, table salt,* and *silver bromide.*

3. What is meant by a *catalyst* in chemistry?

4. Write the structural formula for *nitric acid* remembering that N and O have the valencies 5 and 2.

5. What is the most useful compound of sulfur and what is its formula?

6. What causes the difference between *white* and *red* phosphorous?

7. Name the two most abundant elements in the earth's crust.

Chapter 11. THE CHEMISTRY OF LIFE

1. Why is the chemistry of carbon so much more complicated than the chemistry of other elements?

2. What chemical compounds are known as *hydrocarbons?*

3. What is the difference between *hydrocarbons* and *carbohydrates?*

4. What are alcohols? Give an example.

5. What are protein molecules formed from?

6. What is the general structure of an amino acid molecule?

7. What is the role of ATP in a living organism?

8. The atoms of which elements are responsible for binding together protein molecules in such tissue as hair, nails, etc.?

9. From how many different units is DNA composed?

10. How is hereditary information stored in DNA molecules?

Chapter 12. THE ELECTRIC NATURE OF MATTER

1. Write the formula for the positive and negative ions in a water solution of nitric acid.

2. A current of 5 amperes passing through water for 4 hours liberates 0.752 gm of hydrogen. How many grams of copper will be liberated by a current of 20 amperes passing through a solution of $CuSO_4$ for 2 hours?

3. If an electric wire carries a current of 100 amperes, how many electrons go through it per second?

4. How long must a current of 10 amperes flow through a wire in order to carry through 1 gm of electrons?

5. What is meant by *isotopes?*

6. What is the difference between Thomson's and Rutherford's atomic models?

7. How did Rutherford come to the conclusion that the positive charge is concentrated in the very center of the atom?

8. What is the correlation between the atomic number of a given element and the number of positive charges carried by the nucleus?

9. What accounts for the proportionality between the electric and thermal conductivity of metals?

10. What is meant by an "electron hole" in the theory of semiconductors?

Chapter 13. ATOMIC MECHANISMS

1. How does the energy of a light quantum vary with the wave length?

2. Assuming that the average frequency ν of light emitted by an electric bulb is 5×10^{14} vibrations per second, calculate the number of light quanta emitted per second by a 100-watt bulb ($h = 6.5 \times 10^{-27}$).

3. How does the number of photo-electrons depend on the intensity of incident light?

4. How does the energy of photo-electrons depend on the intensity of incident light?

5. When a beam of X-rays is scattered when passing through matter, does the frequency of the scattered radiation decrease or increase with the increasing angle of scattering?

6. How do the radii of Bohr's circular orbits increase with the increasing quantum number n?

7. What is the Pauli principle?

8. What will be the de Broglie wave length for:
   a) A mass of 5 gm moving with the velocity of sound (0.3 km/sec).
   b) A proton moving with ⅔ the velocity of light.

9. Why is Heisenberg's uncertainty principle important only in the case of very small masses?

10. How much energy will be liberated if one kilogram of ordinary matter is brought together with an equal amount of antimatter?

Chapter 14. NUCLEAR PHYSICS

1. If an atomic bomb explosion produces 320 gm of a radioactive fission product with a halflife of four months, how much of it will be left two years after the explosion?

2. What products are obtained by:
   a) Hitting an N^{14} nucleus with an α-particle.
   b) Hitting an Li^7 nucleus with a proton.

3. What makes the track of a charged atomic particle visible in a cloud chamber?

4. What is the principle of Van de Graaff's high-tension machine?

5. In what nuclear reaction were neutrons first discovered?

6. Why are there more neutrons than protons in heavy nuclei?

7. What is the characteristic difference between nuclear and electrostatic forces?

8. Is the structure of an atomic nucleus similar to the structure of a solid, a liquid, or a gas?

9. What kind of forces cause the fission of heavy nuclei?

10. Why will a nuclear chain reaction not go in a sample of fissionable material that is not large enough?

Chapter 15. OUR SOLID EARTH

1. At what depth under the surface of the earth does the temperature of rock reach the melting point of lead (327°C)?

2. Why do the rocks forming the mantle remain solid even though the temperature rises above their melting point?

3. What is meant by "tides in rocks"?

4. What is the comparative height of tides in rocks and tides in oceans?

5. What is the core of the earth made of?

6. Why are there *two* tidal bulges in the oceans on the opposite sides of the earth?

7. What is meant by *isostatic equilibrium?*

8. Name two kinds of seismic waves that propagate through the body of the earth.

9. If an earthquake takes place in Japan, which kind of seismic waves will be observed in San Francisco and in Buenos Aires.

10. According to present views, what is the cause of the permanent magnetic field of the earth?

Chapter 16. THE "BOOK OF SEDIMENTS"

1. Why do sedimentary deposits not follow exactly the chapters of the earth's history?

2. How did the surface of the earth look during most of its geological history?

3. Name three eras in the history of the earth and discuss their relative duration.

4. What geological revolution is responsible for the formation of the Rocky Mountains and the Himalayas?

5. What could be the cause of the periodic glaciations in the past history of the earth?

Chapter 17. OCEAN OF WATER AND OCEAN OF AIR

1. What is the cause of ocean currents?

2. What is meant by *troposphere?*

3. Why does the temperature of the air decrease continuously when we rise above the surface of the earth?

4. Describe the change of temperature in the atmosphere up to very high altitudes.

5. What is the cause of winds?

6. If the earth were not rotating, what would be the general pattern of winds?

7. What is the effect of the rotation of the earth on atmospheric circulation?

8. What is the difference between *cyclones* and *anticyclones?*

9. What is the cause of clouds?

10. In Boulder, Colorado, located immediately east of the Rocky Mountains, the air is always dry, and the sun shines 328 days a year. Can you figure out the reason why?

Chapter 18. THE PLANETARY SYSTEM

1. How is the *retrograde motion* of the outer planets explained by the Copernican theory?

2. Give the geometrical definition of an *ellipse,* a *parabola,* and a *hyperbola.*

3. State Kepler's second law.

4. Imagine two planets *A* and *B* revolving around some star along nearly circular orbits. If the distance of planet *B* from the star is 9 times larger than that of planet *A* and its revolution period is 54 years, what is the revolution period of planet *A*?

5. Name the planets of our solar system in the order of their distance from the sun.

6. Under what assumption does the Titus Bode law hold for the nine planets of our solar system?

7. What is Saturn's ring made of?

8. Name the satellites of Mars.

9. Why does Venus shine so brilliantly?

10. Do comets have tails when they travel far away from the sun?

Chapter 19. OUR SUN

1. How do astronomers notice the rotation of the sun around its axis?

2. How does one prove the existence of strong magnetic fields in sunspots?

3. What is the explanation of the "mysterious" spectral lines that were previously ascribed to the hypothetical element, "coronium."

4. Name terrestrial phenomena that are undoubtedly connected with the periodic changes in the number of sunspots.

5. What is the state of matter inside the sun?

6. What is the "contraction hypothesis" and why doesn't it work?

7. What is the difference between a carbon cycle and an H-H reaction?

8. How old is our sun, and how long will it last?

9. What is the difference between a "point source" and a "shell source" model of a star?

10. How can we contain the material in the thermonuclear reactors of the future?

Chapter 20. STARS AND STELLAR SYSTEMS

1. Suppose stars *A* and *B* have magnitudes of +5 and +7 respectively. Which star is brighter and by what factor?

2. How do astronomers measure the distance of the stars?

3. If the parallax of a certain star is found to be 0.10″, what is its distance in light-years?

4. What is the condition necessary for a binary star to be observed as an eclipsing variable?

5. Suppose the surface temperature of a certain star is 50 per cent higher than that of the sun (in °K) and its radius is also 50 per cent larger. How much brighter is it than the sun?

6. How much brighter than the sun is a star that is 5 times more massive than the sun?

7. What is the basic difference between stars belonging to the main sequence and all other stars?

8. What are *white dwarf stars*?

9. What method was used by H. Shapley to measure the size of the Milky Way?

10. How did Oort prove that our galaxy is rotating?

Chapter 21. GENERAL RELATIVITY AND COSMOLOGY

1. What is Einstein's equivalence principle?

2. What is a "geodesic"?

3. Give examples of a surface of positive curvature and a surface of negative curvature.

4. How does the sum of the angles of a triangle differ from 180° in the case of positive and negative curvature?

5. Name the three basic tests of Einstein's general theory of relativity.

6. What observation has supplied the evidence that our universe is expanding?

7. A galaxy located 10^9 light-years away from us shows a red shift amounting to 20 per cent. Derive from these data the age of the universe.

8. Some people might say that the drawing in Fig. 21-5 is incorrect, since the earth moves around the sun in a *counterclockwise* direction. Explain why this criticism does not apply.

ANSWERS

Chapter 1

2. Yes.

4. Expands or shrinks its body in order to change its mean density with respect to water.

6. The 3,000 cubic meters of air displaced by the blimp weigh 3,000 kg, while the weight of an equal volume of helium is only 3,000/8 = 370 kg. Thus the lifting power of the blimp is 3,000 − 370 = 2,630 kg.

8. Since the circumference of the free water surface in the second case is twice as large as in the first case, the total capillary force supporting the second column of water will also be twice as large. On the other hand, since the weight of a water column is proportional to the cross-section of the tube, the weight of the second column would be $2^2 = 4$ times larger than that of the first column if their heights were the same. Thus the height of the second water column must be only one-half that of the first column.

10. Since the gauge shows the difference between the pressure in the tire and the atmospheric pressure, the pressure in the tire was 2 atmospheres in the first case and 3 in the second. Thus the amount of air in the tire had to be increased by 50 per cent.

Chapter 2

2. The Boulder Dam station is $\frac{400 \times 200}{500 \times 50} = 3.2$ as powerful as the Niagara Falls station.

4. Yes it will. The motion of the bullet can be considered to be composed both of the motion along a straight line towards the original position of the monkey and of the simultaneous free fall. Since both the bullet and the monkey fall at the same speed, the bullet will hit the monkey before it gets to the ground.

6. A 10-horsepower pump develops 7.45×10^{10} ergs per second or 2.7×10^{14} ergs per hour. To lift a weight of one ton (10^6 gm) to a height of 50 meters (5×10^3 cm) requires $10^6 \times 981 \times 5 \times 10^3 = 4.9 \times 10^{12}$ ergs. Thus, the amount of water pumped up in the course of one hour will be:

$$\frac{2.7 \times 10^{14}}{4.9 \times 10^{12}} = 55 \text{ tons}$$

8. $a = d = f = i$; $b = k$; $c = g$; $e = h$.

10. The period of the pendulum will be longer by a factor of $\sqrt{5.9} = 2.4$, while the period of the weight suspended on a spring will not change.

Chapter 3

2. From the formula on p. 62 we see that T is proportional to $\sqrt{\frac{l}{s}}$. If l is twice as large, s must be twice as small (to maintain the same volume) so that the ratio l/s is four times as large. Thus, the square root of it, which determines the vibration period, will be twice as large.

4. Very little.

6. Because the TV and sound equipment was located on the atoll much closer to point zero than the ships.

8. By measuring the time delay of the sound waves reflected from the bottom.

10. Yes.

Chapter 4

2. In cooling down from $100°C$ to $T°C$, a liter of water liberates $(100 - T) \times 10^3$ calories. To heat up 300 grams of alcohol from $20°C$ to $T°C$, we need $0.232 \times (T - 20) \times 300$ calories. Since the two amounts of heat must be equal, we have:

$$(100 - T) \times 10^3 = (T - 20) \times 69.6$$

which leads to:

$$T = \frac{101.4}{1.07} \cong 95°C$$

4. The mechanical energy liberated in the fall is:

$$10^3 \times 981 \times 5 \times 10^4 = 4.9 \times 10^{10} \text{ ergs}$$

or about 1,000 calories. To melt 10 gm of ice one needs 800 calories. The remaining 200 calories will be used to raise the temperature of the water produced in the melting from $0°C$ to $20°C$.

6. In the case of heat conduction, heat flows through the material which is itself at rest, while in the case of heat convection, heat is carried bodily by the moving material masses.

8. In the first case the mechanical energy of motion can be completely turned into heat, for example, through friction. In the second case only a certain fraction of heat can be turned into mechanical energy, while the rest of it flows from the high-temperature region into the low-temperature region.

10. Entropy characterizes the direction in which physical processes go in a natural way, such as the transformation of mechanical energy into heat or the flow of heat from hot regions into cooler ones. For an isolated system, the entropy can only remain constant or increase.

Chapter 5

2. Perpendicular to a plane passing through the wire and the suspension point of the needle.

4. The electric current flowing through a wire is directly proportional to its cross-section, and to the change of electric potential per unit length of the wire.

6. They considered electric and magnetic fields to result from the stresses in an all-penetrating "world ether" filling the entire space of the universe.

8. A *diode* tube transmits electric current only in one direction and thus can be used as a *rectifier*. A *triode* tube passes or stops the current (in one direction) depending on the potential applied to the grid. Thus, this tube can be used to *modulate* the current.

10.

```
10011010          101010 × 101
+ 111100
----------
11010110              101010
                      101010
                    ----------
                    11010010
```

Chapter 6

2. What one actually sees in this case is the *second reflection* as shown in the accompanying figure. Because of the sym-

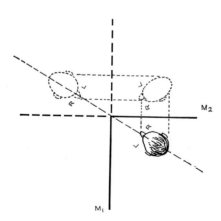

metry, the line connecting the second image with your eyes always passes through the joining edge of the two mirrors. To prove that you see the second image, close your right eye. You will see that, instead of closing its left eye (as it does in the case of a single mirror), your image will also close its right eye thus proving that it was reflected twice.

4. If we plot equal lengths along the incident and the refracted rays, the ratio of their projections on the boundary line between two substances will be the same for any two given substances.

6. The deflection of electron beams in a magnetic field.

8. Because in the case of gases the atoms fly freely through space so that their proper vibrations are undistorted, while in the case of solids they are tightly squeezed together and cannot vibrate freely.

10. The change of the wave length is 0.43 Å which is one ten-thousandth of the original wave length. Thus the velocity of the star (in radial direction) is one ten-thousandth of the velocity of light, i.e., 30 km/sec. Since the observed wave length increased, the star is receding from us.

Chapter 7

2. Because light waves, which were allegedly propagating through it, are transverse waves.

4. The early assumption that all material bodies moving through the "world ether" shrink in the direction of their motion by a factor of $\sqrt{1 - \dfrac{v^2}{c^2}}$.

6. The bomb liberates a total of $(2 \times 10^7) \times (5 \times 10^{13}) = 10^{21}$ ergs of energy. Its mass is $10^{21}/c^2 = 10^{21}/9 \times 10^{20}$, i.e., about *one gram*.

8. In the case of a double star, the two sources of light move alternately towards us and away from us. If the velocity of light were affected by the motion of its source, there would be a considerable difference between the arrival of light from the two components of the double star, and the observations of binary stars would go haywire.

10. The four-dimensional distance between two events remains invariant. Since the motion is equivalent to the rotation of the four-dimensional space-time coordinates, the projections of the four dimensional distance on the space axis and on the time axis change correspondingly.

Chapter 8

2. In a random motion of a large number of particles, the average kinetic energy per particle is the same independent of its mass.

4. He sent a molecular beam through a pair of rotating coaxial cogwheels.

6. See the discussion on p. 201.

8. Since the thickness of the layer is about 10^{-7} cm, the total volume of oil needed is $10^5 \times (10^5)^2 \times 10^{-7} = 10^8$ cm³, i.e., 100 cubic meters.

10. Although they are built from the same carbon atoms, the diamond carbon atoms are arranged in a rigid three-dimensional array, while in graphite the same atoms are arranged in plain sheets only loosely connected with each other.

12. The energy necessary to build more complicated molecules and the "negative entropy" necessary to produce highly organized molecular structures.

Chapter 9

2.

4. (H, Na), (F, Cl), and (He, A).

Chapter 10

2. HF; NaCl; AgBr.

4.

6. The internal arrangement of atoms in these two kinds of crystals.

Chapter 11

2. A sequence of C-atoms in a linear form or in the form of a ring, with all the free valencies saturated by H-atoms.

4. Alcohol is obtained when an H-atom in a hydrocarbon is replaced by an —O—H group. For example, using ethane, we get ethyl alcohol:

6. It is formed by a carbon atom (α-carbon), the four valencies of which are saturated by four different units: 1) a hydrogen atom, 2) an amino group —NH₂ 3) a carboxyl group, COOH, and 4) a molecular group (residue) distinguishing one amino acid from another.

8. Sulfur atoms in cysteine molecules.

10. It is defined by the order in which the four units are arranged along the DNA molecule.

Chapter 12

2. Since the current in the second case is 4 times stronger but lasts only half the time, the total amount of electricity that passes through the $CuSO_4$ solution is twice that which passes through the water. Since, on the other hand, an ion of copper carries twice the amount of electricity carried by an ion of hydrogen, the number of atoms of copper deposited on the cathode in the second case will be the same as the number of hydrogen ions deposited in the first case. Since cop-

per atoms are 63.5 times heavier than those of hydrogen, the weight of the deposited copper will be $63.5 \times 0.752 = 47.8$ gm.

4. Since 10 amperes of current carry 10 coulombs per second, and since the charge-mass ratio of an electron is 1.76×10^8 coulombs per gram, it would require 1.76×10^7 seconds or about half a year.

6. In Thomson's model the electrons were distributed *inside* a positive charge that occupied the entire volume of the atom, while in Rutherford's model the electrons move *outside* the positive charge concentrated in the center.

8. They are equal to one another.

10. The spot that could be occupied by an electron, but isn't. (For a more detailed discussion see pp. 281-286.)

Chapter 13

2. The energy of the light quantum of that frequency is $6.5 \times 10^{-27} \times 5 \times 10^{14} = 3.2 \times 10^{-12}$ erg. A 100-watt bulb emits 10^9 ergs per second. The number of light quanta emitted per second is $10^9/(3.2 \times 10^{-27}) = 3 \times 10^{35}$.

4. It is independent of it.

6. The radii are proportional to n^2.

8. a) $\lambda = \dfrac{6.5 \times 10^{-27}}{5 \times 3 \times 10^4}$
$\cong 3.4 \times 10^{-32}$ cm.

b) $\lambda = \dfrac{6.5 \times 10^{-27}}{1.65 \times 10^{-24} \times 2 \times 10^{10}}$
$\cong 2 \times 10^{-13}$ cm.

10. Since in this case all mass goes into energy, the total amount of energy will be:
$$2 \times 10^3 \times c^2 = 2 \times 10^3 \times 9 \times 10^{20}$$
$$= 1.8 \times 10^{24} \text{ ergs}$$

Chapter 14

2. a) O^{17} and a proton.
   b) Two α-particles.

4. An electric charge is continually brought into the inside of a large metallic sphere by means of a running belt.

6. Because of the coulomb repulsion between the protons.

8. A liquid.

10. Because a large fraction of fission neutrons will escape from the material before having a chance to cause another fission.

Chapter 15

2. Because of the very high pressures existing at those depths.

4. Tides in rocks are about one-third the tides in the oceans.

6. Because the ocean water on the side turned towards the moon is attracted more strongly than the solid body of the earth which, in its turn, is attracted more strongly than the ocean water on the opposite side.

8. Longitudinal and transverse waves.

10. Electric currents in the molten iron core of the earth that result from the thermal convection in the core.

Chapter 16

2. Flat and featureless since the high mountains formed by the crumpling of the earth's crust were comparatively quickly obliterated by erosional processes.

4. The Laramide revolution, the latest one.

Chapter 17

2. The layer of air up to an altitude of about 20 km in which the convective currents cause a continuous mixing of gaseous material.

4. The temperature drops to about $-60°C$ at an altitude of about 20 km, then rises to the freezing point of water, and then drops again to $-90°C$ at an altitude of about 80 km. Above 80 km there is a steady rise of air temperature, and it reaches the melting point of lead at 250 km.

6. Cold air would move along the meridians from polar regions to the equator; there would be steady arctic winds everywhere in the Northern and Southern Hemispheres.

8. Cyclones correspond to a region of low pressure; the air masses move *towards*

its center and are spun *counterclockwise* by the earth's rotation around its axis. In an anticyclone, which corresponds to a high-pressure region, the air masses *diverge* from the center and are spun in a *clockwise* direction.

10. The moist air coming from the west climbs the slopes of the Rocky Mountains, cools, and loses its moisture in the form of rain or snow. Coming down on the eastern side, the air warms up and its relative humidity drops quite low.

Chapter 18

2. These three curves are *conical sections*, being formed by the intersection of a circular cone with planes forming different angles with its axis. A parabola is obtained if that angle is equal to half the cone's opening. We get an ellipse or a hyperbola if that angle is larger or smaller than half the cone's opening.

4. According to Kepler's third law, we have:

$$\left(\frac{\text{revol. per. of } A}{\text{revol. per. of } B}\right)^2 = \left(\frac{\text{distance of } A}{\text{distance of } B}\right)^3$$

or:

$$\left(\frac{\text{revol. per. of } A}{54 \text{ years}}\right)^2 = \left(\frac{1}{9}\right)^3$$

From this it follows that:

$$\text{revol. per. of } A = \sqrt{\left(\frac{1}{9}\right)^3} \times 54 \text{ years}$$

$$= \frac{1}{27} \times 54 = 2 \text{ years}$$

6. If we assume that the ring of asteroids corresponds to an extra planet, thus ascribing to Jupiter the ordinal number 6.

8. Phobos (fear) and Deimos (horror).

10. No, because their tails are formed by gases that are driven away by intense solar radiation.

Chapter 19

2. By observing the splitting of Fraunhofer lines of sunspot spectra into several components (Zeeman effect).

4. Polar lights and radio reception.

6. The assumption that solar heat is produced by the gravitational contraction of the sun's body. The energy liberated in such a contraction is not large enough to explain the long life of the sun as established by paleontological data.

8. It is five billion years old and will lasts about that much longer.

10. By the use of a magnetic field that will cause the charged particle to wind around the lines of force.

Chapter 20

2. By their parallactic displacement in the course of six months.

4. The line of vision must lie in the orbital plane of the two stars (or at least very close to it).

6. Eighty times brighter (approximately).

8. They represent the last stage of stellar evolution. No thermonuclear reactions take place any more in their interior, and they are hot simply because they have not yet had time to cool down.

10. See the discussion on p. 524.

Chapter 21

2. The shortest distance between two points. In Euclidean geometry, a straight line.

4. Larger than 180° for positive curvature, and smaller than 180° for negative curvature.

6. The red shift in the spectra of distant galaxies.

8. There is no absolute *up* and *down* in space, nor is there an absolute *clockwise* or *counterclockwise* rotation. Conventionally, we draw the earth with its north pole up, but it can just as well be drawn with the north pole down. Since in Fig. 21-5 the direction of the earth's axis is not shown, the world line could be drawn winding in either direction. In fact, the world line in the figure looks the way an Australian physicist would draw it. In the countries down under, Polaris is down, while the Southern Cross is up. Thus, according to the Australians, the earth rotates clockwise, unless one turns the clock dial downwards (upwards for us).

INDEX